MW00848670

RENEWALS 458-4574
DATE DUE

GAYLORD   PRINTED IN U.S.A.

EXTRUSION

SECOND EDITION

Editors

M. Bauser

G. Sauer

K. Siegert

Translated from German by

A.F. Castle

ASM
INTERNATIONAL

The Materials
Information Society

ASM International®
Materials Park, Ohio 44073-0002
www.asminternational.org

Originally published as *Strangpressen*
© 2001 Aluminium-Verlag, Düsseldorf, Germany

First printing, December 2006

Comments, criticisms, and suggestions are invited, and should be forwarded to ASM International.

Prepared under the direction of the ASM International Technical Books Committee (2006–2007), James Foley, Chair.

ASM International staff who worked on this project include Scott D. Henry, Senior Product Manager; Charles Moosbrugger; Editor, Diane Grubbs, Editorial Assistant; Bonnie Sanders, Production Manager; Madrid Tramble, Senior Production Coordinator; Diane Wilkoff, Production Coordinator; Pattie Pace, Production Coordinator; Kathryn Muldoon, Production Assistant

Library of Congress Cataloging-in-Publication Data
Extrusion / editors, M. Bauser, G. Sauer, K. Siegert. — 2nd ed.
p. cm.
Includes bibliographical references and index.
ISBN-13: 978-0-87170-837-3
ISBN-10: 0-87170-837-X
1. Metals—Extrusion. 2. Aluminum alloys. I Bauser, M. (Martin) II. Sauer, G. (Günther) III. Siegert, Klaus.

TS255.E78 2006
671.3′4—dc22   2006050365
SAN: 204-7586

ASM International®
Materials Park, OH 44073-0002
www.asminternational.org

Printed in the United States of America

Contents

Foreword

The book *Extrusion: Processes, Equipment, Tooling,* edited by Kurt Laue and Helmut Stanger, was published in 1976 by the Aluminium-Verlag GmbH, Düsseldorf. The excellent, wide, and often deep overview enabled experienced engineers as well as students and academics to understand extrusion processes, equipment, and tooling. For a long time, this book, which was also translated into English, was the standard reference on extrusion.

Because it has been out of print for several years, it made sense to republish the book *Extrusion* in a fully updated version. The editors have attempted to retain the character of the book as an overview of the processes, equipment, and tooling. Extruded products have been discussed in more detail to demonstrate the range of applications of extrusion and to stimulate the industrial application of extrusion beyond that used today.

In addition, the metallurgical fundamentals of the extrusion process are covered in detail, because the editors believe that extrusion can only be optimized by taking the materials technology into account.

The discussions on extrusion equipment, plant, and tooling attempt to extend the overview with application examples. Actual applications, however, require the cooperation of the customer, extruder, tool maker and equipment manufacturer.

The book *Extrusion* is intended for both students and research engineers as well as engineers in extrusion plants, manufacture of machinery and plant, tool manufacture, as well as the designers, process developers, and managers of automotive companies, building industries, and plant manufacture. The book should give an introduction to and an overview of extrusion. More detailed discussions and the latest research results can be found in the technical literature.

The authors thank the co-authors of this book and the numerous companies that have helped in its realization by providing the material for the figures and technical discussions. Specific mention should be made of the support from Wieland-Werke AG, Ulm, and by the companies Alusuisse Neuhausen and Alusingen. We should also thank the members of the "Extrusion Technical Committee" in the DGM for the valuable information they provided. These include, in particular, Dr. J. Baumgarten, Dr. G. Fischer, and Dipl.-Ing. Rethmann. Thanks are also due to Y. Ismailoglu of IFU-Stuttgart and A. Schug of Wieland-Werke Ulm for the preparation and production of numerous photographs, drawings, tables, and diagrams.

The editors also give special thanks to the Aluminium Verlag for fulfilling the requests and requirements of the editors and the authors and for the careful preparation of the contributions for printing.

Sadly, one of the three editors, our dear colleague and friend, Professor Dr. Ing. Günther Sauer, died on October 7, 2000. He gave a great deal of commitment and effort to the realization of this book and completed all of his promised contributions to it before his sudden death. Unfortunately, he was not allowed the pleasure of seeing this book in its final format. We would like to express our sincere thanks for being a good colleague and a friend.

We hope this book fulfills the expectations of the reader and contributes to the further development of extrusion.

Dr. rer. nat. Martin Bauser   Prof. Dr.-Ing. Dr. H.C. Klaus Siegert

Authors

Dr. Rudolf Akeret, Neuhausen, Switzerland
Adolf Ames, Duchtlingen bei Singer (Hohentwiel)
Dr. rer. nat. Martin Bauser, Senden bei Ulm
Dr. rer. nat. Amit K. Biswas, Kaarst
Dipl.-Ing. Wolfgang Eckenbach, Iserlohn
Dr. rer. nat. Adolf Frei, Neu-Ulm
Horst H. Groos, Mettmann
Willi Johnen, Simmerath
Dr.-Ing. Klaus Müller, Berlin
Dr. Josef Putz, Simmerath
Prof. Dr.-Ing. Günther Sauer, Kronberg/Ts.
Dr.-Ing. Günther Scharf, Bonn
Prof. Dr.-Ing. Wolfgang Schneider, Bonn
Dr.-Ing. Gottfried Schreiter, Kleinwaltersdorf bei Freiberg
Prof. Dr.-Ing. Dr. H.C. Klaus Siegert, Stuttgart
Dipl.-Ing. Detlef Smolarek, Pfeffikon, Switzerland

CHAPTER 1

Introduction*

1.1 Basic Principles of Extrusion

THE EXTRUSION OF METALS, in which a billet, usually round, is pressed by a stem at high pressure through a tool of the desired shape, the die, to one or more lengths, first achieved its important position in the semifinished product industry in the twentieth century. The process was used mainly for the production of bar, wire, tubes, and sections in aluminum alloys and copper alloys. However, stainless steel tubes, steel sections, and semifinished products in other metals also are produced in small quantities by extrusion.

Figure 1.1 illustrates the two most important types of extrusion:

- In *direct extrusion,* a stem, usually with a pressure pad in front, pushes the billet in a stationary container through a tool of the desired shape, the die. Relative movement takes place between the billet and the container.
- In contrast, in *indirect extrusion,* the die is located in front of a hollow stem and pushed against the billet by the forward movement of the container closed at the back. There is, therefore, no relative movement between the billet and the container.

During extrusion, a compressive stress state is developed within the billet, which enables large deformations to be achieved with a low risk of cracking. The ratio of the billet cross-sectional area to that of the extruded section is known as the extrusion ratio. It usually falls in the range 10 to 100. In special cases—for example, brass wire—the extrusion ratio can be as high as 1000. However, this requires the material's being extruded to have a low flow stress

in addition to a high specific press pressure of up to 1000 N/mm^2. Extrusion is therefore normally carried out at a high temperature: aluminum alloys usually in the range 400 to 500 °C, copper alloys between 600 and 900 °C, and stainless steels and special materials up to 1250 °C.

Mention should also be made of the special processes of hydrostatic extrusion, the conform process, and cable sheathing also described in this book.

In hydrostatic extrusion (Fig. 1.2), the billet is surrounded by a pressurized fluid. This has the advantage of negligible liquid friction between the billet and the container. The only friction that has to be taken into consideration is between the material and the die. Because the

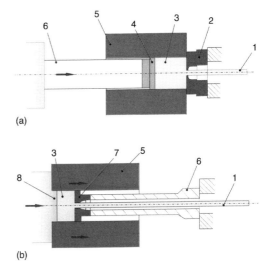

(a)

(b)

Fig. 1.1 Extrusion processes. (a) Direct extrusion. (b) Indirect extrusion. 1, extrusion; 2, die; 3, billet; 4, dummy block; 5, container; 6, stem; 7, dummy block with die; 8, sealing tool

*Historic Development of Extrusion, Martin Bauser

process is difficult to operate and the pressurized fluid can withstand only relatively low temperatures, which restricts the extrusion ratios that can be achieved, the process has only limited applications in spite of initial great hopes.

In the conform process (Fig. 1.3), a continuous feedstock is extruded through the die by a rotating friction wheel with a groove that is closed by a semicircular shoe. Small cross sections and relatively low deformation ratios are possible. Only a few applications are known.

The standard processes, i.e., direct and indirect extrusion, have step by step reached high levels of productivity and quality combined with a simultaneous reduction in operating personnel associated with improvements in machine technology and upstream and downstream equip-

ment, modern control technology, and the optimization of tooling materials and tooling design.

Knowledge of the fundamental principles of metallurgy, as well as the basics of deformation technology, machinery, and tooling, is needed to understand the extrusion process. All these aspects are discussed in this book.

Historic Development of Extrusion*

Martin Bauser

Joseph Bramah described in a patent in 1797 a "press for the production of pipes of a specific diameter and length without joints in lead and other soft metals" (Fig. 1.4). Joseph Bramah used liquid lead forced from a melting vessel A

---

*Historic Development of Extrusion, Martin Bauser

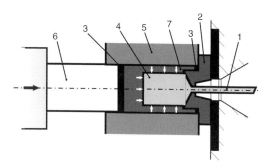

Fig. 1.2 Hydrostatic extrusion. 1, extrusion; 2, die; 3, seal; 4, billet; 5, container; 6, stem; 7, hydrostatic medium

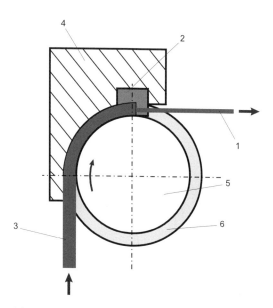

Fig. 1.3 Conform process. 1, extrusion; 2, die; 3, feedstock; 4, shoe; 5, friction wheel; 6, groove

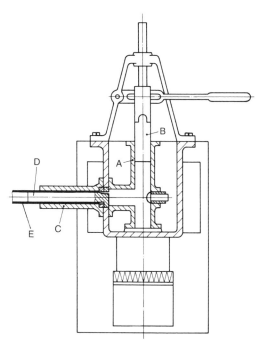

Fig. 1.4 Bramah's lead piston press, 1797. A, melting chamber; B, piston; C, tube support; D, tube mandrel; E, extruded tube

by the piston B through a valve into the cylinder. The liquid material is then pushed by the piston as split metal streams through annularly located openings in the mandrel support so that the metal streams combine and solidify in the annular gap formed by the tube mandrel D and the tube support C to form a tube E.

Pure lead melts at 327 °C, and most of its alloys at an even lower temperature, so that this material can be formed with low loads even at 80 °C. Therefore, lead was the only important extruded material up to the end of the nineteenth century. Many of the important elements of the process used today were, however, developed during this period.

The first known design of a (vertical) hydraulic extrusion press for lead tube was developed by the Englishman Thomas Burr in 1820 (Fig. 1.5). It had a container A, an extrusion stem with a machined-in pressure pad, a threaded mandrel, and a replaceable die B.

England played a leading role in extrusion as well as in many engineering fields. Lead pipes were used there relatively early for water supply pipes. English inventions from the nineteenth century include the bridge die, the hydraulic accumulator, the gas-heated container, and the indirect extrusion process. Specific mention should be made of the invention of I. and C.

Hanson, who, as early as 1837, were producing lead tubes from a solid billet through a multipart bridge die with a replaceable fixed pressure pad (Fig. 1.6).

The first two-piece container heated with gas was developed by Hammon in 1867.

The start of electrification opened a new market for lead as a cable sheathing material. The first cable sheathing press was built by Borell in 1879 in which lead was extruded directly onto the cable core. The process was improved in 1882 by Werner von Siemens.

Alexander Dick, who lived in England, succeeded in developing from lead extrusion the processing of metals with higher melting points. He is therefore quite correctly considered to be the "father of extrusion."

In 1894, Dick registered a patent for an extrusion press designed specifically for brass rod (Fig. 1.7) [Dic 94]. His idea was to cast liquid metal into the vertically orientated container and to let it solidify. After rotating the container into the horizontal position, the product was extruded from this initial heat through a replaceable die, F. Direct water pressure pushed the stem forwards. A pressure pad protected it from the billet heat and prevented back extrusion of the metal. The die and die holder, E, were sealed against the cross head by two wedges, D. These were

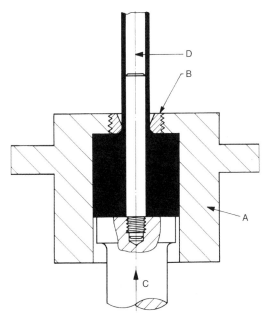

Fig. 1.5 First hydraulic lead press (Th. Burr, 1820). A, container; B, die; C, extrusion stem with machined dummy block and threaded mandrel; D, extruded tube

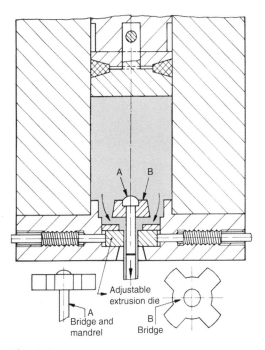

Fig. 1.6 First bridge die by I. and C. Hanson (1837)

opened at the end of the extrusion process, and the die discard and pressure pad ejected using the stem (Fig. 1.8).

Because the one-piece container made from cast iron or steel tended to crack under the thermal stresses developed by the casting of the hot metal, a multipiece container was introduced in 1896. However, the individual cylinders were not prestressed but merely insulated from each other by powdered graphite and borax.

The time-consuming process copied from lead pipe extrusion of filling the container with liquid metal was soon replaced by the use of preheated cast billets. Alexander Dick described over a period of time many important details in numerous patents: the loose pressure pad, various mandrel designs for tubes, dies for multihole extrusion, and even a hollow section die. The three-piece bridge die patented by Alexander Dick in 1897 is shown in Fig. 1.9 [Dic 97]. The billet is divided into six streams that weld together in the shape forming aperture.

The manufacture of extrusion presses with press capacities of more than 7 MN enabled larger billets to be used, thus giving an economic

production. The water hydraulic extrusion press was powered by a pressurized water system consisting of pumps and accumulators. The hot billets were manually loaded into the container using tongs. Hand-operated valves were used to control the operating sequence of the extrusion press. The extruded products had to be handled manually with tongs.

Rapid developments at the start of the twentieth century resulted in the extrusion process completely replacing the previously standard process for the production of bars, sections, and wire in copper alloys of section by rolling of cast billets. More than 200 extrusion presses, mostly for brass, had been built by 1918 (mainly by the German company Krupp-Gruson). However, even steel sections were being extruded by 1914.

Although it was possible to produce tubes on standard presses by the development of "floating mandrels," which were a loose fit in the hollow billet and were heavily tapered toward the die, this was replaced—following a patent by Arnold Schwieger in 1903—by a piercing system located behind the main cylinder (Fig. 1.10).

The mandrel holder passing through the main cylinder carries the mandrel at its tip, which can pierce the solid billet. This then forms the internal contour of the tube in the die. These presses, which can naturally also be used to extrude solid bars by removal of the mandrel, were built up to the 1950s. Then the internal piercer enabled the press length to be shortened and the alignment of the mandrel to be improved (Fig. 1.11).

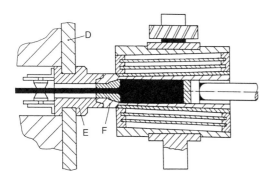

Fig. 1.7 First brass extrusion press. D, wedges; E, die and die holder; F, replaceable die (A. Dick, 1894)

Fig. 1.8 Hydraulic extrusion press (1895)

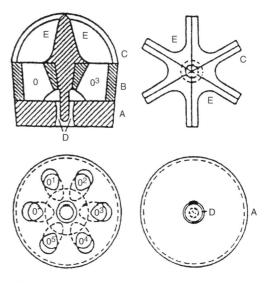

Fig. 1.9 Bridge die by A. Dick (1897)

In the 1920s, experience showed that that the concentricity of internal and external tube walls was better on vertical hydraulic presses because of the favorable influence of gravity. The mandrel was rigidly screwed to the stem and pre-pierced billets used. In the 1950s, numerous vertical tube presses were built (by the companies Schloemann and Hydraulik) but now with independent mandrel movement and automatic operation for the production of copper and brass tubes. The manufacture of vertical presses stopped around 1965 when it became possible

to improve the alignment of the press centerline, the guiding of the container, stem, and mandrel to such an extent that tubes with adequate concentricity were produced on horizontal presses. In spite of the high cycle speeds, the presses with a maximum capacity of 16 MN did not have sufficient power to process billets of sufficient size.

Around 1933, the vertical mechanical tube presses patented by Singer started to mass produce steel tubes. These vertical tube presses with a high number of strokes per minute for the mass production of steel tubes have been largely replaced by rolling processes that operate more economically with a higher productivity.

Containers, which had for a long time been produced as multipiece units but without any interference fit could operate only with specific press extrusion pressures of approximately 300 N/mm². It was only the introduction of two- or three-piece prestressed containers that enabled higher extrusion pressures to be used. Movable containers enabled the billet loading and the removal of the discard to be improved. The introduction of electric container heating (resistance and later induction heating) in 1933 replaced the previously used gas or coal heating and enabled aluminum to be processed (Fig. 1.12).

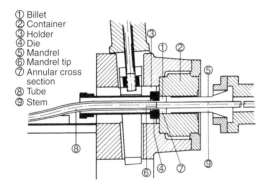

① Billet
② Container
③ Holder
④ Die
⑤ Mandrel
⑥ Mandrel tip
⑦ Annular cross section
⑧ Tube
⑨ Stem

Fig. 1.10 First rod and tube press (Arnold Schwieger, 1903)

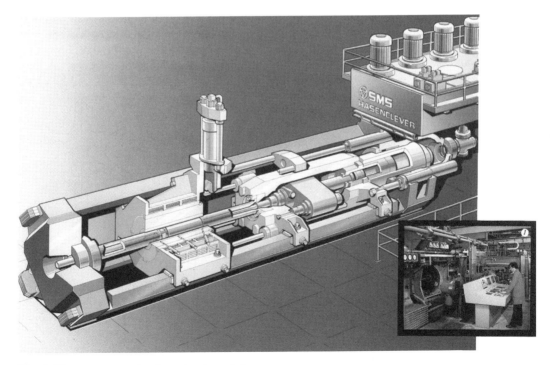

Fig. 1.11 Extrusion press for tubes with an internal piercer

Fig. 1.12 Three-piece container with induction heating

The rapid expansion of extrusion technology since 1925 gave rise to intensive investigation into the flow processes and deformation technology theories. These resulted in new developments in press construction and tooling technology.

For a long time it was standard practice to design each press from new to meet the needs of the application and the customer. Around 1960, multipurpose extrusion presses that could be used universally were developed in Europe.

Although Alcan has processed aluminum on horizontal presses since 1918, the breakthrough in aluminum extrusion came with the construction of airships and aircraft. Difficult-to-extrude high-strength aluminum alloys were developed in the 1930s (aluminum copper), and large product cross sections required powerful presses. The largest extrusion presses built up to 1945 had a press power of 125 MN. Around 1950, the preassembled short stroke press with variable direct oil drive (mounted above the press), and die slide or die rotate for rapid die changing, was developed in the United States. This enabled short dead cycles to be developed. These presses for aluminum alloys were built with press loads from 10 to 30 MN. They provided optimal production in combination with a high-speed gas-fired billet furnace in front of the press and a handling system with stretcher and saw for the profiles after the press. Aluminum profiles for windows and curtain walling could then be produced economically. The full layout of an aluminum extrusion plant is shown in Fig. 1.13.

Although experiments by R. Genders (1921, in England) into indirect extrusion resulted in the manufacture of theses presses by 1925, the breakthrough of this process came with the indirect extrusion of brass wire (Hydraulik Co.). Improved designs and the application to difficult-to-extrude aluminum alloys ensured the increasing application of this indirect extrusion process. In contrast, the hydrostatic extrusion process has succeeded in only very specialized applications in spite of extensive research and numerous publications. One example is the extrusion of composite materials.

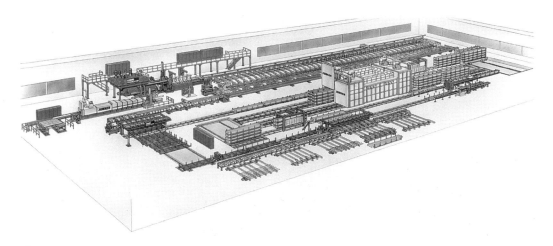

Fig. 1.13 Complete aluminum extrusion plant (SMS Hasenclever)

REFERENCES

[Bau 82]: M. Bauser and E. Tuschy, Strangpressen—Heutiger Stand und Entwicklungstendenzen (Extrusion—Present Position and Development Trends), *Z. Metallkd.,* Vol 73, 1982, p 411–419

[Bis 73]: A. Biswas and F.J. Zilges, Direktes, indirektes und hydrostatisches Strangpressen—Verfahrensbeschreibung und geschichtliche Entwicklung (Direct, Indirect and Hydrostatic Extrusion Process Description and Historic Development), *Aluminium,* Vol 49, 1973, p 296–299

[Dic 94]: A. Dick, Deutsches Patent 83388, 1894

[Dic 97]: A. Dick, Deutsches Patent 99405, 1897

[Nus 90]: A.J. Nussbaum, Extrusion of Metals: The First Hundred Years, *Light Met. Age,* Vol 48, 1990, p 8–33

[Pea 61]: C.E. Pearson and R.N. Parkins, *The Extrusion of Metals,* Chapman & Hall, 1960

[Pet 59]: E. Petsch, Neues indirekt-Strangpreßverfahren für Metalldraht (New Indirect Extrusion Process for Metal Wire), *Z. Metallkd.,* Vol 50, 1959, p 629–637

[Wei 66]: F. Weitzel, *Die Entwicklung der Strangpresse (The Development of the Extrusion Press),* Edelstahlwerke Buderus AG, Wetzlar, 1966

[Wie 70]: H. Wieland, *Die Geschichte des Strangpressens im Blicke der Wieland-werke (The History of Extrusion from the Viewpoint of Wielandwerke),* Wielandwerke AG, Ulm, Germany, 1970

CHAPTER 2

Extruded Products

Günther Sauer*

THE HOT-WORKING PROCESS extrusion is used to produce semifinished products in the form of bar, strip, and solid sections as well as tubes and hollow sections. The high mean compressive stresses in the deformation zone of the container enable materials to be worked that cannot be processed into semifinished products by other hot-working processes, for example rolling, because of their limited workability. The extrusion process also enables semifinished products to be produced from powder metallurgy-based materials, composite materials, and the production of semifinished products from clad composites with material combinations including aluminum/copper and aluminum/steel using the cladding process. Finally, the sheathing of electrical cables with lead or aluminum alloys using the transverse extrusion process has been a standard process for a long time, as has the production of multicore solders with integrated flux cores using the same process.

The pushing of the material being extruded through the shape-forming aperture of the extrusion die enables cross-sectional shapes to be produced that cannot be manufactured by any other hot-working process. The favorable deformation conditions with nonferrous metals such as tin and lead alloys as well as magnesium and aluminum alloys with good welding properties and working temperatures that can be withstood by the tool materials also enable the billet to be divided into several metal streams, and then rewelded in the shape-forming region of the extrusion die to form tubes and hollow sections. The production of hollow sections is one of the main applications of extrusion. This process can also be used for certain copper alloys; however, the materials used for the extrusion tooling cannot withstand the thermo-mechanical stresses. Billet-on-billet extrusion enables coiled tubes of long length to be produced, for example, aluminum alloy heat exchanger tubes and tin and lead alloy multicore solders.

The extrusion process generally produces a semifinished product close to the finished size with materials with working temperatures up to 600 °C. This occurs in one production step in contrast to other processes used to form semifinished products. Therefore, the design of the cross section of the semifinished product can practically ignore any limitations associated with subsequent processing operations. The most suitable cross-sectional geometry can be freely selected for the specific application. Simple matching of the cross-sectional geometry of the extrusion to the static, dynamic, and geometric requirements combined with the wide range of joining methods in assembly characterize the high functionality of the products produced by this working process.

2.1 Tin and Lead Extruded Products with a Deformation Temperature Range of 0 to 300 °C

Tin alloy extruded products are mainly soft solders with or without flux cores for use in electrical engineering and electronics. Tin alloys are significantly more common than are lead alloys.

---

*Extruded Products from Materials with a Working Temperature Range of 600 to 1300 °C, Martin Bauser

They are produced on horizontal presses and drawn, coiled, or wound to the customers' desired finished sizes on multispindle wire drawing machines as shown in Fig. 2.1. The production processes are described in section 5.3. Other extruded products are anodes used for electrochemical plating with tin, for example, tin plating for corrosion protection. Tin alloy extruded products are also used in the manufacture of chemical equipment.

Lead alloy products have lost a large part of their market since World War II because of the toxic properties of these alloys. Even in the 1950s, extruded lead alloys were still used for water supply pipes up to the fittings on sinks. These materials were also used for extruded water waste pipes. This has changed completely. Lead alloys may no longer come into contact with food products because they can form very poisonous lead salts. Drinking water counts as a food and, therefore, lead drinking water pipes are no longer permitted. Nevertheless, lead alloys offer a range of advantages that make alternative materials difficult or even impossible to find. Lead alloys have good resistance to fluoric and sulfuric acids as well as phosphoric acid, ammonia, chlorine, and soda. They are therefore useful alloys for the chemical industry.

The high density makes lead alloys particularly suitable for radiation and noise protection. Good workability combined with low melting points means that lead alloys are also used for the manufacture of soft solder, which is described in section 5.3. Lead alloys, similar to tin alloys, are also suitable for the production of custom shaped anodes as shown in Fig. 2.2 for electrochemical plating. An example is the approximately 20 μm thick and soft running surface in plain bearings such as bearing shells and bushes. Although the use of specific lead alloys for the production of cable sheaths cannot be classified as environmentally harmful, the cable industry prefers alternative plastic and aluminum-base materials. High-voltage cables are still sheathed in lead. Spacers for double glazing (Fig. 2.3) are also extruded from lead alloys. Fishing nets and curtains are usually weighted with lead lines produced by horizontal extrusion. Some examples are shown in Fig. 2.3.

Lead alloys can be made relatively resistant to corrosion by the addition of tin. They can also be recycled relatively easily. However, the environmental political pressure will affect the current applications because of the toxic properties of this material.

Fig. 2.1 Soft solder with one or more flux cores (tube solder), extruded and drawn to the finished dimensions and coiled on plastic spools. Source: Collin

Fig. 2.2 Extruded sections and tubes in lead base and tin alloys for use as anodes for the electrochemical coating, supply tubes for aggressive media, materials for seals and radiation protection, etc. Source: Collin

Fig. 2.3 Extruded solder with several flux cores, lead sheathed cable, and window spacer sections in lead alloys for double glazed windows, as well as lead lines for fishing nets and curtain weights. Source: Collin

2.2 Magnesium and Aluminum Extruded Products with a Working Temperature Range of 300 to 600 °C

2.2.1 Magnesium Alloy Extruded Products

Magnesium alloys are light materials with useful mechanical properties. Their density of approximately 0.0018 kg/m^3 is about 36% less than that of the aluminum alloys. The Young's modulus (E) is approximately 45 GPa and, therefore, about 65% of the E-modulus of aluminum alloys. For this reason, they are, in principle, more interesting than aluminum alloys as a construction material for light components. However, the corrosion resistance of magnesium components is not usually as good as that of aluminum components. They, therefore, have to be given more surface protection. The corrosion sensitivity of magnesium alloys can be lowered significantly by reducing the trace element content of copper, iron, manganese, and nickel into the ppm region. The corrosion behavior of high-purity magnesium alloys approaches that of aluminum alloys. This has considerably increased the interest in magnesium alloys as construction materials. However, the mechanical behavior of magnesium components is very directional de-

pendent because of the hexagonal lattice structure. In addition, any partial cold working of magnesium components, as is necessary, for example, for the aluminum alloy side door beam in Fig. 2.24, in the section "Passenger Cars," is practically impossible because of this hexagonal lattice structure. Magnesium alloys naturally have good machining characteristics. Unlike aluminum alloys, they do not need any chip-breaking alloying additions such as lead and bismuth. Consequently, extruded semifinished products are eminently suited to the production of turned components including ones in daily use, for example, pencil sharpeners. A typical profile can be seen in Fig. 2.4 [Fuc 96]. In the past, the market for extruded magnesium alloy products was limited in spite of the products' good properties, in particular, their low density. The reason for this is both the lattice-related poor cold-working properties, and the hot-working properties that are very alloy dependent. The main application for magnesium alloys is, therefore, still cast components. The most well-known application is the engine and gearbox housing used after World War II in the air-cooled flat twin engine in the Volkswagen Beetle.

Basically, magnesium products are used where the weight saving, e.g., components with a low mass, has high priority. The main areas of application are automobile and machine manufacture. The extruded products shown in Fig. 2.5 and 2.6 are suited primarily for machine components subjected to high acceleration and braking, for example, in textile machine components [Fuc 96]. These products are also used in the aerospace industry and in military applications.

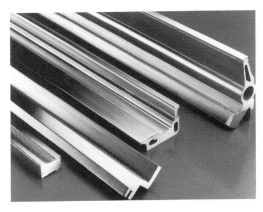

Fig. 2.4 From left to right: Section in MgAl2Zn for the production of pencil sharpeners, two sections in MgAl3Zn for warp knitting machine, and test arm sections for disc magazines. Source: Fuchs-Metallwerke

Fig. 2.5 Extruded section in MgAl3Zn for textile machines. Source: Fuchs-Metallwerke

Fig. 2.6 Hollow section in MgAl3Zn for the external rotor of a turbocharger for automobile engines. Source: Fuchs-Metallwerke

Magnesium alloys are being developed further because of their suitability for light components with the intention of achieving higher static and dynamic mechanical properties as well as improving the working properties [Tec 96/97/98, Gar 93]. Interest in magnesium alloy components is increasing, particularly in the automobile industry.

In the past, hot-worked semifinished products in the form of magnesium alloy sheet and ex-

truded products were used to a significant degree in the period before World War II. Complete fuselages in hot-rolled and section-reinforced magnesium sheets were produced for small aircraft [Bec 39]. Bus trailers were manufactured almost entirely from hot-worked magnesium alloys, including a welded frame of extruded magnesium tubes clad with magnesium sheet [Bec 39]. Welded seat frames for passenger aircraft were made from extruded magnesium tubes.

The increasing interest by the automobile industry in light extruded products in order to save energy by reducing vehicle weight has resulted in increasing examination of extruded semifinished products in magnesium alloys. This will gain in importance if the further development of the magnesium alloys results in higher values of static and dynamic strength and improved working and corrosion properties. It can, therefore, be assumed that magnesium alloys will also be used to an increasing extent for load-carrying components as well as safety components, which require a good proof stress and elongation. Magnesium alloys are, moreover, as easily recycled as aluminum alloys.

The extrusion of magnesium alloys is described in section 5.5.

2.2.2 Aluminum Alloy Extruded Products

The main application of the hot-working process extrusion is in the general production of bars, tubes, and wire in aluminum alloys and, in particular, the manufacture of aluminum sections. No other material is used as a semifinished product to the same extent in practically all areas of technology. Acceptable materials properties and modulus of elasticity, weight saving from the low-density, good surface quality, good dimensional accuracy and minimum subsequent machining, and ease of recycling make aluminum alloys both economically and environmentally interesting. These properties, as well as the largely unrestricted shape of the cross-section geometry, are the basis for the trend to the development of ever more functional components with good appearance and corrosion resistance.

The reason for the predominance of aluminum profiles in extrusion is due to the moderate working temperatures of the aluminum alloys. The extrusion tooling can then withstand the thermo-mechanical stresses. In general, the working temperature of aluminum alloys is below the annealing temperature of the hot-working tool steels normally used to manufacture aluminum extrusion tools. This has played a decisive role in the development of the design of extrusion tooling for aluminum profiles. Very demanding aluminum profiles can now be produced. In recent years, the development of extrusion tools for the production of large profiles has been particularly successful.

Large profiles are used today in almost all areas of industry. In Europe alone there are four large extrusion presses with press powers of 72,000 to 100,000 kN used to produce them. Standard solid and standard hollow sections with a circumscribing circle diameter of approximately 600 mm can be produced from 650 mm round containers on the 98,000 kN direct extrusion press operated by Alusuisse in Singen (Germany) (Fig. 2.7). Solid flat sections with maximum dimensions of 800 by 100 mm (width by height) and flat hollow sections with a maximum size of 800 by 60 mm can be produced from the

same round container by using spreader techniques. West European aluminum extrusion plants today can produce extruded sections ranging from 10 g/m to 130 kg/m. The section "Extrusion of Semifinished Products in Aluminum Alloys" describes the extrusion processes used today for aluminum alloys.

The large profile technology was first developed in the second half of the 1970s for the construction of railway rolling stock. Until then, the technical advantages of aluminum aroused some interest in its use as a construction material, but the classic method of construction of railcar body shells using sheet and small extruded profiles could not compete with the proven construction material steel. A light steel design of the body shells was about 50% cheaper than a comparable one made from aluminum alloys. The light steel construction was, therefore, preferred. This changed with the introduction of

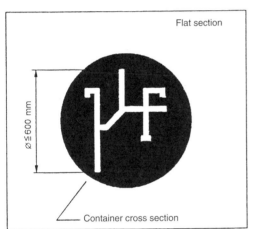

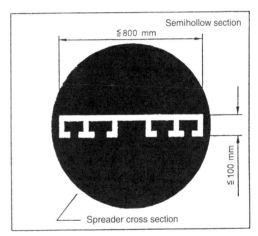

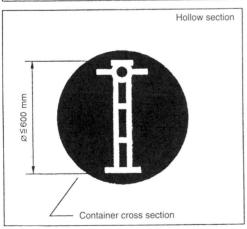

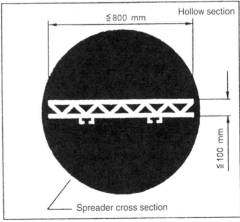

Fig. 2.7 Large sections produced from containers with a circular bore on the 98,000 kN direct extrusion press in Singen. Adapted from Alusuisse

large profiles the length of the rolling stock that could be automatically welded to each other. The assembly cost of the railcar body shells could be reduced to an extent that not only compensated for the higher material cost of the aluminum but also reduced the total cost of the aluminum wagon by approximately 30% of that of the steel wagon [Wis 92, Cor 95].

Aluminum designs using large profiles that simplified assembly then started to compete with steel. Today, aluminum large profile technology has become the economic solution in many branches of technology. Large profiles enable several fabricated classic components to be replaced. Extruded profiles can be supplied as integral components ready for installation. Large profiles not only can replace several classic components but also, in addition to their static and dynamic functions, take on additional functions in addition to the overall function with the minimum of additional material as shown in Fig 2.8, which depicts cross-sectional views of a carriage of the Paris Metro [Alz 85].

The mechanical properties of the aluminum alloys used for the production of large aluminum profiles are adequate for most applications where good design enables the profile geometry to be adequately dimensioned. Nevertheless, difficult to extrude and, to some extent, moderately difficult to extrude aluminum alloys (those with a higher alloy content) do not offer the same profile geometry options as the low alloyed and easily welded aluminum alloys such as AlMgSi0.5 and AlMgSi0.7.

Figure 2.9 shows a body shell of the Paris Metro type MF 77 utilizing welded large profile technology. The carriage cross section is shown in Fig. 2.8, together with some of the large profiles necessary for its construction. Figure 2.10 shows the right longitudinal rib needed to stiffen the floor frame of the carriage of the San Francisco Metro in the alloy AlMgSi0.7 on the runout table of the 98,000 kN direct press in Singen, Germany.

Since the introduction of the integral construction utilizing large section technology, aluminum designs can increasingly compete with steel designs in spite of the higher material cost of the aluminum. The specific properties of aluminum alloys play a role here including the low E-modulus of the various alloys and their low density. Whereas the E-modulus of aluminum alloys can be assumed to be approximately 70 GPa, that of steel is approximately 210 GPa, three times as high. At the same time, the aluminum designs can be given the same stiffness as steel designs to avoid unacceptable bending or vibrations with significantly lower weights because of the low density of 2.7 g/cm^3. In addition, the elastic properties of aluminum de-

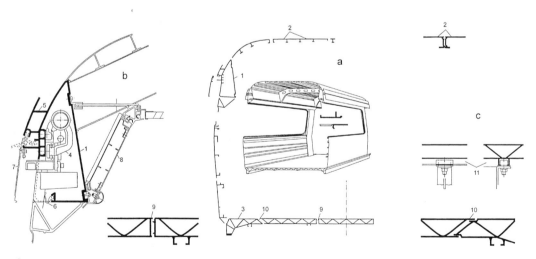

Fig. 2.8 Shell of a type MF77 carriage of the Paris Metro, self-supporting in welded large section technology (Alsthom Atlantique/ Alusuisse, 1977/1981) manufactured in sections from the age-hardened material AlMgSi0.7. a, Multifunctional longitudinal stringer; b, construction of the carriage body in the roof longitudinal stringer region; c, weld joint geometry between the individual extruded sections; 1, multifunctional longitudinal stringer; 2, section in roof region with extruded weld preparations; 3, longitudinal stringer to ensure adequate stiffness of the floor group; 4, door mechanism; 5, rainwater gutter extruded on section 1; 6, door seal location extruded on section 1; 7, roof closure section; 8, roof internal cladding; 9, floor section with extruded legs for the welded joints as well as extruded center locations; 10, floor group sections with extruded slip seating for tolerance equalization; 11, section view of the floor sections with extruded locations for bolt heads. Source: Aluminium Zentrale

signs offer significant advantages. Aluminum alloys have significantly higher elastic or energy absorption capacity relative to steel because of their low E-modulus. This is an advantage that should not be undervalued for aluminum designs subjected to impact loads, for example, in rail or road transport vehicles.

2.2.2.1 Transport Construction

Rolling Stock. Efficient low-weight rolling stock has always been of interest to railway operators. Low weights provide higher load capacities with lower energy consumption and enable higher vehicle accelerations when starting and higher vehicle deceleration on braking, as well as a reduction in rail wear. These advantages are mainly utilized by local traffic with its many stops, e.g., underground trains, but also by long distance traffic, in particular, high speed rail traffic.

Toward the end of the 1920s, the transformation of weight reduction in rolling stock resulted in the replacement of steel internal fittings by fittings made in aluminum alloys, initially in passenger carriages. However, in 1934, the Baltimore and Ohio Railroad Company, at that time

one of the largest North American Railway companies, had built for them, excluding the conventional locomotive design, an aluminum example of the semistreamlined steam-powered "Royal Blue," traveling between Chicago and St. Louis [Hug 44]. Only the wheel trucks, couplings, and buffers of the eight passenger cars were made in steel, all other components from alloys of the alloy group AlCuMg. Long extruded profiles were used for the load-carrying components of the car underframe. Even the columns of the side walls were made of extruded profiles, which were also used for the necessary stiffening in other places in the carriage. Formed sheets in the same aluminum alloy were used for the cladding of the carriage walls, for the train car roof as well as for the floor.

Sections and sheet were joined together with rivets and arc welding. In addition, the internal fittings of the carriage, for example, the tables and seats in the dining car, also were made from aluminum alloys. The eight carriages built completely from aluminum had a total weight of 350 metric tons in contrast to the identically constructed steel carriages with 650 metric tons, i.e., 54% of the weight of the steel carriages.

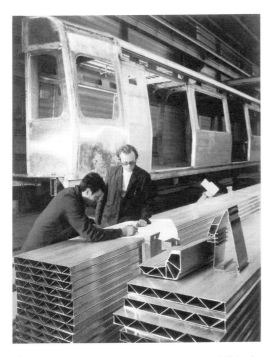

Fig. 2.9 Assembly of an aluminum MF77 type shell for the Paris Metro using welded large section technology together with some large sections ready for assembly. Source: Alusuisse

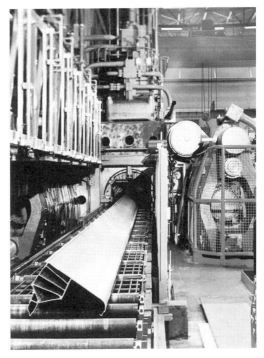

Fig. 2.10 Large section in the aluminum alloy AlMgSi0.7 for aluminum carriages for the San Francisco Metro using large section welded technology on the runout table of the 98,000 kN direct extrusion press at Alusuisse Singen. Source: Alusuisse

Fig. 2.11 Diesel power car of the Trans Europa Express (TEE) on the Rhine section

The desire to reduce the weight of rolling stock by using aluminum alloys continued to develop after World War II. In the second half of the 1950s, the German Rail Company operated several of the advanced for the time fast diesel locomotives designated VT 11.5 with a maximum speed of 160 km/h for the lucrative long-distance service.

The carriages were made from riveted and spot-welded AlMgSi1 sheets with longitudinal and transverse stiffeners in extruded solid AlMgSi1 sections. Both types of semifinished products were used in the age-hardened temper. Only the main transoms in the under frame of the carriage as well as the wheel trucks and coupling carriers were made in St52 steel as well as the coupling system. Figure 2.11 shows this diesel train on the Rhine section, and Fig. 2.12 shows a cross section of the conventionally built and thus correspondingly expensive carriage.

The multiunit railcar train shown in the photographs with its design that is still modern by today's standards traveled as the Trans Europa Express (TEE) in Inter-European long-distance travel. It consisted of five carriages as well as the two power cars, each with a diesel engine, at the front and the back. The basic concept of this diesel multiunit railcar, two external power cars with the carriages in between, is practically the basis of the German InterCity Express trains ICE1 and ICE2 used today.

During the postwar decades, the European national railways built their rail networks initially

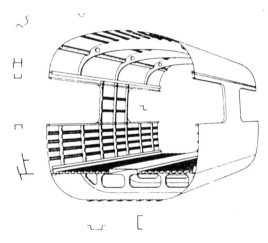

Fig. 2.12 Carriage body of the Trans Europa Express (TEE) in riveted and spot-welded ALMgSi sheets with longitudinal and transverse stiffeners in extruded sections of the same alloy in the heat treated temper

for train speeds up to 200 km/h, speeds that could be achieved using electric locomotives. In the context of the further technical development of the wheel/rail system, the tracks have been prepared in the past 10–15 years for significantly higher speeds. In the near future, the European railways are targeting future high-speed rail traffic with speeds of 350 km/h (220 mph). Large advances along this path have been made by the French national railway SNCF with its TGV, which set a world record of 515 km/h (320 mph) on test runs. In the next 20 years in Europe, a certified rail network for high-speed trains with multiple current systems and corresponding signal and control systems will develop in Europe to allow inter-European long-distance trains to travel the national rail networks. These stretches are operated for inter-European long-distance train travel with train concepts that do not follow the previously conventional train system of "a locomotive with carriages." One example is the Eurostar, a special design of the TGV with a multiple current system that can travel between Paris and London in three hours through the Channel Tunnel. The ICE3 of the DB follows a similar concept.

From this perspective, the European railway operators have a vital interest in trains with the lowest possible weight for the high-speed rail network as described previously. Low weights minimize the energy requirements for powering these trains as well as the wear of the tracks and permit high accelerations when starting and decelerations on braking.

The big breakthrough for the economical application of aluminum alloys in carriage construction was the development of the large profile technology in the 1970s by Alusuisse. This enabled rolling stock to be entirely and economically produced from aluminum at a significantly lower cost than comparable rolling stock in steel lightweight construction. This involves the use of easily extruded, relatively corrosion insensitive, and easily age-hardened aluminum alloys such as AlMgSi0.5 and AlMgSi0.7, without which the very demanding cross-sectional geometries of the large profiles could not be produced. These extrusion alloys also provided significant freedom in the design of the cross section to match the strength needed in the component. Until now, this could not be achieved with moderate to difficult to extrude alloys used previously in the manufacture of rolling stock. Modern concepts were also developed for the steel lightweight designs of rolling stock, but these could not significantly reduce the price advantage of the aluminum large profile technology [Aug 77, Wis 92]. The rolling stock produced from welded large profile technology also offers weight advantages over those produced from the high-strength steels. Both these factors resulted in the extensive application of the aluminum lightweight construction incorporating the large profile technology in Europe and the United States in the 1980s [Dav 79,

Ing 91]. Further development resulted in interest in the aluminum large profile technology for the multiunit railcars for the high-speed rail traffic. In this period, the percentage of rolling stock produced using large aluminum alloy profile technology increased out of proportion. At the start of the 1970s, it was approximately 5% but has now increased to over 60% [Ing 91].

Whereas the French high-speed train TGV of the SNCF with its respectable power and proven ability over several years was manufactured in steel, the German Railway decided to build its 280 km/h (175 mph) high-speed trains InterCity Express 1 (ICE1) and InterCity Express 2 (ICE2), as well as the 330 km/h InterCity Express 3 (ICE3), and the 230 km/h InterCity Express T (ICET), basically using self-supporting welded large aluminum profile technology. The only exception was the power cars of the trains ICE1 and ICE2, which were manufactured in steel to ensure that the driven four axles per power car could apply sufficient normal force onto the track to obtain the torque needed to achieve high acceleration and deceleration.

This, however, results in high track loading because each wheel truck of these power cars places a load of 40 metric tons onto the rails. Throughout Europe, however, the track can only be loaded to a maximum of 34 metric tons per wheel truck. For this reason, the two high-speed trains ICE1 and ICE2 cannot use the inter-European rail network. This, however, changed with the introduction of the high-speed train ICE3, which in contrast to the power car train is designed as a multiunit train; i.e., the driven axles are spread along the entire train with every second axis being driven. These trains apply a load less than 34 metric tons weight on the track per wheel truck and are therefore suitable for participation as multisystem trains for the Inter-European traffic [Tas 93]. The InterCity Express T (ICET) is in certain ways a special design of the ICE3 fitted with tilting technology developed in Italy. With this design, the multiunit train can travel around curved rails with high speed. Figure 2.13 shows an example of the ICE1 framed with a schematic diagram of the extruded profiles for the floor group, the longitudinal member of the floor group, and the connecting edge wall profile of the left side of the passenger carriage. The joint aids visible on the section corners in Fig. 2.13 for the longitudinal joining of the extruded sections are of interest.

Finally, Fig. 2.14 describes the design of the passenger carriage with all the large profiles for

Fig. 2.13 High-speed ICE1 of the Deutsche Bahn AG framed by the large sections of the carriage cross section shown in Fig. 2.14. Source: Alusuisse

the left half of the carriage. In addition, Fig. 2.15 shows a view of the design of the passenger carriage of the high-speed trains ICE2 and ICE3.

Other European national railways, for example, Denmark, England, Italy, and Norway, as well as Spain and Sweden, have learned the value of the self-supporting aluminum large profile technology in welded designs for high-speed trains as well as intercity passenger carriages and intercity rail cars. This technology has, for example, been used for building the 250 km/h (155 mph) high-speed Advanced Passenger Train of British Rail and the 300 km/h (185 mph) ERT 500 of the Italien Ferrovie dello Stato (FS). The French TGV Duplex, a double decker, new high-speed train of the SNCF, will be manufactured using welded aluminum large profile technology to control the track loading.

Self-supporting large profile aluminum technology is used not only for high-speed trains running on rails. The carriages of the track guided fast magnetic levitation Transrapid, with a maximum speed of 500 km/h (310 mph) are built using the self-supporting aluminum large profile technology in a bolted design [Mil 88]. The prototype is shown in Fig. 2.16. This assembly method is described in the section "Bus Manufacture" later in this chapter.

Naturally, thought has been given to reducing the wagon weight in rail freight transport with the aim of reducing transport energy costs. For a long time, there has been increasingly rigorous competition with other methods of transport, including road transport. Initially, this involved increasing the load capacity of the freight wagon by using individual, usually movable, aluminum alloy components for the same wagon axle load. Consideration was then given to significantly improving the handling of the construction elements. Sliding roofs, folding roofs, as well as sliding doors and shutters, were manufactured from aluminum sheet and reinforced with extruded sections by the German railway, DB, as well as the Swiss Federal Railway, SBB. With time, complete wagon bodies also were built from aluminum alloys. The structure of these wagons consisted of roll formed 1.5 to 2.0 mm thick AlMg3 sheets reinforced with AlMgSi0.5 extruded sections, apart from the under frame and the vertical end wall columns, which were made in steel. In addition, the aluminum construction offers not only the advantage of weight reduction but is also maintenance friendly, i.e., in contrast to steel designs, no painting is needed because of the corrosion resistance of the aluminum alloys used.

Tilting sidewalls on open goods wagons for specific transport applications are manufactured from AlMgSi0.5 and AlMgSi0.7 extruded profiles, as shown in Fig. 2.17. These sidewalls can

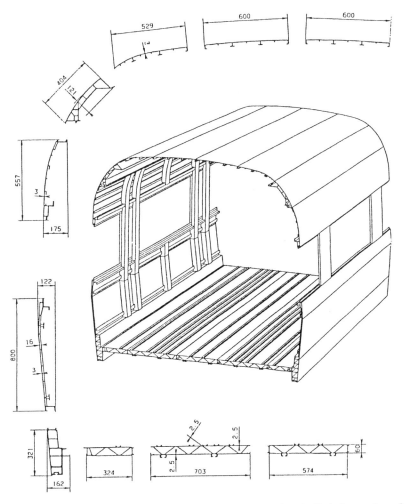

Fig. 2.14 Passenger carrier design on the high-speed train ICE1 of the Deutsche Bahn AG with the large sections of the left carriage section. Source: Alusuisse

be highly loaded and do not require any surface protection because of the corrosion resistance of the aluminum alloys.

The focal point of European rail transport is mixed cargo transport where the loading space of a wagon is more important than the load-carrying capacity. Consequently, the application of aluminum alloys is usually limited to movable components as described previously. Bulk goods transport by rail has only a limited role in Europe.

This differs in other countries, including Australia, Canada, South Africa, and the United States, with, for example, rich surface reserves of coal and minerals. The extraction site is usually a long distance from the processing plant so that bulk goods have to be transported over large distances. This process is usually carried out using rolling stock with the optimum load capacity. The optimum storage capacity of these wagons can be achieved by using self-supporting welded aluminum large profile technology, which makes them particularly economical compared with wagon designs in steel. Figures 2.18 and 2.19 show an example of a coal silo wagon built with aluminum large profile technology. The sidewalls as well as the chassis of this coal silo wagon consist mainly of large extruded profiles in the aluminum alloy AlMgSi0.7 with large format sheets of AlMg2.7Mn in the floor area. The assembly of the silo wagon involves the use of the same automatic welding systems that are used for personnel carriages.

Silo wagons of this design were designed and built by Alusuisse to U.S. standards. In spite of the high material costs of the aluminum silo wagons, their manufacturing cost per ton payload is approximately 10% less than that of a steel wagon.

Road Vehicles. The development of automobile manufacture including both cars and

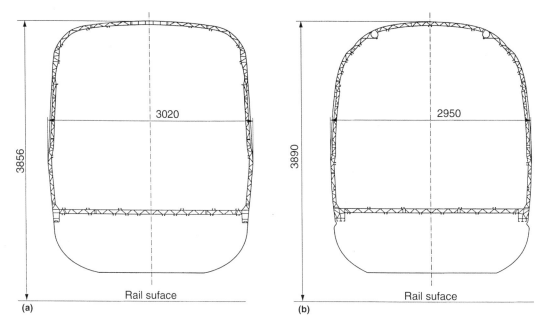

(a)

(b)

Fig. 2.15 (a) Carriage shell cross section ICE2 and (b) carriage shell cross section ICE3, self-supporting using welded large section technology. Source: ADtranz

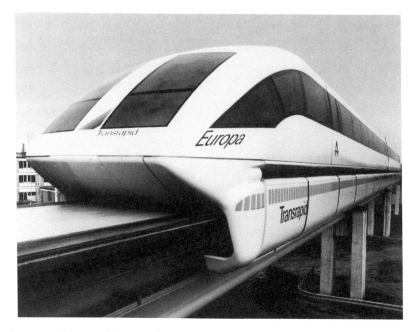

Fig. 2.16 Prototype of the magnetic levitation Transrapid manufactured with bolted aluminium large profile technology using aluminium AlMgSi0.7 extruded sections. Source: Alusuisse

Fig. 2.17 Tilting trailer walls of an open goods wagon finished in extruded hollow sections in the alloys AlMgSi0.5 and AlMgSi0.7. Source: Alusuisse

Fig. 2.18 Coal silo wagon produced in welded self-supporting large extrusion technology to U.S. standard. Source: Alusuisse

freight vehicles has been associated with the use of aluminum alloys from the beginning. Aluminum gearbox and motor housings were already being reported in the latter years of the nineteenth century. In 1924, the Swabische Hüttenwerk developed a car with a self-supporting aluminum design. In 1937, BMW fitted the well-known two-seater sports car 328 with an aluminum alloy body. In racing car manufacture, the well-known Silver Arrow manufacturer Auto Union, BMW, and Mercedes Benz used aluminum alloys to produce the lightest chassis possible. Toward the end of 1920s, the first buses with aluminum bodies were built, particularly in Switzerland (Fig. 2.20).

After World War II, this development increased rapidly. The use of aluminum alloys in road vehicles increased continuously. Today, after steel, aluminum alloys are the most important material in the manufacture of automobiles. In 1993, in Germany alone 315,000 metric tons of aluminum were used in the manufacture of cars and 58,000 metric tons in freight vehicles [Gor 94]. The main applications of aluminum are castings for engine and gearbox housings, pistons, and cylinder heads, as well as car wheels. It is also used as a semifinished product in the form of sheets or strip for the manufacture of bonnets and boot lids, water and oil coolers, and also sometimes for complete sports cars bodies

Fig. 2.19 Design and construction of the coal silo wagon shown in Fig. 2.18

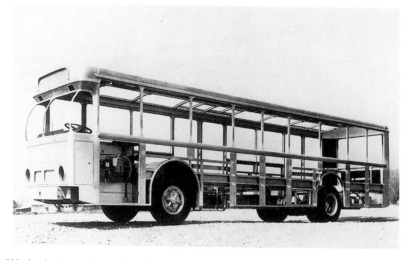

Fig. 2.20 Older bus body manufactured from aluminum alloys in Switzerland with a frame in extruded sections. Source: Alusuisse

as well as extruded semifinished profiles for the production of trim and widow frames, and for safety components such as side-impact beams in car doors. Car superstructures and bus bodies, goods vehicle superstructures, and sidewalls, in addition to forgings for the manufacture of wheels and engine components, are also made from aluminum. This increasing use of aluminum alloys provides these well-known advantages to the automobile industry:

- Lower vehicle mass and thus savings in motive energy, i.e., fuel. According to [Her 90], the replacement of 200 kg of steel by 100 kg of aluminum in a car reduces the gasoline

consumption by about 0.6 to 0.8 l/km (increases mileage 3.5 to 4.7 mpg).
- Lower environmental pollution from exhaust gases as a result of the reduced fuel consumption.
- Reduction in maintenance costs due to the better corrosion resistance of the aluminum alloys
- Simple recycling of the aluminum alloys used as secondary aluminum

Passenger Cars. In 1958, Opel in Germany introduced the Rekord shown in Fig. 2.21 as a new design to the market. The car had as a new feature for the European automobile industry window frames in extruded and age-hardened aluminum alloy for the front and rear windscreens, as well as the side windows in the doors. The aluminum frames were attached in such a way to the steel sheet that the top of the door consisted only of the window frames with the window glass, as shown in Fig. 2.21. The extruded profiles that formed the frames were designed in such a way that the rubber sections that sealed against the body could be easily located in the aluminum window frames. The extruded profiles were formed to the window frames on stretch bending machines, welded together, ground, and polished and anodized to a thickness of 4 to 6 μm. The section material used by Opel was initially Al99.8ZnMg and, later, Al99.8MgSi.

Opel introduced this design within Germany following pressure from the United States. The design was quickly adopted by Audi, BMW, and Ford. The aluminum alloy solution heat treated during the billet heating was extruded into water (standing wave). The sections had a weight per meter of only 0.150 to 0.850 kg. In the early

years, high demands were placed on the decorative appearance, in particular, on the optimum polish. Good mechanical properties were also required. The top of the door consisted only of an aluminum frame, and this frame should not bend when the door was closed. Aluminum extruded profile window frames appeared in many car models for over a decade. During this period, between 150,000 and 200,000 metric tons aluminum sections flowed into this project. Car manufacturers finally stopped using this decorative aluminum window frame construction on the doors mainly because of the wind noise between the window frame and the body associated with the rapidly increasing speeds. The cause of the wind noise was the speed-related suction forces acting externally on the window surfaces and also the pressure forces from the operation of internal fans on the inside of the window surfaces. This revealed a weakness in the aluminum window frame design. As a consequence of the E-modulus of the aluminum alloys used for the window frames being one-third that of a suitable steel, the aluminum window frames deformed elastically three times as much as a steel frame of the same design. Profile cross sections with higher moments of inertia could not easily be incorporated into the door design.

This did not exclude, however, the further use of extruded profiles as frames for the front and rear car windscreens, as shown, for example, in the E class Mercedes in Fig. 2.22. In addition,

Fig. 2.21 Automobile window frame in extruded, age-hardened, and anodized aluminum sections on an Opel Rekord manufactured in 1958. Source: Opel

Fig. 2.22 Rear window frame of the Mercedes W124 manufactured from extruded aluminum sections. The front windshield of the vehicle had a similar frame. Source: Erbslöh

numerous extruded profiles are used in car bodies for a wide range of applications, including steering wheel adjustment, seat rails, sliding roof guides, and also for water and wind deflectors in the roof area of the body and side window guides. Figure 2.23 depicts the metal frame for the folding top cover of the SL class made from an extruded profile.

Aluminum extruded profiles are particularly suited in special cases for the manufacture of safety components for the automobile because the cross-sectional shape can be exactly matched to the loading. They also offer favorable mechanical properties and density and the low E-modulus as well. A typical example is the side door beam that can fulfill its role in a very functional way. Side impact causes 30% of all road deaths in 25% of all car accidents in Germany. The car sides cannot be protected for space reasons by crumple zones as, for example, used in the front and rear. Therefore, the car manufacturers have over the years made great efforts to protect the sides of cars using effective side-impact beams as well as air bags. Figures 2.24, 2.25, and 2.28 show this technology in Audi vehicles.

The impact beam must be able to absorb the transmitted impact energy from an impact on the side door over a defined deformation displacement without breaking, buckling, or even displacement in order to protect the passengers. Research results have shown that extruded aluminum alloy profiles with a symmetrical

cross-sectional geometry and sufficient proof stress and elongation are particularly suitable for this application [Fra 89]. A correctly designed impact beam in an extruded aluminum alloy with materials properties comparable to a geometrically similar steel impact beam can possess approximately three times the elastic deformation capability before plastic deformation occurs.

Interest in the extruded age-hardened aluminum alloy side-impact beam combined with a

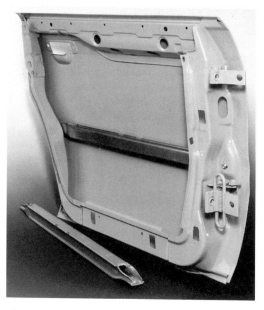

Fig. 2.24 Side door of the Audi 100 with built-in chromatized for corrosion protection, extruded section in the aluminum alloy AlMgSi1, F 31 with $R_{P0.2} = 260$ N/mm² and $A_5 = 10\%$. Source: Alusuisse

Fig. 2.25 Side-impact beam from the Audi 8 consisting of two extruded sections. Alloy AlMgSi1, F 31. The side-impact beam can be seen installed in Fig. 2.27. Source: Alusuisse

Fig. 2.23 Hood container cover of the Mercedes 300 SL and 500 SL class with extruded aluminum section frames. Source: Erbslöh

side air bag is increasing because the good physical and mechanical properties, in particular, the elastic behavior, enable the safety requirements to be fulfilled. Many automobile manufacturers are now installing them.

Naturally, there are numerous safety components that are manufactured from extruded aluminum profiles. Figure 2.26 shows a steering linkage in which the left-hand link consists of sections of extruded profiles, whereas the flexible right-hand part is manufactured from impact extruded tube sections with formed bellows. In an accident, the bellows deform so that the impact on the steering column is reduced. The good experience obtained with the deformation behavior of side-impact beams made from extruded age-hardened aluminum hollow sections has now been used in automobile plastic bumper beams with integrated aluminum hollow sections in the alloy AlMgSi0.5 or AlMgSi0.7. These sections naturally have to match the profile of the bumper beam, i.e., they have to be bent. Whereas this bending operation is carried out today on a large scale on stretched extruded profiles with significant cost for the bending, depending on the section geometry, possibly followed by a sizing operation, these deformation processes can be carried out in the United States during the extrusion process. The low hot flow stress of the aluminum alloy aids the bending process.

The introduction of defined and legally required targets of weight saving, energy saving, and simple recycling of the materials used has initiated significant innovations in recent years in the automobile industry. Previously, aluminum alloys were generally used for simple parts.

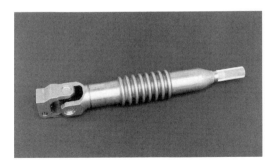

Fig. 2.26 Steering link in the alloy AlMgSi1, F 31. The connection on the left-hand side is from an extruded section, whereas the round, easily deformed in the event of a crash, corrugated section with the transition to the steering column was manufactured from an extruded tube. The corrugated region is heat treated to a strength of F 22 to F 25. Source: Alusuisse

However, in cars this did lead to weight reductions of about 60 kg in Europe and about 80 kg in the United States. The desire for larger weight savings now has resulted in greater use of light materials. In the future, engine and gearbox housings will be made primarily from aluminum alloys. Car manufacturers are also replacing load-carrying steel automobile components with aluminum. This gives an additional weight savings of 60 to 70 kg and a definite improvement in the ride because of the significantly lower undamped weights.

Meanwhile, the automobile driver has become increasingly more demanding. The stability of the body, the airbag, and the side-impact beams, ABS and effective crumple zones provide passenger protection. In addition, air conditioning, CD systems, navigation systems, and other luxurious fittings should make traveling in a car as pleasant as possible. Simultaneously, the fuel consumption should decrease and the materials from old vehicles be easily recycled.

In the future, these conflicting demands will be met by the use of light body designs in steel, aluminum alloys, improved magnesium alloys, and to a limited extent by fiber-reinforced plastic, if necessary, up to self-supporting structures. As early as 1950, Pakiney built the DYNA PANHARD car with extensive use of AlMg3 sheet and, later, AlMgCu. The car weighed only 650 kg and was extremely economical. In 1990, Honda developed the sports car NSX with AlMgSi1 sheet, and Rover has used for many years in the Land Rover aluminum sheets for the body; initially, AlMgCu and, today, AlMgSi1 [Alp 94]. The decisive step was made by AUDI AG with the production of the AUDI A8 shown in Fig 2.27. The body is made entirely of aluminum.

This breakthrough of aluminum into the steel domain has both shocked and challenged the wide strip manufacturers (body sheet). They are trying to counter this development with intelligent solutions for complete steel chassis, for example, with the use of prefinished body parts, tailored blanks. Tailored blanks are cut to size, designed for the load, body panels laser welded together from steel sheets of different thickness, strength, and surface quality. These prefinished body parts, for example, complete wheel housings, enable assembly costs and also weight to be reduced. This is the start of a process that should finish with the ultralight steel car body. However, the high point of this development today is the Audi A8 and the Audi A2 with the space frame construction of Alcoa. This construction principle can be seen in Fig. 2.27 to 2.29. Audi uses for the production of the aluminum body aluminum alloys containing the same alloying elements, a basic requirement for ease of recycling. The extruded sections needed to assemble the space frame are produced in the age-hardening alloys AlMgSi0.5 and AlMgSi0.7. Supporting floor panels consist of the age-hardening alloy AlMgSi1Cu, small sheet parts from the non-heat-treatable alloy AlMg5Mn. The die cast nodes necessary for joining the preformed and age-hardened extruded profiles to balance out the tolerances for the space frame of the Audi A8 were manufac-

Fig. 2.27 Audi A8 Quatro with a body of age-hardened aluminum alloys using the Alcoa space frame concept. Source: Audi

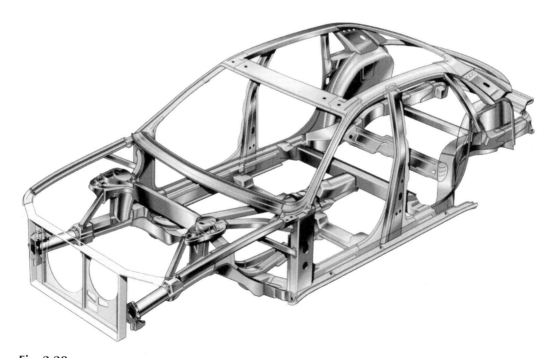

Fig. 2.28 Space frame of the Audi A8 shown in Fig. 2.27

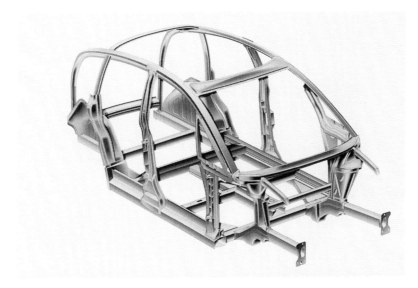

Fig. 2.29 Space frame of the Audi A2 in extruded sections, sheet and castings. Source: Audi

tured with the vacuum casting process in the heat-treatable alloy AlSi10Mg. Other cast components consisted of AlSi7. Die cast components for tolerance compensation were not used for the space frame of the A2.

Finally, cold-worked strip sections in the flow line free (Lüders lines) and heat-treatable aluminum alloy AlMg0.4Si1.2 were used as exterior body panels. Table 2.1 provides an overview of the materials used to build the aluminum body of the Audi A8.

The automobile manufacturer joins the delivered prefinished and age-hardened profile sections to assemblies by MIG welding with the aid of jigs. The complete space frame is then built using the same joining technique. The floor panels and, in particular, the 1.0 to 1.15 mm thick sheets for the body exterior skin were fixed using other joining techniques including, among others, self-piercing rivets. Finally, the finished body in white is age-hardened at a temperature of 230 °C for 30 min. It is mainly the body pan-

els that harden during this heat treatment. The sections of the space frame heat more slowly because these are shielded by the body outer skin during the heat treatment. For this reason, the bent profile sections for the space frame have to be supplied age-hardened in such a way that they harden only slightly during the age-hardening process described and do not over age. In particular, the softened peripheral zones of the section welded from the MIG welding should as far as possible reharden. The complete aluminum body of the Audi A8 is approximately 200 kg lighter than a conventional steel body of the same size.

Bus Manufacture. The manufacture of buses from aluminum alloys has a tradition in Switzerland, as shown in Fig. 2.20. The Alpine country started to consider the reduction in weight of goods vehicles in the 1920s. The engine powers available at this time were still very limited and could therefore be better utilized with a lower weight. The Swiss with their mountainous re-

Table 2.1   Aluminum alloys used for the aluminum body of the Audi A8

	Material	AA(a)	Temper	$R_{p0.2}$ (N/mm²)(b)	R_m N/mm²(c)	A_5 %(d)
Sheet	AlMg0.4Si1.2	6016	T6	200	250	14
	AlMgSi1Cu	6009	T6	230	280	10
	AlMg5Mn	5182	. . .	135	270	25
Vacuum die casting	AlSi10Mg	. . .	T6	120–150	180	15
Permanent mold casting	AlSi7	. . .	T6	200	230–250	15
Extruded section	AlMgSi0.5/0.7	. . .	T6	210–245	1.08 $R_{p0.2}$	11

(a) Aluminum Association designation. (b) $R_{p0.2}$ is 0.2% proof stress. (c) R_m is tensile strength. (d) A_5 is elongation after fracture. Source: Audi

gions never lost sight of this basic principle; it increased in importance after World War II. Other countries, including Germany, also became interested in these solutions.

Extruded profiles in aluminum alloys were the natural solution for the economical lightweight construction of buses. Their low density and good mechanical properties, as well as the optimum shape-forming capability combined with the use of modern joining techniques, provided not only the prerequisite for economic designs of bus superstructures but also for a rational transport of the passengers.

The bus construction concept is based in principle on a lattice frame design of extruded aluminum sections similar to the space frame of the Audi A8 (Fig. 2.28). These profiles are welded together as shown in Fig. 2.30. The body panels are attached with suitable joining techniques. Buses built entirely of aluminum according to

this system are in operation today in Switzerland, Denmark, and Norway. System-built bus superstructures are also common in the United States with sidewalls in extruded sections similar to those used today in Europe for railway rolling stock [Alp 94].

More than a decade ago, Alusuisse developed a bolted bus superstructure with good results. The nucleus of this aluminum bus superstructure is the bolted corner elements as shown in Fig. 2.32, which, combined with the system sections, provide for simple assembly. After successful trials in their own country, other European countries became interested in the process. The two companies Schweizerische Aluminium AG and the German company Kässbohrer presented to the International Automobile Association (IAA) in 1987 a study commissioned by the Ministry for Research and Technology of a bus manufactured of aluminum using the bolted design under the name SETRA CONCEPT BUS. This bus is shown in Fig. 2.31 and the design of the bolted corner joints of the Alusuisse system M5438 in Fig. 2.32.

The bolted design of the supporting aluminum lattice frame had considerable advantages over a similar welded design. The bus superstructure can be produced extremely economically and quickly without labor-intensive reworking as a result of welding distortion. There is also the advantage for the vehicle owner that accident repairs can be carried out in a relatively short time and to a relatively high quality. This assembly system has been successful in many countries. Moreover, the Swiss have also used this method of assembly for light rolling stock for passenger traffic. The carriage bodies of the experimental vehicles of the magnetic levitated Transrapid described in the section "Rolling Stock" and Fig. 2.16 are built from bolted extruded aluminum sections.

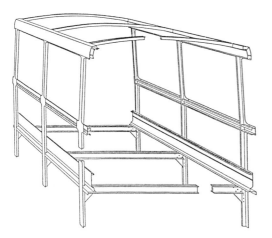

Fig. 2.30 Old lattice design for coach construction as shown in Fig. 2.20 manufactured from extruded aluminum sections. Source: Alusuisse

Fig. 2.31 The study of a coach presented at IAA 1987 with bolted, supporting lattice frame construction in extruded aluminum sections. Source: Alusuisse

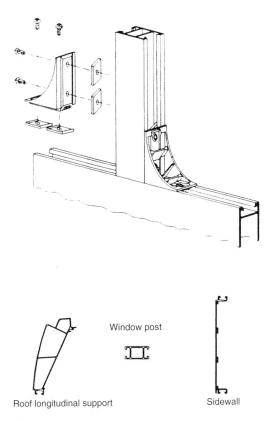

Window post

Roof longitudinal support   Sidewall

Fig. 2.32   Bolted Alusuisse system M5438. Source: Alusuisse

Road Freight Vehicles. For a long time, transport companies in Europe have been subjected to increasing ruinous competitive pressure with increasing costs. Consequently, there is ongoing great interest in freight vehicles with low weights, but with optimum load capacity and low maintenance costs. This leads to a reduction of the transport costs and an increase in the competitiveness.

The increase in the transport capacity can be achieved in two ways:

- By increasing the size of the freight vehicles, which has also been carried out in the past. Today, freight vehicle sizes have reached their limit because of the permitted road loads.
- By reducing the vehicle weight using specific lightweight construction without any further increase in the road loading. This approach offers potential for the future.

Specific aluminum alloys and, in the future, also magnesium alloys, are available for the development of lightweight commercial vehicles. These alloys are characterized by the low densities, adequate material properties, corrosion, and weather resistance with low maintenance costs as well as optimum design capabilities. As in many such applications, extruded semifinished products are particularly suitable, particularly sections with their unlimited cross-sectional shapes. The relatively simple recycling of these materials as secondary materials also plays a role.

Systems for the assembly of truck planking, in particular, truck sides, had already been developed in the first half of the 1960s by the aluminum industry in conjunction with the manufacturers of freight vehicle superstructures. The sidewalls manufactured from extruded hollow sections shown in Fig. 2.33 have proved to be more stable and require less maintenance than the old wooden sidewalls and also are decorative. It is possible today to produce on large presses small truck sides in one piece as shown by the profiles in Fig. 2.34. Trucks with the old wooden superstructures disappeared within a few years with aluminum profiles replacing wood for many loading space floors.

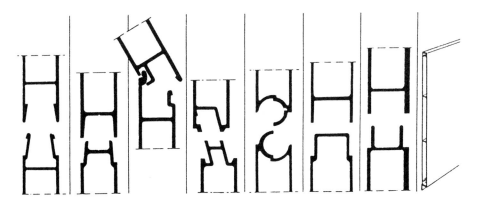

Fig. 2.33   Typical aluminum hollow sections for goods vehicle sides in the alloy AlMgSi0.5. Source: Alp 94

The use of aluminum alloys for truck and trailer constructions for the transport of bulk goods and liquids has proved to be particularly economic, for example the silo rolling stock in Fig. 2.18. This also applies to coarse bulk goods transported with road vehicles. Silo trailers are frequently manufactured entirely from aluminum alloys. The chassis of the trailer is frequently manufactured from extruded aluminum sections. In Europe, silo and liquid transporters predominantly use this type of aluminum superstructure [Koe 88]. Figure 2.35 also shows a loose-goods vehicle for building sites, with a tipping aluminum body made in AlMg4.5Mn sheets with transverse reinforcement (round spars) of extruded AlMgSi1 sections. Finally, Fig. 2.36 shows a trailer with a covered tipping body made entirely of aluminum sections. All aluminum tipping body shells have low wear.

Planked superstructures in extruded aluminum sections have also proved successful as shown in Fig. 2.37. In spite of the higher material costs for aluminum alloy designs, these are viable because of the increase in load capacity derived from the weight saving. In contrast to other European countries, in Switzerland, the planked trailers are made completely from aluminum, including the load-carrying parts of the chassis. In the United States, the use of aluminum alloys for goods vehicles raises fewer questions than in Europe.

The use of aluminum components made from extruded semifinished hollows for superstructures as well as chassis, but also from strip and sheet for the manufacture of containers and wheel rims and so forth, will increase in the future for goods vehicles. The aim is an optimum low vehicle weight with optimum carrying ca-

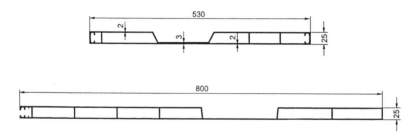

Fig. 2.34 Five-core hollow section for goods vehicles sides with a width of 530 mm and a height of 25 mm and a six-core side section 800 mm wide and a height of 25 mm manufactured in AlMgSi0.5, F 25. Source: Alusuisse

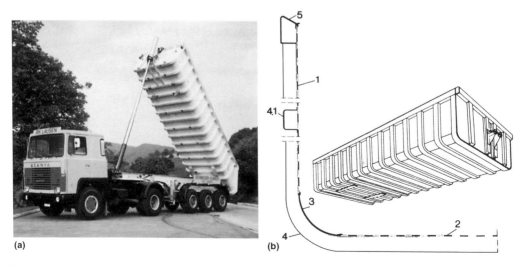

(a) (b)

Fig. 2.35 (a) Tipping wagon with welded tilting body in aluminum sheet reinforced with round spars of extruded aluminum sections. Source: Alusuisse. (b) Tilting body from (a) constructed from: 1 and 2, sheets of AlMg4.5Mn; 3, extruded aluminum curved section in AlMg4.5Mn; 4, round spar with AlMgSil extruded aluminum sections and a cross-sectional geometry of 4.1: 5, top edge in extruded aluminum section

pacity. Aluminum is well suited for this. Finally, the recycling of the used aluminum from old, no longer usable goods vehicles is relatively simple.

Aircraft manufacture is one of the oldest applications of aluminum. As early as 1897, aluminum-base materials were used for the construction of airships, and age-hardening aluminum alloys enabled the German aircraft manufacturer Junkers to introduce the complete metal airplane (Ju-4) in 1917. Whereas today, certain components of modern aircraft such as elevators, rudders, and landing flaps are made from specific weight saving and carbon fiber-reinforced plastics (CFP), aluminum will remain

in the future the dominating metallic-base material for the manufacture of aircraft in the form of plate, sheet, extruded sections, and cast components. Aluminum alloys still have potential for further development. The aircraft outer skin will still be made from aluminum alloys. Important parts of the wings, stiffeners in the shape of spars and stringers are also made from high-strength aluminum alloys as well as window frames, connection nodes, and landing gear components, including the forged aluminum wheel rims. However, in spite of their being the dominant materials used, the trend is for the use of aluminum alloys in the entire Airbus fleet to reduce, as shown in Fig. 2.38. Carbon fiber-

Fig. 2.36 Tipping trailer with covered body made entirely from extruded multicore hollow sections for the transport of fine powdered goods. Source: Alusuisse

Fig. 2.37 Trailer with planked construction and chassis in extruded aluminum sections. Source: Alusuisse

reinforced plastic materials do have a lower density and much higher mechanical properties, but they also have a high impact crack sensitivity with low ductility and toughness. Moreover, their manufacture involves complex production and quality control processes. They are therefore correspondingly expensive [AlH 71, Alt 88, Alp 94].

Extruded sections are used in aircraft in different places for load-carrying or reinforcement functions. For example, they are used as longitudinal stiffeners for the sheet skin of the aircraft fuselage in the form of stringers. Figure 2.39 shows stringer profiles as longitudinal stiffening of an airbus fuselage where the external skin is produced from roll clad aluminum sheets in the alloy 2024. Extruded sections are used for the seat rails and the floor transverse supports. The latter can also be easily seen in Fig. 2.39. The cross-sectional geometry and the relative size of the extruded profiles used are shown in Fig. 2.40. Spars for transverse stiffening of the fuselage skin as shown in Fig. 2.39 are made from AA2024 strip.

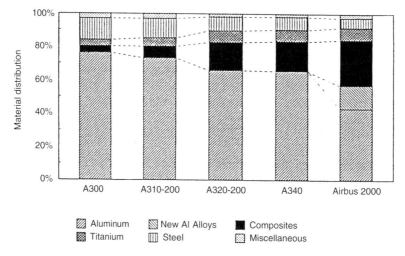

Fig. 2.38 The percentage of metallic materials in the Airbus fleet. Source: Daimler Benz Aerospace Airbus

Fig. 2.39 Airbus fuselage cell with roll clad AA2024 sheet skin longitudinally reinforced with extruded stringer sections in AA2024 and with transverse reinforcement of spars in roll clad AA2024 sheet. The clearly visible cabin floor supports are manufactured from AA7075 extruded sections. Source: VAW

The fraction of extruded profiles within the total of semifinished products used for aircraft in the Airbus fleet is around 11%; in contrast to Boeing aircraft, where it is 41%. As Fig. 2.41 shows, with Boeing, the fraction of extruded aluminum profiles used dominates when compared with other semifinished products. With the Airbus fleet, sheet forms the largest fraction.

Weight reduction also plays an important role in modern aircraft manufacture. The demand is for low-density materials with good mechanical properties that can be stressed optimally to the operating safety limit. Since Wilm's chance discovery in 1909 at the Dürener Metallwerke of the age-hardening capability of AlCuMg, the

aluminum industry has focused on the aim of producing high-strength alloys that can be hot and cold worked. The alloy groups AlCuMg and AlZnMgCu, as well as the new somewhat difficult AlLi alloys, offer the aircraft industry aluminum alloys that can be statically and dynamically loaded to high stresses and processed to semifinished products by rolling, forging, and extrusion. Aluminum alloys with high hot strengths are also available for supersonic aircraft [Alp 94].

The classic aluminum alloys for aircraft construction have been modified over the years and their heat treatment so specialized that today, they not only achieve optimum materials prop-

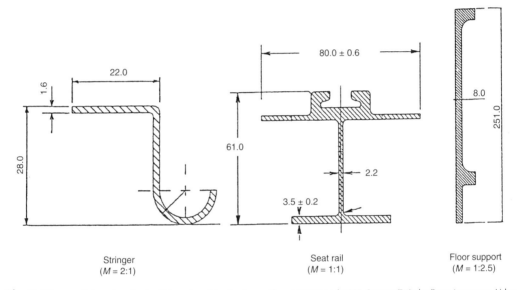

Fig. 2.40 Extruded sections for the Airbus aircraft in aluminum alloys AA2024 and 7075. Source: Daimler Benz Aerospace Airbus

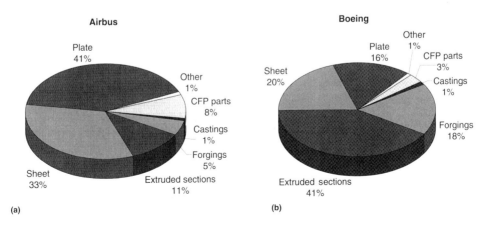

Fig. 2.41 Distribution of the semifinished products used in (a) the Airbus fleet compared with (b) the Boeing fleet. Source: Daimler Benz Aerospace Airbus

erties, but also largely meet the corrosion requirements of the aerospace industry. In contrast, the aluminum alloy AA8090 has been recently developed specifically for aircraft construction. Compared with other high-strength aluminum alloys, it has a density 10% lower with good static and dynamic properties and an *E*-modulus that is approximately 10% higher [Ren 97]. Because of the extreme material loading in aircraft, the aerospace industry naturally still demands the further development of existing aluminum alloys and the development of new aluminum alloys with even higher mechanical properties. Further developments for the Airbus fleet concentrate at the moment on the higher-strength alloys in the AlZnMgCu alloy family with better corrosion resistance and the new development of particle reinforced aluminum alloys. An AlMgSiCu alloy Aluminum Association 6113 (AA6113) reinforced with 25% volume SiC particles has an *E*-modulus double that of nonreinforced alloy variants [Ren 97].

The development of high-strength aluminum alloys for aircraft construction and the requirement for ever larger and more expensive sections has naturally had an effect on extrusion plants. The high-strength aluminum-base alloys are all difficult to extrude. To meet the materials properties required by the aerospace industry, they have to be handled carefully after extrusion. Not only are optimum material properties for static as well as dynamic loading required for aircraft alloys, but also the residual stresses of the first type have to be as low as possible for stress and machining purposes.

There is not only ongoing further development in aerospace materials, but also, naturally, in aircraft construction itself. New fuselage constructions with integrated stringer sections are being developed for the Airbus fleet. These enable the aircraft fuselage sections to be manufactured with 10% less weight and are up to 25% less expensive than the conventional riveted method of construction. Two concepts are favored:

- External skin in sheet, which is welded together to form the fuselage and then bonded with extruded aluminum stringer sections by laser welding
- Extruded external skin with 1.6 to 4 mm wall thickness and integrated stringer sections as shown in Fig. 2.42 to 2.44, e.g., in principle an aircraft fuselage using the welded alumi-

Fig. 2.42 Extruded tube with integral stringers in the aluminum alloy AA6013. Source: Daimler Benz Aerospace Airbus

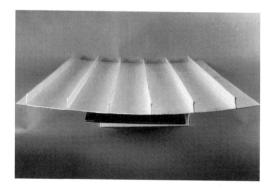

Fig. 2.43 Extruded tube from Fig. 2.42 opened out for the fuselage skin. Source: Daimler Benz Aerospace Airbus

num large section technology used in the manufacture of ICE wagons.

Both concepts are associated with the replacement of the roll clad sheet material 2024 by the new weldable materials AA6013 and AA6056 based on the AlMgSiCu family.

The second concept leads to a new perspective in the use of very wide extruded profiles for

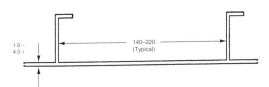

Fig. 2.44 Extruded cross-sectional geometry of the extruded external skin with integrated stringers. Source: Daimler Benz Aerospace Airbus

the fuselage external skin, a special demand on aluminum extrusion plants with large extrusion presses. Whereas the fuselage construction today involves sheets 2500 mm wide, even the largest extrusion press in the industrialized countries cannot, at the moment, produce equivalent sections with a flat cross-sectional geometry. Therefore, the production of extruded section tubes with integrated stringers as shown in Fig. 2.42 has been considered among other ideas. They can be opened out into a wide profile as shown in Fig. 2.43. Using this production method, which is not unusual for extrusion, external skins up to 2100 mm wide can be produced. However, the required wall thickness of 1.4 to 4 mm presents process-related extrusion problems. It is not possible to avoid a certain variation in wall thickness in the extruded tube because of the tendency of the mandrel to eccentricity, i.e., movement from the press axis. Therefore, extremely serious considerations being given within extrusion plants for the solution to this problem, assuming a solution is indeed possible.

Watercraft. A low weight also brings significant advantages to ships. As with other methods of transport, low weights can be achieved by the use of low-density construction materials. Suitable aluminum alloys are also available for watercraft. Lightweight construction methods provide the following advantages to watercraft:

- The carrying capacity of the watercraft is increased: its radius of action can thus be increased.
- The stability of the ship is improved by lightweight superstructures lowering the center of gravity.

- The draft of the ship can be reduced.
- Painting and other surface protection measures can be spared by the use of seawater-insensitive materials including AlMg3, AlMg5, and AlMg4.5Mn for ship components that come into contact with seawater. This reduces maintenance costs.
- The antimagnetic properties of the aluminum alloys simplify navigation.

In spite of this, the complete aluminum ship has not prevailed. Some examples were built in the decades after World War II, for example, the Binnentanker motorboat *Alumina* in the 1960s in Germany with a draft of 1000 metric tons, as well as in 1967, in the United States, the sea ship *Sacal Borincano*. Its construction required approximately 345 metric ton of sheet and extruded sections in the alloy AlMg4.5Mn. The 119 m long completely aluminum ship with a welded design was used to transport semitrailers between Miami and Puerto Rico.

Today, the production of entirely aluminum ships is limited to small ferries and passenger ships for coastal and inshore operation as well as special ships such as rescue boats and hovercraft. Private yachts, in particular, are made entirely of aluminum. The usual method of construction preferred for these ships is a combination of spars in extruded AlMgSi1 sections and an outer skin of AlMg or AlMgMn welded sheet. The extruded profiles used are, therefore, the load-carrying structural components.

The superstructure of large ships with steel hulls is completely different. The superstructure is preferably made using aluminum lightweight construction techniques for stability reasons. The lightweight construction technique enables the center of gravity of the ship to be lowered or the height of the superstructure increased without impairing the stability of the ship with a higher center of gravity. The design of the superstructure in the lightweight construction method has to take into account the different E-modulus of iron and aluminum alloys to cope with the temperature-dependent stresses that occur between the two materials, as well as prevent contact corrosion at steel/aluminum joints by the use of insulating elements [Alh 71, Alt 88, Alp 94].

Large ships need considerable quantities of aluminum semifinished products in the form of sheet and profiles for aluminum superstructures (Fig. 2.45). The superstructures of the passenger ships *United States, Norway,* and the *Queen Elizabeth II* each required approximately 2000 metric tons of aluminum. Modern large aircraft carriers require similar large quantities of aluminum semifinished products for their superstructures. Finally, large section technology has also been used for lightweight construction techniques in ship superstructures. The use of large profiles reduces the assembly costs.

Extruded large multicavity sections are used, for example, in ships in the fishing industry as rack floors with through flowing coolant for the storage of fish in the cold rooms. Mobile intermediate decks for ships for the transport of animals can be produced from large aluminum profiles for economic reasons, as shown in Fig. 2.46. The alloys AlMgSi0.5, AlMgSi0.7, and AlMgSi1 are used for these and for the sup-

porting structures within the superstructures of the ships.

2.2.2.2 Machine Manufacture, Electrical Machines, and Electrical Equipment

The manufacture of machinery and electrical machines was, for a long time, dominated by iron-base materials, but with time this has changed. Other materials with their favorable properties are threatening the domination of the iron-base alloys. During the past 20 years, personnel costs have increased more rapidly than the material costs. Aluminum-base materials with their very specific materials properties have

Fig. 2.45 Aluminum superstructure of a passenger ship. Source: Alusuisse

Fig. 2.46 Multicore hollow section for mobile intermediate ship decks for sheep transport. Source: Alusuisse

today secured a respectable position in this field [Cor 95].

For a long time, the use of aluminum alloys in machine manufacture was restricted to the smaller components that could be produced by casting, forging, stamping, or even extrusion. The future emphasis for manufacture with aluminum alloys will be on the large section technology. This gives the designer a new design element to be used to achieve optimum technical and economical solutions [Alp 94]. The load and functional related shape capabilities of these extruded profiles as well as the high dimensional accuracy have revolutionized many designs, as shown in the examples depicted in this section.

Low density and good mechanical properties make aluminum alloys interesting for moving machine components with high accelerations and decelerations. Nonmagnetic properties, as well as good thermal conductivity, ensure that aluminum alloys play an important role in the manufacture of electrical machines and electrical equipment. Electric motor housings belong to the most important aluminum products in the electrical industry, as shown in Fig. 2.47(a). Weight advantages, free choice of shape, and the good thermal conductivity of low-alloyed aluminum materials have resulted in aluminum replacing cast iron and steel for electric motor housings [Joh 85, Tas 93]. Extruded aluminum

sections provide for electric motor housings along with the functional related cross sectional geometry:

- A large heat-conducting housing surface with extruded cooling fins with significantly narrower spacings and thinner wall thickness than cast housings
- Integrated cooling channels depending on requirements as shown in Fig. 2.47
- An extruded material with high strength and good elongation significantly superseding the mechanical properties of the earlier cast housings
- Housing material not susceptible to corrosion

Electric motor housings with extruded feet, cooling fins, and cooling channels can literally be obtained as finished components by cross cutting the extrusion. Even with small or moderate production runs, the manufacturing costs of the extruded motor housings are well below those of cast aluminum housings. Bus bars (Fig. 2.48) from aluminum sections with pressure clad and, more recently, mechanically bonded layers of ferritic steel are produced to supply S and U trains.

The options of large section technology include the assembly simplifying large section showed in Fig. 2.49 for the tool carrier of a ma-

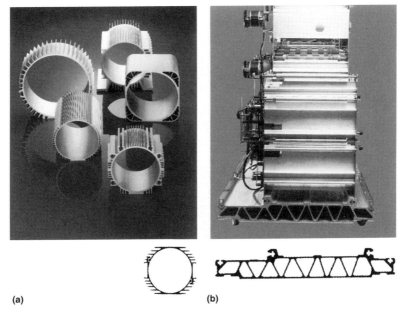

(a)   (b)

Fig. 2.47 AlMgSi0.5 extruded section for electric motor housings (a) and a large section for the console of a high-speed printer (b). Source: Alusuisse

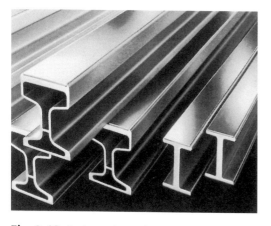

Fig. 2.48 Bus bar sections in aluminum alloys with pressure clad layer of stainless steel. The bus bars from S and U trains collect the electrical energy through the stainless steel layer. Source: Alusuisse

Fig. 2.49 Installation-friendly large section in the alloy AlMgSi0.5 for the tool holder of a machining center. Source: Alusuisse

chining center as well as the carrier and housing section for the scanner of a carpet tufting machine in Fig. 2.50. Frequently, the aluminum profile leaves the extrusion plant as a ready-to-install machine component, i.e., application and function specific extrusion, age-hardened, and cut to length. In this sense, the aluminum large section can practically be conceived as a finished system component for simple installation. The cross-sectional geometry of the extruded section can be almost ideally matched to the function and loading, and the lattice geometry of the extrusion profile makes the large section very stable and stiff. Aluminum large sections for ma-

chines, fixtures, and transport systems can therefore make a significant, and perhaps even the most important, contribution to the entire design. Last but not least are the significant economic advantages that make aluminum sections eminently suitable for the manufacture of machines and electrical machines as well as for the manufacture of numerous traditional products. Large section technology and integral design reduce the assembly costs. They replace complete steel designs with one section and thus eliminate many manufacturing steps.

Using a hot circular saw and a food slicing machine for sausage and cheese as examples,

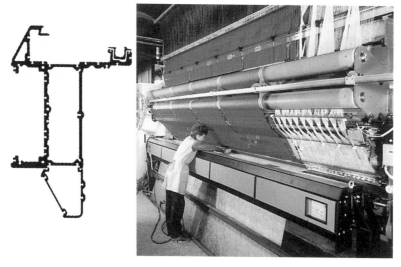

Fig. 2.50 AlMgSi0.5 support and housing sections for the scanner of a carpet tufting machine. Source: Alusuisse

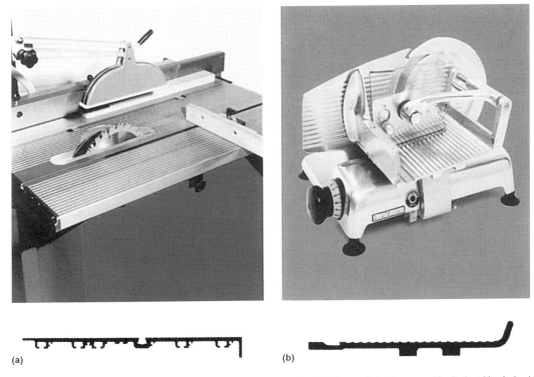

Fig. 2.51 Application of large sections in the alloy AlMgSi0.5 for (a) the table of a wood circular saw and for (b) the table of a food slicer. Source: Alusuisse

Fig. 2.51 illustrates the ideal way an extruded section can be matched to the function of a machine and its operation [Als Pr].

The large section shown in Fig. 2.52 for the manufacture of fixing plates for pneumatic control elements shows an example of these capabilities. Figure 2.53 demonstrates the cost saving, production technological possibilities as well as the process technical advantages of func-tion matched aluminum extruded sections designed as a section for the manufacture of electrical pneumatic control units. Rotor blades of wind electrical generators are usually made from multicavity hollow sections. Extruded aluminum sections dominate as the supporting elements in transport systems such as modular transfer systems, linear vibration conveyors, and

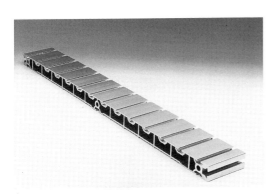

Fig. 2.52 Cross section of an 800 mm wide large section in the alloy AlMgSi0.5 for the production of fixing plates for pneumatic control elements. Source: Alusuisse

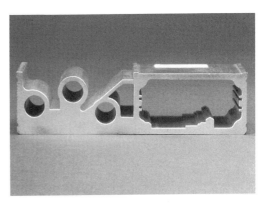

Fig. 2.53 Aluminum section in the alloy AlMgSi0.5 for the manufacture of electropneumatic control units. Source: Alusuisse

Fig. 2.54 Extruded blanks in AlMgSi0.5 for rotors of the air
compressor of a pneumatic tanker pumping unit
for sewage. Source: Honsel

so forth. It is not only aluminum large sections
that have proved to be advantageous for machine design, small sections can also offer significant advantages, for example, the extruded
blanks for the rotor of an air compressor. The
slots to receive the vanes are extruded in the
section. Figure 2.54 shows this quite clearly. The
slots have to be milled out of the blanks in steel
rotors.

Pure aluminum and low-alloyed aluminum alloys including AlMgSi0.5 are good conductors
of heat. Extruded tubes and sections in these materials are therefore used for heat exchangers and
cooling elements. Nests of tubes made from extruded pure aluminum are required in large
quantities in the chemical, petrochemical, and
food industries. In air conditioners, small, flat
multicore hollow sections are used. Tube sections are used in recuperative and regenerative
systems, including heat exchangers and also solar panels. The use of hollow sections in condensers for liquid nitrogen tanks is well known.
The high-power electronic industry requires
high-power cooling bodies as shown installed in
Fig. 2.55. Using separately extruded base and
finned sections joined together by a rolling process in which the finned sections are firmly
rolled with their feet in the slot of the base section, high-power cooling elements are manufactured as shown in Fig. 2.56 [Tas 93].

Naturally, this description of the application
possibilities of extruded aluminum sections in
the manufacture of machinery, electrical machines, and electrical equipment can only just
touch on the full range and the versatility. The
ready-to-install integral component made from
an extruded section has become an important
factor in the industries mentioned thanks to large
section technology. This gives the designer the
ability to develop machine specific solid and
hollow sections the practical nature of which reduces the cost of the product.

2.2.2.3 Architecture

Buildings. The destruction of the West European cities initiated a building boom in the 50
years after World War II. Large quantities of
building elements including windows and doors
were needed. Many new commercial buildings
as well as offices were fitted with aluminum
cladding, which had been seen in the United
States.

This accelerated the penetration of aluminum
into building. In addition, architects appreciated
the silver metal.

Since then, large quantities of aluminum
semifinished products are consumed by the
building sector. Today, aluminum is one of the
most important materials in buildings. Over the
years the metal has gained a specific market
with its decorative surface finish and its good
corrosion properties. Today, the building sector

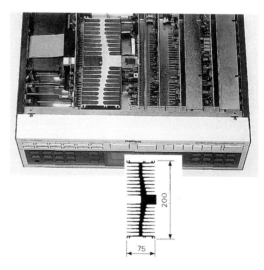

Fig. 2.55 Example of a heat sink in the alloy AlMgSi0.5 for
the cooling of the thyristors of a compact disc
player

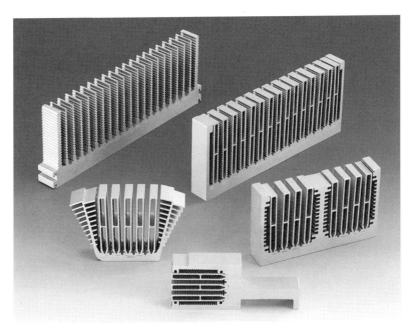

Fig. 2.56 Various high-efficiency heat sinks constructed from extruded AlMgSi0.5 elements to remove the heat produced from electronic systems. Source: Alusuisse

alone accounts for 15% of the total aluminum consumption of Germany and is therefore the second largest consumer of this material after the transport sector [Alz 97]. The main applications are the door and window sectors as well as building façades, followed by roofs, internal walls, conservatories, and building entrances.

Aluminum façades are usually used for imposing buildings, for example, large retail stores, company head offices, and large bank buildings and official buildings. Over time, specific flexible building systems have been developed that can be easily installed. The base structure of extruded sections provides the support for the façade and is usually invisible after installation. Aluminum-base structures can also be used for building façades in other materials.

The high strength of the aluminum alloys used in building applications enables ambitious filigree but reliable designs to be produced. However, when this material is used with other materials, such as steel, the different physical properties of the materials have to be taken into account. In particular, the significantly lower E-modulus and the higher linear coefficient of thermal expansion of aluminum have to be allowed for. Also, the lower solidus temperature of the aluminum alloys used in high-rise buildings

compared with steel has to be considered in the context of fire prevention measures. The AlMgSi-base metallic construction materials have a solidus temperature of only about 580 °C.

Fig. 2.57 Skyscraper of the Dresdner Bank in Frankfurt, Germany, with a naturally anodized aluminum façade

Fig. 2.58 Aluminum glass façade of a commercial building. Source: Hueck

Over time, different types of building façades have been developed in addition to the entire aluminum façades shown in Fig. 2.57. Aluminum glass façades as shown in Fig. 2.58 are becoming more popular. They provide a lot of light; are easy to maintain; and energy producing elements such as photovoltaic modules [Alp 94], which fulfill specific heating requirements, can be included. Building façades of mixed designs, for example, stone and aluminum as well as stone and aluminum-glass, are found to an increasing extent, as shown in Fig. 2.58 and 2.59. Finally, pure stone façades with stove enameled aluminum windows and frames make a good impression as can be seen in Fig. 2.63.

Frequently, in imposing buildings glass roofed courts with curved glass roof constructions are integrated into the building as shown in Fig. 2.60. These are usually associated with the entrances to the building. These can also be found in smaller buildings. Today, curved glass roof designs can be produced easily from bent extruded sections as shown in Fig. 2.61. Thermally insulated aluminum sections are used as with windows and doors.

The different systems for building façades include the fixing to the building wall. Frequently, a steel skeleton is fixed to the wall onto which

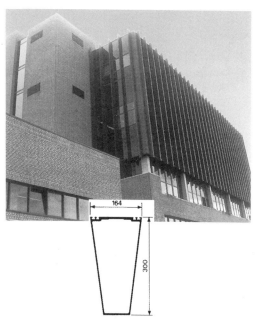

Fig. 2.59 Aluminum façade of the post office in Odense, Denmark, with the supporting vertical façade section. Source: Alusuisse

Fig. 2.60 Aluminum glass façade in combination with an illuminated courtyard and curved roof over the entrance of the Euro-Cetus-Complex in Amsterdam, Netherlands. Source: Hueck

Fig. 2.61 Curved glass roof with aluminum sections for an illuminated courtyard of a sports center in France. Source: Cintro Systems

the curtain wall is then fitted. Figure 2.62 clearly shows this in the aluminum glass façade wall design from Erbslöh-Aluminum for the entrance of the Neuss fire station in Hammerdamfeld.

The largest amount of aluminum used in buildings is for windows and doors. They are the central part of building architecture. The use of suitable aluminum alloys such as AlMgSi0.5 and sometimes AlMgSi0.7 ensures that the building components are low maintenance compared with other window materials, with the exception of plastic-based materials. The hot-working process extrusion enables visually very ambitious and decorative window designs to be developed, a possibility that is hardly possible with, for example, wood. This, combined with the surface treatment of the aluminum building components, can have a strong influence on the appearance of a building's façade as (Fig. 2.63).

Windows and doors have a major influence on the office and domestic quality as well as the energy efficiency of the building. Before the energy crisis in the 1970s, aluminum windows and door frames and sashes were installed without thermal insulation. Earlier designs did not even

include double glazing. This had the disadvantage of cold bridges forming because of the good thermal conductivity of the aluminum alloys used. At low external temperatures, the aluminum material transported the cold to the inside of the window and the moisture condensed from the room air onto the section surface and could even freeze in winter. An ice film formed. In the sun's rays, the reverse happened, even with low external temperatures. The metallic window frames heated up and transferred their heat to the room air. The metallic window frames acted as radiators.

This changed during the energy crisis toward the middle of the 1970s. Whereas previously, windows and doors were usually considered from the architectural viewpoint, the requirement for thermal insulation and sound insulation rapidly grew. The window and door sections were insulated using inherently stable plastic bridges with low thermal conductivity as shown in the sash section in Fig. 2.64. This process was also introduced for the manufacture of aluminum façades. Figure 2.64 also shows the use of the extruded aluminum spacers for double glazed windows in Fig. 2.65.

A special aluminum window design, the wood aluminum window, was developed at a relatively early stage even before the energy crisis of the 1970s. This design arose from the concept of having the well-proven and warm wood window frame on the inside, while outside, the aluminum section used made the window weather tight with all the advantages of the corrosion-resistant aluminum alloy with a surface treatment such as anodizing, wet painting, or powder coating for additional protection. This is shown in Fig. 2.66.

Conservatories built onto domestic houses as shown in Fig. 2.67 have been popular for many years. These extensions can increase the living area, as well as improve the climate of the living area by light, plants, and solar energy.

Aluminum extrusions are naturally best suited for the design of these conservatories. Their good strength with low weight and the production of application suited section geometry enables architecturally attractive buildings to be produced. In special cases, very light houses with conservatory-based design have been built using extruded aluminum sections (Fig. 2.68).

Movable interlocking walls also benefit from the low weight of the aluminum alloys used and from the solid appearance of the sections. With the good formability of the alloys used, curved

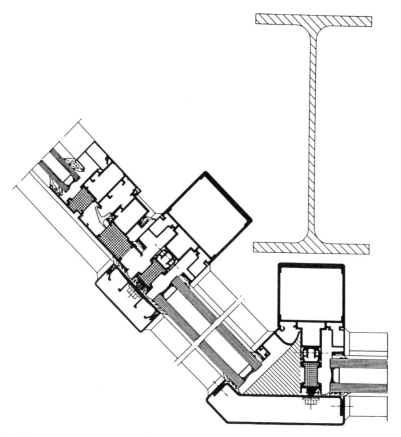

Fig. 2.62 Ekonal-FV70 aluminum glass façade system from Erbslöh-Aluminium for the Neuss fire station in Hammerdamfeld. The steel framework for fixing the façade is shown by the double T beam on the right-hand side of the drawing. Source: Erbslöh-Aluminium

Fig. 2.63 Refurbishment of the NCR at Spree-Ufer in Berlin, Germany, with the blue baked painted aluminum window frames

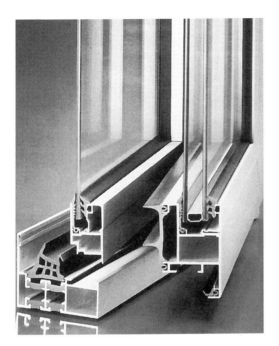

Fig. 2.66 Wood-aluminum window system from Schüco's Comex 515 system. Source: Schüco

Fig. 2.64 Insulated glass window with thermal break in the aluminum section. A typical hollow aluminum section is used as the spacer between the two panes of the double glazing. The frame of the window has two brown plastic bars to reduce extensively the heat conduction. Source: Hueck

and undulating structures can be produced economically.

Roller shutter and sectional doors in extruded aluminum sections for fire stations and hospitals and transport companies (Fig. 2.69) also depend on the beneficial properties of the alloys used. Aluminum shutter doors last longer and are

more stable than those produced in plastic. Extruded aluminum sections are usually used for the closures of flat roofs and frequently for windowsills on house external walls. Extruded sections are valued in buildings, and the international development of buildings shows a corresponding increase in the use of aluminum for architectural applications.

The refurbishment of curtain walling, windows, and doors can produce large quantities of aluminum as building scrap. This scrap can be easily melted like that from machines, automobiles, and rolling stock, and converted to sec-

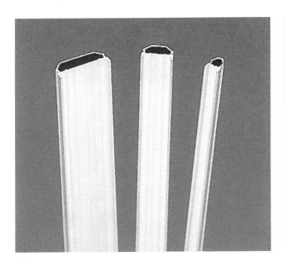

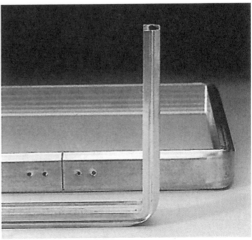

Fig. 2.65 Extruded spacers for the double glazed windows shown in Fig. 2.64. Source: Erbslöh-Aluminium

Fig. 2.67 Conservatory extension in extruded and thermally broken aluminum sections. Source: Sykon-Systems

Fig. 2.68 House with conservatory-type construction based on aluminum extruded sections. Source: Sykon-Systems

ondary aluminum. Melt refining, alloying correction including optimum degassing and continuous grain refinement during the log casting produce a quality that can hardly be distinguished from primary aluminum. The aluminum alloys produced by remelting can be reused as a building material without restriction.

Civil engineering covers the area between machinery and buildings. Design with metallic materials including, for example, iron and aluminum alloys, predominates. Civil engineering construction includes all types of bridges, ship jetties, railway station supporting structures, industrial greenhouses, airport building, lifts and industrial transport systems, parabolic reflectors

for flattop antennae for telecommunications, movable external and industrial steps, and sign gantries on main roads and freeways, as well as offshore plants including oil platforms with helicopter landing stages and so forth.

The use of aluminum alloys for load-carrying designs has proved successful for specific applications. The use of these alloys in civil engineering is specifically linked to their properties, including low density, acceptable mechanical properties, good corrosion resistance, and good workability in the production of extruded profiles matched to both application

Fig. 2.69 Roller shutter door in extruded aluminum sections. Source: Alusuisse

Fig. 2.70 Movable stairs for embarkation and disembarkation from aircraft at airports manufactured in extruded aluminum sections. Source: Alusuisse

Fig. 2.71 Industrial stairs manufactured in extruded aluminum sections including those shown in Fig. 2.72. Source: Alusuisse

(a)

Fig. 2.72 Extruded aluminum sections for the manufacture of stairs and landing ramps. The bottom large profile had a width of 600 mm and a height of 28 mm. Source: Alusuisse

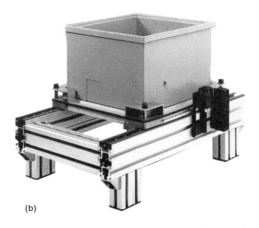

(b)

Fig. 2.73 Application of extruded sections in AlMgSi0.5 for transport systems in production applications and warehouses. (a) A multicore hollow section for the rail of the overhead conveyor of an assembly line (Alusuisse, Cie Francais des Convoyeurs) and (b) part of a transport line in extruded sections for a modular transfer system. Source: Alusuisse/Bosch

and loading. The aluminum semifinished product supplies a specialized market, although the use of aluminum-base building materials is not so marked by spectacular designs and buildings as is steel [Alp 94]. However, aluminum pedestrian bridges, pedestrian drawbridges as well as gangways for ships, planking for quays and, in particular, the Bailey bridges built in large num-

bers in West Germany in the 1960s in extruded AlZn4.5Mg1 and AlMgSi1 bear impressive witness to the advantageous use of aluminum alloys in specific cases. Equally, the use of extruded aluminum sections in civil engineering is versatile, for example, the manufacture of movable steps for airports and static industrial steps as can be seen in Fig. 2.70 to 2.72. Extruded sec-

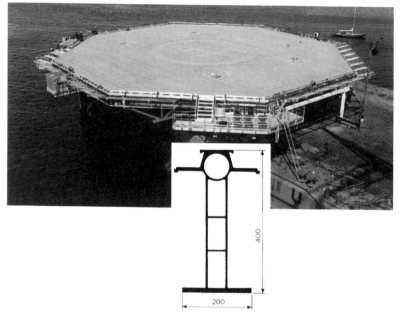

Fig. 2.74 Helicopter landing platform manufactured from aluminum alloys with the multicore large section shown as the supporting profile with multifunctions including integrated fire extinguisher foam pipe in the upper part of the section. Source: Alusuisse

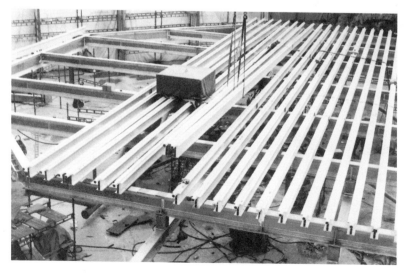

Fig. 2.75 Assembly of the supporting profiles shown in Fig. 2.74 for the helicopter landing platform. Source: Alusuisse

tions are also suitable for the manufacture of conveyor systems (Fig. 2.73). The load carrying parts of marquees are usually made from extruded aluminum semifinished products, and movable lifting platforms depend on their light telescopic aluminum arms. Even in underground workings, reusable extruded aluminum formwork is preferred.

For some time, aluminum large-scale constructions have been used in offshore applications. Their use for accommodation modules and helicopter landing decks, as shown in Fig. 2.74, is related to the good physical and, in the marine atmosphere, good corrosion resistance of the aluminum alloys used along with the good assembly options of the large aluminum sections and, thus, the favorable assembly costs. The helicopter landing deck in Fig. 2.74 and 2.75 gives an impressive illustration of this. Similar advantages are shown by the use of extruded semifinished products in suitable alloys for display signs on freeways and main roads in the salt-laden atmosphere during the winter.

Extruded Products from Materials with a Working Temperature Range of 600 to 1300 °C

Martin Bauser*

2.3 Copper Alloy Extruded Products

The temperatures used for the extrusion of copper alloys are 600 to 900 °C, significantly higher than those for aluminum alloys. Consequently, only semifinished products with simpler cross-sectional geometries and thicker-walled sections can be produced because of the more severe thermal loading of the shape-producing tools. Whereas extruded sections form the "lion's share" of all extruded aluminum sec-

tions, with copper alloys extrusion is used in most cases as the preliminary step for subsequent cold-drawing operations (with intermediate annealing when necessary), which produce the finished dimensions of the required products sold by the semifinished product plant—bar, wire, section, and tube.

The German standards list almost 90 wrought copper alloys. In addition, there are numerous special custom alloys. This clearly illustrates the wide range of alloys and the fine differentiation to be found in copper and copper alloy specifications. This, together with the large dimensional range of the semifinished products produced by section and tube extrusion, makes it impossible to describe all applications.

The copper alloys are divided into the groups:

- Pure copper
- Low-alloy copper
- Copper zinc alloys (brass), also with additional elements (special brass)
- Copper-tin alloys (tin bronze)
- Copper-aluminum alloys (aluminum bronzes)
- Copper-nickel alloys
- Copper-nickel-zinc alloys (German silver)

The high electrical and thermal conductivity—for pure copper, both are the highest of all metals—the alloy dependent more or less good workability at room temperature (cold workability) or at high temperature (hot workability), the corrosion resistance against different media, and the decorative appearance are decisive factors in the selection of suitable alloys. With this wide range of positive properties, extruded copper alloys can be found in an extremely wide range of industrial products—often only as a few individual parts such as electrical contacts in household machines. Copper alloys form the major component in only a few products, for example, bathroom fittings, some decorative metal products, or brass instruments.

In the past few decades, a large part of the market for copper alloys has been partly or completely lost. One example is cutlery, which previously was largely made from silver or chromium-plated brass and nickel silver and which is now almost exclusively stainless steel. Another example is in electronics, in which relays fitted almost exclusively with copper alloys have been replaced as switching elements by electronic components.

Plastics are now used to a large extent for zippers and ball point pens, although a small market remains for high-value products. There are other

*Extruded Products from Materials with a Working Temperature Range of 600 to 1300 °C, Martin Bauser

Fig. 2.76 Copper bus bars from extruded semifinished products. Source: KM-Kabelmetall AG

sive. A useful detailed description of the different applications can be found in the information literature of the German Copper Institute (DKI).

The majority of current carrying products made in copper, the ideal electrical conductor, are wires produced by rolling processes. Square and shaped bars as well as simple profiles for bus bars are, however, produced by extrusion (Fig. 2.76). They are used in electrical switch gear or for slip rings in electric motors. Hollow sections are used for water-cooled conductors in heavy duty transformers, in generator stators and strong electromagnets in large research installations.

Bars made of copper tellurium (CuTe) and copper sulphur (CuS) should be mentioned as low-alloy copper machining variations, from which, for example, welding torch nozzles and fittings are manufactured. This group of materials includes age-hardening alloys that are usually alloyed with chromium and zirconium and are associated with a high conductivity with good wear resistance even at high temperatures. They are therefore suitable for welding electrodes for spot, seam, and butt welding. The use of welding robots in the automobile industry has significantly increased the demand for these semifinished products.

examples of the loss of large-market segments to competitive materials, mainly plastic and steels. However, new fields have opened for copper alloys, for example, in module technology in computers, radio and television equipment, or in the central electronics in motor vehicles where a large number of connectors are made from copper alloys.

The most important industrial products for the different semifinished product groups are described subsequently, without being comprehen-

Brass bars, sections, and wire are the most important of the extruded products in the copper processing semifinished products industry. Particular mention should be made of the lead-containing machining versions available in different compositions depending on the application. The standard bar for automatic lathes used to man-

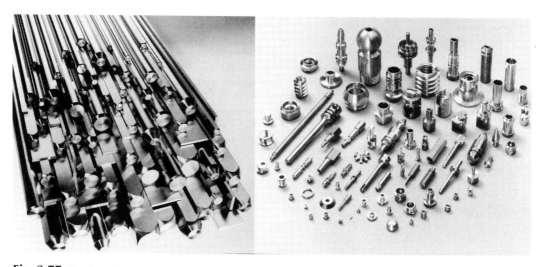

Fig. 2.77 Bar, shaped bar, and turned components in free machining brass. Source: Wieland-Werke AG

ufacture bolts, nuts, and other small parts is CuZn39Pb3 (Fig. 2.77).

Household water fittings can be produced from extruded bars of the hot-working alloy CuZn40Pb2 by hot stamping followed by machining. Bars in other copper alloys including special brasses and copper-nickel alloys are machined to fixing elements and so forth where corrosive attack is feared.

The severe competition by plastic for the use of brass shaped wire for zippers has already been mentioned. However, even today, metal is sometimes preferred for high-quality applications. This also applies for many parts in equipment in daily use, where to some degree there has been a return to metallic materials, which retain their shape even after prolonged use and also are less likely to break.

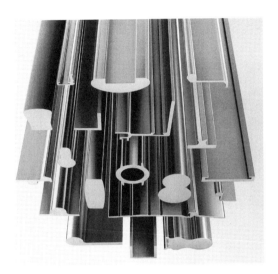

Fig. 2.78 Brass extruded sections. Source: Wieland-Werke AG

Fig. 2.79 Furniture fittings in extruded brass sections. Source: Wieland-Werke AG

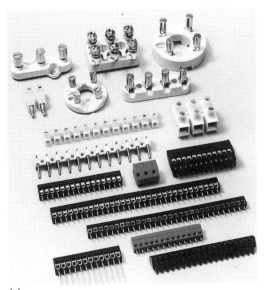

(a)

(b)

Fig. 2.80 Brass section extruded sections. (a) Terminal blocks. (b) Lock cylinders. Source: Wieland-Werke AG

Fig. 2.81 Brass instrument made from extruded tombac tubes. Source: Wieland-Werke AG

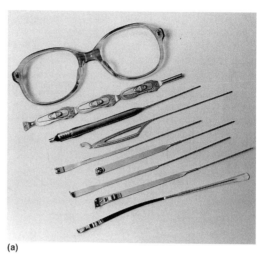

(a)

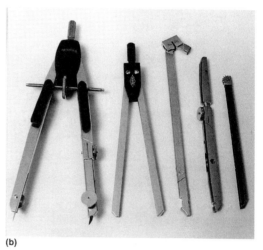

(b)

Fig. 2.82 Pressed products from extruded nickel-silver sections. (a) Glass frames. (b) Drafting instruments. Source: Wieland-Werke AG

Windows and façades are made from sheet and sections of special brass alloys (CuZn40Pb2) for specific requirements; this is naturally not an inexpensive option (Fig. 2.78). However, copper-zinc alloys are often found in the form of sections for furniture fittings and stair banister rails and tubes for light fittings as well as many other products in the metal goods industry (Fig. 2.79).

Brass sections are, moreover, used in terminal blocks for electrical connections (usually supplied in long strips) and in lock cylinders (Fig. 2.80). Bars and sections are supplied for equipment manufacture in special brasses matched to the application.

Copper-zinc alloys with high copper content (tombac) can be easily cold worked. Brass instruments are predominantly made from these alloys (CuZn28–33). They have no competition, not only because of their excellent red-yellow color and their hygienic properties, but also because of their good workability. Tubes are mainly used for this application as well as sheet and bars (Fig. 2.81).

Nickel-silver alloys have a special role in optics and fine machinery, for example, drafting instruments and spectacle parts (hinges and frames) (Fig. 2.82).

These alloys are also appreciated in other applications. For example, model railway rails are made from extruded nickel-silver wire. The almost silver appearance of this group of materials along with the good workability (bending, stamping and machining) are the decisive factors in the selection of the material. Small sections and shaped components are mainly brought to the finished shape from round bars by section rolling and drawing because the alloys are difficult to extrude.

Tubes in the corrosion-resistant special brass alloys (alloyed with aluminum or tin) predominate in power station construction (mainly in condensers) and in contact with seawater (in desalination plants). Copper-aluminum and copper-nickel alloy tubes are also used in these applications.

Bearing sleeves in special copper-zinc alloys are used extensively in the manufacture of machines, mechanical engineering, power stations, and automobiles because of their good wear and corrosion resistance. They are also being used to an increasing extent as piston gudgeon pin bearings in engine manufacture (Fig. 2.83).

The largest use of copper tube extrusion by far is the manufacture of copper tubes for domestic water tubes (Fig. 2.84). The oxygen-free copper SFCu has gradually almost completely replaced steel and lead pipes since World War II. Today, copper tubes are converted from the extruded shell to the finished product by numerous drawing operations on rotary drawing machines. However, plastic pipes recently have started to compete against copper tube in low-quality water because of copper solubility and occasional corrosive attack.

Copper tubes have also made their mark in heating and air conditioning applications where tubes are used for under-floor heating, radiator

(a)   **(b)**

Fig. 2.83   (a) Bearing bushings in extruded special brass. (b) As installed

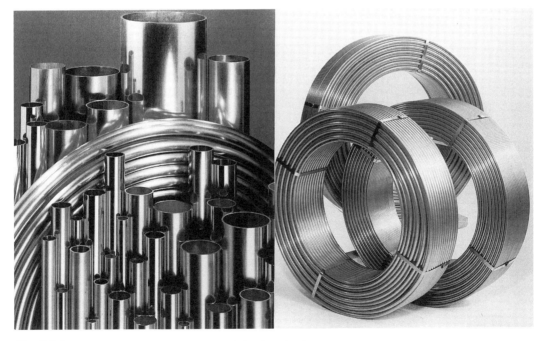

Fig. 2.84   Extruded and drawn copper tube in straight lengths and coils

connections, and tubes in air-conditioning plants (Fig. 2.85). The tubes are purchased in straight lengths or small coils from the semifinished product manufacturer for domestic applications, although large coreless coils with a preferred weight of 130 kg are used for industrial applications (Fig. 2.84).

Finned tubes are more suited for heat exchanger tubes than tubes with smooth surfaces. Different fin shapes are formed from smooth tubes on roll machines, depending on the application. These finned tubes are also made in other materials (special brasses and copper nickel) if the medium in which they are used is corrosive (Fig. 2.86).

In sanitary applications, water outlet components are preferred in lead-free brass tubes; this is also due to the outstanding plating characteristics with nickel and chromium (Fig. 2.87).

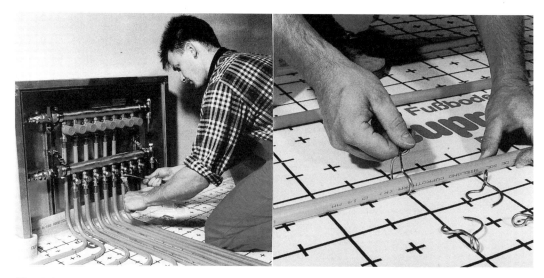

Fig. 2.85 Domestic insulation and under-floor heating in extruded and drawn (plastic-insulated) copper tubes. Source: Wieland-Werke AG

Fig. 2.86 (a) Tube coils and finned tubes in extruded copper tubes. (b) Test stand for finned tubes. Source: Wieland-Werke AG

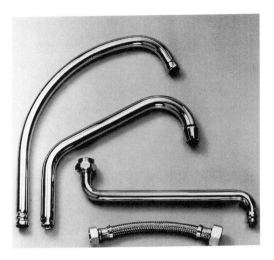

Fig. 2.88 Manometer springs in extruded and drawn tin-bronze tubes. Source: Wieland-Werke AG

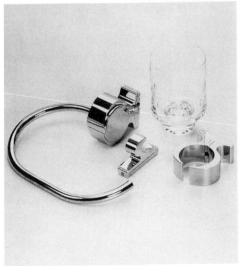

Fig. 2.87 Water supplies and bath fittings in extruded lead-free brass tubes. Source: Wieland-Werke AG

The pressure-gage springs shown in Fig. 2.88 are manufactured from thin tin-bronze tubes produced from extruded tubes by numerous drawing operations with intermediate annealing.

The use of copper alloys processed by the extrusion press and subsequent processing plants to bar, wire, section, and tube extend well beyond the examples mentioned. These can, however, serve as typical examples of the wide-ranging possibilities for the application of copper and its alloys.

2.4 Extruded Titanium Alloy Products

Titanium alloys possess, depending on the alloy, good to high mechanical properties retained

for long periods up to 480 °C and short periods up to 550 °C. In addition, they also have good corrosion resistance due to the formation of a resistant passive coating, a relatively low density of 4.5 g/cm^3 and an outstanding creep resistance under thermo-mechanical stresses. These properties, which are described in more detail in the section "Extrusion of Semifinished Products in Titanium Alloys," ensure that these alloys are used as specific construction materials for high-operating-temperature applications.

The starting material for construction applications can be produced as bar, tubes, and sections using the standard extrusion processes used for iron alloys. The extrusion of semifinished products with dimensions close to the finished size is possible but expensive. This is also described in the section "Extrusion of Semifinished Products in Titanium Alloys."

The manufacture of aircraft, spacecraft, and rockets cannot be imagined without titanium alloys. Extruded titanium alloy products are used, in particular, where weight reduction under thermo-mechanical loading is required, including turbine blades in jet engines. In addition, components in extruded titanium alloys are used because of their high strength and low density in aircraft undercarriage, in the manufacture of helicopters and in the automobile industry for the manufacture of, for example, cardan shafts. Extruded tubes are used to transport aggressive media in the chemical industry as well as in the manufacture of chemical equipment, including heat exchangers, pressure vessels, and in plants that operate with salt-containing liquids, for example, saltwater. Their good skin compatibility as well as their visual appearance makes extruded titanium alloys useful as the starting material for the manufacture of glass frames and watch housings. For the same reason, titanium alloys are used for the manufacture of implants and surgical tools [Mec 80, Alp 94].

Titanium alloys have certainly not reached their full potential because of their good properties. Their further development from the point of view of even higher thermo-mechanical loading and more economic production will open other areas of application. Titanium alloys also lend themselves to recycling.

2.5 Extruded Products in Iron Alloys and Other Hot-Working Alloys

Various hot-rolling processes threaten the market in extruded iron alloy semifinished products. Only a few segments remain for extrusion, where the geometry of the extrusion, the special alloy, or the small demand is preferred to the other processes geared to high throughputs in standard alloys and standard shapes.

Extruded volume steel tubes—previously the staple extruded product—have not been produced on presses for some time. The production of round and shaped bars is also moving away from extrusion.

With stainless steels, high-alloy ferritic and austenitic steels are extruded as tubes. Downstream cold pilger and drawing operations bring the tubes to the final dimensions required by the customer. The severe requirements associated with corrosive media—frequently associated with high temperatures—are the reason stainless steels of suitable composition are used in the chemical and petrochemical industries, power stations (both fossil fired and also nuclear), and in marine technology. Extremely high specifications frequently have to be fulfilled and evidence of numerous quality tests provided because of the high safety requirements and the long service life demanded.

The same hot-working processes used for stainless steels are also used for nickel-alloy tubes as well as high-alloy high hot strength materials. However, in these applications, extrusion plays a significantly more important role than with stainless steels, because only small quantities in very precisely alloyed materials are usually required and the price of the very high requirements is not the controlling factor.

A wide range of applications of nickel alloys is found in the chemical and petrochemical industries, in turbine and jet engine manufacture, in aerospace, ship construction, and the food industry.

Whereas tubes produced by extrusion usually consist of high-alloy and difficult to hot-work alloys, easily worked versions are preferred for the extrusion of profiles to enable useful cross sections to be produced. The extrusion temperature is approximately 1250 °C so that the shape-producing tools can withstand only low extrusion pressures and are so deformed after only one extrusion that they have to be reworked. Subsequent stretching and correction operations, possibly calibration and brightening drawing operations, give the section the final shape. Higher-alloyed and thus difficult to extrude stainless steels can be extruded only into the simplest shapes (Fig. 2.89).

Fig. 2.89 Extruded stainless steel tubes. The thin wall sections that can be seen under the extruded sections are produced by roll forming. Source: Krupp-Hoesch

Fig. 2.90 Special sections as support tubes in a walking beam furnace for heating steel slabs

Fig. 2.91 Special sections as guide plates, guide wheels, scraper edges, and stringers for construction machinery. Source: Krupp-Hoesch

The application palette for these profiles is extremely wide ranging. In the manufacturers' brochures there are, for example, sections for vehicles (railway superstructure, automobile doors, and valve blocks), ship construction, and elevator guides, to mention only a few. Figures 2.90 and 2.91 give two examples.

As with the tube manufacturers, the section producers also prefer to use the more economic hot-rolling process for suitable section geometries and quantities.

REFERENCES

[Alh 71]: *Aluminium-Handbuch* (*Aluminum Handbook*), VEB Verlag Technik, Berlin VLN 201/DG.-Nr. 370/13/17, Abschnitt, Chapter 19, 2.6, p 638–641

[Alp 94]: D. Altenpohl, *Aluminium von innen* (*Aluminum from the Inside*), Aluminium Verlag, Düsseldorf, 1994, p 320–370

[Als Pr]: *Prospekte Alusuisse* (*Aluminum Brochure*)

[Alt 88]: *Aluminium*, taschenbuch (*Aluminum, paperback*), Aluminium Verlag, Düsseldorf

[Alz 85]: Prospekt, *Konstruieren mit Aluminium-Strangpreßprofilen* (brochure: *Designing with Aluminum Extruded Profiles*), Aluminium-Zentrale

[Alz 97]: *Bauen und gestalten mit Aluminium* (*Building and Construction with Aluminum*), Aluminium-Zentrale e.V., 1997

[Aug 77]: G. Augehrn and I. Zehnder, *Aluminium im Fahrzeugba* (*Aluminum in Vehicle Construction*), Neue Züricher Zeitung, Beilage Forschung und Technik, Vol 13 (No. 162), July 1977

[Bec 39]: A. Beck, *Magnesium und seine Legierungen* (*Magnesium and Its Alloys*), Springer-Verlag, Berlin, 1939

[Cor 95]: P. Cordes and V. Müller, *Moderne Stahl-Zeichenbaukonstruktionen für den Schienenfahrzeugbau* (*Modern Steel Designs for Rolling Stock*), Blech, Rohre, Profile 42 (No. 12), 1995

[Dav 79]: W. David, S-Bahn-Wagenkästen aus Aluminium in Voll-Integral-Bauweise (S-Bahn Rolling Stock Bodies in Aluminum Integral Construction), *Aluminium,* Vol 55 (No. 7), 1979

[Fra 89]: S. Frank and F. Wehner, Der Seitenaufprall (The Side Impact), *Aluminium,* Vol 65 (No. 9), 1989

[Fuc 96]: O. Fuchs, Metallwerke: *Prospekt Strangpreßprodukte* (*Extruded Products Brochure*), 1996

[Gar 93]: F. Garber, Magnesium-Schwierigkeiten überwunden (Problems with Magnesium Overcome—New Opportunities in View), neue Chancen im Blick, *Metall.,* Vol 47 (No. 6), 1993

[Gor 94]: I. Goroncy, Leichtmetalle Im Aufwind (Aluminum on the Ascent), *Metall.,* Vol 48 (No. 10), 1994

[Her 90]: I. Hermans, *Vorteile und Chancen für den Einsatz von Aluminium im Automobilbau* (*Advantages and Opportunities for Aluminum in Automobile Manufacture*), Vortrag der VAW AG, 1990

[Hug 44]: AD.-M. Hug, Aluminium-Fahrzeuge bei Bahnbetrieben (Aluminum Vehicles in Railway Operations), *Aluminium,* May/June 1944

[Ing 91]: Aluminium-Schienenfahrzeuge, Integralbauweise mit Großprofilen (Aluminum Rolling Stock, Integral Assembly with Large Sections), *Ing.-Werkst.,* Vol 3 (No. 10), 1991

[Ing 91]: Aluminium-High-Tech-Werkstoffe mit Zukunft (Aluminum-High-Tech-Materials with a Future), *Ing.-Werkst.,* Vol 3 (No. 6), 1991, p 10–14

[Joh 85]: P. Johne, *Trotz hoher Materialkosten oft wirtschaftlich* (*Frequently Economic in Spite of High Material Costs*), Industrieanzeiger

[Koe 88]: A. Koewius, Komfort und Leistungsanspruch, Sicherheits—und Umweltdenken—eine Herausforderung an den Automobilleichtbau, Teil II: Nutzfahrzeuge (Comfort and Performance Requirement, Safety and Environmental Considerations—A Challenge for Lightweight Automobile Manufacture), *Aluminium,* Vol 64 (No. 4), 1988, p 355–365

[Mec 80]: E. Meckelburg, Eigenschaften and Anwendung von Titan als Konstruktionswerkstoff (Properties and Applications of Titanium as an Engineering Material), *Maschinenmarkt,* Vol 86 (No. 9), 1980, p 154–158

[Mil 88]: L. Miller, Einsatz von Aluminiumwerkstoffen für moderne Verkehrssysteme (Application of Aluminum Alloys to Modern Transport Systems), *Aluminium,* Vol 64 (No. 1), 1988, p 24–28

[Ren 97]: K.H. Rendigs, C. Melzer, and G. Broden, Aluminium Strangpreßprodukte im Airbus (Extruded Aluminum Sections in the Airbus), Vortragstexte des Symposiums *STRANGPRESSEN,* Vol 9 and 10, Oct 1997 in Garmisch-Partenkirchen, DGM-Informationsgesellschaft, Verlag

[Tas 93]: W. Taschner, Mit Aluminium in die Elektrotechnik (Aluminum in Electrical Engineering), *Ing.-Werkst.,* Vol 5 (No. 4), 1993, p 72–73

[Tas 93]: W. Taschner, Mit Aluminium auf die Schiene (Aluminum on the Railway), *Ing.-Werkst.,* Vol 5 (No. 3), 1993

[Tec 96/97/98]: Techn. Universität Clausthal/ Universität Hannover, Sonderforschungsbereich 1515 Magnesiumtechnologie (Special Research Project 1515 Magnesium Technology Financial Support Contract), Finanzierungsantrag, 1996/97/98

[Wis 92]: G. Wisniewsky, Metall, Schlüsselwerkstoff in der Umformtechnik (Metal, Key Material in Deformation Technology), *Ing.-Werkst.,* Vol 4 (No. 11), 1992

CHAPTER 3

Rod and Tube Extrusion Processes

Klaus Siegert*

THE ROD AND TUBE extrusion processes can initially be classified into cold-working and hot-working processes:

- *Cold working:* The material being processed is not heated, i.e., loaded into the working process at room temperature.
- *Hot working:* The material being processed is heated to a temperature above room temperature and then loaded into the working process.

As hot working is the standard process in rod and tube extrusion, the terminology usually used is rod and tube extrusion instead of hot rod extrusion and hot tube extrusion.

The cold rod and tube extrusion processes are, however, always referred to as such, which emphasizes that they are special processes.

In rod extrusion wire, strip, bar, solid sections, and hollow sections are produced. The latter are extruded through welding chamber dies. In these, the material is welded in the deformation process within the die. This is referred to as *extrusion welding*. In hollow sections it produces the extrusion weld seam. Tubes produced in this way are considered under rod extrusion.

Tube extrusion is referred to, however, when seamless tubes are produced using a mandrel passing through the billet to produce the internal contour and a die for the external contour.

Rod extrusion is the extrusion of wire, strip, sections, bars, and hollow sections through a die.

Tube extrusion is the extrusion of seamless tubes as well as seamless hollow sections over a mandrel passing through the billet.

Rod extrusion is discussed first, while tube extrusion is considered later.

The rod extrusion process can be divided into:

- Direct extrusion
- Indirect extrusion
- Hydrostatic extrusion including the thick film process
- Special processes, e.g., the conform process and cable sheathing

Figures 3.1(a) and (b) show the direct and indirect extrusion process versions discussed in this book. Figure 3.1(c) lists both hydrostatic extrusion processes described in the book, and Fig. 3.1(d) shows the special processes covered in the book.

It should be pointed out that only the processes that are of practical importance are discussed. Variations that do not appear to be important for the future are deliberately excluded.

The processes mentioned in Fig. 3.1(a) to (d) are described individually. The direct extrusion process is considered first. There are, in principle, four versions according to Fig. 3.1(a). The extrusion of aluminum and copper alloys are used as examples in the discussion of direct and indirect extrusion. The thermal conditions that occur in hot copper alloy extrusion are significantly different from those in hot aluminum alloy extrusion.

3.1 Direct Extrusion

Direct extrusion is the extrusion process used most frequently. The main application of the

*Hydrostatic Extrusion, Gottfried Schreiter; Conform Process, Klaus Siegert; Cable Sheathing, Martin Bauser; Tube Extrusion Process, Klaus Siegert

direct extrusion is the extrusion of semifinished products of aluminum. However, all other metallic materials including steel, copper, brass, lead, and zinc can be deformed by the direct extrusion process. Fig. 3.1(a) depicts the most important direct extrusion processes discussed in this book.

The process can be divided into direct extrusion with lubrication and direct extrusion without lubrication, depending on whether there is a

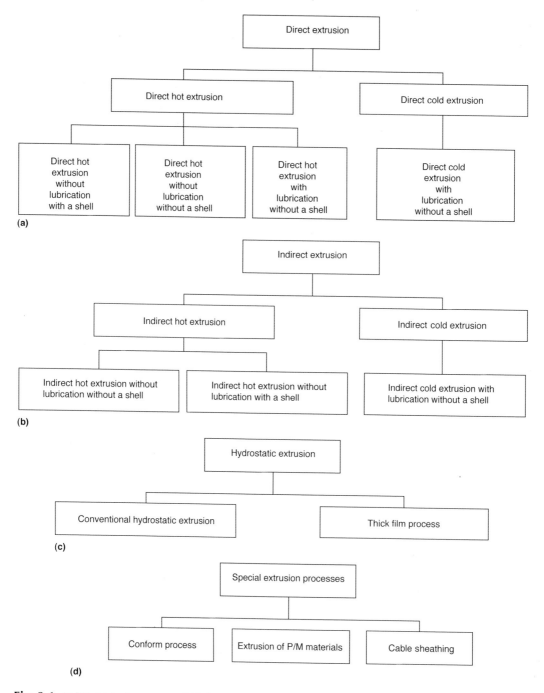

Fig. 3.1 (a) Direct extrusion processes. (b) Indirect extrusion processes. (c) Hydrostatic extrusion processes. (d) Special extrusion processes

film of lubricant between the material being deformed and the tooling:

- *Direct extrusion with lubrication:* There is a film of lubricant between the material being deformed and the tooling.
- *Direct extrusion without lubrication:* There is no film of lubricant between the material being deformed and the tooling.

As shown in Fig. 3.2, in direct extrusion without lubrication, the material being deformed is loaded as a billet between the container and the stem, pushed along with the pressure pad by the stem into the container, upset in the container, and then pushed through a stationary die. The die aperture determines the external contour of the section.

The process-defining feature in direct extrusion is the friction between the material being deformed and the container because the upset billet is pushed during extrusion in the container toward the die.

Characteristic feature of direct extrusion: friction between the material being deformed and the container. As mentioned previously, the direct hot extrusion process is first described using direct hot extrusion of aluminum alloys as an example. This is followed by the direct hot extrusion of copper alloys. Hot extrusion of aluminum alloys is usually carried out without lubrication and shell (Fig. 3.2).

Direct hot extrusion without lubricant with a shell is considered in section 3.1.2 using the direct hot extrusion of copper alloys as an example.

3.1.1 Direct Hot Extrusion without Lubrication and Shell (Aluminum Alloys)

Hot extrusion is, according to the German Standardization Institute (DIN), when the billet is loaded into the container at a temperature above room temperature. Usually, the billet in hot extrusion is heated to a temperature above the recrystallization temperature of the billet material. The container, die, and pressure pad are also heated to approximately the same temperature, providing the thermal properties of the tooling permit this. The maximum permitted operating temperature for hot-working steels is approximately 500 °C.

Aluminum alloys can be extruded above the recrystallization temperature under the following conditions: The billet temperature ϑ_B is approximately the same as the container temperature ϑ_R.

This is only a basic statement. Temperature changes in direct hot extrusion are discussed in Sections 3.1.1.5, 3.1.2.5, and 3.1.3.4.

Approximately 80% of the extrusion process direct extrusion without lubrication and shell involves aluminum alloys. If aluminum extrusion is mentioned, this usually means the direct hot extrusion of aluminum alloys without lubrication and shell.

3.1.1.1 Process Sequence of Direct Hot Extrusion without Lubrication or Shell

There are principally two possible methods of loading the pressure pad:

According to Fig. 3.2, the billet is loaded with the pressure pad between the stem and the container and then pushed into the container by the stem. Alternatively, the pressure pad can be fixed to the stem. Figure 3.3 shows the sequence.

The actual extrusion process starts with the upsetting of the billet in the container. The process stops when the discard length l_R is reached. The container then opens a short distance so that the discard can be separated from the die and the extrusion by a shear blade. The extrusion can then be pulled from the die. The container and the stem (with a loose dummy block) or the container, the stem and the fixed dummy block are then returned to the starting position.

In billet-on-billet extrusion, the extrusion is usually cut by a shear or a saw located behind the end housing (Fig. 3.4).

3.1.1.2 Variation in the Extrusion Load with Stem Movement in Direct Hot Extrusion without Lubrication or Shell

As shown in Fig. 3.5, when the billet is upset in the container, the extrusion load F_{St} increases to a maximum value $F_{St\ max}$. The actual deformation process commences at this value. When the extrusion leaves the die, the billet in the container moves toward the die by an amount corresponding to the volume extruded. If the extrusion ratio V is the ratio of the container cross-sectional area A_0 to the product cross-sectional area A_S and the ram speed is u_{St}, then the speed of the extrusion u_S is given by:

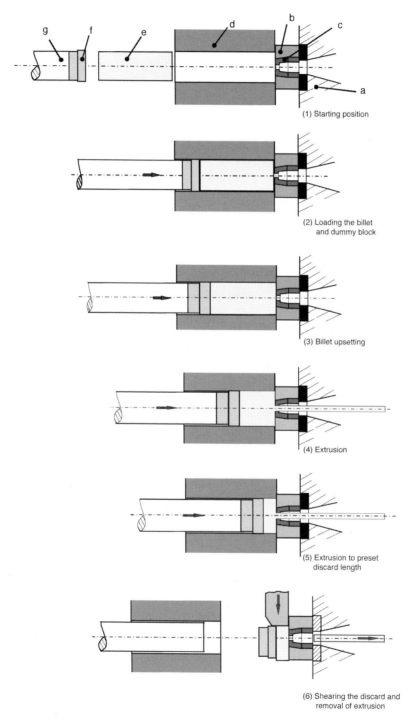

Fig. 3.2 Process sequence of direct hot extrusion without lubrication and without a shell, with loose dummy block. a, platen; b, die holder; c, die; d, container; e, billet; f, dummy block or pressure pad; g, extrusion stem

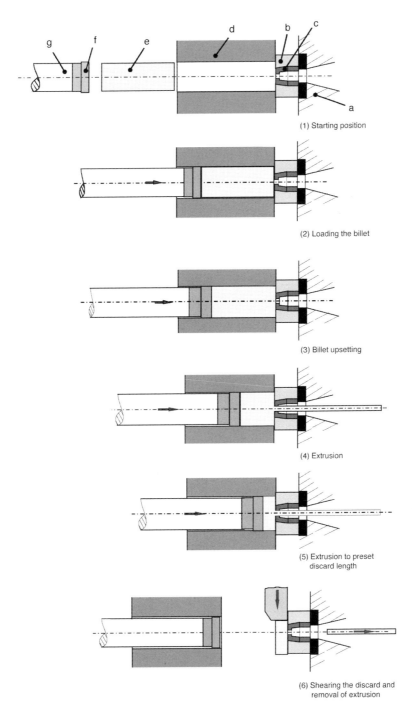

Fig. 3.3 Process sequence of direct hot extrusion without lubrication and without a shell, with dummy block fixed to the stem. a, platen; b, die holder; c, die; d, container; e, billet; f, dummy block or pressure pad; g, extrusion stem

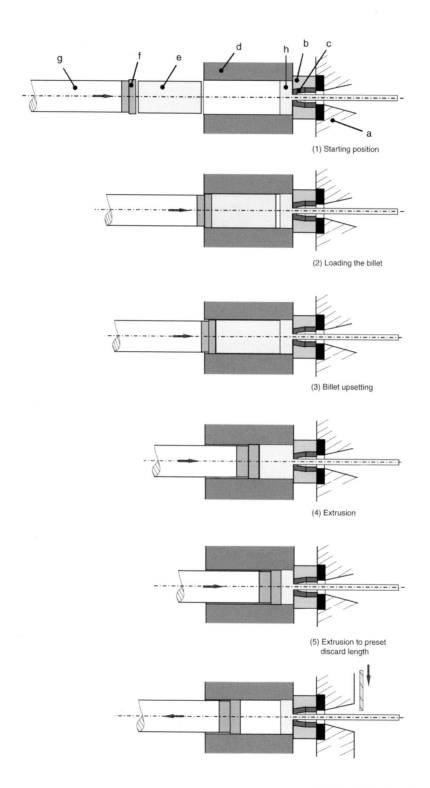

(1) Starting position

(2) Loading the billet

(3) Billet upsetting

(4) Extrusion

(5) Extrusion to preset
discard length

(6) Withdrawal of the stem with
the dummy block, operation
of the section saw

Fig. 3.4 Billet-on-billet direct hot extrusion without lubrication and without a shell, with dummy block fixed to the stem. a, platen; b, die holder; c, die; d, container; e, billet; f, dummy block; g, extrusion stem; h, discard from the previous extrusion

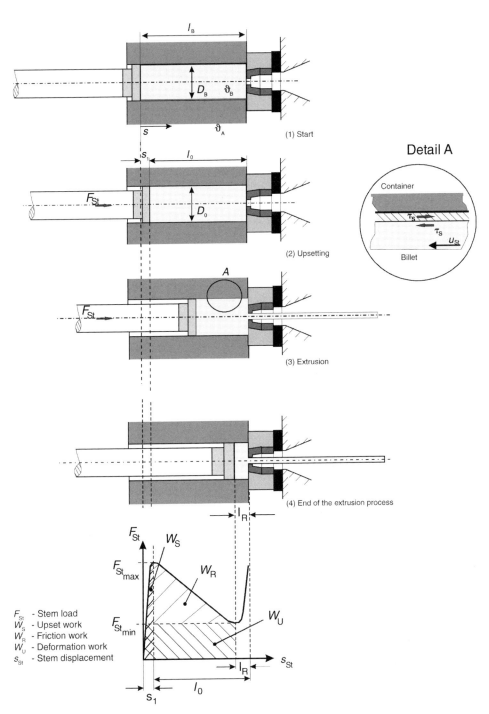

Fig. 3.5 Variation of the stem load F_{St} over the stem displacement s_{St} in direct hot extrusion without lubrication and without a shell (initial billet temperature $\vartheta_B \cong$ container temperature ϑ_R). l_B, initial billet length; D_B, initial billet diam; l_0, upset billet length; D_0, container diam; τ_S, shear stress; s, stem displacement; l_R, discard length; ϑ_B, initial billet temperature; ϑ_A, container temperature; u_{St}, stem speed

Extrusion ratio $\quad V = \dfrac{A_0}{A_S}$ (Eq 3.1)

$A_0 \cdot u_{St} = A_S \cdot u_S$
$u_S = V \cdot u_{St}$ (Eq 3.2)

After upsetting in the container and ignoring the friction between the dummy block and the container, the extrusion load can, in principle, be considered to be the sum of the friction load needed to push the billet through the container and the axial load F_M on the die, as shown in Fig. 3.5. As an approximation $F_{St\ min} \approx F_M$, where F_M is the load actually needed to deform the billet to the section. This statement ignores the friction between the material being extruded and the die. It can be seen that at the start of the extrusion process, approximately 50% of the maximum extrusion load $F_{St\ max}$ is needed to overcome the friction between the billet and the container.

If the extrusion process is not stopped when the minimum extrusion load $F_{St\ min}$ is reached but carried on, the load F_{St} increases again because the remaining billet disc between the die and the container can only flow in the direction of the die aperture under very high axial stresses. The extrusion process is usually stopped before the minimum is reached to ensure that defect-free extrusions are produced. This is covered in more detail in the discussion of the material flow.

Based on experimental investigations [Sie 76] it can be assumed that $F_{St\ min}$ is reached at a discard length of approximately:

$l_R \cong \dfrac{D_0}{6}$ (Eq 3.3)

where D_0 is the container diameter.

If the load displacement graph in Fig. 3.5 is studied, it can be seen that a significant part of the extrusion load needed at the start of extrusion is necessary to overcome the friction between the billet and the container, whereby the initial billet l_B is approximately 3.5 to 4.5 times the container diameter D_0. The other part of the extrusion load is needed for the deformation whereby the friction between the material being extruded and the die and the friction between the dummy block and the container are ignored. In direct extrusion without lubrication the upset billet length l_0 has an effect on the maximum extrusion load needed $F_{St\ max}$.

Accordingly, in direct hot extrusion without lubrication and without a shell (e.g., aluminum), the extrusion load F_{St} is approximately equal to the friction load needed to push the billet through the container F_R and that for the deformation at the die F_M:

$F_{St} \cong F_R + F_M$ (Eq 3.4)

It should also be taken into account that the maximum friction load is proportional to the length l_0 of the upset billet in the container.

In the extrusion of aluminum alloys, a layer of the material being extruded forms on the container wall; i.e., the container wall is not in direct friction contact with the billet, but shearing of the billet takes place along a boundary surface (see Fig. 3.5, detail A).

In the boundary surface, the axial velocity of the material being extruded changes from zero (velocity of the material being extruded that adheres to the container wall) to the stem speed u_{St} (mean axial velocity of the billet). If the boundary surface length is taken to be $l_0 - l_R$ and the critical shear stress is τ_S, which depends on the shear velocity and the temperature for a specific material, then, under the assumption that the shearing process starts when the billet is upset in the container and the upset displacements s_1 is reached:

$F_{R\ max} = \pi D_0 (l_0 - l_R) \tau_S$ (Eq 3.5)

$F_R = \pi D_0 (l_0 - l_R + s_1 - \dot{s}_{St}) \tau_S$ (Eq 3.6)

Thus, the shearing of the billet along the shear surface takes place under the influence of a critical shear stress τ_S.

The critical shear stress of a specific material is a function (f) of the temperature and the shear strain rate. In some cases, the critical shear stress is also dependent on the mean principal stress (Mue 84). This has not, however, been scientifically verified.

It is therefore assumed in the following discussion that any possible influence of the mean principal stress on the critical shear stress is negligible. Thus:

$\tau_S = f(\text{material, temperature, shear rate})$ (Eq 3.7)

3.1.1.3 Material Flow in Direct Hot Extrusion

In axisymmetric extrusion it is possible to investigate the material flow using the visio-plastic

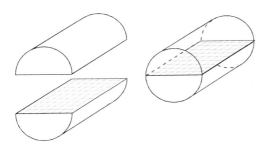

Fig. 3.6 Split billet for visio-plastic study of material flow

method with grid lines on billets sectioned in the longitudinal direction (Fig. 3.6).

The billet center line falls in the section plane. A billet half is prepared with a rectangular, usually square, grid. A separating agent is applied to the billet halves and then both halves are extruded together as a billet. A relatively small step, e.g., the grid spacing, is selected. Comparing the grid before and after one or more deformation steps (stages) enables deductions to be drawn about whether the material flow is quasi-stationary or not; whether dead zones, i.e., volumes that do not participate in the material flow, exist; which regions form the actual (primary) deformation zones; and which shape changes can be attributed predominately to the friction between the tooling and the billet. As well as these qualitative evaluations, the displacement of individual volumes during the deformation can be quantitatively studied [Wil 69].

After one deformation step s_0 with the ram speed V_{St} in the time $t = s_0/V_{St}$ the grid point A has been displaced to point B. B has moved to C and C to D. A, B, C, D, fall on a flow line (Fig. 3.7). In quasi-stationary deformation, the flow line is a flow tube.

With small deformation steps the straight line joining point H to point I is a measure for the value and direction of the local velocity. This gives a mean speed V_M for the point M in the center of the line joining H and I. If this is carried out for all points on the linear net, an approximate velocity field of the process is obtained [Wil 69]. Figure 3.8 shows a visio-plastic material flow picture of an extrusion stage in the direct extrusion of AlMg3.

It can be seen that the friction between the billet and the container naturally influences the material flow. It retards the flow of the external billet zones so that these are held back while the inner zones flow forward. This has the advantage that the impurity containing external skin of the billet does not flow into the extruded product, but material from the interior of the billet forms the product. The external skin remains in the discard, providing this is the correct size.

Figure 3.8 clearly shows that the external billet zones are held back by the friction between the billet and the container and, consequently, the billet core flows forward. The influence of the friction between the billet and the container is such that a geometrically narrow deformation zone does not form in front of the die. The de-

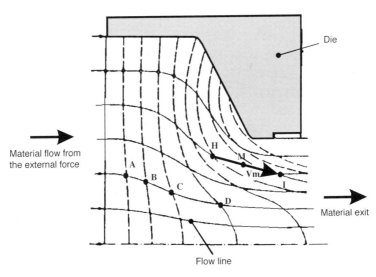

Material flow from the external force

Die

Material exit

Flow line

Fig. 3.7 Determination of the velocity field of the distorted network [Wil 69] visio-plastic material flow investigation

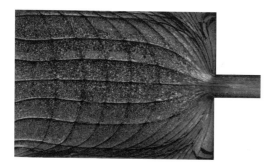

Fig. 3.8 Stage in hot direct extrusion of AlMg3 without lubrication and without a shell (container diam = 140 mm; extrusion ratio V = 50; initial billet length = 450 mm; initial billet temperature = container temperature = 450 °C)

- An actual deformation zone—referred to as the primary deformation zone—that is not clearly defined. It can be considered to be the area within the shear surfaces bounded by the dead metal zones. This has a conical shape in axisymmetric extrusion.
- A friction affected peripheral zone. The friction between the billet and the container results in the billet external zones undergoing a shear deformation.
- A secondary deformation zone that results from retention of the billet external zones by the friction between the billet and the container. Oxidized and impure material can flow from this zone into the deformation zone toward the end of extrusion, giving rise to the back end extrusion defect (Fig. 3.10).
- The billet core is largely unaffected by the other zones mentioned.

formation zone can only approximately be defined geometrically by a marked shear zone between the billet volume in front of the die, which does not participate in the material flow (dead metal zones) and the billet interior. The shear zone that borders the dead metal zones has a conical shape in direct hot extrusion with an included angle of $2\alpha \cong 90°$ This angle depends on the extrusion ratio, the extrusion stage, and the magnitude of the friction between the billet and the container.

In principle, as shown in Fig. 3.9, the material flow in direct hot-extrusion without lubrication through a flat die consists of:

- A dead metal zone that forms in front of the die

As already mentioned, a secondary deformation zone forms in front of the dummy block as a consequence of the retarding of the billet external zones and the resulting acceleration of the billet internal zones as the extrusion process proceeds. It is possible for impure oxidized billet external zones to flow from this secondary deformation zone into the section, which forms an invisible back end or pipe extrusion defect under the surface of the extrusion (Fig. 3.10). This defect can be avoided by reducing the billet length and/or increasing the discard thickness as well as selection of an adequately large discard.

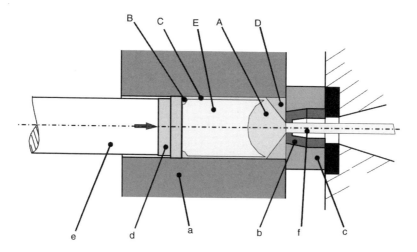

Fig. 3.9 Material flow zones in direct hot extrusion without lubrication and without a shell. A, primary deformation zone; B, secondary deformation zone; C, friction affected peripheral zone; D, dead metal zone; E, billet core; a, container; b, die; c, die holder; d, dummy block; e, stem; f, extrusion

Dürrschnabel [Due 69] defined the following principal material flow types as shown in Fig. 3.11.

Flow type S is based on the assumption of negligible friction between the billet and the container as well as between the billet and the die front surface, and is also based on the assumption that no shear zones form in the billet. With these assumptions and homogeneous billet material, the material being deformed must move across the die front surface and the billet surface becomes the surface of the extrusion. *Flow type S is purely theoretical and does not occur in practice.*

Flow type A applies to homogeneous billet materials, low friction between the billet and the container as well as significant friction between the billet and the die front surface. It is characterized by a "dead metal zone" that forms in front of the die and a narrow shear zone between the dead metal zone and the billet. This shear zone approximates to a funnel that borders the primary deformation zone. The billet zones outside this funnel are not influenced by the deformation. The material volume at the billet surface can flow via the shear zone into the outer regions of the extrusions.

Flow type B applies to homogeneous billet materials, significant friction between the billet and container as well as significant friction be-

tween the billet and the die surface. The friction between the billet and the container results in the outer layer of the billet being held back relative to the billet interior. The dead metal zones are more marked than with type A. The deformation zone then encompasses a significantly larger billet area.

Flow type C is formed by the same friction conditions as type B but in this case the difference is an inhomogeneous billet. This occurs when the flow stress of the billet outer zones is significantly higher than that of the billet core. Severe cooling can result in the billet outer zone having a lower temperature than the billet core. This occurs when the container temperature is much lower than the initial billet temperature. With certain materials, e.g., (α-β) brass, phase, differences are possible as a consequence of the low temperature of the billet outer zones, such as β brass (body-centered cubic lattice) in the billet interior and α brass (face-centered cubic lattice) in the billet outer zones. The billet periphery of material with the higher flow stress is restrained relative to the billet core, builds up in front of the dummy block, and is diverted into the billet interior with further extrusion finishing up under the extrusion surface in the center of the product. This material flow results in a secondary "deformation zone." The result is an extrusion defect known as the piping defect (Fig.

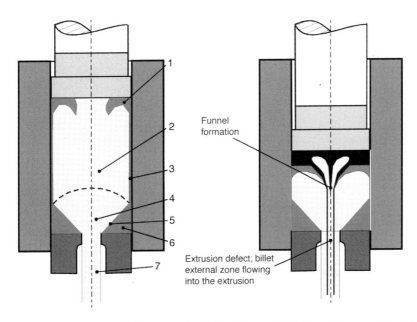

Funnel formation

Extrusion defect; billet external zone flowing into the extrusion

Fig. 3.10 Formation of extrusion piping defect. 1, secondary deformation zone; 2, billet core; 3, shear zone; 4, primary deformation zone; 5, shear zone; 6, dead metal zone; 7, extrusion

3.10). It is necessary to reduce the billet length and/or lengthen the discard thickness to prevent this piping defect.

The material flow in direct extrusion without lubrication can be summarized as:

Flow type S is purely theoretical and does not occur in practice.

Flow type A assumes little friction between the billet and the container. These conditions rarely occur in unlubricated extrusion. They can develop in the extrusion of, for example, lead or copper where special conditions, e.g., relatively severe oxidation of the billet surface and a freshly cleaned container occur.

The two most important flow types for direct extrusion without lubrication and with flat dies are types B and C, although the boundary between the two is flexible. They occur in the extrusion of aluminum alloys and copper alloys and are shown in principle in Fig. 3.11.

3.1.1.4 Calculation of the Axial Loads in Direct Hot Extrusion without Lubrication and Shell (Aluminum Alloys)

Calculation of the Friction Load F_R. As already discussed, the stem load F_{St} can be assumed to consist of the sum of the axial load F_M acting on the die, which is necessary for the deformation of the material being worked in the primary deformation zone, and the axial load F_R required to overcome the friction between the billet and the container. From Eq 3.4:

$$F_{St} \cong F_R + F_M$$

From Fig. 3.5 the friction load F_R can be calculated by assuming that there is shear stress τ_S with which the billet shears along the boundary surface. The maximum value of the shear load

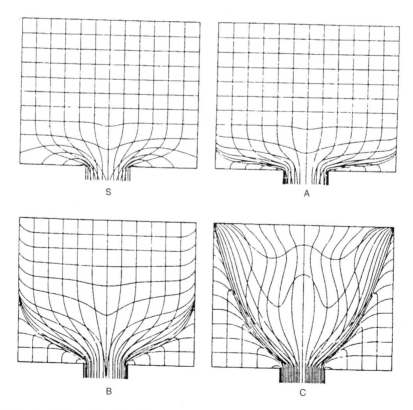

Fig. 3.11 Direct extrusion flow patterns [Due 69]

$F_{R\ max}$ occurs after the billet has been upset in the container where $S_{St} = S_1$ at the start of the actual extrusion process given by, according to Eq 3.5:

$$F_{R\ max} = \pi D_0 (l_0 - l_R)\tau_S$$

Equation 3.6 gives the variation of the load F_R with stem displacement:

$$F_R(s_{St}) = \pi D_0 \cdot \tau_S(l_0 - l_R + s_1 - s_{St})$$

The discard length is l_R where the friction load F_R is zero.

According to Eq 3.3:

$$l_R \cong \frac{D_0}{6}$$

The stem displacement s_1 needed to upset the billet in the container is obtained from the constant volume:

$$\frac{\pi}{4} D_0^2 \cdot l_0 = \frac{\pi}{4} D_B^2 \cdot l_B$$

$$s_1 = l_B - l_0 = l_B\left(1 - \frac{D_B^2}{D_0^2}\right) \qquad \text{(Eq 3.8)}$$

where l_B is the initial billet length, D_B is the initial billet diameter, l_0 is the upset billet length, and D_0 is the container diameter.

As mentioned previously, the shear stress τ_S is the stress at which a specific material is sheared along a boundary surface at a specific temperature and a specific speed. According to Eq 3.7:

$$\tau_S = f(\text{material, temperature, shear rate})$$

If in the direct extrusion of a specific material $F_{R\ max}$ is measured along with the temperature of the billet and the ram speed, the shear stress τ_S is, according to Eq 3.5:

$$\tau_S = \frac{F_{R\ max}}{\pi D_0(l_0 - l_R)} \qquad \text{(Eq 3.9)}$$

It is therefore possible to determine the shear stress τ_S in the direct extrusion of aluminum from the stem load stem displacement diagram. Because the temperature is not constant over the complete length of the billet in contact with the container, there is some inaccuracy in the determination of the shear stress τ_S.

Figure 3.12 shows the variation of the shear stress τ_S with the shear rate at different temperatures ϑ for Al99.5, and Fig. 3.13 shows τ_S as a function of the temperature for shear rates between 2 and 6 mm/s.

Another method of determining τ_S is by piercing an upset billet using a lubricated mandrel avoiding material flow against the mandrel movement [Sie 76b].

As shown in Fig. 3.14, the billet is first upset in a container with the die closed by a sealing piece supported against the bolster. The sealing plate is then rotated through 90° so that it can be removed through the rectangular aperture of the bolster. Piercing is then carried out with a lubri-

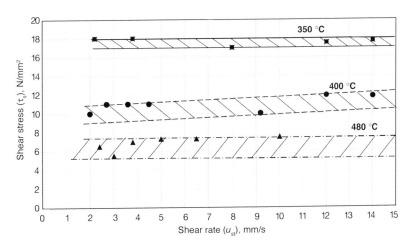

Fig. 3.12 Variation of the shear stress with the shear rate for Al99.5 at different temperatures

cated mandrel. The die diameter is only slightly larger than the mandrel diameter. Fixing the dummy block avoids the material flowing back against the piercing ram movement during piercing.

The macrographs in Fig. 3.15 show that during piercing, the narrow shear zone formed is narrow enough to be designated a boundary surface. After piercing the core length must be equal to the upset billet length. For a piercing load F_D over the mandrel displacement S_D and

ignoring the friction between the billet and the mandrel:

$$F_D = \tau_s \cdot D_D \pi (l_0 - s_D) \qquad \text{(Eq 3.10)}$$

where l_0 is the upset billet length in the container and D_D the mandrel diameter.

From Eq 10:

$$\tau_s = \frac{F_D}{D_D \pi (l_0 - s_D)} \qquad \text{(Eq 3.11)}$$

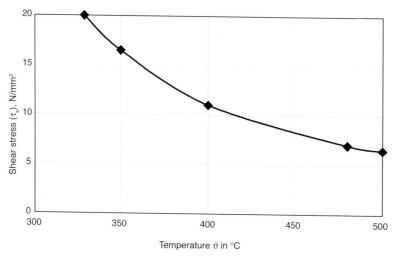

Fig. 3.13 Variation of the shear stress with temperature for shear rates between 2 and 6 mm/s for Al99.5

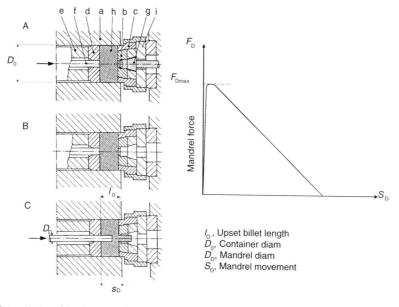

Fig. 3.14 Determination of the shear stress τ_S by piercing an upset billet. A, upsetting the billet; B, opening the die; C, piercing; a, container; b, die; c, die holder; d, dummy block; e, stem; f, mandrel; g, sealing piece; h, billet; i, sealing plate

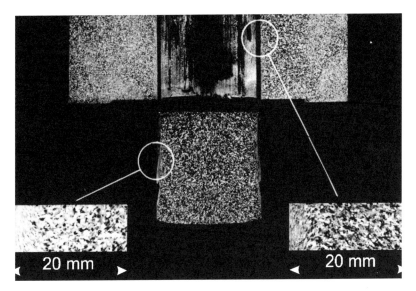

Fig. 3.15 Macrographs of a shearing process

From the maximum piercing load $F_{D\ max}$ at the start of piercing when $S_D = 0$:

$$\tau_s = \frac{F_{D\ max}}{D_D \pi l_0} \qquad \text{(Eq 3.12)}$$

It is therefore possible to experimentally determine τ_S and show it in diagrams. In the determination of the shear stress τ_S, it is assumed that the mean stress state in the billet (usually referred to as the hydrostatic stress) does not influence the shear stress. The validity of this assumption still has to be scientifically verified.

Calculation of the Deformation Load F_M. The following discussion covers the axial load F_M acting on the die necessary for the deformation of the material located in the primary deformation zone.

If the initial billet temperature is approximately the same as the container temperature, which is the case in the hot extrusion of aluminum, then F_M is approximately constant over the stem displacement. There is only a maximum at the start of extrusion, which is associated with the temperature in the deformation zone at the start of extrusion being the initial billet temperature. A temperature increase occurs in the deformation zone as extrusion continues because of the work of deformation. This results in decreasing deformation loads as the flow stress is reduced by the increasing temperature. If approximately constant strain, velocity, and temperature conditions occur in the deformation

zone, a quasi-stationary deformation process is referred to. The maximum in the axial load F_M occurs in the nonstationary state.

For the quasi-stationary state:

$$F_M = C \cdot \varphi_{g_{ges}} \cdot \bar{k}_f \pi \frac{D_0^2}{4} \qquad \text{(Eq 3.13)}$$

where $\bar{k}_f$ is the mean flow stress for the primary deformation zone, $\varphi_{g_{ges}}$ is the logarithmic total strain (Eq 3.14), and C is a factor that is die specific and includes a shape efficiency factor η. $\varphi_{g_{ges}}$ is obtained from the extrusion ratio (Eq 3.1):

$$\varphi_{g_{ges}} = \ln V = \ln \frac{A_0}{A_S} \qquad \text{(Eq 3.14)}$$

where A_0 is the container cross-sectional area and A_S is the section cross-sectional area. The flow stress k_f is the stress at which plastic flow of a material occurs in a uniaxial stress state. The flow stress k_f is a function of the material, the deformation temperature, the logarithmic principal strain φ_g, and the logarithmic principal strain rate $\dot{\varphi}_g$.

Flow Stress $k_f = f(\text{material}, \vartheta, \varphi_g, \dot{\varphi}_g)$.

The mean flow stress $\bar{k}_f$ in Eq 3.13 can be obtained from quasi-adiabatic flow curves found in the literature for:

- The temperature ϑ_E that the material being deformed enters the deformation zone

- The mean logarithmic principal strain $\bar{\varphi}_g$
- The mean logarithmic principal strain rate $\bar{\dot{\varphi}}_g$
- The specific material

$\bar{\varphi}_g$ and $\bar{\dot{\varphi}}_g$ are mean values that apply to the entire material being deformed in the deformation zone.

$\bar{k}_f = f$(material, entry temperature ϑ_E, mean logarithmic principal strain $\bar{\varphi}_g$, mean logarithmic principal strain rate $\bar{\dot{\varphi}}_g$).

From the literature [Sie 76a]

$$\bar{\varphi}_g = 2\ln \frac{3}{\dfrac{D_S}{D_0} + 2} \quad \text{(Eq 3.15)}$$

$$\bar{\dot{\varphi}}_g = \frac{V - 1}{l_U} \cdot u_{St} \quad \text{(Eq 3.16)}$$

where l_U is the length of the deformation zone. In the extrusion of round bars of diameter D_S, then, for a conical deformation zone with an opening angle $2\alpha = 90°$:

$$l_U = \frac{D_0 - D_S}{2 \tan \alpha} \quad \text{(Eq 3.17)}$$

If it is assumed for the hot extrusion of a round bar the deformation zone is conical with $\alpha = 45°$, then from Eq 3.16 and 3.17:

$$\bar{\dot{\varphi}}_g = \frac{2[V - 1]}{D_0 - D_S} \cdot u_{St} = \frac{2\left[\left(\dfrac{D_0}{D_S}\right)^2 - 1\right]}{D_0 - D_S} \cdot u_{St} \quad \text{(Eq 3.18)}$$

If the extruded section does not have a round cross section, an equivalent diameter D_S^* should be used to replace D_S:

$$D_S^* = \sqrt{\frac{4 \cdot A_S}{\pi}} \quad \text{(Eq 3.19)}$$

where A_S is the section cross-sectional area.

From the literature [Ake 66], [Stu 68], and [Stu 71], the approximation for direct hot extrusion attributable to Feltham [Fel 56] is:

$$\bar{\dot{\varphi}}_g = 6 \cdot \frac{u_{St}}{D_0} \cdot \varphi_{g_{ges}} \quad \text{(Eq 3.20)}$$

This approximation does, however, give significantly lower values than does Eq 3.18, which

appears to better describe the velocity behavior in the deformation zone and will therefore be used to determine the mean flow stress for the primary deformation zone.

Figure 3.16 shows for Al99.5 in a double logarithmic format the flow stress k_f as a function of the logarithmic principal strain φ_g.

This graph gives straight lines for $k_f = f(\varphi_g)$. These have been extrapolated from $\varphi_g = 1.1$. The values in the range $0.4 \leq \varphi_g \leq 1.1$ are taken from the measured values from the work [Bue 70]. These flow stress values are show for the logarithmic principal strain rates $\dot{\varphi}_g = 0.25, 4.0$, and 63 s^{-1}. It can be seen that as the temperature increases, the influence of the logarithmic principal strain rate also increases.

Figure 3.17 shows for aluminum in double logarithmic format the flow stress as a function of the logarithmic principal strain rate.

These values were measured for the principal strains $\varphi_g = 1, 3$, and 5 [Alu]. Figure 3.18 shows that in the temperature range 350 to 500 °C, the influence of the logarithmic principal stress on the flow stress is small. Flow stress values as a function of φ_g, $\dot{\varphi}_g$, and ϑ for metallic materials can be found in the literature, e.g., [DGM 78].

The factor C in Eq 3.13 contains:

$$C = \frac{f_p}{\eta_F} \quad \text{(Eq 3.21)}$$

where f_p is the profile factor, and η_F the deformation efficiency factor.

If the axial load on the die for the extrusion of a specific section is compared with the axial load for the extrusion of a round bar of the same extrusion ratio:

$$f_p = \frac{F_{M\ \text{section}}}{F_{M\ \text{round}}} \quad \text{(Eq 3.22)}$$

The deformation efficiency factor η_F is defined as the ratio of the theoretical deformation load needed $F_{M\ \text{theor}}$ to the actual measured load $F_{M\ \text{gem}}$:

$$\eta_F = \frac{F_{M\ \text{theor}}}{F_{M\ \text{measured}}} = \frac{\bar{k}_f \cdot \varphi_{g_{ges}} \cdot \dfrac{\pi D_0^2}{4}}{F_{M\ \text{measured}}} \quad \text{(Eq 3.23)}$$

If no experimental results are available, $\eta_F = 0.5$–0.6 can be assumed.

If a round bar is being extruded, the factor C is given by:

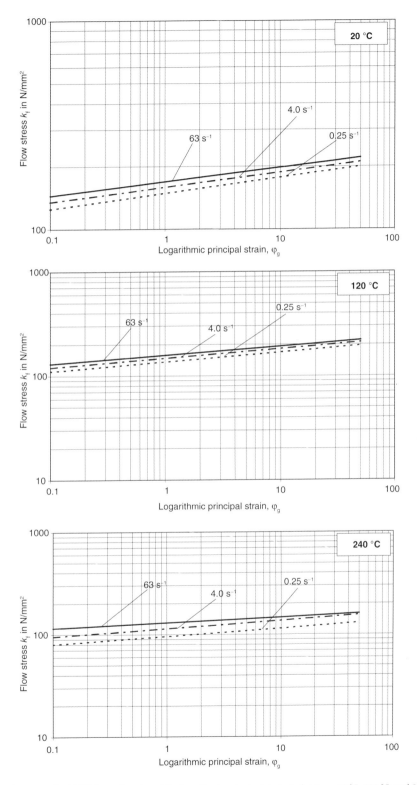

Fig. 3.16 Flow stress k_f of Al99.5 as a function of the logarithmic principal strain φ_g for $\vartheta_E = 20$ °C, 120 °C, and 240 °C (values in the range $0.4 \leq \varphi_g \leq 1.1$ taken from [Bue 70])

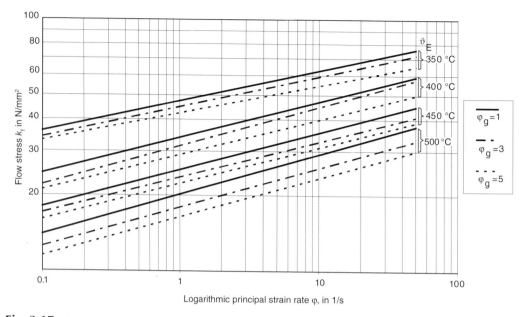

Fig. 3.17 Flow stress k_f of Al99.5 as a function of the logarithmic principal strain rate $\dot{\varphi}_g$ (values from [Alu])

$$C = \frac{1}{\eta_F} \qquad \text{(Eq 3.24)}$$

Example:

Material:	Al99.5
Container diam	$D_0 = 140$ mm
Initial billet diam	$D_B = 136$ mm
Initial billet length	$l_B = 500$ mm
Product	Round bar 19.8 mm
Initial billet temperature = container temperature	400 °C
Ram speed	10 mm/s

Then:

Equation	Parameter	Result
3.1	Extrusion ratio	$V = 50$
3.14	Logarithmic principal strain	$\varphi_{g_{ges}} = 3.9$
3.15	Mean log. Principal strain	$\bar{\varphi}_g = 0.674$
3.16	Mean log. Principal strain rate	$\bar{\dot{\varphi}}_g = 8.15 \text{ s}^{-1}$

With $\bar{\dot{\varphi}}_g = 8.15 \text{ s}^{-1}$, $\bar{\varphi}_g = 0.674$, and $\vartheta = 400$ °C, then the mean flow stress over the full deformation zone from Fig. 3.17 is:

$$\bar{k}_f = 31 \text{ N/mm}^2$$

Equation	Parameter	Result
3.21	Factor C for $f_p = 1$ and $\eta_f = 0.6$ (estimated)	$C = 1.67$
3.13	Deformation load	$F_m = 3100$ kN
3.8	Upset displacement	$s_1 = 28$ mm
3.8	Upset billet length	$l_0 = 472$ mm
3.3	Discard length	$l_R = 23$ mm

With $u_{St} = 10$ mm/s, $\vartheta = 400$ °C, then for Al99.5 from Fig. 3.12, the shear stress is $\tau_S = 10 \text{ N/mm}^2$:

Eq 3.6 friction load $F_R = 4396$ N/mm
$$\cdot (477 - s_{St}) \text{ mm}$$

Eq 3.6 Stem load $F_{St} = F_M + F_R = 3100$ kN
$$+ \ 4396 \text{ N/mm} \cdot (477 - s_{St}) \text{ mm}$$

For the maximum of the stem load at the start of extrusion where $s_{St} = s_1$ mm. Then:

$$\text{Max stem load } F_{St \ max} = 5074 \text{ kN}$$

The stem load minimum at $s_{St} = l_0 + s_1 - l_R$ gives:

$$\text{Min stem load } F_{St \ min} = 3100 \text{ kN}$$

The result is the principal variation of the stem force over the stem displacement shown in Fig. 3.18.

3.1.1.5 Thermal Changes in Direct Hot Extrusion of Aluminium

The process input parameters are the initial temperatures of the dummy block, the die, and the billet immediately before the start of extrusion.

The temperature of the container is also an important process parameter.

Whereas it is adequate to only input the mean initial temperature of the dummy block and the die, an understanding of the temperature of the billet and the container is needed in both the axial and the radial direction.

It is possible with an induction billet furnace to develop temperature gradients in the billet,

but it is possible for these to change during the period between heating and upsetting.

The variation in the billet temperature in the axial and radial direction immediately before the upsetting of the billet is of interest.

The temperature distribution in the container is more difficult to analyze.

Figure 3.19 shows the axial temperature profile along the container wall in the static empty condition. This shows that the actual temperature ϑ_A displayed at the control desk is exceeded

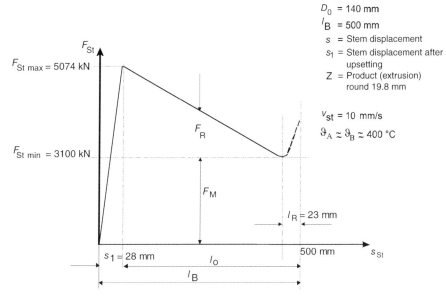

Fig. 3.18 Calculated variation of the stem load F_{St} over the stem displacement for Al99.5. The result is the principal variation of the stem force over the stem displacement shown in the figure.

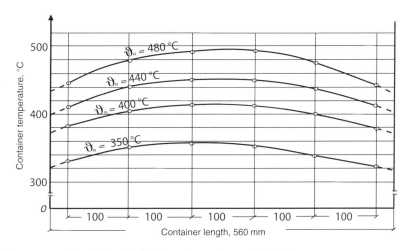

Fig. 3.19 Temperature variation in the axial direction at the container wall [Sie 76a]

in the middle of the container, and the temperature toward the end faces is significantly lower. In the stationary empty condition the maximum temperature occurs in the center of the container. Figure 3.20 shows the change in the container temperature fields for different extrusion intensities. These show that as the intensity of the extrusion operation increases, the temperature maximum moves toward the die, and with an intense press operation, the temperature increase comes entirely from the friction and deformation with the container heating switched off.

Considering the heat sources in extrusion the deformation work in the primary deformation zone is converted to heat.

Thus:

$$F_M \cdot s = Q_U \qquad \text{(Eq 3.25)}$$

In a quasi-adiabatic process, this heat in the material being extruded produces a temperature increase of:

$$\Delta \vartheta_U = \frac{\bar{k}_f \cdot \varphi_{g_{ges}}}{\rho \cdot c} \qquad \text{(Eq 3.26)}$$

where ρ is the density and c the specific heat of the material being extruded. This relationship first applies in the quasi-stationary extrusion process because at the point of upsetting, not all the billet volume will pass through the deformation zone but, depending on the location in front of the die, will experience a reduced deformation. The extrusion will initially have the initial billet temperature ϑ_B, and once the first billet section has passed through the entire deformation zone undergoing the full deformation $\varphi_{g_{ges}}$ will have the exit temperature given by ϑ_A where:

$$\vartheta_A = \vartheta_E + \Delta \vartheta_U \qquad \text{(Eq 3.27)}$$

Here, ϑ_E is the temperature of the material being extruded as it enters the deformation zone. It is assumed that no heat flows back from the deformation zone into the billet.

It is also assumed that no heat flows from the deformation zone into the container and die in contact with the deformation zone. The entry temperature ϑ_E is determined from the model assumption that the material being extruded consists of flat parallel discs perpendicular to the center line between the deformation entry plane and billet end. With the assumption of a boundary surface within which the material being extruded shears as the billet moves through the container, the thermal conditions in a disc can be considered as shown in Fig 3.21.

The disc has a thickness of 10 mm and a diameter D_0. It is pushed through the container with a stem speed u_{St}. In the time t, the quantity of heat Q_τ that develops in the boundary surface is:

$$Q_\tau = (\pi \cdot D_0 \cdot 10 \text{ mm}) \int_0^t \tau_S \cdot u_{St} \cdot dt \qquad \text{(Eq 3.28)}$$

From this quantity of heat Q_τ a fraction Q_B flows back into the billet and a fraction Q_R into the container.

According to Lange [Lan 71]:

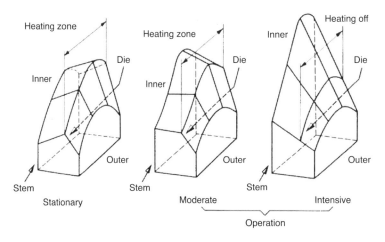

Fig. 3.20 Principal variation in the container temperature for different working conditions [Ake 71]

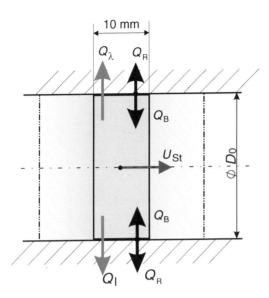

Fig. 3.21 Heat balance in a billet slice [Sie 76b] with reference to [Lan 71]

$$Q_T = Q_B + Q_R \qquad \text{(Eq 3.29)}$$

$$Q_B = \frac{b_B}{b_B + b_R} \cdot Q_T \qquad \text{(Eq 3.30)}$$

where b is the heat penetration coefficient, which is the square root of the product of the thermal conductivity λ, specific heat c, and density ρ. For the billet material:

$$b_B = \sqrt{c_B \cdot \lambda_B \cdot \rho_B} \qquad \text{(Eq 3.31)}$$

and for the container material:

$$b_R = \sqrt{c_R \cdot \lambda_R \cdot \rho_R} \qquad \text{(Eq 3.32)}$$

It is therefore possible to calculate from Eq 3.30, taking the relationships Eq 3.1, 3.28, and 3.32 into account, the quantity of heat Q_B that is transferred into the billet disc in time t from the shearing of the material being extruded as it is pushed through the container.

It is still necessary to determine the quantity of heat Q_λ that flows into the container from the billet disc in the time t when the container temperature is less than the billet temperature. If the mean temperature of the region of the container along which the disc is pushed immediately before the start of extrusion is ϑ_R, and if ϑ_B is the mean temperature of the disc at the start of extrusion, then from ([Lan 71] and [Sie 76b]):

$$Q_\lambda = (\pi \cdot D_0 \cdot 10 \text{ mm}) \frac{2 \cdot b_B \cdot b_R \cdot (\vartheta_E - \vartheta_R)}{\sqrt{\pi(b_B + b_R)}} \sqrt{t} \qquad \text{(Eq 3.33)}$$

In the time t, the quantity of heat transferred to the billet is Q_B and the quantity of heat removed is Q_λ. The difference is:

$$\Delta Q = Q_B - Q_\lambda, \qquad \text{(Eq 3.34)}$$

This difference gives the temperature increase:

$$\Delta\vartheta_B = \frac{\Delta Q}{\frac{\pi}{4} D_0^2 \cdot 10 \text{ mm} \cdot \rho_B \cdot c_B} \qquad \text{(Eq 3.35)}$$

From this it is possible to calculate the mean temperature ϑ_E with which the individual billet disc enters the deformation zone depending on the shear displacement and the time:

$$\vartheta_E = \vartheta_B + \Delta\vartheta_B \qquad \text{(Eq 3.36)}$$

where ϑ_B is the temperature of the disc at the start of the extrusion process. The temperature increase $\Delta\vartheta_B$ is obtained taking (Eq 3.34) into account from the difference of the heat added Q_B and the heat conducted away Q_λ.

The shear displacement up to entry into the deformation zone and thus the amount of shear heat transferred into the disc depends on the location of the disc in the container at the start of extrusion. The amount of heat that flows into the disc in the container depends on the extrusion speed and the location of the disc in the container. The difference between the container temperature and the billet temperature has a major influence.

Of interest is the section exit temperature as a function of stem displacement or extruded length. The extruded length is obtained by multiplying the stem displacement S_{St} by the extrusion ratio V:

$$L_s = S_{St} \cdot V \qquad \text{(Eq 3.37)}$$

A constant exit temperature is desired to achieve constant product properties over the extruded length.

Figure 3.22 shows in principle the influence of the shearing of the material being extruded along the container wall on the temperature increase in the deformation zone and the section exit temperature.

From Fig. 3.22:

- The entry temperature ϑ_E is not constant during the process but increases with the stem displacement because of the shearing of the material being extruded as the billet is pushed through the container.

- It should be noted that ϑ_E influences the flow stress k_f of the material being extruded in the deformation zone. As the entry temperature ϑ_E increases, the flow stress decreases. From this, as the stem displacement or extruded length increases, there is a decrease in $\Delta\vartheta_U$.

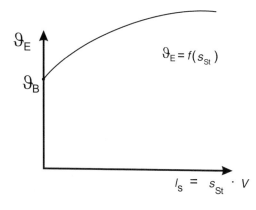

Principle variation of the temperature ϑ_E of the billet material as it enters the deformation zone over the length of the section or the stem displacement

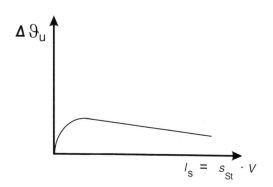

Principal variation of the temperature increase $\Delta\vartheta_u$ of the billet material in the deformation zone over the length of the section or the stem displacement

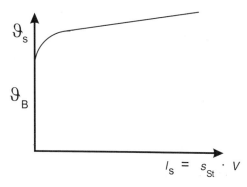

Principal variation of the section exit temperature over the section length or the stem displacement

Fig. 3.22 Influence of the friction between the billet and container on the increase in temperature in the deformation zone and on the exit temperature in direct extrusion without lubrication and without a shell for $\vartheta_R = \vartheta_B$

However, as a rule, the influence of the entry temperature as a result of the shear friction dominates so that the exit temperature increases with increasing stem displacement. Thus, the section exit temperature ϑ_S over the stem displacement S_S or section length follows, in principle, the profile shown in Fig. 3.22 for the direct hot extrusion of aluminum alloys.

Figure 3.23 shows the measured section exit temperature for the aluminum alloy AlZnMgCu0.5 over the section length. This temperature was measured with a micromantle thermocouple Th in the die land. Figure 3.23 also shows the maximum possible exit temperature without the occurrence of section transverse cracks (hot cracking).

The aim for an economic extrusion process is to use the maximum ram speed possible. However, specific material-related limiting temperatures should not be exceeded to avoid hot cracking. The structure and thus the product properties can also change with the section exit temperature ϑ_S.

For high productivity in extrusion, the stem speed over the stem displacement should be as high as possible.

The exit temperature ϑ_E should be as constant as possible over the product length to ensure a defect-free product. Specific limiting temperatures at which transverse cracks can occur should never be exceeded.

The following possibilities exist to obtain an exit temperature as constant as possible. These are usually not used individually but together:

- Optimization of the difference between the initial billet temperature and the container temperature
- Axial billet temperature profile (this requires an induction billet heating furnace)
- Stem speed as a function of stem displacement
- Zone heating and zone cooling of the container with the aim of maintaining the temperature fields in the container largely independent of the extrusion process

If the material being extruded enters the deformation zone with a constant exit temperature ϑ_E then, as shown in Fig 3.24, the section exit temperature is constant over the extrusion length after an unsteady upset process. The product properties are then constant over the length of the extrusion.

3.1.2 Direct Hot Extrusion without Lubrication and with a Shell (Copper Alloys)

Copper alloys are usually extruded by direct or by indirect hot extrusion without lubrication and with a shell. Both processes will be discussed to enable a direct comparison to be made between them for the extrusion of copper alloys.

Thus, *The extrusion of copper alloys is usually carried out without lubrication and with a shell by the direct or indirect hot extrusion process.*

In direct hot extrusion without lubrication and with a shell the contaminated and oxidized peripheral zone of the upset billet in the container is sheared to leave a tubular shell on the container wall. The thickness of the shell is determined by the gap between the container and the dummy block. The shell ensures that only defect-free material enters the extrusion. The disadvantage is that the shell has to be removed from the container.

3.1.2.1 Process Sequence for Direct Hot Extrusion without Lubrication and with a Shell

As shown in Fig 3.25, in this process the billet is pushed into the container along with the loose dummy block by the stem. This is followed by the actual extrusion process until the preset dis-

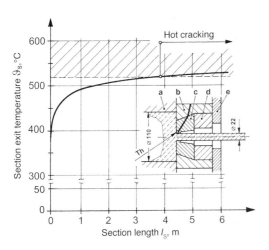

Fig. 3.23 Section exit temperature over the length of the extrusion for the alloy AlZnMgCu0.5 [Sie 76b]. a, container; b, die holder; c, die; d, die support; e, press platen; Th, measurement location of microsheathed thermocouples

card length is reached. A shell that adheres to the container wall is formed between the dummy block and the container wall. At the end of the extrusion process the stem is withdrawn. The container is then opened far enough to allow the section to be sawn and a discard tool to be loaded between the die and the container. The stem then scalps the shell from the container wall using a cleaning disc and pushes the dis-

card, shell, dummy block, and discard into the discard tool.

The stem is then withdrawn to the starting position. The container then travels back far enough to enable the discard tool to be swung out. The container then returns to its starting position.

With some extruded alloys there is the option of using a combination block (Fig. 3.46). This

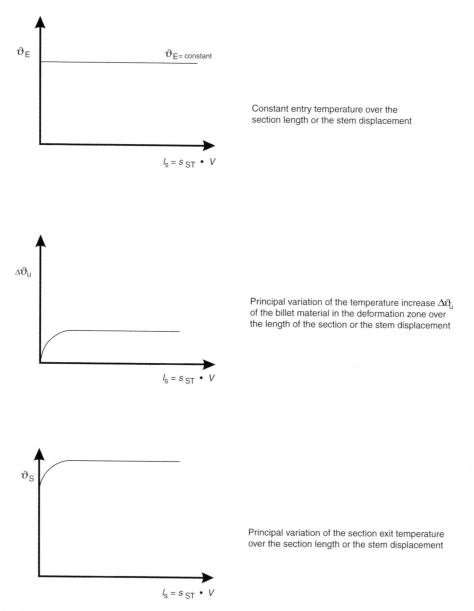

Fig. 3.24 Constant entry temperature ϑ_E as the requirement for a constant exit temperature over the length of the extrusion or over the stem displacement in direct extrusion without lubrication and without a shell (billet temperature increasing toward the front of the billet and ram speed decreasing over the stem displacement as well as in some cases zone heating and cooling of the container)

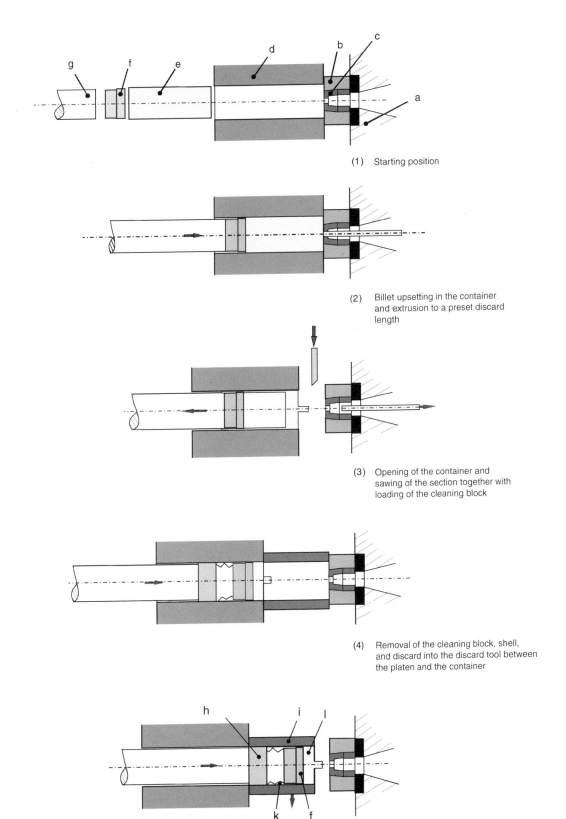

(1) Starting position

(2) Billet upsetting in the container and extrusion to a preset discard length

(3) Opening of the container and sawing of the section together with loading of the cleaning block

(4) Removal of the cleaning block, shell, and discard into the discard tool between the platen and the container

(5) Removal of the discard tool followed by return to the starting position

Fig. 3.25 Process sequence in direct hot extrusion without lubrication and with a shell of copper alloys. a, platen; b, die holder; c, die; d, container; e, billet; f, dummy block; g, extrusion stem; h, cleaning billet; i, discard tube; k, shell; l, discard

process uses a combination of the dummy block and the cleaning disc with an intermediate chamber into which the shell is compressed. It is then possible with this combination block to eliminate the process sequence shown in Fig. 3.25 of withdrawal of the stem, loading of the cleaning block, and cleaning by moving the stem forward.

3.1.2.2 Variation in the Stem Load over the Stem Displacement in Direct Hot Extrusion without Lubrication and with a Shell

In principle, the stem load variation over the stem displacement in direct hot extrusion without lubrication and with a shell should be the same as in direct extrusion without lubrication and without a shell. In direct hot extrusion without lubrication and without a shell, e.g., aluminum, a film of the material being extruded coats the container wall and shearing of the material being extruded has to take place similar to extrusion with a shell.

In the extrusion of copper alloys, the initial billet temperature ϑ_B is usually higher than the container temperature ϑ_R. Heat then flows from the billet into the container. This is usually larger than the heat transfer into the billet from the shearing of the shell.

As the stem displacement increases the billet volume enters the deformation zone with a decreasing entry temperature ϑ_E. As the entry temperature ϑ_E decreases, the flow stress k_f rises and the deformation load F_U increases with stem displacement. Figure 3.26 shows the variation in the stem load F_{St} over the stem displacement s as the sum of the deformation load F_U and shear or friction load F_R. The deformation load F_U is equal to the axial load acting on the die F_M ($F_U = F_M$).

3.1.2.3 Material Flow in Direct Hot Extrusion without Lubrication and with a Shell

Figure 3.27 shows stages in the direct hot extrusion without lubrication and with a shell for $CuCo_2Be$. As the stem moves forward (decreasing billet length), the friction between the billet and the container results in an extremely severe distortion of the grid lines. The hotter internal zones accelerate forward, and the peripheral zone restrained by the friction between the material being formed and the container wall flows in as a secondary deformation zone at the back of the billet (compare with Fig. 3.9 and 3.11 and the discussion in section 3.1.1.3). The material flow in direct hot extrusion without lubrication and with a shell can be classified as flow pattern C in Fig. 3.11.

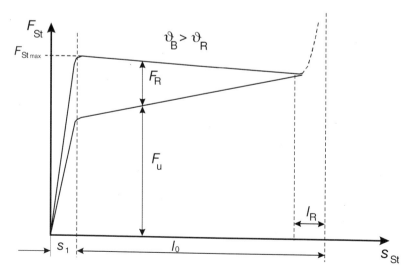

Fig. 3.26 Principal variation of the stem load F_{St} and the deformation load $F_U = F_M$ over the stem length s_{St} for the direct hot extrusion with a shell for the initial billet temperature ϑ_B that is significantly above the container temperature ϑ_R, which is the case for direct hot extrusion with a shell of copper alloys

3.1.2.4 Calculation of the Axial Forces in Direct Hot Extrusion without Lubrication and with a Shell

The calculation of the axial forces for direct hot extrusion without lubrication and with a shell can, in principle, follow the procedure described in section 3.1.1.4. One factor to take into account is that in the determination of the shear load (friction load) over the stem displacement $F_R = f(s_{St})$, the shear stress τ_S is obtained for the temperature in the billet peripheral zone. The temperature of the material being deformed in the billet peripheral zone will decrease with increasing billet/container contact time despite transfer of the heat from the shearing. The time of contact can be obtained from the stem speed and the upset billet length. The mean temperature in the billet peripheral zone can be roughly estimated to be:

$$\bar{\vartheta}_{Ba} = \frac{\vartheta_B + \vartheta_R}{2} \qquad \text{(Eq 3.38)}$$

where ϑ_B is the initial billet temperature and ϑ_R the container temperature. A mean shear stress $\bar{\tau}_S$ can then be obtained for $\bar{\vartheta}_{Ba}$ taking into account the stem speed (shear rate) providing shear flow curves are available.

Allowance should also be made for the decrease over the stem displacement of the entry temperature ϑ_E of the material being deformed into the deformation zone. The flow stress k_f will then increase over the stem displacement. The calculation of the entry temperature can be carried out following the method of Lange [Lan 71] in section 3.1.1.4.

3.1.2.5 Thermal Conditions in Direct Hot Extrusion without Lubrication and with a Shell

Copper alloys are extruded at working temperatures over 600 °C. Typical initial billet temperatures for copper alloys fall in the range 600 to 800 °C. However, the thermal resistance of hot-working steel extrusion tools has a maximum temperature of 500 °C. The tool temperature should therefore be below this value. Some heat therefore will flow from the billet into the container. This heat loss is higher than the heat gain from shearing the shell.

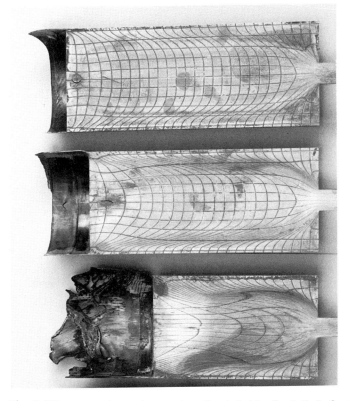

Container temperature	D_A = 460 °C
Container diam	D_0 = 110 mm
Billet length	l_B = 300 mm
Billet diam	D_B = 106.7 mm
Billet temperature	ϑ_B = 950 °C
Product	22.5 × 11.3 mm
	V = 37.4
Upset speed	32 mm/s
Stem speed	30 mm/s
Billet lengths (mm)	271.3 (above)
	246.1 (middle)
	176.0 (below)

Fig. 3.27 Stages in the direct hot extrusion with a shell of the alloy CuCo$_2$Be (Source: K. Müller, Srangpreβzentrum Berlin)

The billet cross-section discs thus enter the deformation zone with a temperature that decreases with stem displacement. This results over the stem displacement in an increasing temperature rise $\Delta\vartheta_U$ in the material being deformed as it passes through the deformation zone throughout the stem displacement.

It is a fact, however, that the temperature ϑ_E decreases with stem displacement in spite of the heat input from the shearing of the shell because of the temperature difference between the initial billet temperature ϑ_B and the container temperature ϑ_R and the associated heat conduction into the container (Fig. 3.28).

The temperature decrease predominates so that the exit temperature ϑ_S decreases over the length of the extrusion.

As a general rule, the cooling of the extrusion billet in the container and the risk of piping defect (see section 3.1.1.3) limits the billet length in the direct hot extrusion with a shell of copper alloys to:

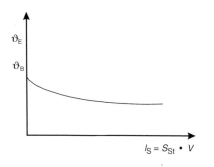

Principal variation of the temperature ϑ_E of the billet material as it enters the deformation zone over the stem displacement or the length of the section

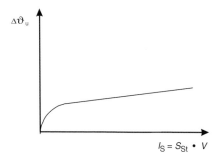

Principal variation of the temperature increase $\Delta\vartheta_u$ of the billet material in the deformation zone over the stem displacement or the length of the section

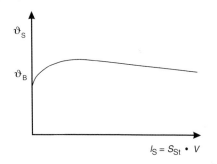

Principal variation of the section exit temperature ϑ_S over the stem displacement or the length of the section

Fig. 3.28 Principal temperature variation over the stem displacement or over the extruded length in direct hot extrusion without lubrication with a shell for the initial billet temperature ϑ_B that is significantly above the container temperature ϑ_R, which is the case for the direct hot extrusion with a shell of copper alloys

$$l_B \leq 3.5 D_0 \qquad \text{(Eq 3.39)}$$

3.1.3 Direct Hot Extrusion with Lubrication and without a Shell (Steel)

Direct hot extrusion without lubrication and without a shell is considered in section 3.1.1 using aluminum extrusion as an example. Direct hot extrusion without lubrication with a shell is discussed in section 3.1.2 using copper alloy extrusion as an example.

Because direct hot extrusion with lubrication and without a shell is used mainly for the extrusion of alloy steels, it is sensible in this context to discuss direct hot extrusion with lubrication without a shell using *the extrusion of steel* as an example.

3.1.3.1 Process Sequence in Direct Hot Extrusion with Lubrication and without a Shell

Horizontal hydraulic extrusion presses are normally used for this process. As shown in Fig. 3.29,

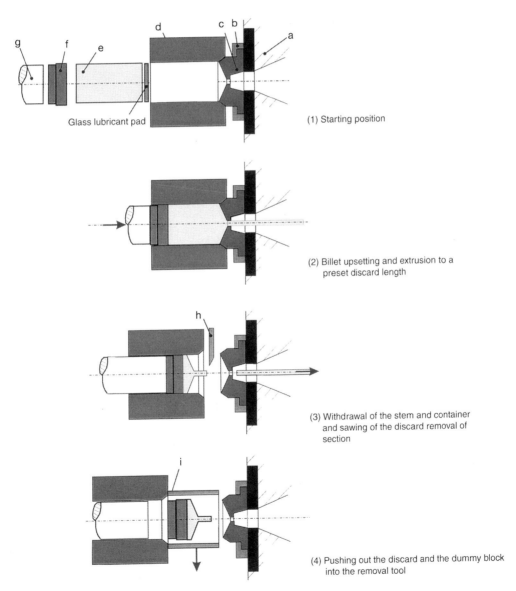

Fig. 3.29 Process sequence in extrusion of steel solid sections. See [Lau 76]. a, platen; b, die holder; c, die; d, container; e, billet; f, dummy block; g, extrusion stem; h, saw; i, discard tool

the billet is loaded together with a glass lubricant disc in the front and a loose dummy block at the back between the container and the stem and then loaded into the container. After the billet has been upset in the container, during which the glass reaches a low viscosity and surrounds the entire billet with lubricant, extrusion continues to the preset discard length. The container is then opened so that the section can be sawn from the discard.

When necessary, the container travels forward to push the section from the die using the residual section on the discard.

Finally, the container travels back to enable a discard tool to be moved between the container and the end housing. The stem then pushes the discard with the dummy block into the discard tool.

So far the discussion has concentrated on the pure process sequence. Special features to consider include:

- The container seal against the die is conical.
- The die is conical so that no dead metals zones form.
- The high billet temperature of over 1000 °C requires a short contact temperature taking into account the tool temperature of approximately 800 °C. This necessitates high stem speeds. Nevertheless, the service life of the die is so low that sometimes a new or reworked die has to be used after each extrusion.
- In addition to the material being extruded, the service life of the die depends on the extrusion ratio and the section exit speed as well as the die shape and the lubricant used.

This should, on one hand, have sufficient lubrication properties to completely separate the material being extruded from the container wall and the die and, on the other hand, the lubricant should also have a low thermal conductivity—in other words, provide thermal isolation. Glass and combinations of grease, oil, and graphite are used as lubricants. Glass provides very good lubrication and simultaneously excellent insulation. Direct hot extrusion of steel is, therefore, usually lubricated with glass.

3.1.3.2 Variation in the Stem Load with Stem Displacement in Direct Hot Extrusion with Lubrication and without a Shell

If the initial billet temperature ϑ_B is significantly higher than the container temperature ϑ_R,

as is the case in the extrusion of steel, then there is a significant heat loss from the billet to the container even with relatively short contact times. The friction between the billet and the container in direct hot extrusion with lubrication and without a shell is extremely low. The heat transfer into the billet from the friction billet/container is comparatively negligible compared with the heat flow from the billet into the container.

As shown in Fig. 3.30 the deformation load F_U increases over the stem displacement because the billet zones enter the deformation zone with a continuously decreasing temperature and thus increasing flow stress as the stem displacement increases. The difference between the stem load and the deformation load is equal to the friction load F_R, which is necessary to overcome the friction between the billet and the container. The friction between the billet and the container can be assumed to be Coulombic friction (see section 3.1.4.2).

3.1.3.3 Material Flow in Direct Hot Extrusion with Lubrication

In direct hot extrusion with lubrication, the deformation zone that develops in the material flow through conical dies is virtually enclosed by the die cone. With large die opening angles it curves into the billet.

The lubrication reduces the friction between the billet and the container to such an extent that it can approximately be assumed that the friction has no influence on the material flow. As shown

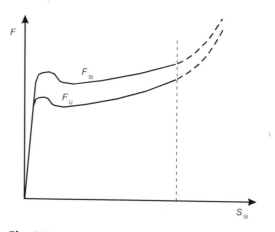

Fig. 3.30 Principal variation in the stem load F_{St} and the deformation load F_U over the stem displacement for direct hot extrusion with a lubricant and without a shell (e.g., steel)

in Fig. 3.31, a deformation zone forms that extends slightly from the die cone into the billet. With this type of material flow, the surface of the extrusion is formed from the billet peripheral zones. They should as far as possible not be oxidized.

3.1.3.4 Thermal Conditions in Direct Hot Extrusion with Lubrication

In the consideration of thermal conditions, attention has to be given to the fact that the billets in the extrusion of steel have temperatures between 1100 and 1200 °C, whereas the container temperature usually cannot exceed 700 °C. There is, therefore, a large temperature difference, which makes it necessary to have the shortest possible contact time between the billet and the container and consequently for the extrusion process.

The mechanical presses used earlier have been largely replaced in recent years because they have proved to be uneconomic for the production of low-alloy steel tubes compared with tube rolling processes (see the section "Extrusion of Iron-Alloy Semifinished Products" in Chapter 5).

Today, horizontal hydraulic presses with accumulator drive are almost exclusively used because the accumulator drive provides high stem speeds.

Over the stem displacement s_{St} or the section length $l_S = V \cdot s_{St}$ billet zones enter the deformation zone with a decreasing temperature (ϑ_E), where there is a temperature increase $\Delta\vartheta_U$ associated with the deformation. The flow stress k_f increases with the decreasing temperature of the material being deformed, and the temperature

increase $\Delta\vartheta_U$, therefore, increases over the stem displacement or the section length.

The influence of the entry temperature ϑ_E over the stem displacement or section length is the dominating factor on the section exit temperature ϑ_S, which decreases over the stem displacement or the section length. See the temperature profiles in Fig. 3.32.

3.1.4 Direct Cold Extrusion with Lubrication and without a Shell

As in all direct extrusion processes, friction between the container wall and the billet has to be taken into account in direct cold extrusion with lubrication and without a shell. This friction is minimized by using a lubricant that is normally applied to the billet before extrusion. Conical dies are usually used to ensure that the lubricant surrounds the material being extruded up to the exit from the die. The billet is also tapered at the front.

Direct cold extrusion with lubrication and without a shell is characterized by the friction between the material being extruded and both the container and the die. This friction is minimized by the use of a lubricant.

3.1.4.1 Process Sequence in Direct Cold Extrusion with Lubrication and without a Shell

Figure 3.33 shows a possible process sequence. The dummy block is fixed to the stem. The billet tapered at the front is coated with lubricant and loaded into the container. It is then extruded to a preset discard length. The container and stem are then withdrawn to enable the discard to be pulled from the die with a manipulator and the section to be cut free with a saw.

The discard is then removed from the press with the manipulator and the section pulled from the die. The container and stem finally travel back to the corresponding starting position.

3.1.4.2 Stresses, Axial Loads, and Temperature Increase

Figure 3.34 shows variation in the axial load $F_U = F_M$ on the die, the axial load F_R required to overcome the friction between the material being extruded and the container, and the stem load F_{St} over the stem displacement s_{St} for direct cold extrusion with lubrication and without a shell. This shows that a constant axial load $\bar{F}_U$ forms during the quasi-stationary deformation

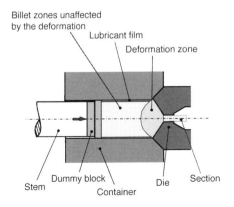

Fig. 3.31 Principal material flow in direct hot extrusion with lubrication without a shell

Billet zones unaffected by the deformation
Lubricant film
Deformation zone
Stem
Dummy block
Container
Die
Section

process after an unsteady initial process, which is characterized by the maximum value $\hat{F}_M$ and $\hat{F}_{St}$, whereas the friction load F_R falls exponentially over the stem displacement.

The stem load F_{St} is obtained from the sum of the deformation load F_U and the friction load F_R.

In direct cold extrusion with lubrication and without a shell, the starting point is the model assumption that the deformation zone is geometrically restrained by the die wall, the die entry plane, and the die exit plane (Fig. 3.35).

The axial force $P_{E_{id}}$ for the ideal deformation in the entry plane is given using the logarithmic total principal strain $\varphi_{g_{ges}}$ (see Eq 3.14) or the extrusion ration V by:

$$p_{XE_{id}} = \bar{k}_f \cdot \varphi_{g_{ges}} = \bar{k}_f \cdot \ln V \qquad \text{(Eq 3.40)}$$

where $\bar{k}_f$ is the mean flow stress for the total volume in the deformation zone. The mean log-

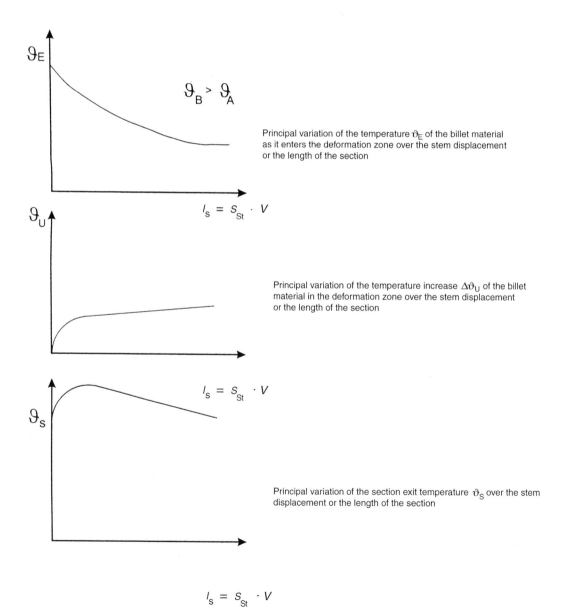

Principal variation of the temperature ϑ_E of the billet material as it enters the deformation zone over the stem displacement or the length of the section

Principal variation of the temperature increase $\Delta\vartheta_U$ of the billet material in the deformation zone over the stem displacement or the length of the section

Principal variation of the section exit temperature ϑ_S over the stem displacement or the length of the section

Fig. 3.32 Principal variation in the exit temperature ϑ_S for direct hot extrusion with lubrication and without a shell for the initial billet temperature ϑ_B that is much higher than the container temperature ϑ_R (e.g., the direct hot extrusion with lubrication and without a shell of steel)

arithmetic principal strain $\bar{\varphi}_g$ at the volume center of gravity S is needed to determine this from the quasi-adiabatic flow curves. The volume centre of gravity of the deformation zone is approximately given by:

$$x = \frac{2}{3} \cdot l_U \quad \text{(see Fig. 3.35)}$$

From this, according to Eq 3.15:

$$\bar{\varphi}_g = 2 \ln \frac{3}{\frac{D_S}{D_0} + 2}$$

The mean logarithmic principal strain rate is, according to Eq 3.18:

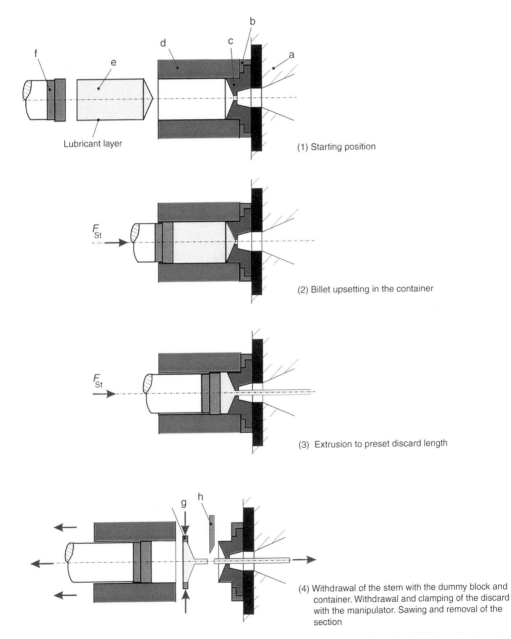

Lubricant layer

(1) Starting position

(2) Billet upsetting in the container

(3) Extrusion to preset discard length

(4) Withdrawal of the stem with the dummy block and container. Withdrawal and clamping of the discard with the manipulator. Sawing and removal of the section

Fig. 3.33 Process sequence in direct cold extrusion with lubrication and without a shell. a, platen; b, die holder; c, die; d, container; e, billet; f, stem with fixed dummy block; g, manipulator; h, saw

$$\bar{\dot{\phi}}_g = \frac{2\left[\left(\dfrac{D_0}{D_S}\right)^2 - 1\right]}{D_0 - D_S} \cdot u_{St}$$

In the cold working of metallic materials, the melting point of which is well above room temperature, it is usually possible to ignore the influence of the logarithmic strain rate on the flow stress. It is, therefore, possible to obtain the flow stress $\bar{k}_f$ for copper and aluminum alloys from adiabatic flow curves for $\vartheta_E = 20\ °C$ and $\bar{\dot{\phi}}_g$ using Eq 3.15.

In the extrusion of low-melting-point materials, e.g., lead and tin, the mean logarithmic strain rate has to be taken into account.

The ideal axial compressive stress $P_{XE_{id}}$ required for perfect deformation on the die entry plane multiplied by a factor C gives the actual axial compressive stress:

$$P_x = C \cdot P_{XE_{id}} \tag{Eq 3.41}$$

here, the factor C from Eq 3.21 contains a profile factor f_p and a deformation efficiency factor (see section 3.1.1.4).

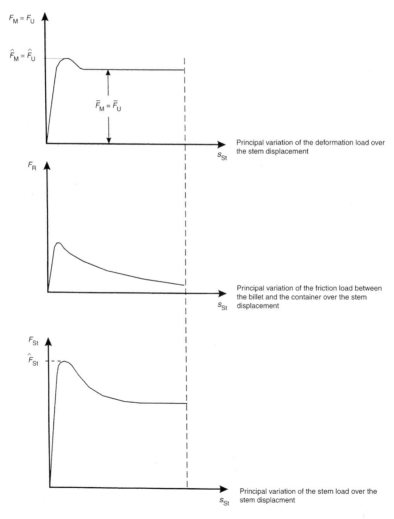

Fig. 3.34 Principal variation in the axial force F_M, F_R, and F_{St} over the stem displacement for direct cold extrusion with lubrication and without a shell

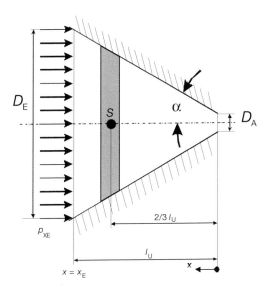

Fig. 3.35 Geometry of the deformation zone in the direct cold extrusion with lubrication without a shell and with a conical die

In direct cold extrusion with lubrication without a shell of round bars through conical dies where $f_p = 1$:

$$C = \frac{1}{\eta_U} = 1.1 \qquad \text{(Eq 3.42)}$$

from Eq 3.40, taking Eq 3.14 and 3.1 into account:

$$p_{X_E} = C \cdot p_{XE_{id}} = 1.1 \cdot \bar{k}_f \cdot \varphi_{g_{ges}}$$
$$= 1.1 \cdot \bar{k}_f \cdot \ln V \qquad \text{(Eq 3.43)}$$

The product of the axial compressive stress and the entry cross-sectional area gives the axial force F_U acting in the entry plane:

$$F_U = p_{X_E} \cdot A_E$$
$$= 1.1 \cdot \frac{\pi \cdot D_0^2}{4} \cdot \bar{k}_f \cdot \ln V \qquad \text{(Eq 3.44)}$$

The stem force F_{St} is the sum of the deformation force F_U and the friction force F_R:

$$F_{St} = F_U + F_R$$

The deformation load remains constant during the quasi-stationary deformation process, whereas the friction load falls exponentially because of the decreasing contact surface with increasing stem displacement between the billet

and the container assuming Coulombic friction (Fig. 3.34).

According to [Sie 76a], [Eis 31], [Sac 37], and [Rat 66], the axial compressive stress in the billet outside the deformation zone is given by (see Fig. 3.36):

$$p_X = p_{XE} \cdot e^{4(\mu_0/D_0)\bar{x}}$$
$$+ k_{f0} \cdot [1 - e^{4(\mu_0/D_0)\bar{x}}] \quad . \qquad \text{(Eq 3.45)}$$

where $\bar{x} = 0$ in the die entry plane (see Fig. 3.36).

The axial compressive stress p_x reaches its maximum value at the end of the billet at the start of extrusion:

$$p_x(\bar{x} = l_0) = P_{XE} e^{4(\mu_0/D_0)l_0}$$
$$+ k_{f_0} \cdot [1 - e^{4(\mu_0/D_0)l_0}] \qquad \text{(Eq 3.46)}$$

The minimum value occurs when:

$$p_x(\bar{x} = 0) = p_{XE} \qquad \text{(Eq 3.47)}$$

The flow stress k_{f_0} is the initial flow stress exhibited in the billet when it is loaded in the press. It can approximately be set as equal to the proof stress of the billet material. Then:

$$k_{f0} \approx R_{p0.2} \quad \text{or} \quad R_{eH}$$

The maximum stem load F_{St} at the billet end at the start of extrusion is, according to (Eq 3.46):

$$F_{St}(\bar{x} = l_0) = p_X(\bar{x} = l_0) \cdot \frac{\pi \cdot D_0^2}{4} \qquad \text{(Eq 3.48)}$$

$$F_{St}(\bar{x} = l_0) = \frac{\pi \cdot D^2}{4} \cdot p_{XE} \cdot e^{4(\mu_0/D_0)l_0}$$
$$+ \frac{\pi \cdot D_0^2}{4} \cdot k_{f_0} \cdot [1 - e^{4(\mu_0/D_0)l_0}]$$
$$\text{(Eq 3.49)}$$

This force reduces during extrusion to a minimum value:

$$F_{St}(\bar{x} = 0) = \frac{\pi \cdot D_0^2}{4} \cdot p_{XE} = F_U \qquad \text{(Eq 3.50)}$$

As shown in Fig. 3.36, the radial compressive stress p_r in the die region is larger than the axial compressive stress p_x by k_f. Outside the die, the radial compressive stress between the material being extruded and the container is lower than the axial compressive stress by k_{f0}.

The temperature increase in the deformation zone has to be taken into account. The work needed for the deformation is almost 100% converted into heat. Thus, for the section exit temperature ϑ_{St} under adiabatic conditions:

$$\vartheta_S = \frac{C \cdot k_f \cdot \bar{\varphi}_{ges}}{\rho \cdot c} + 20 \ °C$$

$$= \frac{C \cdot k_f \cdot \ln V}{\rho \cdot c} + 20 \ °C \qquad \text{(Eq 3.51)}$$

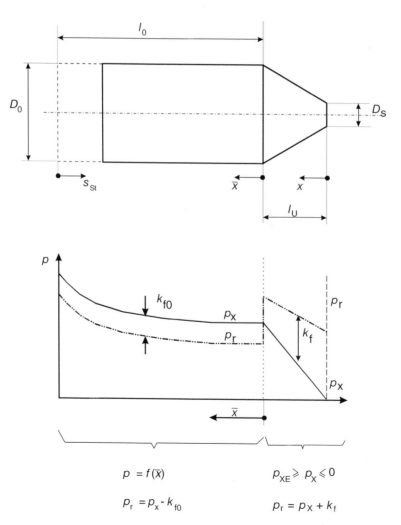

$$p = f(\bar{x})$$

$$p_r = p_x - k_{f0}$$

$$p_{XE} \geqslant p_X \leqslant 0$$

$$p_r = p_X + k_f$$

Fig. 3.36 Principal representation of the variation of the axial compressive stress p_x and the radial compressive stress p_r in direct cold extrusion with lubrication without a shell. l_0, upset billet length; s_{St}, stem displacement; D_0, container diam; D_S, extrusion diam; l_U, length of the deformation zone

The higher the strain, the higher is the section exit temperature ϑ_E. It can be several hundred degrees Celsius in cold extrusion.

Example (see Fig. 3.37):

Material	Al99.5
Container diam	$D_O = 85$ mm
Initial billet diam	$D_B = 82.5$ mm
Initial billet length	$l_B = 450$ mm + tip
Product	Round/12.02 mm
Initial billet temperature = container temperature	20 °C

Equation	Parameter	Result
(3.1)	$V = 50$	Extrusion ratio
(3.14)	Logarithmic total principal strain	$\varphi_{g_{ges}} = 3.9$
(3.15)	Mean log. Principal strain	$\bar{\varphi}_g = 0.674$

With $\bar{\varphi}_g = 0.674$ and $\vartheta_E = 20$ °C, then from Fig. 3.16:

$$\bar{k}_f = 160 \text{ N/mm}^2$$

Equation	Parameter	Result
(3.40)	Ideal axial compressive stress in the die exit plane	$p_{XE_{id}} = 626$ N/mm²
(3.41)	Actual axial compressive stress	$p_{X_E} = 690$ N/mm²
(3.44)	Deformation load	$F_U = 3900$ kN
(3.8)	Upset billet length	$l_0 = 424$ mm
(3.46)	Axial compressive stress at the start of extrusion at the billet end	$p_X(\bar{x} = l_0) = 970$ N/mm²
(3.49)	Stem load at the start of extrusion	$F_{St}(\bar{x} = l_0) = 5500$ kN

3.2 Indirect Extrusion

The principle of the indirect extrusion process has been known since 1870 and was used commercially in 1930 for the extrusion of brass semifinished products. The breakthrough in indirect extrusion, however, first occurred around 1960 with the extrusion of brass wire and sections in high-strength aluminum and copper alloys. Figure 3.1(b) shows the basic indirect extrusion process.

The indirect extrusion process can be classified into hot indirect extrusion or cold indirect extrusion, depending on whether the billet is loaded into the container heated or cold, i.e., at room temperature:

- *Hot indirect extrusion:* A heated billet is loaded into the container.
- *Cold indirect extrusion:* A cold (room temperature) billet is loaded into the container.

The hot indirect extrusion process can be divided into hot indirect extrusion without lubrication and without a shell and hot indirect extrusion without lubrication and with a shell.

Hot Indirect Extrusion without Lubrication and without a Shell. No lubricant is used

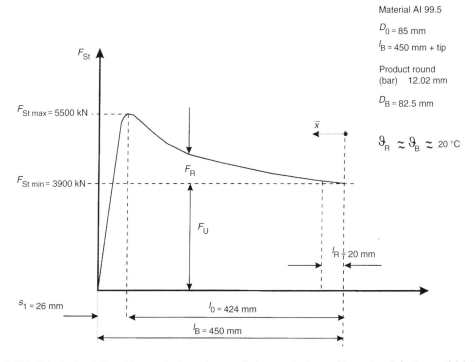

Fig. 3.37 Calculated variation of the stem load over the stem displacement in direct cold extrusion of aluminum with lubrication and without a shell. $D_0 = 85$ mm; $V = 50$; $l_B = 450$ mm + tip; $\mu = 0.02$; $R_{eH} = 120$ N/mm²

during extrusion. No shell is produced between the external die wall and the container wall.

Hot Indirect Extrusion without Lubrication and with a Shell. No lubricant is used during extrusion. A shell is produced almost as a second extruded product between the external die wall and the container wall.

The cold indirect extrusion process can be divided into extrusion with lubrication and extrusion without lubrication. In extrusion with lubrication the upset billet in the container is surrounded by a lubricant film. This lubricant film flows during extrusion both in the contact zone between the die wall and the billet as well as in the contact zone between the die external wall and the container wall. No shell is produced in either process.

Cold Indirect Extrusion without Lubrication and without a Shell. No lubricant is used during extrusion.

Cold Indirect Extrusion with Lubrication and without a Shell. A lubricant is used to reduce the friction between the die and the billet and to reduce the friction between the die external wall and the container wall.

3.2.1 Hot Indirect Extrusion without Lubrication and without a Shell (e.g., Aluminum Alloys)

As shown in Fig. 3.38, in hot indirect extrusion without a shell (and without a lubricant) the material being deformed is loaded as a billet between the hollow stem and the container and pushed along with the die into the latter by moving the container.

The billet can also be loaded between the container and the sealing stem. This does, however, have the disadvantage that when the billet slides into the container, pieces of the material being extruded adhering to the container wall can be shaved off by the billet and pushed in the direction of the billet. This can then flow into the extruded product during extrusion, resulting in extrusion defects.

This is avoided if the billet is loaded between the hollow stem and the container. In this case, any shavings of the material being extruded from the container wall are pushed in the direction of the sealing stem and remain in the discard.

In indirect extrusion the billet should preferably be loaded between the hollow stem and the container so that if any of the material being extruded is shaved from the container wall as

the billet is loaded, this will finish in the discard and not in the extrusion.

The operating sequence in indirect extrusion with a loose die in front of the hollow stem is shown in Fig. 3.38. It can be seen that a short sealing stem seals the container and pushes this over the die and hollow stem. After loading the billet is upset in the container and then extruded. The extrusion load is then transferred through the sealing stem. The discard can be sheared by a shear located on the container.

As well as using a loose die it is also possible, as shown in Fig. 3.39, to screw the die directly to the hollow stem or to locate it together with a die backer in a die holder attached to the hollow stem by a bayonet connection.

Figure 3.40 shows an example of a hollow stem with a screwed-on hollow stem extension fitted with a bayonet connection. The die holder is fitted to the latter by the bayonet connection.

A rigid connection between the die or the die holder and the hollow stem results in withdrawal loads and therefore places stresses on the thread or bayonet connection (Fig. 3.39). There is also the risk that billet material is shaved from the container wall by the rear edge of the die during the return stroke. This has to be removed before the next cycle.

It is also possible to extrude with a loose die guide ring (Fig. 3.39d). This does, however, have to be changed after each extrusion. There is no shaving of the billet material on the return stroke with this method of operation and no high-return loads.

The design of the sealing stem is very important in indirect extrusion.

As shown in figure Fig. 3.41, this can include a chamber. The material being extruded then flows into the container when the billet is upset in the container.

The friction between the material being extruded and the chamber wall enables the discard to be torn away or pulled away from the die at the end of the actual extrusion process as shown in Fig. 3.41. The removal of the discard with a "loose die guide ring" is shown in Fig. 3.42.

The following methods of die guiding can be used in indirect extrusion:

Loose Die Guiding. The loose die is loaded in front of the hollow stem and pushed out after shearing at the end of extrusion (Fig. 3.39). It is also possible to saw between the hollow stem and the discard after pulling back the discard together with the extrusion with a special chamber design in the sealing stem. The pull-out load comes from the friction between the deformed material in the chamber of the sealing stem and the chamber wall. The loose die is then removed along with the discard by a pusher located in the sealing stem (Fig. 3.41, 3.42).

Die Rigidly Attached to the Hollow Stem. In this case there are two possibilities. On one hand, the die can be screwed to the hollow stem. On the other hand, it is possible to attach a die

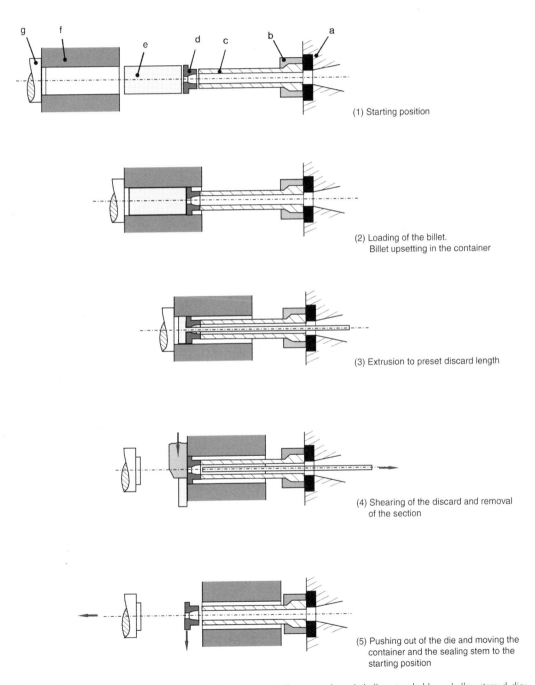

(1) Starting position

(2) Loading of the billet.
Billet upsetting in the container

(3) Extrusion to preset discard length

(4) Shearing of the discard and removal of the section

(5) Pushing out of the die and moving the container and the sealing stem to the starting position

Fig. 3.38 Process sequence in indirect hot extrusion without a shell. a, press platen; b, hollow stem holder; c, hollow stem; d, die; e, billet; f, container; g, sealing stem. See [Bis 73].

holder to the hollow stem with a bayonet connection (Fig. 3.39, 3.40).

Die Rigidly Attached to the Hollow Stem with a Loose Die Guide Ring. This arrangement enables the discard to be separated with a saw because it is possible with the special design of the sealing stem to pull out the discard to-

gether with the die closure ring (Fig. 3.39d, 3.42).

3.2.2 Hot Indirect Extrusion without Lubrication and with a Shell

In hot indirect extrusion with a shell the latter forms as a quasi-second (tube-shaped) extruded

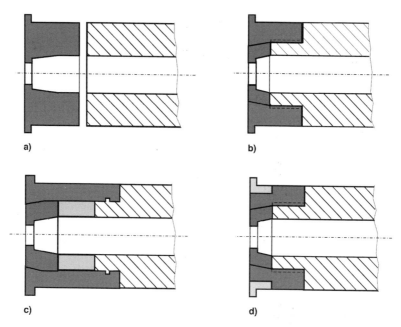

Fig. 3.39 Die guiding in indirect extrusion. See [Zie 7]. (a) Loose die in front of the hollow stem. (b) Die rigidly screwed to the hollow stem. (c) Die holder attached to the hollow stem by a bayonet connection. (d) Die rigidly attached to the hollow stem with a loose die guiding ring

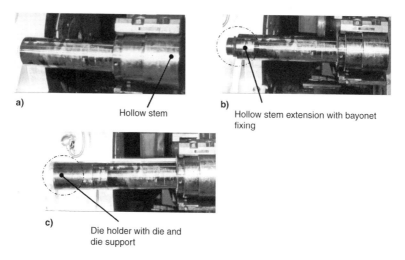

a) Hollow stem
b) Hollow stem extension with bayonet fixing
c) Die holder with die and die support

Fig. 3.40 (a) Hollow stem with internal thread. (b) Hollow stem with screwed-on extension with bayonet adapter. (c) Hollow stem with screwed-on extension and die holder attached by bayonet connector

product between the die guiding land and the container wall. The gap between the die and the container and the length l_{Ma} of the die land are set so that a perfectly complete shell is formed around the circumference and over the extrusion stroke and remains bonded to the container wall (Fig. 3.43).

The compressive stress state in the billet in front of the die has a significant influence on the selection of the gap and the length of the die guide land. The higher the extrusion ratio, the larger is the gap. This means that the gap should be increased for low extrusion ratios, as shown in Fig. 3.44.

Hot indirect extrusion without lubrication and with a shell has the advantage that billets with

impure or peripheral zones can be extruded as these peripheral zones remain in the shell. The disadvantage is that this process needs a special operating sequence "shell removal." Figure 3.45 shows the cycle.

It can be seen that the shell together with the die are pushed into a discard collector loaded between the container and the sealing stem during the cleaning cycle.

One possibility for indirect extrusion with a shell but without a special cleaning cycle is to use a so-called combination die (Fig. 3.46). The shell is compressed into a space behind the die guiding land. These combination dies have been used successfully in the indirect extrusion of brass.

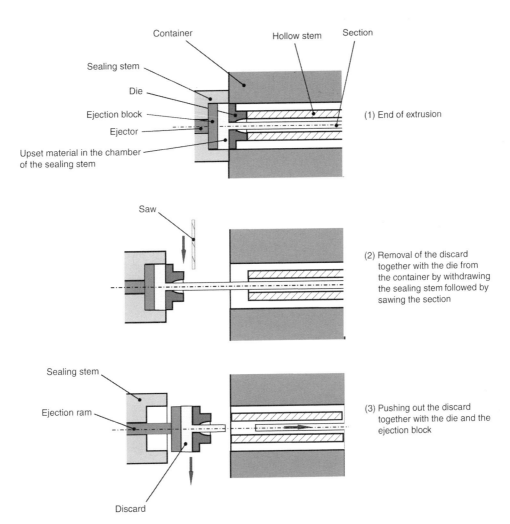

Fig. 3.41 Sealing stem with recess for withdrawal of discard and die

3.2.3 Material Flow in Indirect Hot Extrusion

As described in the section on direct hot-extrusion, the material flow can be studied by visio-plasticity (see section 3.1.1.3).

Figure 3.47 shows stages in the hot indirect extrusion without lubrication or shell of CuZn42. The distortion of the grid shows that a small deformation zone forms directly in front of the die face. The billet volume adjacent to the deformation zone is completely unaffected by the extrusion process. The material flow is, therefore, not affected by the billet length. From the material flow point of view there is no limit on the billet length. The billet length is limited only by the thermal conditions and the buckling length of the hollow stem.

The die and the deformation zone formed in front of the die are pushed through the container during indirect hot extrusion. It should be noted that the billet in front of the die face does not flow toward the die opening but forms a so-called dead metal zone. The material flow can, therefore, not be described by the flow type S (see Fig. 3.11). This has been claimed in the past by some authors but has since been clearly seen to be incorrect. Figure 3.48 shows a section of an AlMg3 billet extruded indirectly without lubrication. The material flow is the same as shown in Fig. 3.47 for brass. This principal material flow also occurs—as shown in Fig. 3.44—

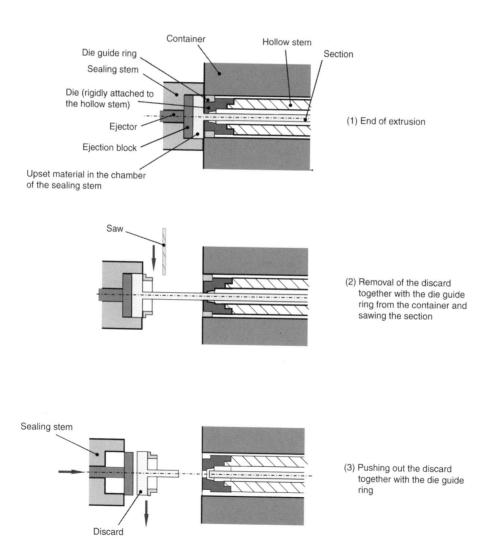

Fig. 3.42 Sealing stem with recess for withdrawal of discard and loose guide ring

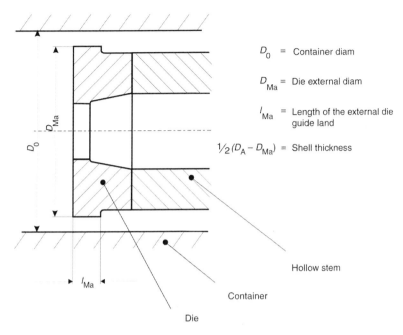

D_0 = Container diam

D_{Ma} = Die external diam

l_{Ma} = Length of the external die guide land

$\frac{1}{2}(D_A - D_{Ma})$ = Shell thickness

Hollow stem

Container

Die

Fig. 3.43 Geometric conditions in indirect extrusion with a shell

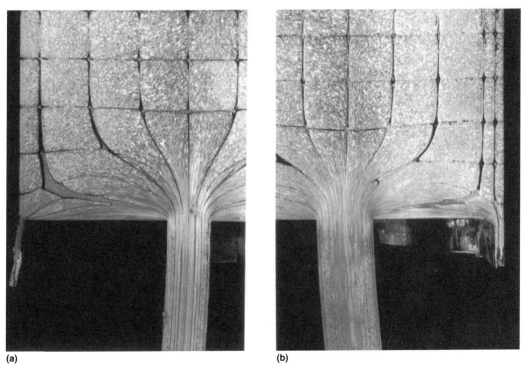

(a)   (b)

Fig. 3.44 Material flow in indirect extrusion with a shell (a) $V = 70$ and (b) $V = 30$. AlMg3, container diam = 140 mm, container temperature = billet temperature = 450 °C [Sie 76a], [Zie 73]

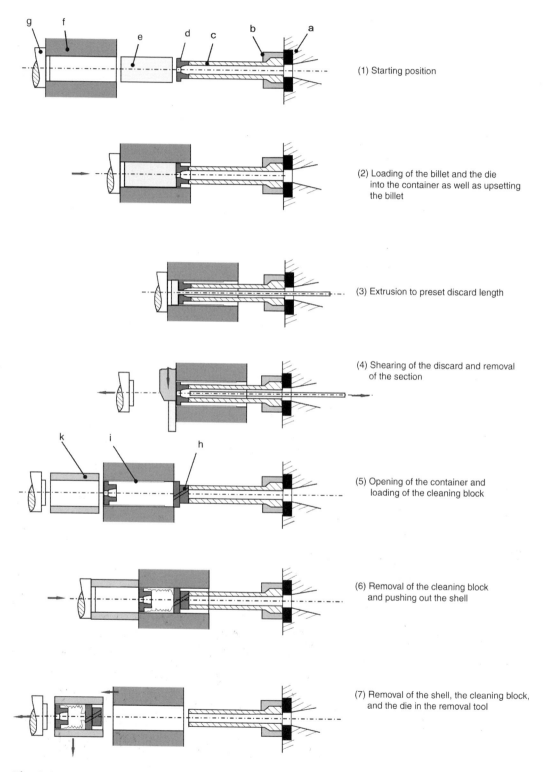

Fig. 3.45 Process sequence for the indirect extrusion without lubrication and with a shell. a, platen; b, hollow stem holder; c, hollow stem; d, die; e, billet; f, container; g, sealing stem; h, cleaning block; i, shell; j, discard tool. See [Bis 75].

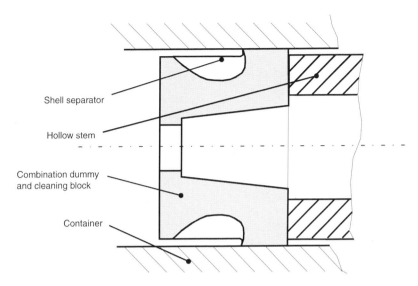

Fig. 3.46 Combination of die and cleaning block [Pet 59, Zie 77]

Fig. 3.47 Material flow (extrusion stages) in indirect hot extrusion without a shell and without lubrication of CuZn42 billets with container diam $D_0 = 110$ mm

for indirect hot extrusion without lubrication and with a shell. In this case there is a quasi second die aperture between the die external guiding surface and the container. The aim is for the shell to adhere to the container wall and is thus no longer than the upset billet length less the discard length.

In principle, the material flow for the indirect hot extrusion without shell can be described as shown in Fig. 3.48. Figures 3.47 and 3.48 show how the billet external zone flows in indirect extrusion without a shell via the deformation zone into the external zones of the extrusion.

To avoid this, extrusion can be carried out with a shell. In indirect hot extrusion the billet material flows in the gap between the external die surface and the container and forms a cylindrical shell almost as a second extruded product given the correct selection of the length of the external die surface and the gap width. This shell should, as far as possible, adhere to the container wall during extrusion; i.e., at the end of extrusion, the shell is no longer than the die movement within the container.

Figure 3.44 shows that if the mean compressive stress in the billet is low, which is the case with small extrusion ratios, the shell has to be thicker. Figure 3.49 shows aluminum shells that have been pushed from the container.

3.2.4 Axial Forces and Extrusion Exit Temperatures in the Indirect Hot Extrusion with an Initial Billet Temperature Equal to the Container Temperature (e.g., Aluminum Alloy Extrusion)

The characteristic feature of all indirect extrusion processes is that there is no friction between the billet and the container. It is, therefore not possible—as is the case with direct extrusion—to influence the material flow by the friction between the billet and the container.

It should also be taken into account that, in contrast to direct extrusion, no axial force is needed to overcome the friction between the billet and the container because it is the die, and not the billet, that is pushed through the container.

If the container displacement load and the load needed to overcome the friction between the container external land and the container is neglected, then the sealing stem load is equal to the hollow stem load.

In indirect extrusion, the sealing stem load F_{VSt} is approximately equal to the hollow stem load F_{HSt}, which is equal to the axial load on the die F_M, if the friction between the die and the container is ignored. This load is equal to the

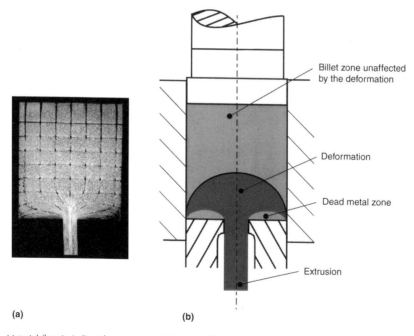

(a)   (b)

Fig. 3.48 Material flow in indirect hot extrusion without a shell and without lubrication. (a) Material AlMg3; extrusion ratio V_{ges} = 50; initial billet length l_b = 500 mm; container diam D_0 = 140 mm. (b) Principal depiction of billet zones in indirect extrusion without lubrication and without a shell [Sie 80]

axial load F_U needed for deformation in the entry plane of the deformation zone during the quasi-stationary extrusion process:

$$\bar{F}_{VSt} = \bar{F}_{HSt} = \bar{F}_M = \bar{F}_U \qquad \text{(Eq 3.52)}$$

For the unsteady start of the extrusion process:

$$\hat{F}_{VSt} \cong \hat{F}_{HSt} \cong \hat{F}_M = \hat{F}_U = 1.1 \cdot \hat{F}_U \qquad \text{(Eq 3.53)}$$

In indirect extrusion, the container temperature should, as far as possible, be equal to the initial billet temperature, although, as discussed in the section on direct extrusion, the container temperature should not exceed 500 °C.

The condition of the container temperature ϑ_R being equal to the billet temperature ϑ_B can be met for all aluminum alloys.

Over the sealing stem displacement S_{VSt} the billet cross-sectional discs always enter the deformation zone with the same temperature ϑ_E if the initial billet temperature is equal to the container temperature ϑ_R. They then undergo a temperature increase $\Delta\vartheta_U$ as a result of the deformation work that is almost 100% converted to heat in the deformation zone.

According to Eq 3.26, with reference to Eq 3.14:

$$\Delta\vartheta_U = \frac{\bar{k}_f \cdot \varphi_{ges}}{\rho \cdot c} = \frac{\bar{k}_f \cdot \ln V}{\rho \cdot c}$$

where ρ is the density and c the specific heat of the billet material.

According to Eq 3.27, the extrusion exit temperature ϑ_S is given by:

$$\vartheta_S = \vartheta_E + \Delta\vartheta_U$$

As shown in principle in Fig. 3.50, after the unsteady start of the extrusion process, the extrusion exit temperature ϑ_S is constant over the sealing stem displacement and over the length of the extruded product $l_S = V \cdot s_{VSt}$ if $\vartheta_E = \vartheta_B = \vartheta_R = $ a constant.

If the entry temperature ϑ_E of the billet volume on entering the deformation zone is constant, which applies when the initial billet temperature ϑ_B is equal to the container temperature ϑ_R, the sealing stem load F_{VSt} is constant after the unsteady start of the extrusion process over the sealing stem displacement s_{VS} (Fig. 3.51).

Accordingly:

- The initial billet length in indirect extrusion is not affected by either the load displacement variations, the material flow, or the thermal conditions if the initial billet temperature ϑ_B is equal to the container temperature ϑ_R.
- The initial billet length is only affected by the maximum (buckling length) of the hollow stem.

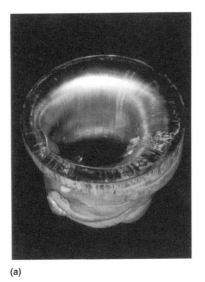 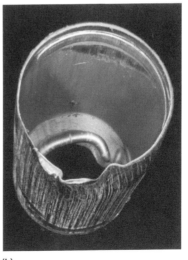

(a) (b)

Fig. 3.49 Removed aluminum shell in indirect hot extrusion with a shell and without lubrication. (a) Upset in the container on removal. (b) Partly upset [Zie 73]

If the initial billet temperature ϑ_B is equal to the container temperature ϑ_R, then in indirect extrusion with a constant sealing stem speed the initial billet length is, according to the above, limited only by the buckling length of the hollow stem.

As a general guide:

$$l_B \leq 7 \cdot D_0 \qquad \text{(Eq 3.54)}$$

The discard length in indirect hot extrusion is approximately 10% of the container diameter:

$$l_R = 0.1 \cdot D_0 \qquad \text{(Eq 3.55)}$$

The axial load $\bar{F}_M$ is as with direct hot-extrusion according to Eq 3.13 and 3.14:

$$\bar{F}_M = C \cdot \varphi_{g_{ges}} \bar{k}_f \cdot \frac{\pi \cdot D_0^2}{4}$$
$$= C \cdot \ln V \cdot \bar{k}_f \cdot \frac{\pi \cdot D_0^2}{4}$$

The calculation of $\bar{F}_M$ is described in detail in section 3.1.1.4. Similar to the example in section 3.1.1.4, Fig. 3.52 shows the variation in the calculated sealing stem load with the sealing stem displacement. It can be seen that in indirect hot extrusion, the sealing stem load is constant over

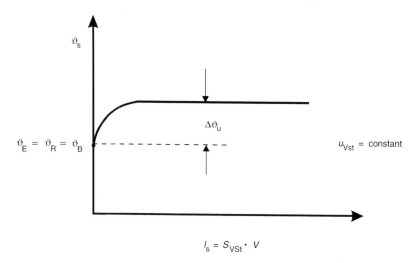

Fig. 3.50 Variation in the exit temperature ϑ_S over the length of the extrusion l_S in indirect hot extrusion for $\vartheta_E = \vartheta_B = \vartheta_R =$ constant (e.g., for aluminum)

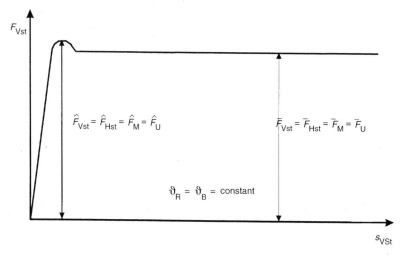

Fig. 3.51 Variation of the sealing stem force F_{VSt} over the sealing stem displacement s_{VSt} in indirect hot extrusion with an initial billet temperature equal to the container temperature

the sealing stem displacement apart from a load peak at the beginning, if the initial billet temperature is equal to the container temperature.

Compared with direct hot extrusion, the load profile is reduced by the friction load F_R. In addition, the initial billet length in indirect hot extrusion can be up to seven times the container length. This is significantly longer than the initial billet length in direct hot extrusion, which is usually less than four times the container diameter. The discard length in indirect hot extrusion is significantly smaller than in direct hot extrusion (see Eq 3.3 and 3.55).

The sealing stem load F_{VSt} in indirect extrusion is lower than the stem load in direct extrusion by the friction load F_R from the friction between the billet and the container.

At the same maximum press load, indirect extrusion offers the following advantages over direct extrusion under the condition that the initial billet temperature is the same as the container:

- For the same product cross section and the same initial billet temperature, the container diameter can be increased; i.e., a higher extrusion ratio can be selected.
- For the same product cross section and the same container diameter, the initial billet temperature can be reduced, which enables the maximum possible extrusion speed to be increased for aluminum alloys.

If the container temperature, product cross section, extrusion speed, and initial billet temperature are held constant, then it is possible to use a press with a lower maximum load compared with hot direct extrusion.

Example:

Material	A199.5
Container diam	$D_0 = 140$ mm
Initial billet diam	$D_B = 136$ mm
Initial billet length	$l_B = 840$ mm
Product	Round bar 19.8 mm
Initial billet temperature = container temperature	400 °C
Ram speed	10 mm/s

Then,

Equation	Parameter	Result
3.1	Extrusion ratio	$V = 50$
3.14	Logarithmic total principal strain	$\varphi_{gges} = 3.9$
3.15	Mean log Principal strain	$\bar{\varphi}_{gges} = 0.674$
3.16	Mean log Principal strain rate	$\dot{\bar{\varphi}}_g = 8.15$ s^{-1}

With $\dot{\bar{\varphi}}_g = 8.15$ s^{-1}, $\bar{\varphi}_g = 0.674$ and $\vartheta = 400$ °C, then the mean flow stress over the full deformation zone from Fig. 3.17 is:

$$\bar{k}_f = 31 \text{ N/mm}^2$$

Equation	Parameter	Result
3.21	Factor C for $f_p = 1$ and $\eta_f = 0.6$ (estimated)	$C = 1.67$
3.13	Deformation load	$F_M = 3100$ kN
3.8	Upset displacement	$s_1 = 47$ mm
3.8	Upset billet length	$l_0 = 793$ mm
3.3	Discard length	$l_R = 14$ mm
3.53	Maximum axial force at the start of the extrusion	$\hat{F}_{VSt} = 3400$ kN

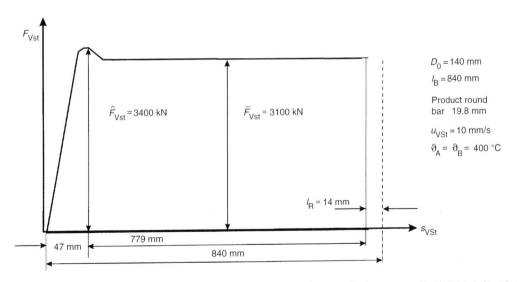

Fig. 3.52 Calculated variation in the sealing stem force F_{VSt} over the sealing stem displacement s_{VSt} for Al99.5 in indirect hot extrusion with an initial billet temperature equal to the container temperature. This gives the variation of the sealing stem force over the sealing stem displacement shown in the figure.

3.2.5 Axial Loads and Exit Temperatures in Indirect Hot Extrusion with an Initial Billet Temperature Higher than the Container Temperature (e.g., in the Extrusion of Copper Alloys)

High productivity is achieved with the indirect extrusion of copper alloys. In contrast to the previous discussions where the initial billet temperature was taken to be equal to the container temperature, with copper alloys, the initial billet temperature is over 600 °C. The container temperature cannot be raised above 500 °C. The billet, therefore, loses heat to the container so that as extrusion continues the billet volume enters the deformation zone with a decreasing entry temperature. If the entry temperature decreases, then the flow stress increases, and this also results in a larger temperature rise in the deformation zone. In spite of this, the exit temperature falls over the sealing stem displacement and over the length of the section because the influence of the decreasing entry temperature over the sealing stem displacement predominates. Figure 3.53 shows the changes in the inlet temperature ϑ_S, the temperature increase in the deformation zone $\Delta\vartheta_U$, and the extrusion exit temperature ϑ_E over the length of the section l_S, which is the product of the sealing stem displacement s_{VSt} and the extrusion ratio V. These changes occur when the initial billet temperature

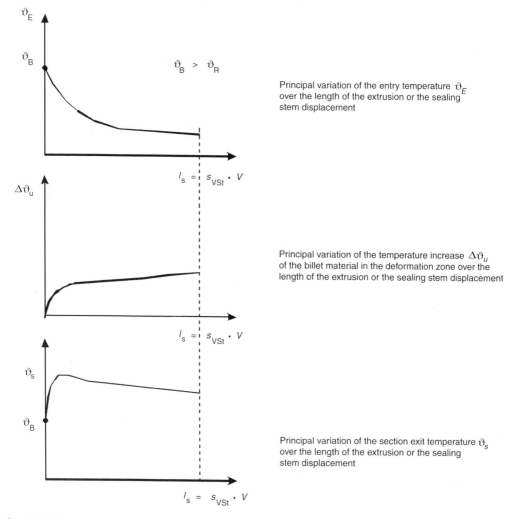

Principal variation of the entry temperature ϑ_E over the length of the extrusion or the sealing stem displacement

Principal variation of the temperature increase $\Delta\vartheta_u$ of the billet material in the deformation zone over the length of the extrusion or the sealing stem displacement

Principal variation of the section exit temperature ϑ_s over the length of the extrusion or the sealing stem displacement

Fig. 3.53 Temperature variation over the sealing stem displacement or the length of the extrusion in indirect hot extrusion with an initial billet temperature ϑ_B that is higher than the container temperature ϑ_R (e.g., for copper alloys)

ϑ_B is higher than the container temperature ϑ_R, which is usually the case for the indirect extrusion of copper alloys.

The sealing stem load increases over the sealing stem displacement s_{VSt} corresponding to the increase in the flow stress associated with the decreasing entry temperature ϑ_E over the sealing stem displacement s_{VSt} as shown in Fig. 3.54. The maximum sealing stem load in indirect hot extrusion with $\vartheta_B > \vartheta_R$ is not at the start of the extrusion process, as is the case with all other processes, but at the end of the extrusion process because of the billet cooling.

This can, in some cases, result in a limitation of the billet length. The aim should, therefore, be to keep the initial billet temperature ϑ_B as low as possible and the container temperature ϑ_R as high as possible. A container temperature $\vartheta_R = 500\ ^\circ\text{C}$ and billet temperatures $\vartheta_B = 600$ to $700\ ^\circ\text{C}$ have proved successful for the indirect hot extrusion of brass. It is also beneficial to select the largest possible billet diameter to obtain a better ratio of the thermal content of the billet to the billet surface area.

3.2.6 Comparison of the Indirect Hot Extrusion Process with Direct Hot Extrusion

Compared with direct hot extrusion with a shell and without lubrication, indirect hot extrusion with a shell without lubrication offers the following *advantages:*

* Because the sealing stem load is lower than the direct extrusion load by the amount of the friction or shearing load, it is possible to

reduce the initial billet temperature and/or increase the container diameter, i.e., increase the extrusion ratio with a significantly larger initial billet length and smaller discard length.
* Reducing the initial billet temperature gives a better product quality (higher proof stress, higher tensile strength) over the length of the extrusion.
* The productivity in indirect hot extrusion is much higher than with direct hot extrusion because of the significantly larger initial billet volume.

The *disadvantages* of indirect hot extrusion compared with direct hot extrusion include:

* The need to have a press specifically designed for indirect extrusion
* A special hollow stem the internal diameter of which is determined by the circumscribing circle of the section and which, in some cases, has to be internally clad with a graphite canister to avoid damage to the section
* The need for a particularly long guided container that usually has both zone and end face heating as well as zone cooling to guarantee a constant container temperature over the container length
* Allowance should also be made for the fact that there is no friction between the billet and the container to prevent the billet outer zone flowing into the deformation zone. There is, therefore, the risk that the impure billet surface flows into the surface adjacent zones in the section. If this has to be avoided, then it is necessary to extrude with a shell.

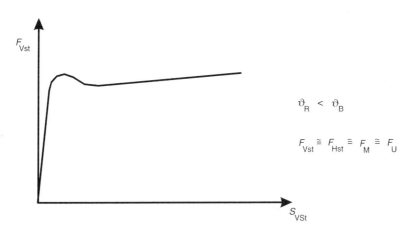

Fig. 3.54 Variation in the sealing stem load with the sealing stem displacement in indirect hot extrusion with an initial billet temperature ϑ_B that is higher than the container temperature ϑ_R (e.g., copper alloys)

Direct extrusion should be used for the extrusion of aluminum bright-finish alloys for products with the best surface quality (anodizing quality). Indirect hot extrusion lends itself to the extrusion of high-strength aluminum alloys for products with less demanding surface properties.

3.2.7 *Indirect Cold Extrusion*

The following processes fall into the heading indirect cold extrusion:

- Indirect cold extrusion without lubrication and without a shell
- Indirect cold extrusion without lubrication with a shell
- Indirect cold extrusion with lubrication and without a shell

The first two processes are indeed theoretically possible but technically unimportant. In these two processes the temperature increase in the deformation zone from the deformation process can produce similar thermal conditions to indirect hot extrusion. The material flow when extruding through flat dies is approximately the same as in indirect hot extrusion, when fast extrusion speeds (sealing stem speeds) and high extrusion ratios are used.

A quasi-adiabatic deformation process, therefore, takes place. The temperature increase in the material being deformed in the deformation zone is calculated from Eq 3.26.

Section exit temperatures of approximately 300 °C can be achieved in the indirect cold extrusion of Al99.5 with extrusion ratios over $V = 100$ and high sealing stem loads.

The industrial application for the two processes, indirect cold extrusion without lubrication and without a shell, and indirect cold extrusion without lubrication and with a shell, is restricted by the relatively high sealing stem load F_{VSt} on the container cross-sectional area A_0 required. This relative load is referred to as the sealing stem pressure p_{VSt}:

$$p_{VSt} = \frac{F_{VSt}}{A_0} \tag{Eq 3.56}$$

Indirect cold extrusion with lubrication and without a shell is more important for the extrusion of composite materials, solders, powder metal (P/M) alloys and materials with relatively low flow stresses.

3.2.7.1 Indirect Cold Extrusion with Lubrication and without a Shell

Process Sequence in Indirect Cold Extrusion with Lubrication and without a Shell. The process was first reported in [Sie 77]. In indirect cold extrusion with lubrication and without a shell, a conical die as shown in Fig. 3.55 is used. The billet with a tapered end is coated with the lubricant and loaded into the container along with the die. Although, it is true that in indirect extrusion a reduction of the friction between the billet and the container cannot be obtained because there is no friction, it is possible to reduce the friction between the die and the container and between the die and the material being extruded [Sie 77].

With suitable design of the die and the sealing stem and the correct selection of a lubricant that usually has high thermal viscosity and high resistance to mechanical stresses, a lubricant buffer forms at the die entry. Lubricant flows from this into the gap between the die external surface and the container as well as into the working area between the die and the material being extruded (see Fig. 3.55).

Introducing seals between the sealing stem and the container and between the die and the container gives a smooth transition between this process to hydrostatic extrusion and the thick film process.

Figure 3.56 shows the sealing stem and the hollow stem as well as the container for a container diameter of 85 mm and a sealing stem load of 8000 kN for indirect cold extrusion with lubrication. The sealing stem load force acting over the cross-sectional area of the container (sealing stem pressure) is 1400 N/mm^2 (see Eq 3.56).

Figure 3.57 shows the process sequence of indirect cold extrusion with lubrication without a shell. It is recommended that loose dies be used because of the extremely high sealing stem pressures usually used.

Material Flow in Indirect Cold Extrusion with Lubrication and without a Shell. Figure 3.58 shows stages in indirect cold extrusion with lubrication. It can be seen that a quasi-stationary deformation process forms within the die cone. The material flow is approximately the same in all stages.

Figure 3.59 shows for different die opening angles that the deformation zone extends into the adjacent billet volume with larger opening angles. However, it can be clearly seen that the billet volume outside the deformation zone is completely unaffected by the deformation process. The billet length is, as in all indirect extrusion processes, not limited by the material flow but merely by the maximum possible length of the hollow stem calculated to resist buckling.

Axial Forces in Indirect Cold Extrusion with Lubrication and without a Shell. Be-cause there is no friction between the billet and the container to be taken into account in any indirect extrusion process, then, according to Eq 3.52:

$$F_{VSt} \cong F_{HSt} \cong F_M = F_U$$

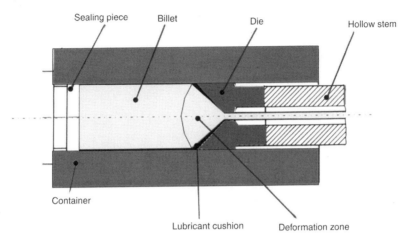

Fig. 3.55 Principal depiction of indirect cold extrusion with lubrication and without a shell [Sie 77]

Fig. 3.56 Sealing stem, hollow stem, and container for a container diam of 85 mm and a sealing stem load of 8000 kN

As in direct cold extrusion in the die entry plane the ideal axial compressive stress is, according to Eq 3.40:

$$p_{XE_{id}} = \bar{k}_f \cdot \varphi_{g_{ges}} = \bar{k}_f \cdot \ln V$$

The mean flow stress for all the material being deformed in the deformation zone is:

$$\bar{k}_f = f(\bar{\varphi}_g, \dot{\bar{\varphi}}_g, \vartheta)$$

and can be obtained from the quasi-adiabatic flow curves for the initial temperature $\vartheta_E = 20$ °C and the mean principal strain (Eq 3.15):

$$\bar{\varphi}_g = 2 \cdot \ln \frac{3}{\dfrac{D_S}{D_0} + 2}$$

In cold working where the deformation temperature is well below the material recrystallization temperature, the influence of the mean logarithmic principal strain rate $\dot{\bar{\varphi}}_g$ is usually negligible. If this is not the case, then $\dot{\bar{\varphi}}_g$ is obtained from Eq 3.18.

The ideal axial compressive stress $p_{XE_{id}}$ needed for perfect deformation in the die entry plane multiplied by a factor C gives the actual axial compressive stress p_{XE} acting in the die entry plane.

According to Eq 3.41:

$$p_{XE} = C \cdot p_{XE_{id}}$$

where the factor C, according to Eq 3.21, contains a profile factor f_p and a shape change efficiency factor η_U (see section 3.1.1.4).

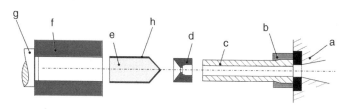

(1) Starting position

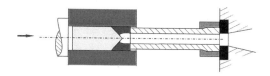

(2) Loading the billet and the die. Upsetting the billet in the container

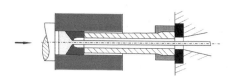

(3) Extrusion to preset discard length

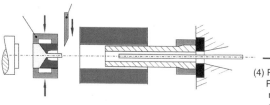

(4) Pushing out of the die and the discard. Removal of the discard and die with the manipulator as well as separation of the extrusion, followed by moving to the starting position

Fig. 3.57 Process sequence for indirect cold extrusion with lubrication and without a shell. a, platen; b, die holder; c, hollow stem; d, die; e, billet; f, container; g, sealing stem; h, lubricant film; i, separator; j, manipulator

In indirect cold extrusion with lubrication and without a shell of round bars through conical dies, then, from Eq 3.42 with $f_p = 1$:

$$C = \frac{1}{\eta_U} = 1.1$$

Accordingly, from Eq 3.43 as with direct cold extrusion with lubrication and without a shell:

$$p_{XE} = C \cdot p_{XE_{id}} = 1.1 \cdot \bar{k}_f \cdot \varphi_{g_{ges}} = 1.1 \cdot \bar{k}_f \cdot \ln V$$

This stress is constant in indirect cold extrusion between the die entry plane and the billet end because there is no friction to overcome between the billet and the container. Thus, the sealing stem pressure is given by:

$$p_{VSt} = \frac{F_{VSt}}{A_0} = p_{X_E} \qquad \text{(Eq 3.57)}$$

Figure 3.60 shows the variation of the radial and axial compressive stresses over the billet length for indirect cold extrusion.

The sealing stem force referred to the container cross-sectional area at the start of extrusion is obtained from:

$$\hat{p}_{VSt} = \frac{\hat{F}_{VSt}}{A_0} = \frac{\hat{F}_{VSt}}{\pi \cdot \dfrac{D_0^2}{4}} \qquad \text{(Eq 3.58)}$$

The relative sealing stem force during the quasi-stationary deformation process is:

$$\bar{p}_{VSt} = \frac{\bar{F}_{VSt}}{A_0} = \frac{\bar{F}_{VSt}}{\pi \cdot \dfrac{D_0^2}{4}} \qquad \text{(Eq 3.59)}$$

The relative sealing stem force $\hat{p}_{VSt}$ at the start of extrusion is approximately 20% higher than the sealing stem force $\bar{p}_{VSt}$:

$$\hat{p}_{VSt} \cong 1.2 \cdot \bar{p}_{VSt} \qquad \text{(Eq 3.60)}$$

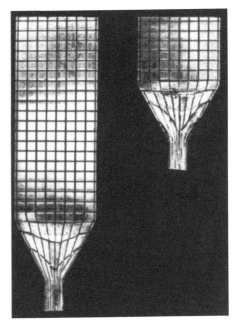

Fig. 3.58 Stages in indirect cold extrusion with lubrication and without a shell of Al99.5

Fig. 3.59 Development of the deformation zone with different die opening angles for cold indirect extrusion with lubrication and without a shell of Al99.5

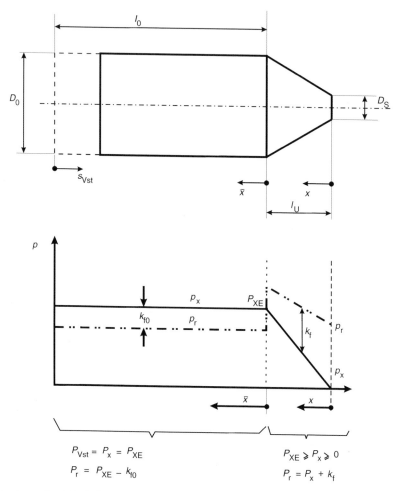

Fig. 3.60 Fundamental variation in the compressive stress p_x and the radial compressive stress p_r over the sealing stem displacement s_{Vst} in cold indirect extrusion with lubrication (l_0, upset billet length in the container without the billet tip; D_0, container diam; l_U, length of the deformation zone

Hydrostatic Extrusion

Gottfried Schreiter*

3.3 Conventional Hydrostatic Extrusion

3.3.1 Process Principles

As shown in Fig. 3.61, in hydrostatic extrusion the billet in the container is surrounded by a pressure medium also known as the hydrostatic medium. The container bore is sealed against the stem and the die. It is important to note that the billet has to be sealed against the die when the hydrostatic medium is compressed to the extrusion pressure to ensure that the extrusion pressure is not lost.

The process, therefore, requires a conical die and careful preparation of the billet tip. The pressure in the hydrostatic medium is increased by moving the stem into the sealed container volume. The actual extrusion process commences at a specific initial pressure $\hat{p}$ when the section starts to emerge from the die. This is then followed by a semistationary deformation process with an extrusion pressure $\bar{p}$ (Fig. 3.62, 3.63).

*Hydrostatic Extrusion, Gottfried Schreiter

The stem does not touch the billet during the compression of the hydrostatic medium to the starting pressure or during the extrusion process. The stem speed and the billet speed, therefore, differ. The speed with which the billet moves in the direction of the die is proportional to the hydrostatic volume displaced by the stem. During the semistatic extrusion process and neglecting the compressibility of the hydrostatic medium and the increase of the volume of the container associated with the elastic deformation to a first approximation: the billet speed u_{billet} is given by the product of the stem speed u_{St} and the ratio of the stem cross-sectional area A_{stem} to the billet cross-sectional area A_{billet}:

$$u_{billet} = u_{stem} \cdot \frac{A_{stem}}{A_{billet}} \qquad \text{(Eq 3.61)}$$

Because the billet does not contact the container wall during extrusion and there is always the hydrostatic medium between the billet and the container wall, there is only fluid friction at the billet surface apart from the area of contact between the die and the extruded product. This is negligible when compared with the stresses and forces in hydrostatic extrusion.

The characteristic feature of hydrostatic extrusion is the fluid friction on the billet surface apart from the contact between the die and the extruded billet. This fluid friction can be considered to be negligible when compared with the stresses and forces in hydrostatic extrusion.

In principle, hydrostatic extrusion can be used for both hot and cold extrusion. However, in hot extrusion it should be remembered that the sealing system and the hydrostatic medium, as well as the system for filling, removing, filtering, and cooling it, will all be exposed to high temperature.

To meet reproducible thermal conditions, the temperature of the hydrostatic medium in the container has to be equal to the initial billet temperature. The maximum permitted temperature (flash point, chemical composition) of the hydrostatic medium therefore determines the maximum initial billet temperature possible. Consequently, *hydrostatic extrusion is primarily a cold working process.*

One process limiting difficulty is the lack of a direct relationship between the billet speed and the ram speed. It is, therefore, possible to have an erratic extrusion with pressure variations in the hydrostatic medium under stick slip conditions. At the transition from sticking to slipping conditions between the extruded material and the die the compressed hydrostatic medium can decompress and the billet be extruded at a high speed. This reduces the pressure in the hydrostatic medium and the deformation process stops. The hydrostatic medium then has to be recompressed to the starting pressure to enable the deformation process to restart. This erratic extrusion occurs particularly when the friction between the extruded material and the die is too high and when the starting pressure is signifi-

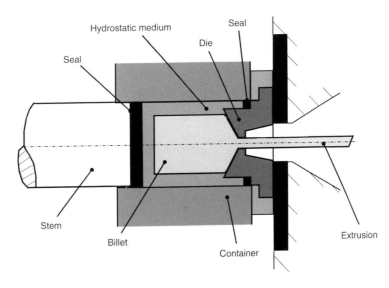

Fig. 3.61 Principle of hydrostatic extrusion

cantly higher than the pressure required for the semistationary deformation process. A large volume of hydrostatic medium increases the likelihood of its occurrence.

The lower the compressibility and the lower the volume of the hydrostatic medium, the steeper the increase in pressure over the stem displacement and the closer is the relationship between the billet speed and the ram speed.

3.3.2 Process Sequence

Figure 3.62 shows the process sequence in hydrostatic extrusion. In principle, the billet can be loaded between the stem and the container or

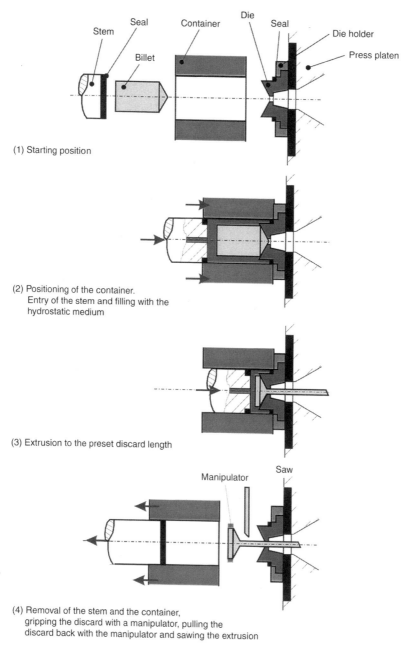

Fig. 3.62 Process sequence for hydrostatic extrusion

between the die and the container. The container volume is filled with the hydrostatic medium (usually castor oil) through a central hole in the stem. When the billet has been extruded to the discard length, the stem and the container travel back far enough to allow the discard to be pulled from the die with a manipulator and the section cut with a saw. Both the seal between the die and the container and the seal between the stem and the container are usually made from an elastomer with a copper beryllium support ring. These seals have a very limited life.

3.3.3 Axial Loads in Hydrostatic Extrusion

The variation of the hydrostatic pressure in the container with the stem displacement is usually studied in hydrostatic extrusion (Fig. 3.63). If it is assumed that the frictional losses in the stem/container seals are negligible, then the hydrostatic pressure p in the container is equal to the stem load F_{St} divided by the stem cross-sectional area A_{St}:

$$p = \frac{F_{St}}{A_{St}} \qquad \text{(Eq 3.62)}$$

The stem load is, therefore, obtained from the product of the stem cross-sectional area and the pressure. The fact that the hydrostatic medium has to be initially compressed must be taken into account when considering the variation in the hydrostatic pressure p over the stem displacement. The actual deformation process commences after the start pressure $\hat{p}$ needed for the deformation has been reached. The pressure then reduces to the constant value $\bar{p}$ required for the semistationary deformation process (Fig. 3.63). The characteristic curve of the pressure increase against the stem displacement depends on the compressibility and volume of the hydrostatic medium, the elastic behavior of the pipe connections, the tooling, and the press frame. (Fig. 3.64).

The gradient of the characteristic curve increases as the volume of the hydrostatic medium decreases. The compressibility of the hydrostatic medium also influences the profile of the pressure increase characteristic curve.

Figure 3.64 shows the variation of the hydrostatic pressure p with the stem displacement for different hydrostatic media and billet lubricants.

The curve with the highest pressures exhibits severe oscillations at the start of the process. These are associated with the erratic transition from sticking to slipping in the tribological system extruded material/lubricant/die known as the stick slip phenomenon. The friction in the tribological system billet/lubricant/die is also very important. Castor oil is usually used as the hydrostatic medium.

If the hydrostatic medium dos not have sufficient lubrication properties, it is possible to add lubricating additions to the hydrostatic medium or to lubricate the billet before it is loaded into the press (see Fig. 3.64).

Figure 3.65 shows in principle:

- The variation of the stem load F_{St} over the stem displacement w
- The variation of the hydrostatic pressure p over the stem displacement w
- The variation of the axial load F_M exerted by the billet onto the die over the billet displacement s.

The stem load and the hydrostatic pressure over the stem displacement have to follow the same principle curve because, according to Eq 3.61, the stem load is derived from the product of the hydrostatic pressure and the stem cross-sectional area, which is a constant.

The axial load on the die F_M behaves differently because it is the product of the billet cross-sectional area and the hydrostatic pressure:

$$F_M = p \cdot A_{Billet} \qquad \text{(Eq 3.63)}$$

During the semistatic deformation process:

$$\bar{F}_M = \bar{p} \cdot A_{Billet} \qquad \text{(Eq 3.64)}$$

For the unsteady upsetting process:

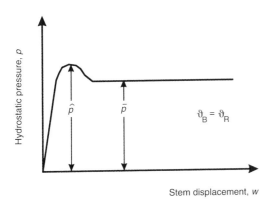

Fig. 3.63 Fundamental variation of the hydrostatic pressure in the container over the stem displacement for hydrostatic extrusion

$$\hat{F}_\mathrm{M} = \hat{p} \cdot A_\mathrm{Billet} \qquad \text{(Eq 3.65)}$$

The maximum value $\hat{F}_\mathrm{M}$ is approximately 15% higher than the value $\bar{F}_\mathrm{M}$:

$$\hat{F}_\mathrm{M} = 1.15 \cdot \bar{F}_\mathrm{M} \qquad \text{(Eq 3.66)}$$

If the axial load F_M applied by the billet onto the die is plotted against the billet displacement s, the curve $F_\mathrm{M} = f(s)$ is comparable to the variation $\bar{F}_\mathrm{M} = f(s)$ for other extrusion processes.

For approximately the same frictional conditions in the interaction between the extruded product and the die, the same die aperture angle and the same extrusion ratio, therefore: The axial load $\bar{F}_\mathrm{M}$ on the die for the semistatic deformation process is approximately the same as for direct cold extrusion with lubrication, indirect cold extrusion with lubrication, and hydrostatic cold extrusion.

3.3.4 Products

Figure 3.66 shows interrupted extrusions of copper wire from copper billets with extrusion ratios of $V = 50$ and an initial billet temperature

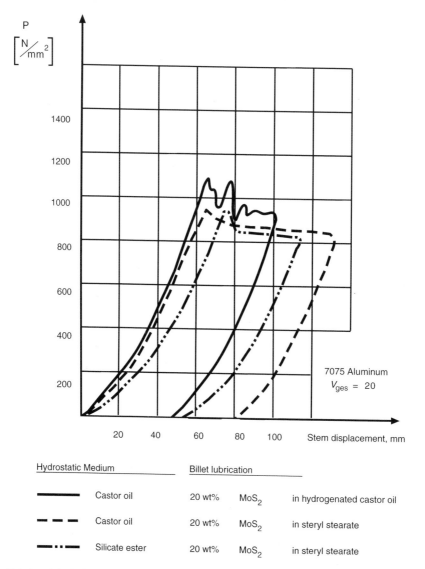

Hydrostatic Medium		Billet lubrication		
————	Castor oil	20 wt%	MoS_2	in hydrogenated castor oil
– – –	Castor oil	20 wt%	MoS_2	in steryl stearate
—·⸱·—	Silicate ester	20 wt%	MoS_2	in steryl stearate

Fig. 3.64 Variation of the hydrostatic pressure over the stem displacement for different hydrostatic media and billet lubrication [Fio 67]

of 20 °C and $V = 800$, and an initial billet temperature of 300 °C and a hydrostatic pressure of 16 kbar.

With pressures up to 20 kbar, hydrostatic extrusion can be used for the cold extrusion of aluminum alloys, copper and copper clad aluminum billets and, to a limited degree, even steel billets to sections (see Fig. 3.67).

It therefore competes with indirect cold extrusion with lubrication and without a shell and, to some degree, also with direct cold extrusion

with lubrication and no shell. Hydrostatic extrusion appears to be particularly suitable for the manufacture of helical sections (see Fig. 3.68). In this case, the billet rotates in the container during extrusion.

Figure 3.68 shows helical gear bars extruded from case-hardening steel cylindrical billets. These helical gear bars can be produced by extrusion only if the billet can rotate in the container completely free of any frictional restraint. This requirement is met in hydrostatic extrusion.

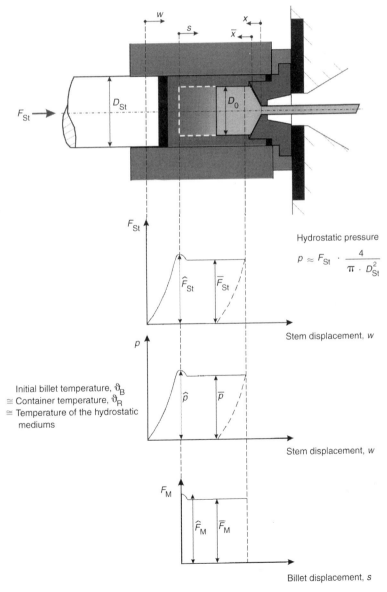

Fig. 3.65 Variation of the stem load F_{St} and the hydrostatic pressure p over the stem displacement w as well as the variation of the axial force F_M over the billet displacement s.

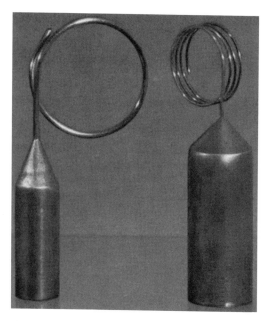

Fig. 3.66 Stages in the extrusion of copper billets to copper wire (Source: ASEA)

It is also possible to extrude tubes with a moving mandrel as shown in Fig. 3.69. This shows a mandrel fitted in an end piece and pressed into a prebored billet. The hole in the billet is slightly smaller than the mandrel diameter.

In the extrusion of copper clad aluminum sections, an aluminum billet is first pressed into a copper tube. The tube is sealed at one end by a pressed-in closure piece and tapered at the other so that it can seal against the die when the container volume is pressurized. Figure 3.70 shows the operating sequence during extrusion.

Figure 3.71 shows the hydrostatic pressure needed plotted against the extrusion ratio for different copper contents. It is clear that the hydrostatic pressure needed increases both with the increasing copper content and increasing extrusion ratio.

3.4   Thick Film Process

The thick film process, also known as the hydrafilm process, is a variation of hydrostatic extrusion.

In this process, as shown in Fig. 3.72, the volume of the hydrostatic medium is kept so low that the stem can contact the billet during extrusion. The stem speed is then the same as the billet speed. This occurs, according to Eq 3.61, if the billet cross-sectional area is approximately the same as the container cross-sectional area.

Thus, in the thick film process, there is merely a thin film of the hydrostatic medium between the billet and the container as well as between the billet and the stem. Because the billet cross-sectional area is approximately the same as the container cross-sectional area, the stem speed is equal to the billet speed.

This process offers the following advantages over conventional hydrostatic extrusion:

- The characteristic compression line is significantly steeper because of the minimized

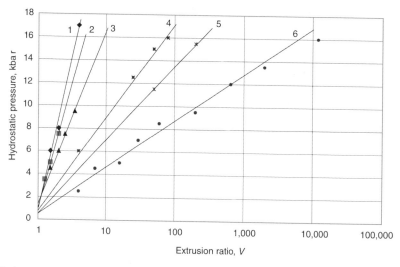

Fig. 3.67 Hydrostatic pressure against the extrusion ratio for different materials (Source: ASEA). 1, high speed steel; 2, mild steel; 3, soft unalloyed mild steel; 4, commercial copper (Cu 99.5%); 5, aluminum alloy 7075; 6, pure aluminum (Al 99.5)

Fig. 3.68 Extruded bars with helical gear teeth in case-hardening steel (Source: ASEA)

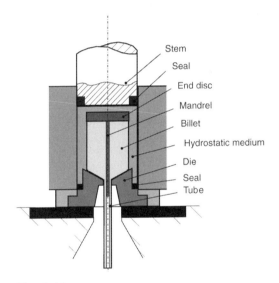

Fig. 3.69 Extrusion of tubes over a moving mandrel

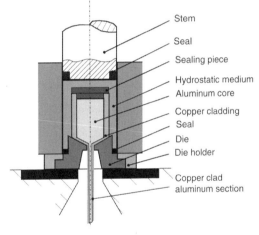

Fig. 3.70 Extrusion of copper clad aluminum section

volume of the hydrostatic medium. This reduces the risk of the stick slip phenomenon occurring.

- The improved utilization of the container cross-sectional area ($A_{\text{billet}} \approx A_{\text{container}}$) increases productivity.

Because the speed with which the billet moves toward the die is almost equal to the stem speed, the extrusion process can be interrupted at any time by stopping the stem movement. The risk of total extrusion usually does not occur in the thick film process.

On the other hand, in conventional hydrostatic extrusion the die is externally supported by the pressure of the hydrostatic medium, which is advantageous for the stresses within the die. The die in the thick film process is supported against the container as is the case with lubricated indirect extrusion.

The billet can also be coated with a lubricant as is the case with hydrostatic extrusion.

The major difference between the thick film process and the hydrostatic extrusion process is that in the thick film process it is possible to coat the billet before loading into the press with a hydrostatic lubricating medium that is solid at atmospheric pressure and viscous at the extru-

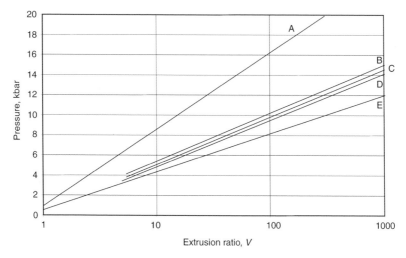

Fig. 3.71 Hydrostatic pressure plotted against the extrusion ratio for different copper contents. A, 100% Cu (pure Cu); B, 20% Cu; C, 15% Cu; D, 10% Cu; E, 0% Cu (pure Al) (Source: ASEA)

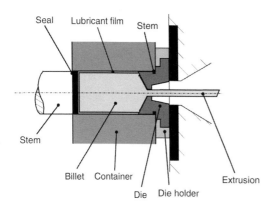

Fig. 3.72 Fundamental depiction of the thick film process

sequence and the lower quantity of the hydrostatic medium make it appear to be more suitable to hot extrusion than hydrostatic extrusion.

The variation in the hydrostatic pressure in the container with the stem displacement is, in principle, taking into account the steeper increase on the upsetting characteristic line, the same as that in hydrostatic extrusion. Both the start pressure $\hat{p}$ as well as the pressure $\bar{p}$ needed for the semi static extrusion process is identical for both processes under the same conditions (material being extruded, temperature, extrusion ratio, extrusion speed.

sion pressure. It is also possible to load the billet along with a disc of a hydrostatic lubricating medium that is solid at atmospheric pressure.

Accordingly, in the thick film process the billet can be loaded into the press with a medium that is solid at atmospheric pressure and viscous at extrusion pressure. It is also possible to load the billet along with a disc of the hydrostatic lubricating medium.

Therefore, in the thick film process there is no need for special systems for the hydrostatic medium including pumps, filters, and coolers.

The thick film process is primarily a cold extrusion process even though the simpler process

Special Processes

3.5 Conform Process

Klaus Siegert*

The conform extrusion process was developed in 1972 by the Advanced Metal Forming Group of the Springfield Nuclear Laboratories, England [Con 84]. The conform process can be used for the continuous extrusion of solid and hollow sections, coating, e.g., steel wires with

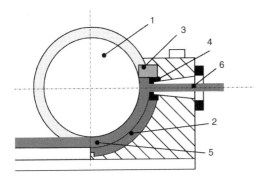

Fig. 3.73 Conform extrusion process (fundamental process). 1, friction wheel; 2, seal segment; 3, sealing piece; 4, die; 5, feedstock (wire); 6, extrusion

aluminum, as well as the cladding of fibers and the sheathing of cables, e.g., with aluminum.

In this context, cladding involves neither a shape nor friction dependant bond with the fiber being clad, e.g., optical fiber. Sheathing involves the pressing of a metallic sheath onto the cable being clad. Aluminum is the most important material processed, e.g., Properzi wire up to 25.4 mm diameter, but copper and non ferrous P/M, materials including zinc, lead, magnesium, silver, and gold can also be extruded by the conform process [Con 84], [Mad 87].

3.5.1 Process Principle

Figure 3.73 shows the principle of the conform process. A rotating wheel, e.g., with a diameter of 500 mm, has a groove around the circumference in which the material being extruded is drawn by the frictional loads between the material being extruded and the groove.

The groove is sealed by a seal segment. The contact area groove/material being extruded is significantly larger than the contact area seal segment/material being extruded so that the friction load drawing in the material being extruded (friction load between the groove and the material being extruded minus the friction load between the seal segment and the material being extruded) is high enough. The groove sealed by the seal segment can be considered as a rotating container. The material being extruded is drawn into this container by the frictional load. The groove is closed at the other end by an abutment so that the material being extruded can emerge only from the die.

As shown in Fig. 3.74, there are, in principle, two different locations of the die. On one hand it is possible, even if geometrically extremely restricted, to locate the die in the abutment giving a tangential exit (Fig. 3.74b). On the other hand, the die can be located between the sealing segment and the abutment giving a radial section exit (Fig. 3.74a).

Even with a radial exit the die is geometrically severely constrained, but not to the same extent as with a tangential exit [Par 84].

By arranging the die behind a prechamber it is possible, as shown in Fig. 3.75, to use larger dies. The cylindrical part of the prechamber has to be heated to maintain the material being extruded at the extrusion temperature. This die arrangement also enables bridge and welding dies to be used for the extrusion of hollow sections.

The material being extruded is usually drawn into the groove at room temperature. The work needed to overcome the friction between the groove and the material being extruded is transformed to heat. This flows into the wheel and into the seal segment as well as into the material being extruded located in the groove. The material being extruded is thus heated to the necessary deformation zone entry temperature ϑ_E as it moves toward the die.

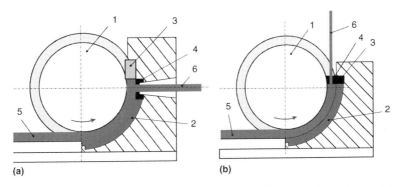

(a)   **(b)**

Fig. 3.74 Conform extrusion press. (a) Radial. (b) Tangential extrusion exit. 1, friction wheel; 2, seal segment; 3, sealing piece; 4, die; 5, feedstock (wire); 6, extrusion [Eth 84b]

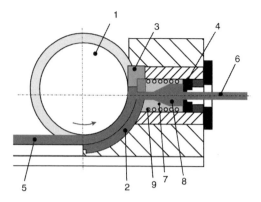

Fig. 3.75 Radial exit with die feeder chamber. 1, friction wheel; 2, seal segment; 3, sealing piece; 4, die; 5, feedstock (wire); 6, extrusion; 7, heated feeder chamber insert; 8, feeder chamber; 9, heating [Mad 87, Lan 88, Eth 84b]

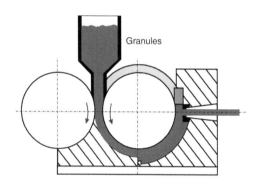

Fig. 3.76 Feeding of granules into the conform system [Mad 87]

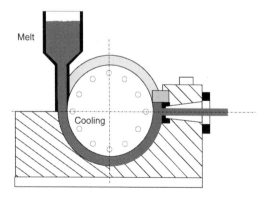

Fig. 3.77 Feed of liquid metal into the conform system—combination of casting and deformation [Lan 88, Con 85]

The friction forces drawing the material in act tangentially in the groove, i.e., act in the longitudinal direction on the material being extruded,

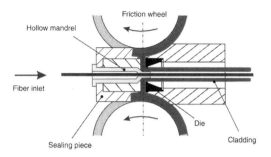

Fig. 3.78 Fiber cladding with the conform extrusion press [Lan 85]

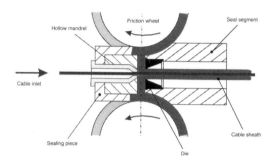

Fig. 3.79 Cable sheathing with the conform process [Lan 85, Par 86]

so that a compressive stress state forms in front of the die in the material being extruded. This is high enough for the material to be extruded through the die.

3.5.2 Process Variations of the Conform Process

3.5.2.1 Extrusion of Granules and Powder

As mentioned previously, it is possible to extrude granules as well as, in some cases, P/M materials. The material being extruded is filled into the groove in the extrusion wheel by gravity through a hopper. A backup roller is used to compact the material being extruded. (see Fig. 3.76). This process variation was primarily developed for recycling material [Eth 84b], [Mad 87], [Par 84]. It does, however, also appear suitable for the extrusion of P/M materials.

3.5.2.2 Combination of Casting and Conform Extrusion

Another variation is the combination of continuous casting and conform extrusion, (Fig.

Fig. 3.80 Holton C400 H conform extrusion system. Friction wheel diam: 400 mm; power supply: 180–250 kW max, rotation speed 36 l/min; max section circumscribing circle: 85 mm without a feeder chamber, 130 mm with feeder chamber; max tube diam: 45 mm without a feeder chamber, 75 mm with a feeder chamber

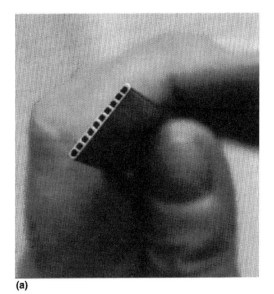

(a)

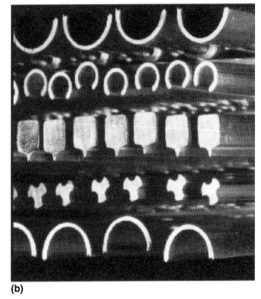

(b)

Fig. 3.81 Sections produced with the conform system, (a) Heat exchanger section. (b) Copper sections (Source: Holton Machinery Ltd.)

3.77). The liquid material is cast directly into the extrusion wheel. A second sealing segment is needed. The extrusion wheel is fitted with cooling channels in this variation to remove the heat from the melt. With optimum process control, the necessary entry temperature and pressure required for extrusion is reached in front of the die [Con 85], [Lan 88].

3.5.2.3 Fiber Cladding by Conform Extrusion

In this context cladding involves the pressing of a protective layer, e.g., in aluminum over a fiber (e.g., optical fiber). There is no frictional or mechanical bond between the sheath and the fiber (Fig. 3.78).

Plants with a single extrusion wheel as well as with two extrusion wheels are used. Figure 3.79 shows the principle arrangement of a symmetrical configuration with two extrusion wheels.

The material being extruded is radially pressed from the grooves of both extrusion wheels into a chamber from which it emerges as a sheath from an annular channel formed by a hollow mandrel and a die. The fiber passes through the hollow mandrel. The tooling between the two extrusion wheels has to be heated to reach the required extrusion temperature. If one extrusion wheel is removed and the corresponding channel to the chamber sealed, then a

system for fiber sheathing with a single extrusion wheel is obtained.

3.5.2.4 Cable Sheathing with the Conform Extrusion Process

In this context, sheathing is the frictional or mechanical pressing of a mantle (aluminum) onto a cable. Single extrusion wheel and twin extrusion wheel plants can be used as with fiber cladding.

Fig. 3.82 Aluminum electrical cable produced with the conform system (Source: Holton Machinery Ltd.)

As shown in Fig. 3.79, the material being extruded is radially pressed from the grooves in the extrusion wheels into a chamber, from which it emerges as a mantle around the cable passing through the hollow mandrel in the die. As with sheathing, the tools have to be heated. It is also possible to work with only a single extrusion wheel.

Figure 3.80 shows an external view of such a conform extrusion machine, and Fig. 3.81 shows a part produced by it. An aluminum electrical cable produced by the conform process can be seen in Fig. 3.82.

3.6 Cable Sheathing

Martin Bauser*

3.6.1 General

The external sheath of power cables and communication cables has to protect the internal elements from mechanical damage and from environmental influences [Kom 89].

Lead cable sheaths have been extruded directly onto cable cores for more than 100 years, since the invention of cable sheathing by Borell in 1879 [Pea 61]. This first application of the extrusion of metals has been extended since

1941 by cable sheathing with aluminum [Zwe 60], which competed with lead, particularly for large diameters. However, the advances in insulation and sheathing technology with plastics and the use of polyethylene layers with embedded aluminum foil has resulted in a reduction of paper and oil insulated energy cable and of paper insulated communication cable and thus to a reduction in metal mantles for both energy, as well as for communication cables. Today, approximately 10% of overland and undersea cables are sheathed with metal, usually lead or aluminum (sea cables usually with lead).

The thickness of the cable sheath is standardized (VDE0255A4) and is usually between 1 and 3 mm (DIN). The sheath has to be completely tight and protect the internal conductor and insulation layers against moisture as well as mechanical, chemical, and thermal influences.

Further requirements are:

- A narrow wall thickness tolerance is prescribed in the standard. The mean value should be at least equal to the nominal value.
- Stop marks (known as bamboo rings) can form when the press is stopped and reloaded. These marks are undesirable because of the associated wall thickness deviations.
- The cable itself should not be damaged by severe temperature effects during the sheathing process.

3.6.2 Principle of Cable Extrusion

The extrusion of cable sheaths is derived from direct extrusion without a shell and without lubrication. Billet-on-billet extrusion without a discard is used to produce a continuous sheath. The dummy block is fixed to the stem.

The difficult material flow conditions and the high friction result in severe material heating at high extrusion loads.

3.6.3 Sheathing with Lead

3.6.3.1 Materials and Process

Lead can be easily worked at relatively low temperatures and has good corrosion resistance. Pure lead is not usually used for cable sheaths because large grains with the risk of intercrystalline cracking can occur. Unalloyed lead is also very sensitive to damage because of its low

---

*Cable Sheathing, Martin Bauser

strength. The cable sheathing alloys are standardized in DIN 17640 part 2. Low-strength alloys are usually alloyed with tellurium and copper. Higher-strength alloys, which are usually used for communication cables, contain antimony. The higher-strength alloys can, however, be processed only on extrusion presses.

In lead sheathing, the extrusion process has had competition for over 70 years from the continuously operating screw press, the design of which is very similar to plastic extruders. They are preferred for pure and low-alloy lead because the machines are less expensive than cable sheathing processes. They are not discussed here.

3.6.3.2   Cable Sheathing with Lead

In lead cable sheathing, liquid metal is poured into a vertical container. Usually, it is filled from an electrically heated crucible containing several tons of the melt through a floor valve with various flow systems at a maximum temperature of 450 °C.

The cast lead should bond well with the discard from the previous filling on the die head to prevent possible defects from inclusions. Air blisters should not form during filling. The lead is, therefore, usually filled under vacuum together with a lost head that is sheared after solidification at the top edge of the container [Rie 63].

The metal solidifies in the water-cooled container under a small load applied by the stem within 5 to 10 minutes after which the extrusion process can begin.

The metal then flows into the bifurcated hollow mandrel from two sides and is pressed into the prechamber. It is then pressed onto the cable and forms the cable mantle as it leaves the die (Fig. 3.83). This also applies to aluminium cable extrusion.

The material flow necessitates longitudinal welds. Particular attention must be paid to these potential sources of defects. The boundary surface between the extruded and the newly filled metal (transverse weld) extends as a tongue over approximately 20% of an extrusion charge and can be scarcely recognized by metallography [Rie 63].

The wall thickness of the extruded cable sheath can be set and adjusted by axial movement of the die [Rie 72].

A cooling ring located immediately behind the die sprays water onto the extrusion providing rapid cooling and hinders coarse grain formation in the lead mantle as well as damage of the temperature-sensitive cable insulation. The cooled cable is coiled directly behind the press.

As mentioned previously, the stop mark between two extrusions, during which the extrusion is stationary for several minutes, is a problem. The bamboo ring that forms has a reduced wall thickness due to the elastic deformation of the die when the load is reduced and the subsequent reduction in the gap between the die and the hollow mandrel. The strength and structure also changes at these stop marks. The pressure at the die also reduces during extrusion from the start of extrusion to the end, resulting in wall thickness variations.

Careful control of the die setting during extrusion and when stopped are used to compensate for this in order to obtain a constant wall thickness. Built-in thermocouples are used to carefully monitor the tooling temperature. Heating elements are used to control the temperature.

So-called continuous cable sheathing extrusion that avoids the stop mark, which is also used for lead, is discussed in the section on aluminum.

The machines used for cable sheathing extrusion with lead range from 6 to 30 MN press

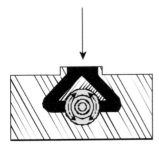
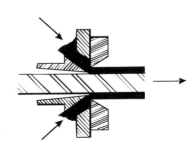

Fig. 3.83   Metal flow in the die head [Kom 89]

power with a container capacity of 135 to 1000 kg lead. The container diameters are selected to give a specific pressure of 350–450 N/mm². Mantle diameters up to 110 mm are standard.

3.6.4 Sheathing with Aluminum

3.6.4.1 Aluminum as a Cable Sheathing Material

Aluminum is significantly lighter than lead and its high conductivity enables it to be used as an earth and with communication cable as the screen against electromagnetic interference. The higher strength compared with lead usually avoids the need for protection against mechanical damage [Sün 69].

The higher bending strength of aluminum compared with lead is, however, a disadvantage because the aluminum sheath extruded onto the cable has to be corrugated for diameters above approximately 50 mm. A further disadvantage of aluminum is the corrosion susceptibility that necessitates careful protective coating, e.g., with bitumen and extruded polyvinyl chloride.

3.6.4.2 General Process

More powerful extrusion presses are needed for aluminum than for lead because of the higher flow stress compared with lead. They usually have capacities of 15 to 35 MN. The extrusion principle is the same as that described for lead except that cast billets, usually Al99.5, are used with aluminum.

If the demand is low, it is not unknown for a cable sheathing press to be used for both materials. Obviously, changing from one material to the other requires extensive modifications and cleaning.

The turned billets are usually heated in an induction furnace to 400 to 500 °C and, depending on the press principle, loaded into the horizontal or vertical container that is also heated. There are two different processes used to avoid air inclusions between the discard and the next billet:

● The container is sealed from above and evacuated before extrusion. This sealing can be produced with either a sealing disc placed on the top or a machined collar on the billet, which contacts the container wall after a short upsetting and seals. The billet is extruded after evacuating for approximately 20 seconds.

● Another method is to produce a temperature profile of approximately 100 °C between the two billet ends in the induction billet furnace [Ste 70]. A uniformly heated billet barrels to the container wall during upsetting and seals the air in on the die side. In contrast, a billet with a temperature profile upsets initially at the hotter side next to the die. In vertical containers the billet contacts the container wall from the bottom to the top so that the air can emerge from the top. Air trapped in front of the die results in blisters and tearing of the metal mantle.

If the operating sequence is interrupted, equalization of the temperature gradient between the billet front and end occurs and, consequently, air blisters cannot be excluded. Therefore, the process mentioned first of sealing and evacuating is preferred.

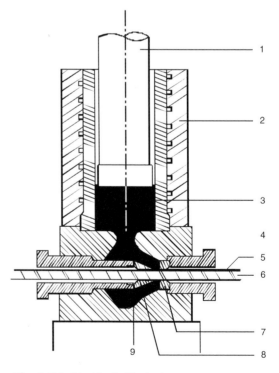

Fig. 3.84 Principle of cable sheathing. 1, extrusion stem; 2, container; 3, cable sheathing material; 4, die head; 5, cable sheath; 6, cable core; 7, die; 8, hollow mandrel; 9, detachable point. The billet is placed in the container and pushed into a feeder chamber. The cable slips through a hollow mandrel in the feeder chamber, is surrounded by the sheathing material, and leaves the feeder chamber through the die, which determines the external diam of the sheath [Pea 61].

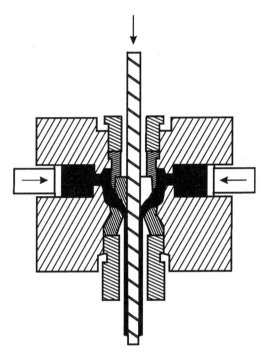

Fig. 3.85 Twin container press [Ste 70]

Fig. 3.87 30 MN cable sheathing press for aluminum [Rie 72]

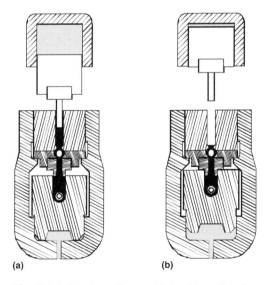

(a)   (b)

Fig. 3.86 Press for continuous cable sheathing. (a) Extrusion. (b) Loading [Rie 72]

3.6.4.3 Discontinuous Extrusion

If extrusion is carried out as shown in Fig. 3.84, the force on one side of the mandrel results in eccentricity and the interruption between two extrusions in a bamboo ring, as described previously for lead. The die therefore has to be adjusted very finely and sometimes the position adjusted relative to the mandrel during the extrusion.

The desire to have a larger press volume and to avoid a single-sided mandrel loading resulted in 1955 in the development of a twin container press (Fig. 3.85) [Ste 70].

In the twin container press, a billet is simultaneously extruded from two opposing containers so that half the cable sheath is formed from each billet and two welds form. There are no side forces on the mandrel and it is easier to hold good sheath concentricity. Since the severe change in direction of the material around the hollow mandrel in the ring piece of the single container press does not occur, the extrusion load is correspondingly lower. This design is, however, no longer pursued.

3.6.4.4 Continuous Extrusion

The worst problem in cable sheathing, the pause between two extrusions, occupied designers relatively early. The best solution is represented by the continuous cable sheathing press first built in 1950 (Fig. 3.86, 3.87). When a new billet is extruded, not only is the cable sheath extruded; simultaneously, the auxiliary container linked to the die head is pushed down and filled with metal. When the lowest position is reached, the residual metal flows exclusively out of the container through the die. As soon as the end of extrusion is reached, and the stem withdrawn to load the next billet, the auxiliary container begins to move upward and the cable sheath continues to be extruded, using its metal filling without interruption but with a slower speed. At the start of this process, a valve in the die head closes to prevent metal flowing up into the main container.

The movement of the auxiliary container lasts long enough to enable a new billet to be loaded and the container evacuated. The valve reopens during the subsequent extrusion and the cycle restarts.

3.7 Tube Extrusion Process

Klaus Siegert*

As mentioned previously, tube extrusion in this context concerns the extrusion of seamless tubes over a mandrel. The extrusion of tubes through a welding chamber die is, therefore, classified under the section extrusion.

Tube extrusion can be classified into:

- Direct tube extrusion
- Indirect tube extrusion

There are also special processes, including hydrostatic extrusion, that can be used for tube extrusion. This is discussed in the section on hydrostatic extrusion.

3.7.1 *Direct Tube Extrusion*

Direct tube extrusion can, according to Fig. 3.88, be divided into direct hot tube extrusion and direct cold tube extrusion. The latter is used only in special cases.

Direct hot tube extrusion can be divided into tube extrusion over a fixed mandrel and tube extrusion over a moving mandrel.

3.7.1.1 **Direct Hot Tube Extrusion over a Fixed Mandrel**

In direct hot tube extrusion without a shell over a fixed mandrel (Fig. 3.89), prebored billets are usually used. The billet bore is slightly smaller than the mandrel shaft diameter.

When the mandrel enters the billet, the bore acts as a pilot hole. Once the mandrel is in the final position, the extrusion process commences by moving the stem forward. The billet is then pushed over the mandrel.

As with all other direct section and tube extrusion processes, there is friction between the material being extruded and the container wall as well as, specific to direct tube extrusion, friction between the material being extruded and the mandrel surface. When the set discard length is reached, the mandrel is withdrawn. The container then opens slightly so that the dummy block and the discard can be pushed out of the container. As the stem moves back, a shear mounted on the press platen separates the discard (Fig. 3.89).

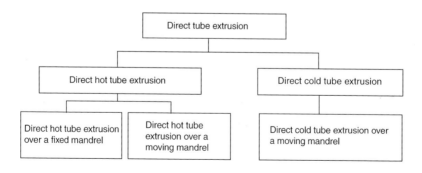

Further classification criteria:

With lubrication/without lubrication
With internal mandrel cooling/without internal mandrel cooling

Fig. 3.88 Direct tube extrusion processes

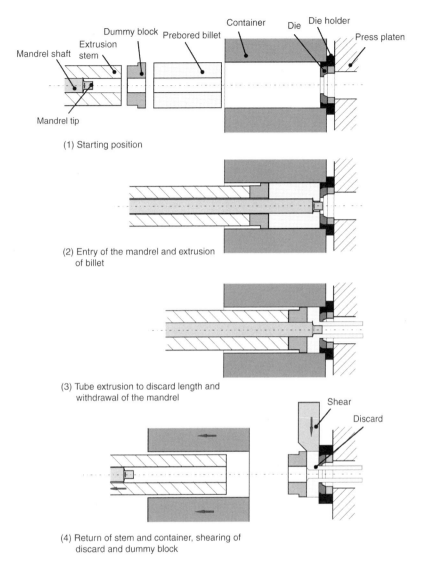

(1) Starting position

(2) Entry of the mandrel and extrusion of billet

(3) Tube extrusion to discard length and withdrawal of the mandrel

(4) Return of stem and container, shearing of discard and dummy block

Fig. 3.89 Process sequence for direct hot tube extrusion without a shell over a fixed mandrel [Bis 75]

This operating sequence can be used for direct hot tube extrusion of aluminum alloys. As with hot section extrusion of aluminum, lubrication is never used.

3.7.1.2 Direct Hot Tube Extrusion with a Moving Mandrel

If extrusion is carried out with a moving mandrel as shown in Fig. 3.90, a cylindrical mandrel without a mandrel tip is used. It is also possible to use slightly conical mandrels.

The mandrel can travel with the stem speed, e.g., coupled to the stem so that there is no rela-

tive movement between the material being extruded and the mandrel outside the deformation zone that forms in front of the die. There is, therefore, no friction in this region. There is, however, an increase in the relative speed between the material being extruded and the mandrel in the region of the deformation zone up to the tube exit speed less the mandrel or stem speed. Friction has to be taken into account in this region. The relative speed between the mandrel and the material being extruded is then lower.

The mandrel can also move relative to the stem when it is possible that the mandrel is

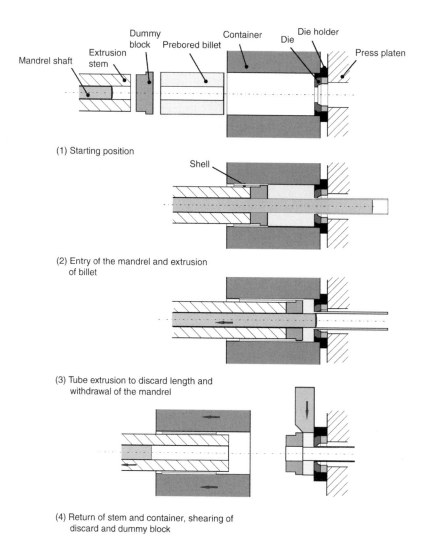

Fig. 3.90 Process sequence for direct hot tube extrusion with a shell over a moving mandrel [Zil 77, Bis 75, Bis 77]

pulled forward by the friction between the material being extruded and the mandrel. This is referred to as direct hot tube extrusion over a moving mandrel with relative movement.

3.7.1.3 Direct Hot Tube Extrusion with a Shell

It is possible to extrude with a shell in both hot tube extrusion with a fixed and with a moving mandrel.

A shell is formed between the dummy block and the container wall in direct hot tube extrusion with a shell if the gap between the dummy block and the container wall is selected correctly.

The shell adhering to the container wall has to be removed at the end of extrusion by a special operation, which is considered to be a disadvantage.

The advantage is, however, that in extrusion with a shell, oxide residues and impurities from the billet peripheral zone finish up in the shell and cannot flow into the extruded product.

Figure 3.90 shows the operating sequence for hot tube extrusion with a shell over a moving mandrel. It is possible to pierce the billet in the container. It is also possible, as shown in Fig. 3.90, to use prebored billets. Then, a longer initial billet length can be used. The removal of the shell is not shown. The shell can be removed in the same way as in direct hot extrusion either by a separate cleaning cycle or a combination block.

It is usual to pierce the billet in the press when extruding with a moving mandrel. The billet is initially upset in the container. The stem then moves slightly back so that the material displaced by the mandrel during piercing can flow in the opposite direction from the piercing direction.

After the piercing operation, the extrusion process continues until the preset discard thickness is reached. The mandrel and the stem then return.

The container is also opened sufficiently to enable the tube to be sawn from the discard.

A cleaning disc then pushes the discard and the shell into a discard tool loaded between the platen and the container. This is the usual operating sequence for the direct hot tube extrusion of copper materials.

3.7.1.4 Analysis of the Axial Forces in Direct Hot Tube Extrusion

Figure 3.91 shows the conditions in direct hot tube extrusion over a stationary mandrel. This extrusion process is usually carried out without a lubricant, e.g., aluminum.

A thin layer of the material being extruded coats the mandrel. As the billet is pushed over the mandrel, the material being extruded shears along a boundary surface concentric to the mandrel surface. Therefore, similar conditions occur at the mandrel as at the container wall. This is discussed in section 3.1.1.4.

If l_0 is the length of the billet upset in the container over the mandrel, s_1 is the upset displacement and l_R is the discard length, which is equal to the difference of the length l_0 and the shaft length in contact with the material in contact, then the mandrel tensile load is given by:

$$F_D = (l_0 - l_R + s_1 - s_{St}) \cdot D_{DS} \cdot \pi \cdot \tau_{S_1}$$
$$+ \frac{D_{DS} + D_D}{2} \cdot \pi \cdot l_R \cdot \tau_{S_2} \qquad \text{(Eq 3.67)}$$

An average mandrel diameter is assumed for the friction between the material being extruded and the mandrel tip:

$$\frac{D_{DS} + D_D}{2}$$

The critical shear stress τ_{S_1} between the material being extruded and that sticking to the shaft surface depends on the localized temperature.

This is lower than that in the deformation zone. The shear stress τ_{S_1} is therefore higher than the shear stress τ_{S_2} in the deformation zone in the boundary surface along the mandrel tip.

The force needed to shear the material being extruded along the container wall is obtained from Eq 3.44:

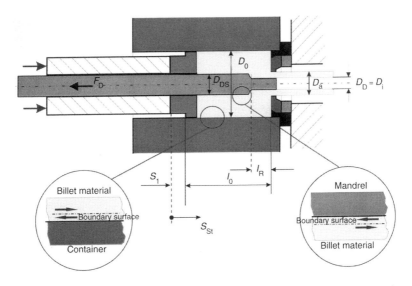

Fig. 3.91 Direct hot tube extrusion over a fixed mandrel (e.g., of aluminum) without lubrication. D_0, container diam; D_{DS}, mandrel bar diam; D_a, tube external diam; D_i, tube internal diam; F_{St}, stem load; F_D, mandrel load; l_0, upset billet length; l_R, discard length; s_{St}, stem displacement; s_1, upset displacement [Zie 78]

$$F_R = \pi \cdot D_0 \cdot (l_0 - l_R + s_1 - s_{St}) \cdot \tau_{S_3}$$
(Eq 3.68)

where τ_{S_3} is the shear stress in the material being extruded at the container wall.

In direct hot extrusion over a stationary mandrel, the extrusion ratio is, according to Eq 3.1:

$$V = \frac{D_0^2 - D_{DS}^2}{D_a^2 - D_i^2}$$
(Eq 3.69)

According to Eq 3.14, the logarithmic principle strain is:

$$\varphi_{ges} = \ln V = \ln \frac{D_0^2 - D_{DS}^2}{D_a^2 - D_i^2}$$
(Eq 3.70)

The axial force needed for deformation in the deformation zone F_M is analogous to Eq 3.13:

$$F_M = C \cdot \varphi_{ges} \cdot \bar{k}_f \cdot \frac{\pi}{4} (D_0^2 - D_{DS}^2)$$
(Eq 3.71)

To determine the mean flow stress $\bar{k}_f$ from quasi-adiabatic flow curves, it is necessary to know the temperature ϑ_E with which the material being deformed enters the deformation zone, as well as a valid mean logarithmic strain $\bar{\varphi}_g$ for the material being extruded in the deformation zone and a mean logarithmic strain rate $\bar{\dot{\varphi}}_g$:

$$\bar{k}_f = f(\text{billet}, \bar{\varphi}_g, \bar{\dot{\varphi}}_g, \vartheta_E)$$
(Eq 3.72)

An equivalent container diameter D_0^* and an equivalent product diameter D_S^* are used to determine the mean logarithmic strain $\bar{\varphi}_g$:

$$D_0^* = \sqrt{D_0^2 - D_{DS}^2}$$
(Eq 3.73)

$$D_S^* = \sqrt{D_a^2 - D_i^2}$$
(Eq 3.74)

Then, according to Eq 3.16 and 3.19:

$$\bar{\varphi}_g = 2 \cdot \ln \left[\frac{3}{\dfrac{D_S^*}{D_0^*} + 2} \right]$$
(Eq 3.75)

The estimation of the entry temperature ϑ_E is more difficult. With increasing ram movement, the billet volume enters the deformation zone with an increasing temperature because of the friction between the mandrel and the material being extruded as well as the friction between the container wall and the material being extruded, if the initial billet temperature is equal to the container temperature.

Initially, the entry temperature ϑ_E is equal to the initial billet temperature ϑ_B. It then increases continuously until the end of the extrusion process, providing a temperature profile produced by an induction billet furnace or a decreasing stem speed over the stem displacement is not used to give a constant entry temperature ϑ_E over the stem displacement.

The temperature increase in the deformation zone corresponding to the work that is converted to heat is given by:

$$\Delta\vartheta = \frac{\bar{k}_f \cdot \varphi_{ges}}{\rho \cdot c}$$

This temperature increase is then constant over the stem displacement if the mean flow

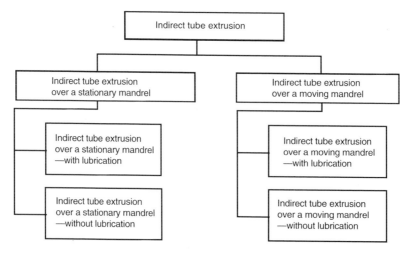

Fig. 3.92 Indirect tube extrusion process

stress is constant, which is the case with a constant entry temperature ϑ_E. This then gives a constant exit temperature ϑ_S over the stem displacement s. This is known as isothermal tube extrusion.

If the initial billet temperature ϑ_B is higher than the container temperature, which is the case in copper tube extrusion, then the billet volume enters the deformation zone at an increasingly lower temperature according to section 3.1.2.5. This tendency compensates the temperature increases from the friction between the container wall and the material being extruded. In addition, the temperature increase in the deformation zone increases with decreasing entry temperature because the flow stress increases. The end effect is a decrease in the exit temperature because of the predominating influence of the de-

creasing entry temperature over the stem movement.

In the extrusion of copper alloys the initial billet temperature of 600 to 800 °C is above the maximum tool temperature of approximately 500 °C. Consequently, mandrel cooling is used to ensure that the mandrel is not overheated.

3.7.2 Indirect Tube Extrusion

Indirect tube extrusion can be divided according to Fig. 3.92 into indirect tube extrusion over a stationary mandrel and indirect tube extrusion over a moving mandrel.

Both processes can, in principal, take place with and without mandrel lubrication and with and without mandrel cooling. If the billet temperature is higher than 450 °C, mandrel cooling should be used.

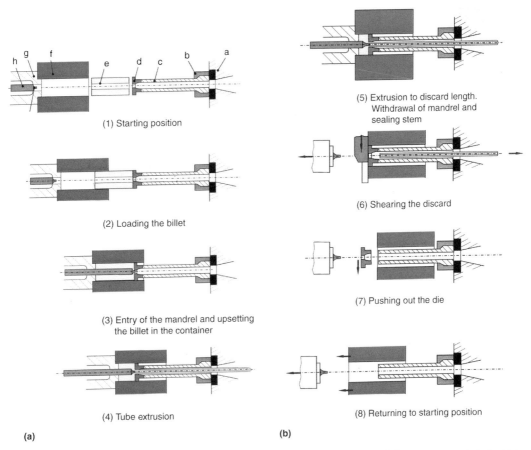

(1) Starting position

(2) Loading the billet

(3) Entry of the mandrel and upsetting the billet in the container

(4) Tube extrusion

(a)

(5) Extrusion to discard length. Withdrawal of mandrel and sealing stem

(6) Shearing the discard

(7) Pushing out the die

(8) Returning to starting position

(b)

Fig. 3.93 (a) Process sequence in indirect tube extrusion over a fixed mandrel (stages 1–4). (b) Process sequence in indirect tube extrusion over a fixed mandrel (stages 5–8). a, extrusion press platen; b, hollow stem holder; c, hollow stem; d, die; e, billet; f, container; g, sealing stem; h, mandrel; i, mandrel tip

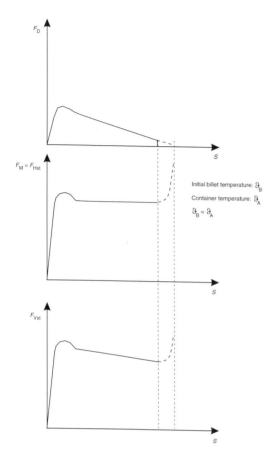

Fig. 3.94 Variation of the axial forces over the sealing stem displacement in indirect tube extrusion over a fixed mandrel (e.g., of aluminum, without mandrel lubrication, without mandrel cooling). F_D, mandrel load (tensile force); F_M, axial compressive load on the die; F_{HSt}, axial compressive load on the hollow stem; F_{VSt}, axial compressive stress on the sealing stem; s, sealing stem displacement

3.7.2.1 Indirect Tube Extrusion over a Stationary Mandrel

This process has been used since 1978. Hollow billets are also used in this process. The internal billet diameter is slightly smaller than the mandrel shaft diameter so that the bore of the billet acts as a pilot hole for the mandrel.

The mandrel is either lubricated or unlubricated, cooled or noncooled, depending on the material being extruded.

The mandrel is usually neither lubricated nor cooled in the indirect tube extrusion of aluminum alloys over a stationary mandrel.

Process Sequence in the Indirect Tube Extrusion over a Stationary Mandrel. Figure 3.93 shows the process sequence. The mandrel first enters the billet until the tip has entered the

die. The billet is then upset and extruded. When the preset discard thickness has been reached, the mandrel withdraws into the sealing stem. The sealing stem and mandrel then move back far enough to allow the discard to be separated by a shear mounted on the container.

As in all other indirect extrusion processes, there is no friction between the billet and the container. However, friction does occur between the mandrel and the material being extruded.

This friction affects both the material flow and the forces on the mandrel (tensile loads) as well as the sealing stem load.

Axial Forces in Indirect Extrusion over a Stationary Mandrel. If the mandrel force is F_D, then with the sealing stem load F_{VSt} and the deformation load F_M acting axially on the die, which is equal to the load acting on the hollow stem F_{HSt}:

$$F_{VSt} = F_M + F_D$$

where

$$F_M = F_{HSt}$$

The mandrel load is calculated in the same way as it is for direct extrusion over a stationary mandrel according to Eq 3.67.

The deformation load F_M is calculated in the same way as for direct extrusion over a stationary mandrel according to Eq 3.71.

The variation in the mandrel load, the deformation load, and the sealing stem load over the sealing stem displacement is shown in Fig. 3.94. The friction between the mandrel and the material being deformed takes the form of shearing within the material being extruded along a boundary zone at the critical shear stress (see section 3.1.1.4).

There is an approximately linear decrease in the mandrel load corresponding to the reduction in the contact area between the mandrel and material being extruded as the sealing stem displacement increases. The sealing stem load is the sum of the mandrel load and the deformation load.

REFERENCES

[Adi 71]: J.F. Adie and S. Harper, Hydrostatisches Strangpressen (Hydrostatic Extrusion) *Z. Metallkd.*, Vol 62 (No. 5), p 343–350

[Ake 66]: R. Akeret and A. Künzli, Ermittlung der Formänderungsfestigkeit kf von Aluminium-Legierung mit hilfe von Torsionsversuchen und Vergleich der Ergebnisse mit denjenigen von Strangpreßversuchen (Determining the Flow Stress of Aluminum Alloys Using Torsion Tests and Comparison of the Results with Those from Extrusion Trials), *Z. Metallkd.,* Vol 57 (No. 11), 1966, p 789–792

[Ake 68]: R. Akeret, Untersuchungen über das Strangpressen unter besonderer Berücksichtigung der thermischen Vorgänge (Investigations into Extrusion with Specific Consideration of the Thermal Processes), *Int. Leichtmetalltagung,* Vol 5, Leoben/Wien, 1968, p 304–307

[Ake 71]: R. Akeret, *Z. Metallkd.,* Vol 62 (No. 6), 1971

[Alu]: *Aluminium-Fließkurven (Aluminum Flow Curves),* Fließkurven-Alu: 2731/101, 2732/101, 2733/101, des Forschungsinstitutes der Schweizerischen Aluminium-AG

[ASEA 70a]: *Quintus Hydrostatic Extrusion Press Type QE,* ASEA pamphlet AQ 14–102T

[ASEA 70b]: *Hydrostatisches Strangpresen (Hydrostatic Extrusion),* ASEA brochure AQ 14–101T

[ASEA 71a]: *Hydrostatisches Strangpressen nach dem Quintus-Verfahren (Hydrostatic Extrusion Using the Quintus Process),* ASEA brochure AQ 14–107T

[ASEA 71b]: *Herstellung von kupferumhülltem Aluminium—ein neues Quintus-Verfahren (Production of Copper Clad Aluminum—A New Quintus Process),* ASEA brochure AQ 14–106T

[Bis 73]: A. Biswas, Direktes, Indirektes und hydrostatisches Strangpressen (Direct, Indirect and Hydrostatic Extrusions), *Z. Aluminium,* Vol 49 (No. 4), 1975, p 296–299 and (No. 5), p 352–356

[Bis 75]: A. Biswas and F.-J. Zilges, Indirektes Strangpressen von Kupfer-Werkstoffen (Indirect Extrusion of Copper Alloys), *Z. Metallkd.,* Vol 29 (No. 4), 1975, p 375–380

[Bue 70]: H. Buehler, H.G. Hoepfner, and J. Loewen, Die Formänderungsfestigkeit von Aluminium und einigen Aluminium-Legierungen (The Flow Stress of Aluminum and Some Aluminum Alloys), *Z. Bänder, Bleche, Rohre,* Vol 11 (No. 12), 1970, p 645–649

[Con 84]: Conform . . . nun das vollendeteste Stranggußverfahren (Conform . . . Now the Most Complete Continuous Coating Process), *Metallurgia,* Vol 51 (No. 6), 1984, p 218–231

[Con 85]: Low Cost Molten Feed Boosts Continuous Extrusion, *Metallurgia,* Vol 32 (No. 6), 1985, p 243–245

[Daw 96]: J.R. Dawson, Conform Machinery for the Manufacture of Round and Multi-Part Aluminium-Tube, *Alum. Today,* April/May 1996, p 11, 12, 17

[DGM 78]: *Atlas der Warmformgebungseigenschaften von Nichteisenmetallen: Bd. 1 Aluminium-Werkstoffe, Bd. 2 Kupfer-Werkstoffe (Atlas of Hot-Working Properties of Non-Ferrous Metals:* Vol 1, *Aluminum Alloys;* Vol 2, *Copper Alloys),* Akeret, Jung, Scharf, Ed., DGM, 1978

[DIN]: DIN 57255A4 = VDE 0255 A4: *Kabel mit massegetränkter Papierisolierung und Metallmantel für Starkstromanlagen (Cable with Impregnated Paper Insulation and Metal Mantle for High Power Plants)*

[Doe 86]: E. Doege, H. Meyer-Nolkemper, and I. Saeed, *Fließkurvenatlas metallischer Werkstoffe: mit Fließkurven für 73 Werkstoffe u. e. grundlegenden Einführung (Flow Curve Atlas of Metallic Materials with Flow Curves for 73 Alloys and a Fundamental Introduction),* Hanser Verlag München, 1986

[Due 69]: W. Dürrschnabel, Der Werkstofffluß beim Strangpressen von NE-Metallen (Material Flow in the Extrusion of NF Metals) I, II, III, *Metall.,* Vol 22, 1968, p 426–437, 995–998, 1215–1219

[Eis 31]: W. Eisbein, "Kraftbedarf und Fließvorgänge beim Strangpressen" ("Load Requirements and Flow Processes in Extrusion"), Technische Hochschule (technical university), Berlin, thesis, 1931, (quoted in [Rat 66])

[Eth 84]: C. Etherington and H.K. Slater, The Extrusion of Aluminium and Its Alloys by Conform Process; Extrusion Productivity through Automation, *Third Int. Aluminium-Extrusion Seminar (Atlanta, GA),* Vol 2, 1984

[Eth 84b]: G. Etherington, Update on Conform—The Continuous Extrusion Forming of Metals, *Chart. Mech. Eng.,* Vol 31, 1984, p 28–32

[Fel 56]: P. Feltham, Extrusion of Metals, *Metal Treatment,* Vol 23, 1956, p 440–444

[Fel 69]: H.D. Feldmann, Betrachtungen zum hydrostatischen Strang-und Fließpressen von Metallen (Considerations on Hydrostatic Extrusion and Impact Extrusion of Metals Parts 1 and 2), Teil 1 und 2, TZ für prakt, *Metallbearbeitung,* Vol 63 (No. 3), 1969, p 116–119 and (No. 8), p 426–433

[Fio 63]: R.-J. Fiorentino et al., Advances in Hydrostatic Extrusion, *Tool and Manufacturing Engineer,* Aug 1963, p 77–83

[Fio 67]: R.-J. Fiorentino et al., New Developments in Hydrostatic Extrusion, *Proc. Int. Conf. Manuf. Techn.,* Sept 1967, p 941–954

[Fio 72]: R.-J. Fiorentino et al., The Thick Film Hydrostatic Extrusion Process, *Metall. and Met. Form.,* June 1972, p 200–205

[Fio 74]: R.-J. Fiorentino et al., Some Practical Considerations for Hydrostatic Extrusion I, II, *Metall. and Met. Form.,* July 1974, p 193–197; Aug 1974, p 210–213

[Har 83]: G. Hartmann, *Untersuchungen über Kräfte und Butzengrößen beim Lochen von Aluminium-Werkstoffen gegen Matrize* (*Investigations into the Loads and Discord Sizes in the Piercing of Aluminum Alloys against Like Die*), D83, Technische Universität Berlin, D83, 1985

[Haw 91a]: D.J. Hawkes and R.E. Morgan, Conform Extrusion, *Wire Ind.,* June 1991

[Hei 77]: H. Heimburg, Verbesserung der Produktqualität und Wirtschaftlichkeit beim Strangpressen von Messing (Improving the Product Quality and Economics of Brass Extrusion), *Z. Metallkd.,* Vol 31 (No. 4), 1977, p 414–417

[Joh 68b]: S. Johnson, Fortschritte beim hydrostatischen Strangpressen (Advances in Hydrostatic Extrusion), *Z. Draht-Welt,* Vol 54 (No. 4), 1968, p 209–213

[Kom 89]: *Kombinat VEB Kabelwerk Oberspree: Kabel und Leitungen* (*Cable and Conductors*), VEB-Verlag Technik Berlin, 1989

[Lan 71]: G. Lange, Der Wärmehaushalt beim Strangpressen (Heat Balance in Extrusion), *Z. Metallkd.,* Vol 62 (No. 8), 1971, p 571–579

[Lan 85]: I. Langerweger and B. Maddock, Sviluppi nell' estrusione continua: il processo conform, *Technologie,* Vol 3 (No. 2), 1985, p 56–59

[Lan 88]: I. Langerweger and B. Maddock, Recent Developments in Conform and Castex Continuous Extrusion Technology, *Light Met. Age,* Aug 1988

[Lau 76]: *Strangpressen: Verfahren, Maschinen, Werkzeuge* (*Extrusion: Processes, Machining, Tooling*), K. Laue and H. Stenger, Ed., Aluminium Verlag, Düesseldorf, 1976, ISBN 3-87017-103-0

[Len 69]: B. Lengyel and L.E. Culver, Properties of Materials Extruded by Orthodox Hydrostatic Extrusion, *J. Inst. Met.,* Vol 97, 1969, p 97–103

[Mad 87]: B. Maddock and B. Eng, Aluminium Rod and Other Products by Conform, *Wire Ind., The British Wire Journal,* Dec 1987, p 720–731

[Met 85]: Low Cost Molten Feed Boosts Continuous Extrusion, *Metallurgia,* Vol 32 (No. 6), 1985, p 243–245

[Mue 84]: K. Müller, Untersuchungen zu den Reibungsverhältnissen beim Warm-Strangpressen von Rohren aus Aluminium-Legierung bei Verwendung von Preßdornen (Investigations into the Friction Behavior in the Hot Extrusion of Aluminum Alloy Tubes Using Mandrels), Forschungsbericht, *VDI-Z,* Reihe 5, Nr. 76, 1984

[Par 84]: J.A. Pardoe, Conform Continuous Extrusion Process—Its Contribution to Energy Conservation, *Met. Technol.,* Vol 11, Aug 1984, p 358–365

[Par 86]: R.D. Parkinson, Continuous Cladding-Conform Process, *Wire Ind., The British Wire Journal,* No. 4, 1986, p 3

[Pea 61]: C.E. Pearson and R.N. Parkins, *The Extrusion of Metals,* Chapman & Hall, 1961

[Pet 59]: E. Petsch, Neues Indirekt-Strangpressverfahren für Metalldraht (New Indirect Extrusion Process for Metal Wire), *Z. Metallkd.,* Vol 50 (No. 11), 1959, p 629–637

[Pug 65]: H.W.D. Pugh and A.W. Low, Hydrostatic Extrusion of "Difficult" Metals, *Sheet Met. Ind.,* Aug 1965, p 572–594

[Pug 72]: H.W.D. Pugh and C.J.H. Donaldson, Hydrostatic Extrusion—A Review, *Annals of the CIRP,* Vol 21 (No. 2), 1972, p 167–186

[Rat 66]: C. Rathjen, "Untersuchungen über die Größe der Stempelkraft und des Innendruckes im Rezipient beim Strangpressen von Metallen" ("Investigations into the Size of the Stamp Force and the Internal Pressure in the Container in the Extrusion of Metals"), TH-Aachen, Diss., 1966

[Rie 63]: H. Riemann, Einrichtungen zum Beschicken von Bleipressenrezipienten (Systems for Loading Lead Extrusion Containers), *Draht,* Vol 14 (No. 8), 1963

[Rie 72]: H. Riemann, Kontinuierliche Ummantelung von Kabeln mit Blei (Continuous Sheathing of Cables with Lead), Bleilegierungen und Aluminium, *Draht,* Vol 4, 1972

[Rup 80b]: D. Ruppin and K. Müller, Kalt-strangpressen von Aluminium-Werkstoffen mit Druckfilm-Schmierung I bis III (Cold Extrusion of Aluminum Alloys with Pressure Film Lubrication I to III), *Z. Aluminium,* Vol 56 (No. 4), 1980, p 263–268; (No. 5), p 329–331; and (No. 6), p 403–406

[Sac 37]: G. Sachs, Spanlose Formgebung der Metalle (Chipless Shaping of Metals), *Handbuch der Metallphysik,* Vol 3 (No. 1), 1937, (quoted in [Rat66])

[Sie 76a]: K. Siegert, "Untersuchungen über das direkte, indirekte und hydrostatische Strangpressen" ("Investigations into Direct, Indirect and Hydrostatic Extrusion"), Technische Universität Berlin, Diss., 1976

[Sie 76b]: K. Siegert, Betrachtung der Reibungsvorgänge beim Strangpressen (Consideration of the Friction Processes in Extrusion), in *Strangpressen Berichte des Symposiums in Bad Nauheim* (in the *Extrusion Papers of the Bad Nauheim Symposium*), 1976, DGM e.V. Oberursel, 1976

[Sie 77]: W. Ziegler and K. Siegert, Spezielle Anwendungsmöglichkeiten der Indirekten Strangpreßmethode (Special Application Possibilities of the Indirect Extrusion Method), *Z. Metallkd.,* Vol 31 (No. 8), 1977, p 845–851

[Sie 78]: Siegert, K., Indirektes Strangpressen von Messing (Indirect Extrusion of Brass), *Z. Metallkd.,* Vol 32 (No. 12), 1978, p 1243–1248

[Sie 80]: K. Siegert, Indirektes Strangpressen von Aluminium-Legierungen (Indirect Extrusion of Aluminum Alloys), *Tagungsbericht der 7, Intern (Report of the Seventh International Aluminum Conference)*, Leichtmetalltagung Leoben/Wien, 1981, p 290–292

[Ste 70]: A. Steinmetz, Doppeltwirkende Presse zum Ummanteln elektrischer Leiter mit Aluminium (Double Acting Press for Sheathing Electrical Conductors with Aluminum), *Aluminium,* Vol 46, 1970, p 3–6

[Stre 82]: W. Strehmel, Untersuchungen zum rechnergestützten direkten Strangpressen von Aluminium-Legierungen (Investigations into Computer Controlled Direct-Extrusion of Aluminum Alloys), Fortschrittsberichte, *VDI-Z (progress report Vol 2),* Vol 2 (No. 51), VDI-Verlag GmbH, Düsseldorf

[Stu 68]: H.P. Stuewe, Einige Abschätzungen zum Strangpressen (Some Assessments of Extrusion), *Z. Metallkd.,* Vol 22 (No. 12), 1968, p 1197–1200

[Stu 71]: H.P. Stuewe, Fließspannung und Verformungsgeschwindigkeit beim Strangpressen (Flow Stress and Deformation Rate in Extrusion), *Z. Metallkd.,* Vol 62 (No. 10), 1971, p 697–701

[Sün 69]: H. Sünderhauf, Die Verwendung von Aluminium in der Kabeltechnik (The Application of Aluminum in Cable Technology), *Aluminium,* Vol 45, 1969, p 111–114

[Wil 69]: H. Wilhelm, "Untersuchungen über den Zusammenhang zwischen Vickershärte und Vergleichsformänderung bei Kaltformvorgängen" ("Investigations into the Relationship between Vickers Hardness and Equivalent Strain in Cold-Working Processes"), Bericht aus dem IFU-Stuttgart (Report from the IFU), No. 9 Girardet, Essen, 1969

[Zie 73]: W. Ziegler and K. Siegert, Indirektes Strangpressen von Leichtmetall (Indirect Extrusion of Aluminum), *Z. Metallkd.,* Vol 64 (No. 4), 1973, p 224–229

[Zie 78]: W. Ziegler, Direktes, indirektes und hydrostatisches Strangpressen im Vergleich (Comparison of Direct, Indirect and Hydrostatic Extrusion), *Z. Drahtwelt,* Vol 12, 1978, p 475–481

[Zil 77]: F.-J. Zilges, Indirektes Strangpressen von Rohren aus Aluminium-und Kuper Werkstoffen (Indirect Extrusion of Aluminum and Copper Alloy Tubes), *Z. Metallkd.,* Vol 31 (No. 4), 1977, p 151–156

[Zwe 60]: W.V. Zwehl, Bewährung von Starkstromkabel mit Aluminiummantel (Protection of Power Cables with Aluminum Cladding), *Aluminium,* Vol 36, 1960 p 666–671

CHAPTER 4

Metallurgical Principles

Martin Bauser*

4.1 Introduction

THE EXTENSIVE USE of metals over thousands of years, but in particular during the industrial age, can be attributed to their specific properties. In addition to their good electrical conductivity—associated with good thermal conductivity—and visual properties, the most important are the mechanical properties and the good workability. The use and range of application of different metals depends on these and many other properties, including, for example, the corrosion resistance. However, the production costs also play a decisive role.

These extend from the accessibility and the extraction of the ore, the cost in the refining up to and including the casting and processing. Extrusion is suitable as a deformation process in different ways for the different materials. The well-used expression "extrudability" is a way of expressing this.

Knowledge of deformation technology alone is not sufficient to be able to understand and control the processes taking place during extrusion. The quality of the billet materials, the processes taking place within the extruded material during extrusion, and the properties of the extruded section can be understood only from a metallurgical viewpoint.

This chapter, therefore, explains the basic terminology of metallurgy—naturally in the context of the aims of this book—to provide the tools needed by those involved in extrusion. More detailed explanations can be found in the literature, e.g., [Hor 67, Guz 70, Ber 83, Sch 81, Dah 93, Hou 93, Blu 93, Alt 94].

This materials science chapter is concerned only with metals. The atoms are held together by the so-called "metallic bond," which differentiates them from the nonmetals (covalent bond, ionic bond). A characteristic of this metallic bond is the ease of movement of the outer electrons, which are no longer attached to individual atoms but form an electron gas. This mobility of the electrons is the reason for the good electrical conductivity of metals.

Nonmetallic crystalline materials can, as a rule, be extruded only with difficulty, if at all. There is insufficient ductility in the working range of temperatures and pressure. Glass with its amorphous structure is, however, an exception because it softens on heating.

Recently, metal and nonmetal composite materials have been extruded. Nonmetallic particles or fibers are uniformly embedded in a metallic matrix, usually artificially, to improve the mechanical properties and often to reduce wear. These materials are also discussed briefly in this chapter.

4.2 Structure

4.2.1 Lattice Structure Single Phase

All metals consist of crystallites (small crystals), the arrangement, size, and shape of which are referred to as the structure. Polishing of

---

*Casting and Cast Structure, Homogenizing of Aluminum Alloys, Wolfgang Schneider; Casting and Cast Structure of Copper Alloys, Adolf Frei; Deformation, Recovery, Recrystallization, Martin Bauser

(a)

(b)

Fig. 4.1 The structure of brass [Wie 86]

metal specimens and suitable methods of etching are used to reveal the structure—usually under the microscope (Fig. 4.1).

The crystallites that form during solidification from the melt change during the cooling. They are stretched by the deformation and reform by recrystallization after annealing a deformed material. They are, however, always crystallites with an ordered lattice structure that constitute the metal.

If a metal consists of only one type of crystallite, it has a *single-phase structure*.

The regular arrangement of the atoms of each crystallite forms the lattice structure. The smallest component of this lattice is referred to as the *unit cell*. A real crystallite, also called a grain, consists of many unit cells arranged uniformly in adjacent rows like building blocks.

The unit cells are very small. The edge length, known as the lattice constant, is of the order of 10^{-7} mm so that a crystallite with a mean diameter of 0.1 mm contains 10^{18} elementary lattice building blocks.

The location of a lattice—a simple cubic lattice is shown in Fig. 4.2—is defined by the direction of the edges of the elementary cell. This is referred to as the orientation of the lattice.

In a real metal body consisting of numerous crystallites, the latter can be differentiated by

their orientation, which is usually completely random.

This is shown schematically in Fig. 4.3. The different types of metal lattices have a significant effect on their behavior during deformation. The most important lattice structures are shown in Fig. 4.4. They are face-centered cubic (fcc), body-centered cubic (bcc), hexagonal, and body-centered tetragonal lattices. Figure 4.4 also shows the lattice structure of the important metals at room temperature.

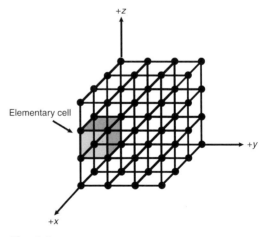

Fig. 4.2 Elementary cell in a simple cubic lattice [Sch 81]

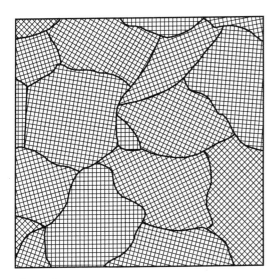

Fig. 4.3   Diagram of a polycrystalline structure

The description of a space lattice by surfaces and direction is usually given by Miller's indices (see the Appendix to this chapter).

In the solid state the metal atoms try to achieve the highest packing density. The fcc and specific hexagonal lattices posses the densest spherical packing. The atoms are assumed to be spheres that preferentially form these arrangements when shaken together. A bcc lattice has a spatial filling of 68%. Face-centered cubic lattices and the hexagonal close-packed structure have a spatial filling of 78% of the maximum possible. It is therefore clear that the density of a metal depends not only on the atomic weight but also on the crystal structure.

The size and shape of the crystallites can be influenced by control of the solidification from the melt and by recrystallisation during the annealing of a deformed metal. Extremely fine

crystallites can have diameters well below 1 μm and large grains several mm. It is also possible to grow single crystals. These are particularly suited for studying the basics of the deformation processed within crystals. Cylindrical specimens several centimeters long are produced for this purpose.

Defect-free ideal crystals do not occur in practice. Indeed, specific defects are necessary for plastic deformation and diffusion processes to occur at all. The most important types of defects are shown schematically in Fig. 4.5 and 4.6 and include:

- *Vacancies:* Numerous lattice sites are unoccupied. The number of vacancies increases exponentially with temperature. In the equilibrium state, e.g., in an undeformed aluminum crystal at room temperature, approximately one in every billion lattice sites is unoccupied. In contrast, one in a thousand is unoccupied just below the melting point.
- *Interstitial atoms:* In pure metals embedded atoms of the same type between the regular lattice sites. In alloys specific foreign atoms that are significantly smaller than the atoms of the base lattice can be embedded into the interstitial places (e.g., C and N in Fe).
- *Foreign atoms that substitute the base metal atoms:* Foreign atoms, particularly those with a similar atomic radius and with a similar lattice structure can replace atoms of the base structure.
- *Dislocations:* Step dislocations are lines at which an atomic plane ends. On one side of the slip plane—so called because the dislocation line can move in this plane—there is one more lattice plane than on the other (Fig. 4.6a). In a screw dislocation, the lattice areas are displaced relative to each other so that

Face-centered cubic lattice
Copper, α-solid solution,
nickel, aluminum, lead

Hexagonal close-packed
lattice
Zinc

Body-centered cubic lattice
β brass lattice,
α iron

Tetragonal body-centered
lattice
Tin

Fig. 4.4   The most important types of metal lattice structures [Wie 86]

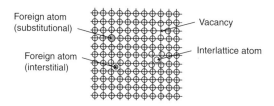

Fig. 4.5 Point type of lattice defect (vacancies, interlattice atoms, substitutional and interstitial foreign atoms)

the atoms are arranged around the dislocation line like a spiral (Fig. 4.6b). A real, usually randomly curved dislocation line in a slip plane can be considered to consist of edge and screw elements. The dislocation line consists of a closed ring or ends at a grain boundary or particle. In an undeformed structure, there can be up to 1 km of dislocation lines/mm^3 (dislocation density 10^6 to 10^8/cm^2.

If the orientation of two adjacent crystallites differs only slightly, the grain boundary between them can be considered to consist of dislocations located above each other (low angle grain boundary; subgrain-boundary) (Fig. 4.7a). Subgrains differ in their orientation from each other by only a few minutes of arc up to a few degrees [Dah 93, Ber 83]. A grain boundary between crystallites with very different orientations (large angle grain boundary) is, in contrast, a severely distorted region with defects of various types (Fig. 4.7b).

Twins represent a special form of crystallites in contact with each other. Their orientation is a mirror image at a plane boundary surface (Fig. 4.8).

A metallic structure that consists of only one type of atom contains dislocations, vacancies, and interstitial atoms. If a metal contains two or more different atoms, it is an alloy containing embedded or substituted foreign atoms. These

can accumulate readily in the more or less severely distorted grain boundaries. Every type of defect naturally causes internal stresses within the lattice. Internal stresses are decreased when foreign atoms migrate to grain boundaries because they are able to fill the voids that are present.

4.2.2 Multiphase Structure—Equilibrium Diagrams

Alloys, materials that consist of two or more metals, can have one or more phases (types of crystal).

If only one type of crystal is present in a metallic material—pure metal or alloy—it has a single phase referred to as a *homogeneous structure*. Correspondingly, a *heterogeneous structure* consists of several types of crystals (phases). The well-known free-cutting brass CuZn39Pb, for example, contains both the fcc α brass as well as the bcc β brass, in addition to undissolved lead inclusions as a chip breaker. Figure 4.1 shows a micrograph of a single phase α brass and a binary phase α-β brass.

The structure, the quantity, and the distribution of the various phases of an alloy depend on the content of the individual metals, the previous history, and the temperature. An alloy can pass through several states as it cools from the melt. The amounts of the individual phases that form in the thermodynamic equilibrium state, i.e., the state with the lowest energy, are described by the equilibrium diagram. The spatial distribution of the crystallites of the phases that occur are studied using metallographic images and image analysis techniques.

4.2.2.1 Binary Systems

The simplest equilibrium diagrams are those with only two alloying partners involved. This is referred to as a binary alloy. The abscissa

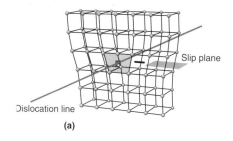

(a)

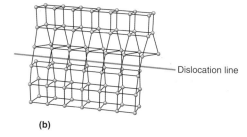

(b)

Fig. 4.6 Dislocation = linear lattice defect. (a) Edge dislocation. (b) Screw dislocation [Wie 86]

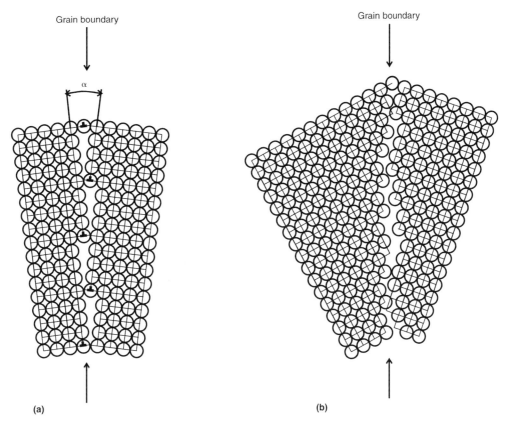

Fig. 4.7 Grain boundary structure. (a) Low angle boundary. (b) High angle boundary [Alt 94, Sch 81]

gives the amount of the two atoms (in weight percent) and the temperature is plotted along the ordinate.

Figure 4.9 shows schematically some of the frequently occurring basic types of binary phase systems. The equilibrium diagrams of most binary systems can be constructed from these examples.

The liquidus temperature (at which solidification commences during cooling from the melt) and the solidus temperature (at which solidification is complete) can be read as well as the occurrence of the phases and the melting interval (the temperature difference between the liquidus and the solidus temperature). In the melting interval, solidified particles float in the melt.

In pure metals, the liquidus and solidus coincide because there is only one solidification temperature. It is identical to the melting temperature as the solid metal transforms to the liquid state at the same temperature on heating.

The different basic types of the equilibrium diagram are shown in Fig. 4.9.

Continuous Solid Solution (Type 1). The lattice type of the parent metal A is retained over the full range of solution up to the pure metal B. The atoms B replace to an increasing extent the atoms A in their lattice positions. This is referred to as atoms B dissolving in lattice A, analogous to the processes in liquids. The solution of one atom type in another is favored where the atom radii differ only slightly from each other, e.g., copper and nickel, which therefore form a continuous solid solution.

In field **a** the metal occurs as a liquid, in field **b** both as solidified particles and as liquid, and in field **c** as 100% solidified solid-solution format.

Because both metals usually have different melting temperatures, the liquidus and the solidus temperature vary with the alloy addition.

Eutectic System (Type 2). In this case, the atoms of type B are completely insoluble in the atoms of type A—usually when there are very large differences between the atom radii. If B is alloyed to A, then B forms its own second phase. The fraction of phase B increases in the equilibrium diagram uniformly to the right and the fraction of phase A decreases accordingly. In the eutectic system there is one concentration E where the liquidus and the solidus temperature coincide at the minimum melting point. A typ-

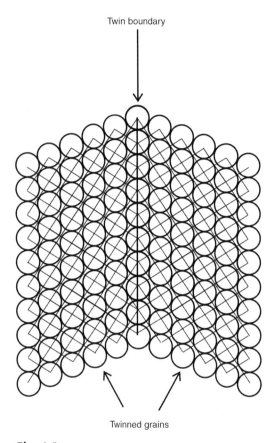

Twin boundary

Twinned grains

Fig. 4.8 Twinned grains and twin boundary

ical eutectic structure forms at this concentration during solidification, usually consisting of alternating layers of atom A and atom B. If, on the other hand, an alloy outside the eutectic concentration on the A-rich side cools, the A phase first solidifies from the melt when the liquidus line is crossed. The residual melt from which the metal A is removed increases in concentration in the metal B as cooling continues. At the eutectic temperature the residual melt has reached the eutectic composition and solidifies entirely eutectically. The structure shows the primary solidified grains of type A surrounded by the eutectoid from the residual melt.

Eutectic System with Solid Solution (Type 3). This type of binary system occurs frequently when the atoms of type B dissolve in small concentrations by substitution of atoms A in the lattice (field **c**). As soon as a limiting concentration is reached, the internal stresses produced by the inclusion of the second atom type B become so high that the formation of a second phase becomes energetically more favorable (field **d**). As mentioned previously, the structure always tries to achieve the state of lowest energy.

The composition of the A-rich phase in field **d** corresponds to the concentration on the left boundary line to **c**, the composition of the B-rich phase to the concentration of the right boundary line c_2 at the corresponding temperature. The more the displacement of the composition of the alloy from the left boundary line to the right, the greater is the number of grains of the B-rich phase and, correspondingly, the fewer the grains of the A-rich phase in this two-phase field.

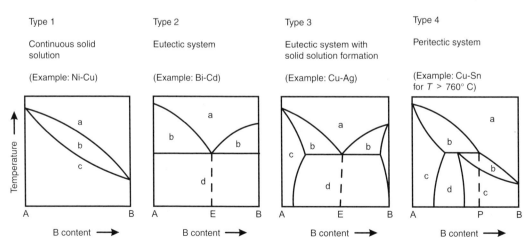

Fig. 4.9 Basic types of phase diagram. a, melt; b, melt + solid crystals; c, solid solution (homogeneous); d, two different crystals (heterogeneous); E, eutectic point; P, peritectic point [Wie 86]

In Fig. 4.10, the structures corresponding to different compositions are sketched under the equilibrium diagram of such a eutectic system with solid solution formation:

- *Concentration α:* Crystals of the phase c_1 solidify here, surrounded by layers of the eutectoid E formed at the eutectic temperature **E**.
- *Concentration β (eutectic composition):* The structure consists only of the layers of the eutectoid of the phases c_1 and c_2.
- *Concentration γ:* Grains of phase c_2 form initially and are surrounded by the eutectoid on further cooling.

As can be seen from the diagram, the solubility of the second atom type decreases in the solution regions (fields c_1 and c_2) with decreasing temperature, which must result in the precipitation of particles of the second phase even after solidification to maintain equilibrium (see also Fig. 4.13, section 4.2.3).

This type of eutectic system equilibrium diagram with solid-solution formation rarely represents the real state of an alloy because the mobility of atoms decreases so strongly with decreasing temperature that the elimination of the nonequilibrum state is possible only after a long holding period, if at all.

The structural state at high temperatures can, therefore, be "frozen" by quenching from this temperature so quickly that the atoms have no time to form the room temperature configuration.

Peritectic System (Type 4). A peritectic reaction occurs when the melt (field **a**) forms a

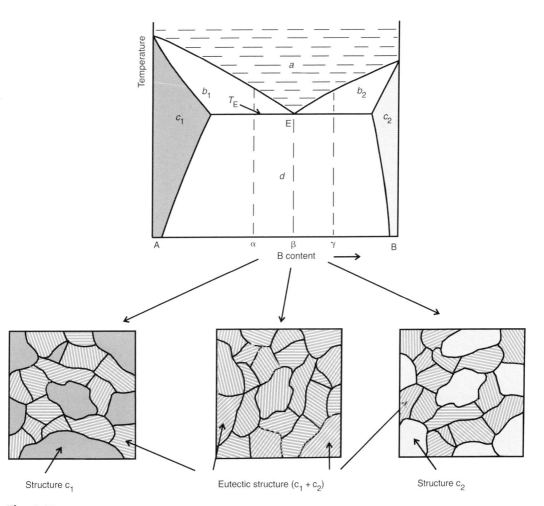

Fig. 4.10 Structure of a eutectic binary alloy [Ber 83]

new solid phase with a primary precipitated solid phase. The α grains are then surrounded by a shell of the β phase. In the peritectic concentration point a peritectoid structure forms that appears similar in micrographs to the eutectoid. The development of the equilibrium state on further cooling is very restricted and can be achieved only after long holding periods at the corresponding temperature.

4.2.2.2 Intermediate Phases

A solid solution consists, as previously mentioned, of the parent metal with interstitial or substitutional foreign atoms that are distributed randomly or only slightly ordered.

Intermediate phases occur when two or more types of atom are bonded together in an ordered, usually complex, structure. Intermediate phases have little or no deformability and are very brittle.

4.2.2.3 Multicomponent Systems

If an alloy consists of more than two types of atoms in a significant amount, it is not possible to depict it completely in a two-dimensional di-

agram. Two different depictions are used for three-part systems (ternary systems), as shown in Fig. 4.11:

- *Isothermal section:* The diagram consists of an equilateral triangle representing the three alloying partners. Each point within the triangle can be related to a specific concentration of the alloying elements A, B, C (in the example point P: 35%A, 40%B, 25%C). This type of diagram naturally shows the state at a specific temperature. In order to represent all phase states, therefore, it is necessary to have numerous similar isothermal sections that are often depicted within each other.

- *Quasi-binary section:* The proportion of two types of atoms are fixed (in the example shown A:B = 3:2) and the phase states studied for increasing amounts of atom type C. This diagram can be read in the same way as a binary system.

4.2.3 Diffusion, Precipitation, Nonequilibrium

The phase diagrams show that in many alloys both the composition of the individual phases of

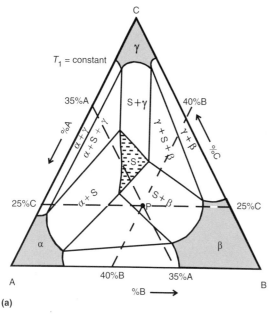

(a)

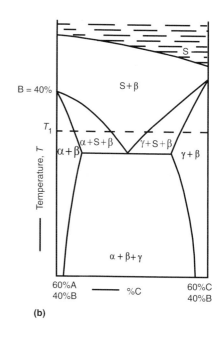

(b)

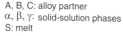

A, B, C: alloy partner
α, β, γ: solid-solution phases
S: melt

Fig. 4.11 Tertiary system representation. (a) Isothermal section (temperature T_1 = constant). (b) Quasi-binary section (alloy component B, e.g., 40%) [Ber 83]

a multiphase structure as well as the fraction of the phases in the structure change during heating or cooling. Atoms have to migrate from one phase to another to maintain the new equilibrium when the temperature changes. This *diffusion* occurs by transposition processes, which, in the case of *substitution solid solutions,* requires a large number of vacancies. The migrating foreign atom always moves to the nearest vacancy position (Fig. 4.12).

The atoms of a crystal lattice are stationary only at absolute zero. As the temperature increases they oscillate more strongly about their location and can then more easily leave their position. When changing places, the migrating atom has to pass through a state of higher energy, known as the activation energy Q, which is easier in the energy-rich state of a higher temperature: diffusion processes occur faster at higher temperatures than at lower.

In interstitial solid solutions the significantly smaller foreign atoms (e.g., carbon or nitrogen in iron) migrate from one interstitial lattice place to the next without the assistance of vacancies. The diffusion activation energy is lower than with substitution solid solutions.

From diffusion laws, which also apply to gases and liquids, the rate of diffusion is not only temperature dependent but is faster the greater the concentration difference between the two regions that will be equalized by the diffusion process.

A precipitation process occurs if a second phase is formed in the solid state of a homogeneous alloy during cooling when the solvus line is crossed. Nuclei first form and continue to grow until phase equilibrium is reached. Typical examples are the age-hardening aluminum alloys (Fig. 4.13).

If a single-phase region is rapidly cooled from the solid solution (e.g., the dashed line X2 in Fig. 4.13), the foreign atoms initially are retained in solution because they are practically immobile at low temperatures. Only when aging occurs at a temperature that enables significant diffusion to take place can nuclei of the second phase form and grow.

Because this process of solution treatment with quenching followed by aging is usually associated with an increase in strength, it is referred to as "age hardening."

Energy also has to be expended for the nucleation of precipitates, but this is usually lower at specific crystal defects or in a grain boundary than in the interior of the undistorted lattice. With a low precipitation pressure—e.g., slow

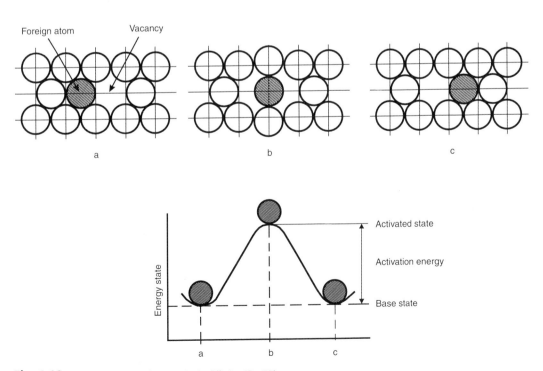

Fig. 4.12 Transposition through vacancies in diffusion [Ber 83]

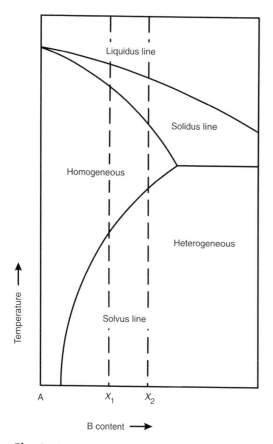

Fig. 4.13 Precipitation of a two-phase system [Wie 86]

cooling—the nuclei preferentially form at these defects and grain boundaries. The foreign atoms have sufficient mobility at higher temperatures to cover large distances to these nucleation points and grow there to precipitates.

However, after quenching and aging at lower temperatures, the precipitation pressure is high enough for large quantities of nuclei to form in the less-distorted zones of the crystal interiors, which can then be reached by atoms in the immediate neighborhood in spite of the lower mobility at these lower temperatures. The precipitates are then so fine that they cannot be detected under the microscope.

If a suitable material is hardened by solution treatment and aging, the rate of cooling from the solution region needed for freezing increases the further the equilibrium state at low temperatures is from the solvus line. Accordingly, with AlMgSi0.5 (line X1 in Fig. 4.13) cooling from the solution temperature at about 500 °C in stationary or slightly moving air is required,

whereas, with AlMgSi1 (line X2), water quenching is needed to retain the solid-solution state.

This ideal picture can change if foreign precipitates or inclusions are present: manganese in AlMgSi0.5 acts as a nucleating agent so that rapid cooling has to be used in this case—similar to the higher-alloyed AlMgSi alloys—in order to retain the solution state [Sca 64].

The change with time (the kinetics) of transformation of the solid solution that is supersaturated by the quenching can be represented in the time-temperature transformation (TTT) diagram. The time is the abscissa and the temperature is the ordinate. The degree of transformation is quantified by curves showing suitable parameters (phase fraction in micrographs, hardness, age hardenability).

The *isothermal TTT diagram* shows the transformation progress of rapidly cooled samples at a constant temperature.

In many cases the *continuous TTT diagram* is more informative. This shows the precipitation behavior for different cooling rates from the solution temperature. The minimum cooling rate can be read from the diagram. Above this, no significant precipitation of the second phase occurs and the full hardening effect is obtained from the subsequent age hardening (Fig. 4.14). This is known as the *critical cooling rate*.

Figure 4.14(a) also shows the *freezing temperature* T_E, below which diffusion processes no longer occur. It occurs approximately at $0.3 \times T_S$ (T_S = the melting point) for diffusing substitution atoms. Figure 4.14(b) shows constant hardness curves in the continuous TTT diagrams.

If the cooling process from the solution temperature can be sufficiently accurately characterized by a specific parameter—e.g., the cooling time t_a to 200 °C—it is possible to use this parameter t_a as the abscissa and to plot against it a parameter that indicates the degree of transformation.

In steels and other materials that have different crystal lattices at different temperatures, the change in the transformation with time analogous to segregation can be depicted by isothermal or continuous TTT diagrams.

Grain growth follows the nucleation of the second phase as additional foreign atoms collect at the nucleus by diffusion. In the case of finely distributed precipitates, a coarsening process finally occurs after further thermal treatment. This is referred to as *coagulation* (Fig. 4.15).

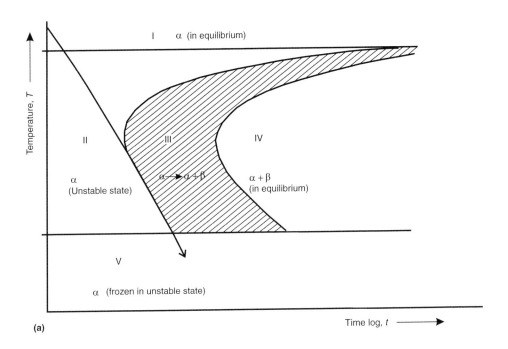

(a)

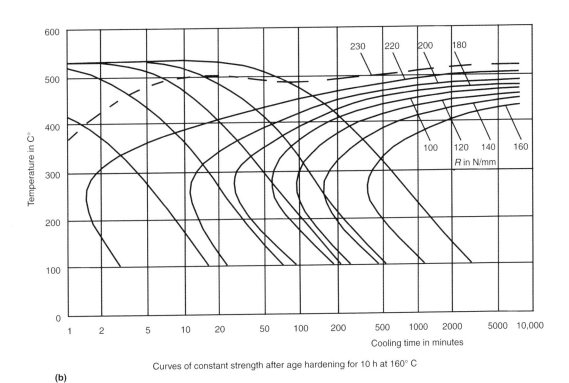

Curves of constant strength after age hardening for 10 h at 160° C

(b)

Fig. 4.14 Time-temperature transformation (TTE) diagram. (a) Principle [Ber 83]. (b) Continuous TTE diagram for AlMgSi0.5. I, solid-solution α (B dissolved in A) in equilibrium; II, solid-solution α (B still dissolved in A) in unstable state; III, second phase β precipitates to an increasing state from the solid-solution α; IV, equilibrium between phases α and β; V, frozen unstable state of the α phase

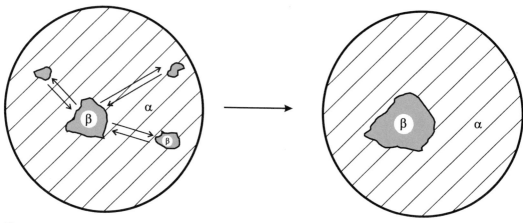

Fig. 4.15 Coagulation of precipitates [Ber 83]

During this coagulation process, atoms migrate by diffusion from smaller to larger precipitates. The small precipitates gradually disappear and only the large precipitates remain. Many small precipitates have a higher total of boundary surfaces between the phases than a few large ones. Because these boundary surfaces are energy rich coagulation reduces the energy levels.

The *martensitic transformation* is a special type of phase transformation in which the atoms adopt new positions without diffusion. This movement takes place extremely quickly after quenching and produces significant stresses between the old surrounding lattice and the new martensitic structure that is usually needle or plate shaped. The formation of martensite is mainly known in the behavior of steels, but it does occur in other materials, including α-β brasses.

4.2.4 Melting and Casting Processes

The structure in the billet is very important for the extrusion process. It has a strong influence on the extrusion load, the maximum possible extrusion temperature and speed, as well as the structure and properties of the extruded section.

The change from chill casting to continuous casting—now used for most metals—alone brought a significant quality improvement. This prevented the severe billet segregation associated with chill casting. The aim of numerous developments in continuous casting initially concentrated on the production of a fine struc-ture with the minimum segregation that solidified from the bottom to the top rather than from the outside to the interior.

The formation of the solid phase by cooling of a melt takes place by nucleation and growth when the liquids line has been crossed in a similar way to the precipitation of a second phase in the solid state described previously. Nuclei first form where the melt is cooler, which is at the mold wall in the casting process. As the undercooling of the melt increases the nucleation work needed reduces so that the number of nuclei increases and a finer structure is produced.

Casting and Cast Structure, Homogenizing of Aluminum Alloys

Wolfgang Schneider*

4.3 Development of the Continuous Cast Structure

Figure 4.16 shows the development of the continuous cast structure in a simplified manner. The heat extraction through the water-cooled mold wall, also referred to as indirect

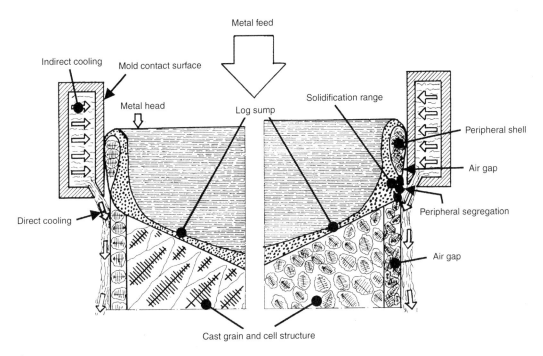

Fig. 4.16 Schematic of the formation of the continuous cast structure

cooling, causes the solidification of the peripheral region, i.e., to the formation of the so-called *peripheral shell*. This shrinks away from the mold wall and forms an air gap between the cast surface and the mold wall. This air gap hinders further heat extraction, resulting in reheating of the peripheral shell up to temperatures in the solidification range; i.e., partial or even complete melting of the peripheral shell is possible. *Peripheral segregation* can form during the dwell time in the air gap region as a result of the partial melting. The surface of the cast log is characterized by this and by the solidification of the peripheral shell itself, particularly in the meniscus region. The cast log finally emerges with the peripheral shell from the bottom of the mold and is hit by the cooling water flowing from the mold to complete solidification, referred to as direct cooling. This results in the formation of the cast grain and cell structure and, finally, the eutectic cast phases on the grain and cell boundaries as well as a characteristic profile of the solidification front across the cast log cross section, which is also known as the cast sump (Fig. 4.16).

The formation of the structure of the cast log is significantly influenced by the mold technology. The parameters of mold technology, which can be assumed to have a controlling influence, are the height of the effective mold wall and the metal head in the mold, the shape of the metal feed into the mold, and the direct cooling of the cast log. The direct cooling of the cast log is carried out by either spray water or mist cooling so that the mold has to have corresponding nozzles that will produce these methods of cooling. In aluminum continuous casting mist cooling predominates because aluminum has a high coefficient of thermal conductivity. In this case the application of a closed water mist below the mold is sufficient for rapid cooling of the cast log, and the use of additional specific cooling zones is not necessary.

The cooling of the cast log by direct cooling results in the development of stresses as a result of the temperature gradient from the interior of the cast log to the periphery; these can lead to the formation of hot or cold cracking, depending on the alloy system. The hot cracks usually form in the center of extrusion billets. Cold cracks, on the other hand, can occur over the full cross section. Alloys of the type AlMgSi are sensitive to hot cracking, whereas cold cracks are more likely to develop in AlCuMg and AlZnMgCu alloys.

The formation of the continuous cast structure is influenced by the casting parameters as well as the mould technology. The most important are the casting speed, the volume of cooling water and the casting temperature or the temperature of the melt as it enters the mould. The casting speed, in particular, is extremely important. Accurate selection of the casting speed and the mould wall height for the alloy composition is very important, for example, to avoid hot and cold cracking.

4.3.1 Peripheral Shell and Peripheral Segregation

The peripheral region of the cast log in the form of a peripheral shell is of particular importance in the continuous casting process. Numerous casting defects can occur within this peripheral shell, and these should not finish up in the semifinished product during subsequent processing of the cast log. Consequently, the extent and the cast structure of the peripheral shell are important and have to be controlled by the casting technology to minimize the peripheral shell thickness and defects.

The extent of the peripheral zone is largely determined by the mold wall height and the alloy composition [Scn 85]. The larger the solidification interval of the alloy being cast and the higher the mold wall, the thicker is the peripheral shell. In comparison, the casting parameters exert only a small influence on the thickness of the peripheral shell.

The cast structure of the peripheral shell usually consists of a fine and a coarse cellular region. The fine cellular zone solidifies in direct contact with the mold wall, whereas the formation of the coarse cellular region can be attributed to the insulation effect of the formation of the air gap already described.

The mechanical properties of the solidifying peripheral zone tend toward low values. They are influenced by the cast structure formation and the temperature of the peripheral zone, in particular by the actual temperature in the solidification interval and subsequently by the fraction of solid phase during the dwell of the peripheral shell in the air gap region [Ohm 88, Ohm 89].

The casting defects that are usually found in the peripheral zone include peripheral segregation. Zones of peripheral segregation are characterized by an above-average high concentration of alloying elements and a sharp concentration jump to the adjacent structure [Mor 69]. There are also often alloying element impoverished zones below the peripheral seg-

regation zones. This can be clearly seen in the example in Fig. 4.17.

The occurrence of peripheral segregations has to be considered in relationship to the solidification of the peripheral shell. Peripheral segregation forms during the dwell of the peripheral shell in the air gap region. Transport of residual melt regions enriched in the alloying elements towards the surface of the cast log takes place. The main transport mechanism is the metallostatic pressure of the melt before the peripheral shell. This is referred to as air gap segregation. A further mechanism for the formation of peripheral segregation is the residual melt enriched with alloying elements overflowing the meniscus curvature of the peripheral shell. This is referred to as meniscus segregation. Both these segregation methods described are shown schematically in Fig. 4.18 [Bux 77].

Various segregation formation shapes can be differentiated in peripheral segregation. Two examples are shown in Fig. 4.19. The nature of the segregation depends on the alloy type but also to some extent on the mold technology.

4.3.2 Cast Log Surface

The surface structure of the cast log is largely determined by the peripheral segregation.

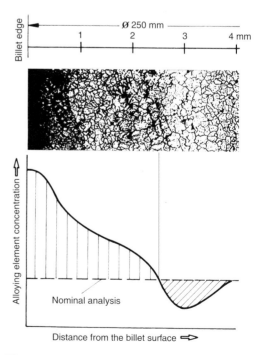

Fig. 4.17 Typical profile of the alloying element concentration in the peripheral segregation region

The different forms of peripheral segregation shown in Fig. 4.19 also result in correspondingly different cast log surfaces. Figure 4.20 shows examples of surfaces caused by different types of segregation.

Cold shuts are one surface feature that is not related to the peripheral segregation. An example is shown in Fig. 4.20. The formation of cold shuts can be attributed to the freezing of the melt meniscus in contact with the mold wall followed

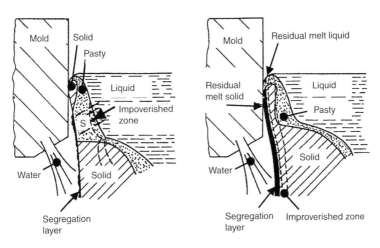

Fig. 4.18 Schematic of the peripheral segregation mechanism [Bux 77]

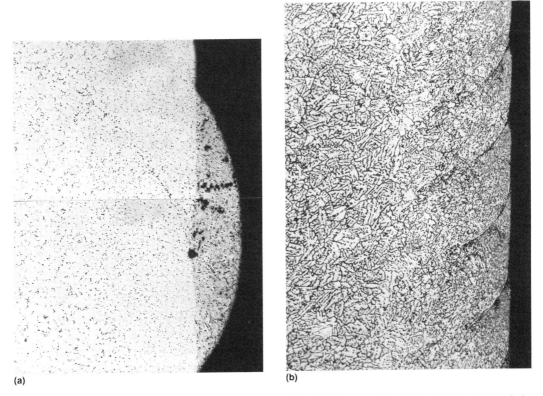

(a)   (b)

Fig. 4.19 Examples of types of peripheral segregation. (a) Sweating beads. (b) Lap segregations. Casting direction downward. The width is approximately 0.75 mm

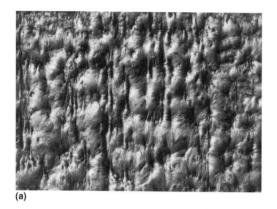

(a)

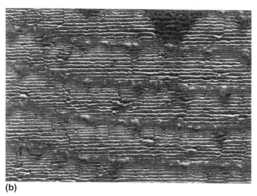

(b)

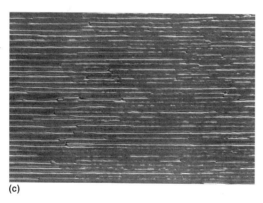

(c)

Fig. 4.20 Examples of types of cast log surfaces. (a) Surface with sweat beads. (b) Surface with segregation beads. (c) Surface with cold laps. Casting direction downward

The types of surface appearance just described are always found on cast logs. The formation of the peripheral shell is indeed important for the formation of the surface. However, a reduction of the peripheral shell thickness should not always be associated with an improvement in the surface quality. In general, the aim is to produce a smooth surface, but in many cases this is merely a purely optical effect. In other words, a smooth surface is not definitely associated with a good peripheral structure quality. This means that more value should be placed on producing a good peripheral structure quality for the subsequent processing of the cast logs.

4.3.3 Cast Grain and Cell Structure, Intermetallic Phases

An important requirement of the structure of the cast log is a fine and uniform globulitic formation of the cast grain structure. The production of a fine cast grain reduces the hot and cold crack sensitivity, depending on the alloy system. In addition, the hot-working behavior of the cast logs and the surface appearance of the extruded product after surface treatment also are affected. The globulitic cast grain structure is achieved using a grain-refining treatment (Fig. 4.21).

Grain-refining alloy additions of the type AlTiB are used [Los 77]. These are added during the casting as a 9 mm thick wire into the melt in the casting launder. The grain-refining action of the AlTiB alloy is attributable to complex nu-

by the melt flowing over the frozen peripheral shell. This surface defect is observed when the casting speed or the casting temperature is too low [Alt 65].

One type of surface that appears on the cast log and is best described as a surface defect is the surface tear that occurs in the form of cracks transverse to the casting direction. These tears are attributed to the frictional forces between the peripheral shell and the mold wall.

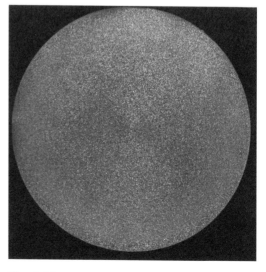

Fig. 4.21 Cast structure of a round billet (200 mm Ø) after grain-refining treatment

cleation processes in the melt [Rei 80]. The most important constituent of the alloys is insoluble TiB_2, which exists as fine particles and plays a direct role in the nucleation processes. Alloy additions of 0.2 to 1.5 kg/t aluminum are needed to obtain adequate grain refining depending on the alloy composition.

The majority of commercial wrought materials cast by the continuous casting process exhibit a cellular to dendritic type of solidification [Fle 74]. This, in turn, determines the cast grain structure. Figure 4.22 shows an example of a cellular/dendritic solidified cast structure.

The grain and cell boundaries of the cast grains are lined with intermetallic phases that occur as eutectics during the solidification. The grain and cell structure is also characterized by grain segregations, i.e., by nonuniform distribution of alloying elements in the structure. These grain segregations, which can be attributed to nonequilibrium solidification with an enrichment of the alloying elements from the grain center to the grain boundary, can result in the formation of eutectic phases on the grain and cell boundaries even in those alloy systems where they cannot occur according to the equilibrium diagram.

The cell structure of a cast log should be fine and uniform [Los 83]. This results in a corresponding fine and uniform distribution of the cast phases in the semifinished product after deformation of the structure. This requirement is particularly important for semifinished products that are given a surface treatment for decorative applications. Variations in the cell size can produce a banded surface.

The cast cell structure of aluminum cast logs exhibit a characteristic profile over the cross sec-

tion as shown in Fig. 4.23 for different billet diameters [Bux 77a].

There is a coarse cellular structure in the peripheral region of the cast log. This is the region of the peripheral shell. Next to this is a region with a very fine cell structure. Toward the center of the cast log, the cell size increases, reaching the maximum in the center. It should also be recognized that the quantitative profile of the cell size strongly depends on the diameter of the cast log. This relationship can be explained using the diagram in Fig. 4.24 [Bux 77a].

The faster the corresponding volume element of metal is transformed from the liquid to the solid state, then the finer the cell structure. If it remains too long in the partially solidified state between the liquidus and the solidus state, coarse cells form because these have a high "local solidification time" [Kat 67].

Figure 4.24 shows that the distance between the liquidus and solidus line varies across the cross section of the cast log. The distance is the greatest in the center of the log where the highest local solidification time occurs and, accordingly, the maximum cell size forms. The cell

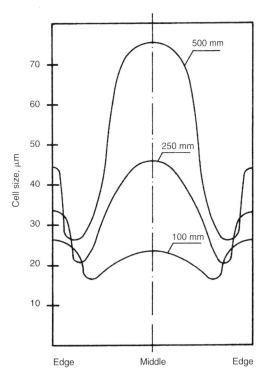

Fig. 4.23 Characteristic variation of the cast cell size over the billet cross section for different billet diameters [Bux 77a]

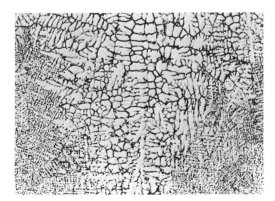

Fig. 4.22 Example of a cellular/dendritic solidified structure. The width is approximately 1.0 mm

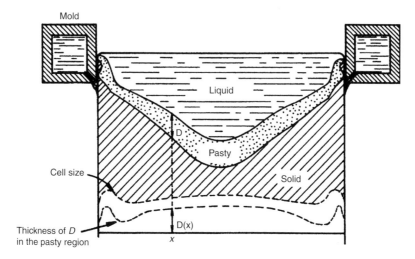

Fig. 4.24 Relationship between the distance between the liquidus and the solidus line and the cell size across the billet cross section [Bux 77a]

size minimum coincides with the contact point of the cast log direct cooling, because this is where low local solidification times exist because of the high solidification rates. Correspondingly, the distance between the liquidus and the solidus lines is smaller than in the log center where the cooling conditions in continuous casting result in the lowest solidification rates.

4.3.4 Homogenizing

The cast structure produced in continuous casting is neither the optimum for the subsequent processing nor for any surface treatment of the semifinished product. As mentioned previously, there is marked grain segregation in the continuous cast structure as well as a supersaturation of alloying elements. The volume fraction of eutectic precipitates is also increased. Therefore, a homogenization treatment consisting of high temperature annealing at temperatures between 450 and 600 °C is carried out to remove grain segregation and supersaturation.

The heating time at the homogenization temperature depends on the cell size and the rate of diffusion of the specific alloying constituents [Ake 90]. A fine cell structure is therefore advantageous because the concentration equalization within a cell can occur more quickly because the diffusion path is shorter.

The cooling of the logs from the homogenization temperature is also important in the homogenization process. Depending on the cool-

ing rate, secondary precipitates form in various quantities and sizes from the α-solid solution as a result of decreasing solubility. The actual precipitation state influences the extrudability of the billets, as is well known from the AlMgSi alloys [Res 92]. If the cooling rate is too slow, coarse Mg_2Si phases can preferentially form on grain and cell boundaries in the temperature range above 400 °C. These coarse phases do not dissolve quickly enough in solution during heating to the extrusion temperature and can melt during extrusion if their melting point is exceeded during the extrusion process. The consequence is a reduction in the extrudability of the billet because surface defects can form on the section even at lower extrusion speeds. Mg_2Si phases that precipitate at temperatures below 400 °C are so fine they can redissolve even during short times at the extrusion temperature.

If the cooling rate from the homogenizing temperature is too high, fewer and finer secondary precipitates form. This is the same as increasing the content of dissolved silicon and magnesium in the α-solid solution. This raises the initial extrusion pressure and reduces the extrusion speed at a constant extrusion load. Figure 4.25 shows the structure of cast logs of AlMgSi0.5 alloy before and after homogenization. Figure 4.25(a) shows the cast state with needles of AlFeSi phases on the cell boundaries. Figure 4.25(b) shows the structure after a defined annealing and cooling. The precipitated secondary phases (Mg_2Si) can be seen in the α-solid solution.

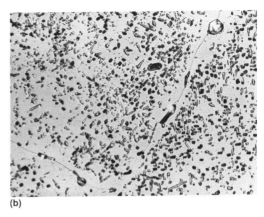

(a)

(b)

Fig. 4.25   Cast structure of AlMgSi0.5 round billet as-cast and after homogenization. (a) As-cast. (b) Homogenized

According to the previous discussion, therefore, the homogenization including cooling should be designed to give fast cooling to 400 °C to avoid the precipitation of coarse phases. This should be followed by slow cooling to reduce the content of dissolved alloying constituents [Ake 88].

Casting and Cast Structure of Copper Alloys

Adolf Frei*

Similar to aluminum alloys, the crystal growth is largely influenced by the temperature profile in the mold. The cast structure usually consists of a narrow very fine grain peripheral zone connected to a coarse globulitic or lamina structure extending to the core. Frequently, some form of single crystal is found in the center of copper billets.

Figure 4.26(a) shows the typical structure of a copper billet with a large columnar grain fraction, and Fig. 4.26(b) shows a brass billet with a globulitic core.

Direct cooling by water impingement is usually situated below a relatively short mold for the continuous casting generally used today for the casting of copper alloys (see Chapter 6). The indirect cooling through the mold wall is

thus reduced and that from the water impingement directly below the casting mold increased (Fig. 4.27).

4.4   Segregation and Gas Porosity

The solidification in the mold is described using a copper-tin alloy with 8% tin as an example (Fig. 4.28). As soon as the liquidus line (at point 1 in Fig. 4.28 at temperature T_1) is crossed, nuclei of the solid phase with composition "a" grow. The residual melt is impoverished in copper atoms and enriched in tin atoms. In the equilibrium state the last residue of the residual melt at temperature T_2 has the composition "b." A fully solidified structure has zones with large variations in composition, i.e., *segregation*, particularly with slow cooling.

Specific crystallographic directions are characterized by high rates of growth leading to preferentially oriented columnar grains that suppress others and enable a cast structure to develop. Preferred growth direction is the reason for the formation of fir tree dendrites seen, for example, in cast iron alloys.

The numerous nuclei that form with rapid cooling and simultaneously grow produce a fine distribution of residual melt constituents in the solid state, which ensures that the segregation is less severe and more finely distributed.

In the solid state, there is both grain segregation, which is a variation in concentration in and around the individual grains of the solidified structure, and billet segregation, which pro-

*Casting and Cast Structure of Copper Alloys, Adolf Frei

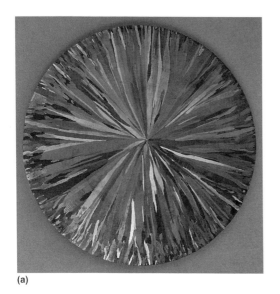
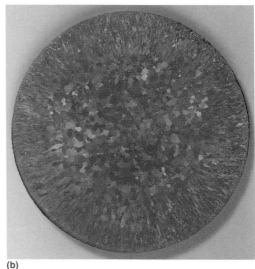

(a)   (b)

Fig. 4.26 Cast structure of copper alloys. (a) Copper billet. (b) Brass billet

duces differences between the billet periphery and the core by the growth of a solidification front from the cold mold wall toward the interior of the billet. The core is richer in the second (in the example the tin containing) phase corresponding to the phase diagram.

If gases are dissolved in a melt (e.g., N_2 or H_2), their solubility in the solid state is usually significantly lower than in the melt; i.e., the gas precipitates in the form of pores during solidification. In chill mold casting where the melt slowly grows from the periphery toward the center, these gas pores collect like pearl strings in the center of the cast billet. In continuous casting they are found in the segregations of the residual melt, i.e., in the boundaries of the grains of the cast structure.

Segregations are, as mentioned previously, supersaturated zones outside the equilibrium state of the solidified structure. The segregations solidified from the residual melt possess a composition that produces crystallites of brittle phases, which hinder working. In addition, because these segregation zones, which solidified at lower temperatures, also melt at lower temperatures than the parent metal during heating, there is a risk of grain-boundary melting during hot working.

4.5   Cooling and Casting Defects

In spite of the indisputable advantages of continuous casting compared with the older processes, there still exists the possibility of defects. Billets with the optimum extrudability can be achieved only by careful control of the casting parameters.

The best billet quality would be obtained with a flat solidification front perpendicular to the casting direction. This would require the entire heat extraction to take place in the direction of the log axis. This can be achieved only with uneconomic casting speeds.

Practice is a long way removed from the ideal case because both indirect and direct cooling remove the heat from the cast log mainly perpendicular to the axis. The casting sump (region of liquid metal in the cast log) has a U- or V-shaped section.

As a rule of thumb, approximately one-third of the heat to be extracted is taken through the mold and the rest by direct cooling of the cast log.

If the direct cooling of the log is not exactly symmetrical, this results in distortion of the emerging log. This bending can quickly become so large that it makes direct extrusion very difficult and indirect extrusion with its longer billet lengths of up to 1.5 m impossible.

4.5.1   Cast Log Surface

The appearance of the surface of the cast log is largely determined by the processes in the mold. The melt transferred into the mold initially solidifies in direct contact with the mold

Principal of continuous casting of logs

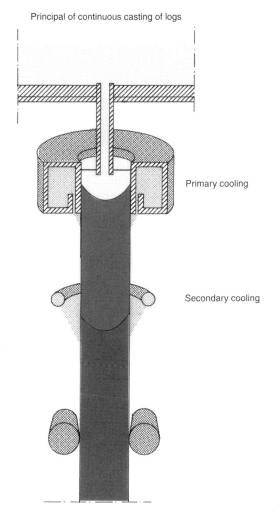

Fig. 4.27 Direct and indirect cooling in the continuous casting mold for copper alloys

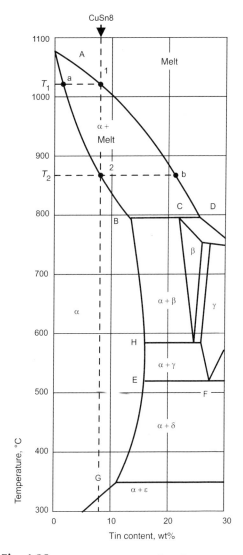

Fig. 4.28 Section of the copper-tin phase diagram [Ray 49]

wall to a thin shell, which pulls away from the mold wall after a few centimeters because of the solidification shrinkage. This produces a shrinkage gap that restricts further heat flow from the cast log. The interaction between the temperature of the melt, the method of metal feed, and the cooling conditions can lead to surface defects as the cast log passes further through the mold:

- Longitudinal cracks when the shell is pushed out by the metallostatic pressure of the melt in the sump and tears because of its low strength
- If the shell is pushed outward as an annular bead into the shrinkage gap, this can cause so much friction at the mold wall that transverse cracks occur ("cold shuts").

- In the extreme case, the log shell can locally melt from the still liquid core. The metal that emerges into the shrinkage gap solidifies as thin strings on the log surface.
- When casting high zinc containing brasses zinc can evaporate from the hot log shell and condense on the cold mold wall. From time to time it is stripped away by the cast log and forms "zinc flakes" on the surface of the log.

In the continuous casting of alloys with wide solidification intervals, for example, tin bronzes, "inverse segregation" can occur. The solidification shrinkage results in the tin-rich residual melt, which solidifies last, being enriched under the log surface and being partially pushed outward into the shrinkage gap. Good extrusion results can be obtained with these billets only by turning off the tin-rich peripheral layer and homogenization. CuSn8 is homogenized at approximately 700 °C for several hours to dissolve segregations of the brittle, tin-rich low-melting-point δ-phases.

The shrinkage gap is reduced in molds that are tapered toward the bottom, and the effects described can at least be suppressed to some degree. These molds are preferred for the casting of copper. The taper has to be carefully matched to the casting speed and the cooling conditions. The optimization is helped by computer programs.

If the metal head in the mold is not constant during the casting, inclusions of the covering agent and slag can occur under the surface of the cast log.

Excessive direct cooling can cause longitudinal cracks in the surface of the cast log, particularly with stress-sensitive alloys.

When casting is carried out with a salt cover, a thin salt film is initially formed on the surface of the cast log, and this has to be rinsed off in the region of direct cooling. If the composition of the covering salt is unsuitable or the direct cooling inadequate, the film can bond firmly to the cast log. It can then act as a lubricant between the billet and the container during extrusion and result in parts of the cast skin flowing into the extruded section, resulting in scrap due to laminations.

4.5.2 Interior of the Cast Log

Perfect results in extrusion can be achieved only from billets with smooth, clean surfaces and a dense structure over the complete cross section. Unsuitable casting conditions not only produce defects on the surface of the extruded section, but also within the section.

With a deep V-shaped casting sump there is the risk that gas bubbles can no longer escape but are retained in the region of the solidification point: porosity in the cast. In the region of the sump tip small zones of liquid metal can also be cut from the casting sump. When they solidify, the shrinkage results in small hollow spaces—solidification blowholes.

Solidification with a V-shaped sump results automatically in stresses in the cast log and, in the worst case, can result in longitudinal cracks in the core of the cast log. With very sensitive materials such as aluminum containing special brasses, these cracks can extend to the surface of the cast logs.

Unfortunately, it has to be assumed that such defects in the center of the billet along with the surface defects do not weld together in the extrusion press but produce material separation in the extruded section and thus scrap.

Exception: in the casting of copper billets with high casting speeds, shrinkage cracks can occur in the core along the grain boundaries with limited longitudinal extension. These "spiders" disappear during extrusion and do not have any detrimental effect on the section.

In the sections "Aluminum Alloys" and "Copper Alloys" in Chapter 6, detailed information on casting plants are given for the different materials.

Deformation, Recovery, Recrystallization

Martin Bauser*

As well as the references given at the start of section 4.2, the following works are recommended for a more detailed discussion of section 4.3: [See 85, Haa 84].

4.6 Deformation of Pure Metals at Room Temperature

4.6.1 Dislocations

In section 4.2.1, dislocations are described as linear defects in the crystal lattice as shown in Fig. 4.6. In real lattices, they form networks and are unevenly distributed (Fig. 4.29).

If an external force is applied, a crystal lattice initially deforms elastically following Hook's law. The elastic deformation is reversible—i.e.,

---

*Deformation, Recovery, Recrystallization, Martin Bauser

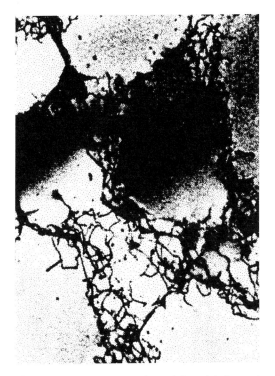

Fig. 4.29 Dislocation network in undeformed single crystal (transmission electron micrograph of aluminum $M = 10,000:1$) [Alt 94]

the lattice returns to the initial state when the load is removed.

As shown schematically in Fig. 4.30, a plastic nonreversible deformation results in atoms in specific planes and direction, the slip system, being displaced by one or more atomic spacings.

If all the atoms on a slip plane are simultaneously moved by one atomic spacing, a theoretical yield stress a hundred to a thousand times the real yield stress is required.

Dislocations make it possible for rows of atoms individually and successfully to spring to the next lattice place with only a low applied load. Figure 4.31 shows schematically the movement of an edge dislocation. As soon as a dislocation has passed through a slip plane, the entire crystal part on one side of the slip plane has been displaced by one atomic spacing relative to the other part.

The slip system in which the dislocation movements occur usually consists of planes with a dense atomic packing but with larger distances between each other. Their slip directions are particularly densely packed atomic rows.

Figure 4.32 shows the possible slip systems in cubic and hexagonal lattices. The planes and

directions are identified by the Miller's indices used in crystallography (see the additional information in the appendix of this Chapter).

There are 12 favorable slip systems in the face-centered cubic (fcc) lattice and eight in the body-centered cubic (bcc) lattice. The close-packed hexagonal spherical packing on the other hand has only three. This gives an indication of the different degrees of workability of such different structures.

If two opposite dislocations meet during their migration on the same slip plane, they mutually cancel each other out. If they are located on two adjacent slip planes, they form a vacancy chain when they meet (Fig. 4.33).

Whereas edge dislocations are tied to their slip planes and can only slip on these, screw dislocations can also move in other slip planes. When they meet barriers they can move to a parallel slip plane by "cross slip" and overcome the barrier (Fig. 4.34).

This cross slip, however, is hindered by stacking faults. The slip of a dislocation by one atomic spacing takes place in two steps when this is energetically favorable. The dislocation is then split into two half dislocations (Fig. 4.35).

The larger the energy needed for the splitting, the "stacking fault energy" of a metal, the smaller is the separation. Therefore, the stacking fault hinders the cross slip because the separation has to be removed by contraction (Fig. 4.34b). The stacking fault energy is therefore a specific parameter for a metallic material—applicable not only to cross slip. It plays an important role in deformation and annealing processes at higher temperatures.

4.6.2 Single Crystals

Single crystals are particularly suitable for experimental investigations and for explaining the deformation processes in metals. If a single crystal is loaded in tension a dislocation moving shear stress is at a maximum at 45° to the specimen axis. Usually, therefore, only the slip system closest to this 45° direction is activated (simple slip in the principal slip system).

During the slip, further dislocations form at *sources* (Fig. 4.36). The dislocations therefore multiply but also hinder one another in real networks. During cold deformation the length of the dislocation lines can increase from originally 1 km/mm^3 in the undeformed state by a factor of 1,000 to 10,000 (dislocation density in the cast structure: 10^6 to 10^8, after a deformation; up to 10^{12}/cm^2) [Hou 93].

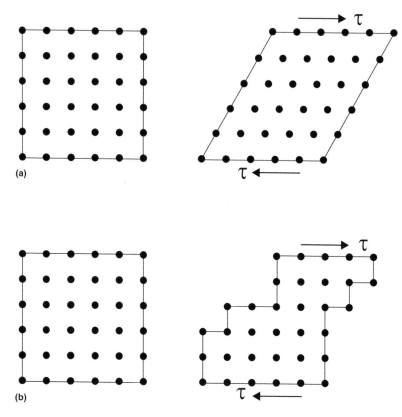

Fig. 4.30 Lattice structure during deformation. (a) Elastic deformation. (b) Plastic deformation

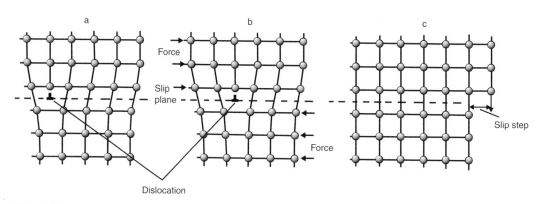

Fig. 4.31 Movement of an edge dislocation [Hou 93]

As slip continues the crystal rotates (Fig. 4.37). More and more slip systems then move into the 45° region and are activated (multiple slip).

In these additional slip systems, the dislocations that move have to cross the original ones and are trapped by them. These locations form defects at which following dislocations pile up.

Strengthening means that dislocation movement is made more difficult by these and other barriers during the deformation.

4.6.3 Polycrystals

A polycrystal can be considered to consist of several single crystals of different orientations.

a) Face-centered cubic, e.g. Cu, Al

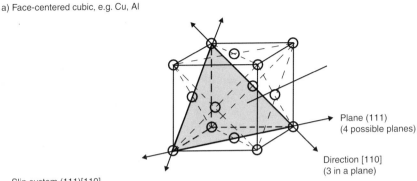

Plane (111)
(4 possible planes)

Direction [110]
(3 in a plane)

Slip system (111)[110]

b) Body-centered cubic, e.g. α-Fe

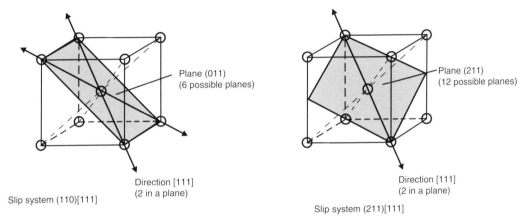

Plane (011)
(6 possible planes)

Direction [111]
(2 in a plane)

Slip system (110)[111]

Plane (211)
(12 possible planes)

Direction [111]
(2 in a plane)

Slip system (211)[111]

c) Close-packed hexagonal, e.g. Zn, α-Ti

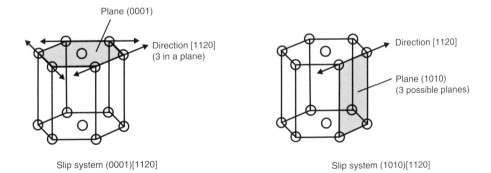

Plane (0001)

Direction [1120]
(3 in a plane)

Slip system (0001)[1120]

Direction [1120]

Plane (1010)
(3 possible planes)

Slip system (1010)[1120]

Fig. 4.32 Slip systems

Each single crystal will deform as discussed above in its principle slip system. The boundaries with the neighboring crystal, however, hinder this free movement.

In order to retain the cohesion between the individual deforming crystallites, at least five slip systems have to be active in each grain, which contributes to the strengthening.

Whereas in single crystals dislocation lines can disappear at the surface, they pile up at grain boundaries in polycrystals. If no grain boundary slip occurs, then the higher the number of grain

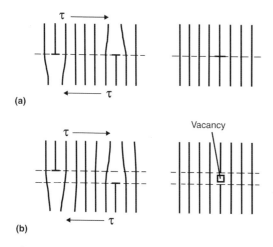

Fig. 4.33 Interaction of parallel dislocations of different signs. (a) Cancellation. (b) Formation of a vacancy

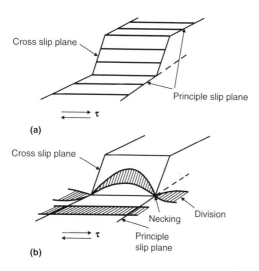

Fig. 4.34 Cross slip of a screw dislocation [Hou 93]. (a) Nondivided dislocation. (b) Split dislocation

boundaries, i.e., the finer the structure, the greater is the strengthening (Hall-Petch relationship).

Twins can form in individual grains during working to relieve the severe internal stresses formed during the deformation of polycrystals (Fig. 4.8).

With severe deformation of a polycrystal, the individual grains extend and align themselves by rotation so that crystal orientations accumulate in the deformed state in specific directions. This is referred to as a *deformation texture* described by Miller indices and pole figures (see Appendix, "Additional Information 2").

The deformation textures of different materials can vary. Also, different methods of deformation produce different textures. A rolling texture is not the same as a drawn texture.

Special *extrusion textures* occur when recrystallization during the extrusion process is completely or partially suppressed [Bag 81].

Textures also signify differences in the deformation behavior in different directions. In extruded bars that have not completely recrystallized, e.g., high-strength aluminum alloys, the strength in the extrusion direction is higher than in the transverse. This is referred to as the *extrusion effect*.

The stress-strain diagrams of polycrystalline materials frequently do not exhibit a marked yield point because individual favorably orientated grains start to flow earlier than others: the transition from the purely elastic to the plastic deformation state is thus smooth. The *0.2% deformation $R_{p0.2}$* is therefore defined as the "yield stress" at which a permanent deformation of 0.2% occurs. The pronounced yield point, which is seen not only in steels, is described in the following section.

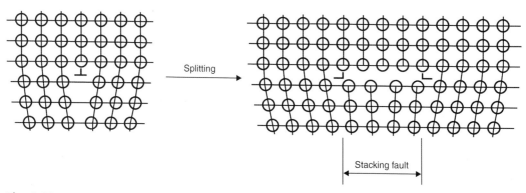

Fig. 4.35 Dislocation split by stacking defects

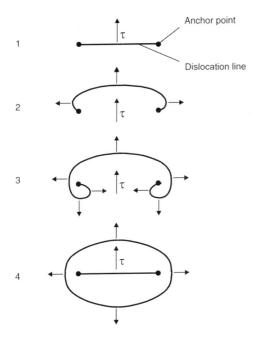

Fig. 4.36 Production of dislocations [Fra 50]

4.7 Deformation of Alloys at Room Temperature

The deformation, i.e., the movement of dislocations, can be hampered in many ways. Foreign atoms embedded in the solid solution or as secondary phases in the form of inclusions or precipitates and the self-producing obstructions from secondary slip systems described previously and neighboring grain boundaries.

In solid solution hardening, a substituted foreign atom in the base lattice causes a local distortion field the size of which increases the greater the difference between the atom radii.

However, even with the base and foreign atoms having approximately the same size, interactions still take place because the foreign atoms influence the bonding forces between the atoms.

The movement of dislocations is therefore hindered by the foreign atoms. Because they have to cross their stress fields—analogous to slip friction between two solid bodies—this is referred to as *solid-solution friction,* which increases the deformation resistance.

The higher mechanical properties of the so-called naturally hard aluminum alloys (AlMg, AlSi) are attributable to solid-solution friction.

The action of foreign atoms in solid solutions is relatively weak compared with the particle hardening described subsequently. The yield stress and the increase in strength, however, do increase significantly with the fraction of dissolved atoms (Fig. 4.38).

Even at slightly increased temperatures, foreign atoms can accumulate at dislocations by diffusion particularly where they reduce the stress field of the dislocation. A dislocation is anchored by these foreign metal clouds (Cottrell clouds) and can only be released and set in movement by higher forces, which produces a *marked yield stress.*

Interstitial foreign atoms, e.g., carbon in iron, move more easily than substitutional atoms. Carbon clouds around dislocations are the cause of the well-known marked yield point of carbon steels.

Particle Hardening. The second phases in an alloy can take on many different shapes, sizes, and distribution, which determine the effect of the particles on the dislocation movement.

Dislocations can pass through so-called *soft particles*; they are "cut" (Fig. 4.39a).

One part of such a particle is displaced by one atomic spacing in the same way as the entire

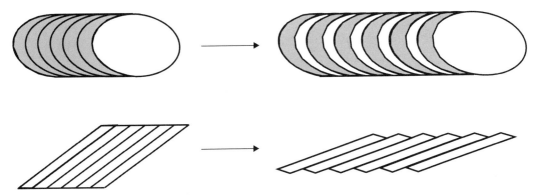

Fig. 4.37 Rotation of single crystal during deformation

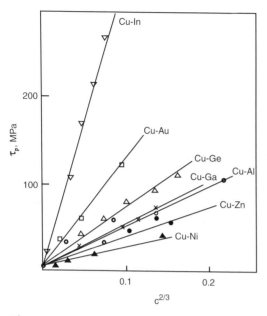

Fig. 4.38 Yield stress of single-phase copper alloys as a function of the content of foreign atoms

lattice along a slip plane. This requires the application of a higher force compared with dislocation movement through a single-phase lattice. The dislocation in the cutting process is therefore stretched like a rubber band and then relaxed after cutting. The greater the number of particles, the stronger is the effect. Only small coherent or approximately coherent precipitates in which the matrix and particle lattices have similar structures and orientations are cut.

An incoherent particle—which includes most precipitates—forms a barrier that cannot be overcome by cutting. The dislocation manages to go around these "hard particles" (Orowan process, Fig. 4.39b); as soon as a dislocation line has been stretched to such an extent that the positive and negative parts move close together, they meet and mutually cancel each other out. A dislocation ring remains around the particle, and this repels the following dislocation. This is because dislocations of the same sign mutually repel each other and those of the opposite sign attract. Therefore, with increasing deformation

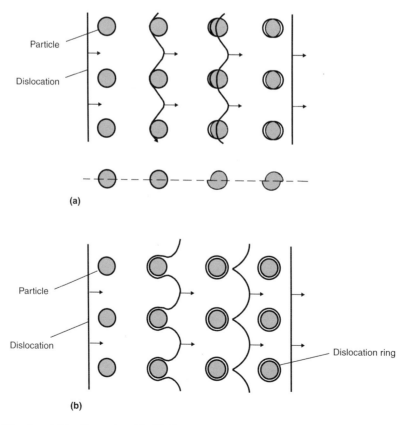

Fig. 4.39 Interaction of dislocations and particles [Ber 83]. (a) Intersection of "soft" particles. (b) Bypassing of "hard particles"

and thus an increasing number of dislocation rings around the particles, an additional type of hardening takes place. This is referred to as *precipitation hardening* or *dispersion hardening*.

The size of the particle does not influence this type of hardening, but their number and distribution do. The higher the number of particles that cannot be cut, the greater is the resistance to dislocation and thus the strengthening.

In hot age hardening, e.g., of a heat treatable AlMgSi alloy, as shown in Fig. 4.40, small and coherent particles of the second phase first form so that they can be cut. As the aging time increases, the particles become incoherent and increase in size and can no longer be cut, which increases the strength. If coagulation occurs after longer heat treatment, as described in Fig. 4.15, large particles grow at the expense of smaller ones and the number of particles decrease. The strength and hardening then reduce. This is known as *overaging.*

AlCu alloys, for example, exhibit an increase in strength even with cold age hardening (aging after solution heat treatment at room temperature) by the formation of coherent groups of copper atoms in so-called Guinier-Preston (GP) zones. They redissolve, however, during subsequent hot age hardening before the hot-age-hardening phases form.

Targeted alloy development and heat treatment enabled extremely high-strength materials with specific deformation properties to be de-veloped. In addition to solid-solution hardening and precipitation hardening, they involve the inclusion of foreign particles as dispersions, e.g., by powder metallurgical processes.

4.8 Higher Temperatures with Pure Metals

As the temperature increases, the thermal movement of the atoms in the crystal increases, which increases the ease of transposition processes by, for example, diffusion.

The *climb of edge dislocations* also takes place (Fig. 4.41). In this process, complete atomic rows are removed or added; the dislocations are thus moved into another parallel slip plane. The climbing, therefore, naturally is only activated when it results in a reduction in the internal stresses and thus to a lowering of the internal energy of the crystal. This can take place by positive and negative dislocations mutually canceling each other and thus reducing the dislocation accumulation.

4.8.1 Annealing of Pure Metals

The first step in stress reduction by annealing of a deformation hardened structure is *recovery*. The crystallites retain their shape and orientation.

Dislocation freed from their forced location by climb and cross slip mutually cancel each

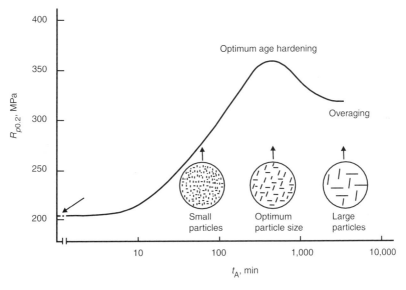

Fig. 4.40 Yield stress of age-hardening aluminum alloy as a function of the aging time [Blu 93]

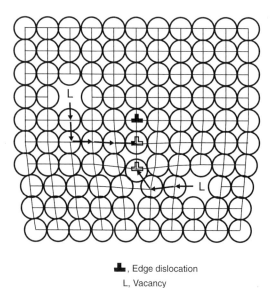

⊥, Edge dislocation
L, Vacancy

Fig. 4.41 Climb of an edge dislocation [Sch 81]

other out, as described previously (positive and negative dislocations), or move and accumulate in low stress subgrain boundaries, which are composed of a chain of dislocations of the same sign.

After recovery heat treatment an entire network of these subgrain boundaries is found— this is referred to as *polygonization* of the crystallite (Fig. 4.42). The orientation of the resulting subgrains differ only slightly from each other. The interior of the subgrains is practically dislocation free.

During recovery the internal stresses are not completely eliminated because there is still a high volume of dislocations in the subgrain boundaries.

Stacking faults hinder not only cross slip but also the climb of dislocations and thus the recovery of metals. Low stacking fault energy metals, i.e., large stacking faults such as copper, nickel, and austenitic steels, therefore exhibit a low tendency to recovery. On the other hand, aluminum and alpha iron with high stacking fault energies and thus small stacking faults easily form subgrains during suitable heat treatment and therefore recover.

If a deformed structure is heat treated at a high temperature, recrystallization takes place. New grains that are largely free of dislocations and thus subgrains are formed during this process. The structure is free of internal stresses and therefore annealed. The deformation behavior largely corresponds with the undeformed cast structure.

Figure 4.43 shows schematically how a healed recrystallized grain grows into a dislocation rich work-hardened lattice.

Recrystallization usually occurs during a suitable heat treatment of a deformed metal without preceding recovery by nucleation after an incubation time.

The nucleation is followed by the growth of a grain that is sustained as primary recrystallization until all the deformed crystals have disappeared. In the subsequent secondary recrystallization (large grain formation), large grains grow at the expense of small recrystallized grains. The internal energy is reduced further by the shortening of the total grain-boundary surface. This is usually undesirable because of the associated irregular grain size [Alt 94].

Figure 4.44 shows the typical recrystallization process with time. As can be seen, after the incubation time there is initially a flat profile during the nucleation and a steep increase during the primary recrystallization. The gradient of the curve decreases with the subsequent secondary recrystallization.

The recrystallization nuclei form mainly at regions of high dislocation density. These can occur at grain boundaries between relatively undeformed original grains. Precipitates can also act as recrystallization nuclei [Wei 94, McQ 75].

During primary recrystallization, these nuclei grow by thermally activated migration of the grain boundaries into the work-hardened structure and consume it. The number of newly formed largely defect-free grains correspond to the number of nuclei capable of development.

Fig. 4.42 Subgrain formation in Al99.99 (hot strip). The width is approximately 8.4 μm [Grz 93]

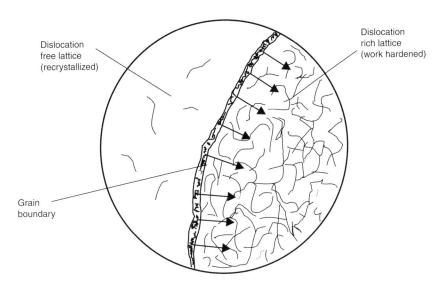

Fig. 4.43 Growth of recrystallized grain

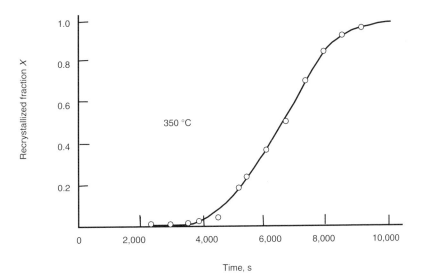

Fig. 4.44 Variation with time of recrystallization (Al99.5 after 5.1% tensile deformation) [And 48]

The rate of migration of the new grain boundaries and thus the rate of recrystallization is the greater the larger the preceding deformation and thus the larger the energy stored in the deformed structure. Naturally, a higher temperature promotes the grain-boundary migration and increases the rate of recrystallization.

Recovery preceding recrystallization, e.g., at low heat treatment temperatures, that has reduced the deformation energy stored in lattice by sub grain formation hinders recrystallization. In metals with high stacking fault energies like aluminum, it can even be completely suppressed by recovery—at low heat treatment temperatures and small deformation.

The recrystallization temperature above which recrystallization can be expected is usually related to the melting point of a metal:

$$T_{recr} \cong 0.6 \cdot T_s [°K]$$

This recrystallization temperature should not be considered unequivocal.

With deformed brass CuZn37, for example, the softening from recrystallization after high deformation starts at 400 °C but only at 500 °C after low deformation. With pure aluminum after 98% deformation recrystallization commences at 300 °C and at 400 °C after 20% deformation [Alt 94].It is, therefore, more correct to refer to a *recrystallization interval* instead of a recrystallization temperature.

If a structure textured by deformation is given a recrystallization heat treatment, the new structure can also exhibit preferred orientation, a so-called *recrystallization texture*. One cause can be that grains of a specific orientation in the deformed structure are less deformed than others. Nuclei of preferred orientation then grow from them into the severely deformed grains.

Deformation and recrystallization textures are closely related to each other but usually differ. Recrystallization textures are also characteristic for the deformation process and for the relevant lattice structure (e.g., AlCuMg [Moc 75]).

4.8.2 Deformation of Pure Metals at High Temperatures

If a pure metal is deformed at a higher temperature, both the yield stress and the work hardening are reduced (Fig. 4.45).

As the temperature increases, the dislocations can start to migrate through their slip systems at lower shear stresses due to thermal activation, which reduces the yield stress. The work hardening—that is, the gradient of the strength curve—is reduced because the vacancy diffusion at higher temperatures is also eased and hence piled up dislocations can move to energetically more favorable positions during the deformation by cross slip and climb. This means that recovery processes can proceed with the formation of a substructure during the work-hardening—and not only after heat treatment following cold working [Mug 84]. This is called *dynamic recovery*.

If deformation is carried out quickly enough at a high temperature, the work hardening can be so high despite the start of recovery that recrystallization can take place even during the deformation—this process is frequently observed in the extrusion of specific materials. It is referred to as *dynamic recrystallization* [Got 84].

The stacking fault energy plays an important role in the boundary between recovery and recrystallization during hot working.

High stacking fault energies and thus fewer divided dislocations occur in bcc alloys (e.g., α-iron, β-brass) as well as in certain fcc alloys (e.g., aluminum). In these cases, the cross slip and climb needed for subgrain formation and recovery is easier—recovery is more likely to take place in these cases in preference to recrystallization during hot working. Low stacking fault energies associated with large divided dislocations are found with a few other fcc lattices (e.g., copper and copper alloys). In these cases, recovery is more difficult, and dynamic recrystallization processes simplified during hot working.

The strength reducing recovery and recrystallization processes during hot working can take place so quickly after reaching a specific work hardening that there is equilibrium between softening and work hardening and the hardening curve remains horizontal (static case). Naturally, the dynamic recovery processes also result in a delay in the fracture-initiating mechanisms (see section 4.11), and the elongation to failure in tensile tests increases with increasing temperature.

If the events occurring within the structure in hot working are studied, it is clear that these processes depend not only on the temperature but also on the rate of deformation.

The slower the deformation rate, the greater is the time for the recovery and recrystallization processes to counteract the work hardening from the multiplication and piling up of dislocations. The work-hardening curve is, therefore, flatter and its horizontal leg lower the slower the deformation rate. At a fast rate of deformation, a relatively high flow stress has to be expected. This explains the high dependence of the deformation resistance on the rate of deformation in

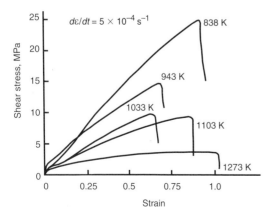

Fig. 4.45 Work-hardening curves of copper single crystals as a function of temperature [Got 84]

hot working compared with cold working (Fig. 4.46).

The dependence of the flow stress on the temperature and the deformation rate in hot working is discussed in section 3 in the Appendix, "Additional Information 3," in this chapter.

The stress-strain curves obtained from torsion tests cover a much larger strain to failure than tensile tests because of the largely tensile-stress-free deformation.

They are therefore more suitable for assessing the behavior of metals in practical hot working, in particular extrusion, which also does not involve any tensile stress (Fig. 4.47) [Fie 57, Ake 66].

The hot stress-strain curves obtained from torsion tests exhibit after the initial increase, in which the number of dislocations and the internal stresses increase significantly, a large stationary region with hardly any additional work hardening. The work-hardening and recovery processes are in balance. The stress-strain curve starts to fall only when structural defects result in fracture.

Usually, no recrystallization occurs during the hot deformation of aluminum and many of its alloys. Subgrains are more likely to develop by recovery and their shape and size hardly change during the stationary region. If the load is removed and the temperature maintained or slow cooling permitted, recrystallization can occur—delayed significantly by the low internal energy. One example is the recrystallization during extrusion of low-alloyed aluminum alloys after leaving the die [McQ 90].

4.9 Alloys at Higher Temperatures

4.9.1 Annealing of Alloys

In the annealing of deformed alloys—from the point of view of the deformation energy—in which there is thermal equilibrium at the annealing temperature, recovery and recrystallization processes play the main role as with pure metals. However, with single-phase alloys, the thermal activation of the climb and cross slip processes initiating thermal activation is more difficult because of the presence of foreign atoms. This also applies to the migration of grain boundaries during recrystallization because grain boundaries are frequently enriched with dissolved atoms and have to be torn away from them.

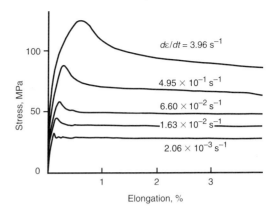

Fig. 4.46 Strain-rate dependence in hot working (stress-strain curves of nickel) [San 75]

If the second phase exists in the form of fine precipitates (in the range of 0.04–0.4 μm diam), these also tend to retard recrystallization because they can exert a significant resistance to the necessary migration of grain boundaries, particularly where they accumulate. This can occur to such an extent that at a moderate annealing temperature recrystallization can be completely suppressed and only recovery takes place. The strength then does not fall completely during annealing and the deformation texture remains.

With two-phase alloys with large crystallites of the second phase, it is possible that only one phase with a low recrystallization temperature recrystallizes during the annealing process, whereas the second phase remains unrecrystallized.

Still more complicated is the case when a deformed alloy is in thermal unequilibrium during annealing. Softening processes then occur by recovery and recrystallization simultaneously with precipitation processes (or, in rare cases, dissolution processes) of second phases [McQ 90, McQ 90a]. The dependence of the mechanical properties on the annealing conditions is therefore complicated and difficult to explain.

There are more vacancies in deformed metals than in undeformed metals, which simplifies the diffusion of foreign atoms to precipitates. Therefore, the precipitation processes during annealing take place more quickly in the deformed structure than in the undeformed state.

It is possible today to construct high-strength materials in which specific alloy composition, heat treatment and deformation precipitation hardening and work hardening are combined without any significant softening processes tak-

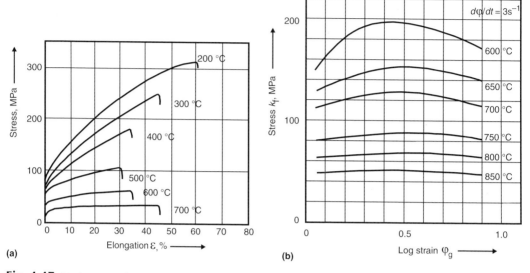

Fig. 4.47 Hot low curves for CuZn8 obtained from different methods. (a) Hot-tensile tests. (b) Torsion tests [Bau 63, DGM 78]

ing place during the permitted time at the intended working temperature [Ber 83].

4.9.2 Deformation of Alloys at Higher Temperatures

In single-phase alloys, the embedded foreign atoms hinder the migration of dislocations as in cold working but also impair dynamic recovery and recrystallization. The hot yield stress, work hardening, and hot strength increase with increasing foreign atom content (Fig. 4.48).

Precipitates, which retard static recrystallization, also naturally hinder dynamic recrystallization processes. Hot-strength curves are therefore steeper with alloys with precipitates and attain the stationary (horizontal) state later or at a higher temperature.

The high hot strength of high-alloy materials naturally makes hot working more difficult and thus materials "more difficult to extrude."

Because, as described above, a high vacancy concentration accelerates the process of precipitation processes, the rate of precipitation increases during the hot working of an alloy not in equilibrium.

The factors that determine whether and at what rate recovery and recrystallization takes place during hot working are the same as those governing annealing after previous cold working.

4.10 Processes in Extrusion

Billet heating before extrusion cannot be considered to be independent of the previous hot processes—casting, hot forging, or homogenization. In addition, the temperature and time of heating are determined by various, often conflicting, requirements:

- Low extrusion pressure
- High extrusion speed
- Limitation of the exit temperature to a maximum (surface quality) and to a minimum (recrystallization, with aluminum alloys solution heat treatment during extrusion).

When determining the preheat temperature, the deformation heat during extrusion (increasing the extrusion temperature) and the heat flow into the tooling (reducing the extrusion temperature) have to be taken into account.

If nonhomogenized billets of age-hardening alloys are used, the homogenizing effect during billet heating increases the longer it lasts. In this case, slower gas furnace heating is more effective than fast induction heating. Not only can segregations harmful to extrusion be reduced, but also precipitates dissolved and supersaturations reduced.

In contrast, previously homogenized billets of suitable aluminum alloys cooled to a specified

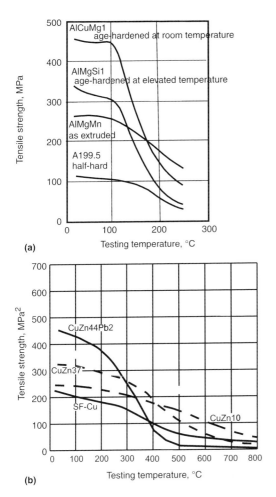

(a)

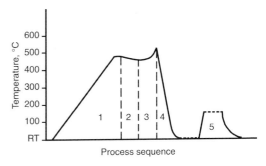

Fig. 4.49 Temperature variation in the processing of age-hardening aluminum alloys by extrusion. 1, Heating the billet; 2, transfer to the press; 3, extrusion = heating from the deformation = solution heat treatment; 4, section cooling; 5, elevated temperature age hardening. RT, room temperature [Alt 94]

(b)

Fig. 4.48 Hot tensile strength of different alloys. (a) Aluminum alloy. (b) Brasses [Alt 94, Wie 86]

degree of solubility have to be heated as quickly as possible and not too high in order not to destroy the desired structure. Induction heating is then recommended.

It is possible with AlMgSi alloys and CuCr and CuCrZr alloys to carry out extrusion at the solution annealing temperature and thus avoid a separate solution heat treatment prior to age hardening (Fig. 4.49).

With brass CuZn39Pb, which has an α-β structure at room temperature, the billet heating can develop a structure corresponding to the phase diagram (see the section "Extrusion of Semifinished Products in Copper Alloys," Fig. 5.51 in Chapter 5), in which the α brass that has poor hot-working properties is dissolved and only the readily hot-worked β brass is present.

The surface of the extruded billet quickly develops the temperature of the container liner wall, which at approximately 500 °C is cooler than materials extruded at moderate and high temperatures. There are materials—such as the free machining brass CuZn39Pb in which the surface cooling of the billet increases the content of the difficult-to-deform α brass—where the flow behavior close to the container wall drastically changes. The β-rich core then flows forward and the α-rich periphery is held back, resulting in the extrusion piping defect (see "Extrusion of Semifinished Products in Copper Alloys," Fig. 5.56, in Chapter 5).

Dynamic and recrystallization processes take place in front of and in the deformation zone of the die during extrusion. The stacking fault energy of the extruded metal plays an important role here. With a low stacking fault energy (copper, α-brass, austenite), dynamic recrystallization occurs in the extrusion deformation zone of the extrusion press at moderate and high extrusion speeds. On the other hand, aluminum and its alloys with a high stacking fault energy can repeatedly only recover—the extrusion leaves the press soft but with a fibrous unrecrystallized structure. However, in some cases, recrystallization processes can occur in the hot extrusion after it leaves the die.

The sketch in Fig. 4.50 schematically shows the influence of the high and low stacking fault energy.

In the shear zones (at the liner wall, at the funnel of the dead metal zones in flat dies and within hollow dies) the deformation in aluminum is up to 60 times larger than in the core [Ake 92].

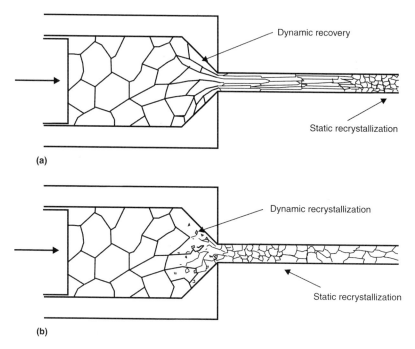

Fig. 4.50 Dynamic recovery and recrystallization processes in extrusion. (a) High stacking fault energy. (b) Low stacking fault energy [McQ 75]

If the fibers with higher deformation (e.g., close to the surface of the extruded section) are very elongated and thin (width approximately two subgrains), adjacent grains can grow together and the fibers appear shorter [McQ 90].

The grain structure, however, is so severely distorted in the shear zones that no grain boundaries are visible under the microscope and the precipitates present are randomly distributed. AlMgSi0.5 sections recrystallize with fine grains but only *after* leaving the die (static and not dynamic).

In alloys with recrystallization retarding additions (e.g., AlMgSi or AlCuMg with additions of Mn, Cr, or Zr), the recrystallization temperature is raised to such a level that no recrystallization occurs even after leaving the deformation zone (particularly following rapid cooling).

However, subsequent solution heat treatment reveals that the peripheral zone from the shear zone is more heavily deformed than the core and, therefore, statically recrystallizes, often with very coarse grains, whereas the more weakly deformed core remains unrecrystallized.

The unrecrystallized structures usually have a strong texture because of the high deformation in the extrusion press, whereby the strength in the longitudinal direction is much higher than in

the transverse direction. This is referred to as the *extrusion effect*.

Recrystallization retarding additions in suitable aluminum alloys can, however, precipitate coarsely during annealing at high temperatures (defective homogenization, billet heating in a gas furnace). A second phase that has no effect on the recrystallization then forms (e.g., manganese in AlMgSi). Then the aluminum material can, as described earlier for AlMgSi0.5, fully recrystallize after leaving the die—while the section is still hot.

In the production of aluminum sections with a decorative surface, structural variations and textures can produce flecks and stripes. Because only the zone immediately below the surface of the section plays a role, attention has to be paid not only to the billet production (see section 4.2.4) but also to the die design. The procedures that have to be taken into account in the manufacture of aluminum sections are described in detail in the section "Extrusion of Semifinished Products in Aluminum Alloys" in Chapter 5.

Independent of the material, in extrusion without lubrication the zones close to the surface of the extruded zone are hotter than the core because of the concentration of the deformation in the shear zone and the friction between the die land and the material. However, at the surface this friction also produces tensile stresses as the core of the extrusion accelerates. It is therefore no surprise that the billets with residual melt segregations with low melting points produce crack-sensitive extrusions. If these segregations are not previously eliminated by homogenization, the only option is to extrude at low temperatures and slow speeds. This prevents the temperature of the section surface from reaching the dangerous region of melting, which results in transverse cracks (see the section "Extrusion of Semifinished Products in Copper Alloys," Fig. 5.45, in Chapter 5).

In the extrusion of copper alloys and steels, spontaneous recrystallization usually takes place during the deformation as the extrusion temperature is well above the recrystallization temperature (which is 0.8–0.9 times the melting point T_S). It can happen that the start of extrusion, where the deformation is low and the temperature high, has a coarse secondary recrystallized structure, but the end of extrusion—where the deformation is high and the exit temperature lower due to cooling during extrusion—is fine grained.

In pure (and low-alloyed) copper so few recrystallization retarding precipitates are present that the grain boundaries migrate relatively easily. After the primary recrystallization in the deformation zone, a secondary coarse recrystallization has to be expected in the emerging extrusion (at 800–900 °C). Rapid cooling is used directly behind the die to prevent this.

4.11 Toughness, Fracture

The toughness of a material is—for the same temperature and the same deformation rate—dependent on the deformation conditions. For example, in a tensile test the toughness defining elongation to fracture is relatively low, but in the torsion test in which the deforming elements are subjected to other forces, it can be higher. In particular, in extrusion with its high hydrostatic contribution to the deforming loads much higher deformations can be achieved than in the simple tensile test. The phenomena occurring in the tensile test up to fracture should be understood (Fig. 4.51). A more detailed explanation is found in [Rie 87].

4.11.1 Ductile Fracture

In metal working the most common type of failure is ductile fracture following deformation. As a rule, the deformed metal is not defect free. During the deformation in the tensile test, initially small voids form at internal boundary surfaces with low adhesion, e.g., at inclusions, coarse precipitates or at existing gas pores, where the stress concentration becomes high enough during the working. Only very pure metals deform in tensile tests without this void formation.

The cross section of the tensile specimen in the region of the voids is reduced. The tensile force therefore exerts a higher stress, which leads to higher elongation in this zone, resulting in a localized necking. Once the necking has started this area continues to reduce in cross section as the stress increases, whereas the sections of the specimen that have not necked elongate only slightly. Soon the pores in the necked zone increase in size and grow together until fracture occurs between them. The fracture surfaces are rough and consist of craterlike depressions, each corresponding to an original void. The ductile fracture usually passes through the grains and is therefore transcrystalline.

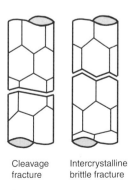
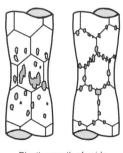
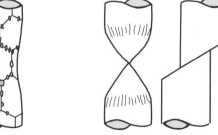

| Cleavage fracture | Intercrystalline brittle fracture | Plastic growth of voids (transcrystalline) (intercrystalline) | Cracking from necking or shearing |

Fig. 4.51 Different failure methods (in tensile testing) [Ash 79]

At higher temperatures, as discussed previously, the yield stress and the work hardening are reduced by the onset of the recovery processes. This means that the stress needed to nucleate the voids, e.g., at inclusions, is first reached after a higher deformation. The elongation to fracture can then increase.

However, at higher temperatures the flow stress and the work hardening react more sensitively to the deformation rate, and accordingly the fracture behavior varies at higher speeds. As a rule, the elongation to fracture decreases as the rate of deformation increases.

Grain-boundary decoration by foreign atoms or inclusions and thin films of segregations can weaken the grain boundaries at high temperatures to such an extent that the crack propagates in an intercrystalline manner.

4.11.2 Brittle Fracture and Mixed Types

Pure deformation-free brittle fracture is rare; more common is low-deformation brittle fracture. Neither of these fracture types occurs during extrusion. Their explanation does, however, increase the understanding of the possible fracture processes.

At sufficiently low temperatures most metals fail without or with only slight deformation by brittle fracture. The starting point is a crack that is already present or forms after slight plastic deformation. The tip of this crack acts as a notch; i.e., a high stress concentrates here under a tensile load, which, when the so-called crack propagation stress is exceeded, results in a deformation free or low deformation cleavage fracture. The fracture surfaces are smooth.

With increasing temperature, the stress peak that forms at the initial crack under load is reduced by local deformation so that the crack propagation stress is reached only after higher work hardening, in other words, higher plastic deformation. The tendency to brittle fracture reduces with increasing temperature or disappears completely.

The cleavage fracture propagates along surfaces with low cohesion. If these are specific crystallographic planes, then the fracture is transcrystalline. With weakened grain boundaries attributed to higher temperatures or accumulated foreign atoms, segregations, or precipitations the fracture propagates between the grains and is thus intercrystalline. Frequently, a fracture shows both transcrystalline and intercrystalline components.

If the deformation is carried out at such a high temperature that existing segregations start to melt, an almost completely brittle fracture occurs.

4.11.3 Fracture during Hot-Working

The processes leading to fracture are now explained using hot torsion tests. Torsion tests correspond more closely to the processes in extrusion, but only a few suitable measured results are available.

Elongation and necking traverse in hot-torsion tests one or two minima. The examples of E-copper and of phosphorous containing tin bronze illustrate this (Fig. 4.52). With E-copper (Fig. 4.52a), the elongation to fracture and the necking initially reduce with increasing temperature (up to a minimum of approximately 500 °C) and then increase. As the temperature increases, severe grain-boundary cracks form perpendicular to the tensile direction. They form and grow by the migration of vacancies to the grain boundaries associated ultimately with weakening due to grain-boundary accumulation. Above the minimum temperature, where the elongation to fracture increases again, the processes of recovery and, in particular, recrystallization occur. Existing voids are dissolved and the susceptibility to fracture reduced.

A second minimum similar to that seen with 8% tin bronze (Fig. 4.52b) can be related to the effect of segregations that have a high mobility and readily melt [Bau 63]. In the example of the tin bronze it is a low melting point phosphorus containing phase on the grain boundaries.

4.11.4 Defects in Extrusion

Tensile stresses are usually required for crack formation and propagation. High shear stresses can also result in cracks—referred to as shear cracks.

In extrusion, the material in the die deformation zone is under three-dimensional compression. Only when it has passed through the die will the tensile stress developed close to the surface by the friction on the die bearing have an effect. The magnitude of this tensile stress depends on the friction and the die design. In lubricated extrusion (glass lubrication with steel and nickel alloys, hydrostatic extrusion) it is lower than in unlubricated (aluminum) or if only a flat die is lubricated (copper). The tensile stresses at the surface of the extruded section

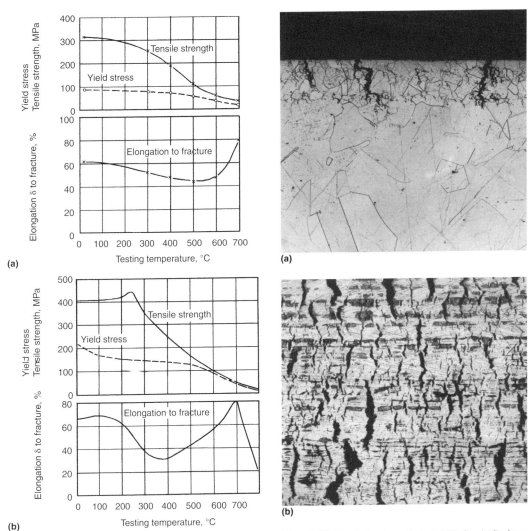

Fig. 4.52 Elongation to fracture as a function of temperature in tensile tests. (a) E-copper. (b) Tin-bronze CuSn8

Fig. 4.53 Cracked surface of a CuZn28Sn (longitudinal section/surface image). (a) The width is approximately 0.66 mm. (b) The width is approximately 1.4 mm [Die 77]

combined with the temperature increase in the peripheral zone result in transverse cracks (fir tree defect) if an existing grain-boundary accumulation is severely weakened or even melted. Under the microscope these grain-boundary accumulations can be detected along with the predominantly intercrystalline nature of the cracks (Fig. 4.53).

Internal cracks in tubes have the same origin: if the friction between the material and the mandrel is high enough at the extrusion temperature to destroy the cohesion between grain boundaries transverse to the direction of extrusion, transverse cracks will form on the internal surface of the tube.

At a small extrusion ratio the core accelerates so quickly during extrusion relative to the surface zone that the shear stresses are sufficient to separate a surface shell from the core. This also requires correspondingly weakened zones.

With very small extrusion ratios, conical-shaped transverse cracks can develop because tensile stresses can occur along the billet axis before the die plane. These can result in voids and cracks at the affected areas.

Both types of defects—the peeling of a surface shell from the core and the core cracking—cannot be detected on the surface. Materials at risk must be tested using nondestructive methods when necessary.

4.12   Solid-State Bonding

Materials can bond together under pressure and at an elevated temperature without macroscopic shape changes (diffusion bonding). However, at least one of the bonding partners has to undergo a significant compressive deformation (compression, rolling, extrusion).

The bonding processes that occur during deformation is the reason for the use of the extrusion process in many cases.

The weld seams in hollow profiles, the production of composite profiles and the processing of composite materials as well as the extrusion of metal powders are discussed in this section.

4.12.1   Bonding Processes

The most common methods of joining two components are welding and soldering. In both cases the liquid phase takes the dominant role. In welding, the boundary layer between the components melts. The resolidified melt forms the "weld seam." In soldering, both the parts remain in the solid state, only the solder between them melts and solidifies. The joint is formed by adhesion and diffusion at the boundary surface.

When bonding in the solid state—referred to as *pressure welding*—the formation of a liquid phase usually is not required. The most common methods are roll cladding, friction welding, and ultrasonic welding (more information on pressure welding is found in [Tyl 68].

If two metallic surfaces meet, they can bond together if the surface atoms of both components are approximately a lattice spacing apart. The faces then act as a grain boundary and the metallic bonding forces of the electron gases act across the boundary surfaces. Experience shows that this adhesion process rarely occurs without the contribution of pressure and temperature. Absolutely flat and clean boundary surfaces are required and it is made easier or possible at all if the two components pressed together have identical, or similar, lattice structures.

A higher surface pressure always flattens very small irregularities and improves by plastic deformation of the roughness peaks the contact between the components pressed together over the maximum contact area. With pure aluminum the pressure welding commences after only 10% deformation of the two surface areas; however, it is only after 70% that the tear resistance of the joint matches the value of the parent metal.

At a higher temperature, this flattening and smearing together of the two surfaces is simplified, atoms changing places with each other can fit with the opposing lattice so well that the bond between the atoms at the boundary surface is optimized. There are hypotheses that the dislocations stacked together by pressure welding can traverse the boundary surface into the other partner.

Any existing coatings, e.g., fine oxide skins or films of lubricant, hinder any adhesive bond. If the areas of the components being bonded are increased during the bonding process, e.g., in roll cladding or extrusion, brittle coatings such as oxides cannot follow this expansion. Instead, they break up into individual pieces. Fresh metal forms between the pieces on the surface and this can now bond with the opposite side. Pressure welding requires both high pressure and a large deformation and thus an increase in the surface area. Since, in roll cladding and extrusion through a hollow section die there is also relevant movement between the two partners and frequently polyganization or even recrystallization occurs by recovery processes the grains orientate themselves into matching positions. If the bond is very good, it is impossible to detect the joint under the microscope (see Fig. 4.55).

If the surface coating can follow the increase in the contacting areas, i.e., smear, then bonding is not possible during the contacting process. One example is the damaging effect of lubricant in the extrusion of hollow aluminum alloy sections. This can prevent the formation of a sound pressure weld.

4.12.2   The Formation of Pressure Welds in Hollow Sections and during Billet-on-Billet Extrusion

If hollow sections are produced using bridge or porthole dies as described in Chapter 5, in the section on the extrusion of aluminum alloys, the divided strands bond together in the welding chamber immediately in front of the die into two or more longitudinal seams. These are not welds, as sometimes stated, but metallic bonds from solid-state adhesion. In these die zones, which are more correctly referred to as *bonding chambers,* the high transverse forces—almost equal to the hydrostatic pressure in the undeformed billet—act on the surfaces of the divided strands producing an increase in the surface area by the reduction of the cross section in the chamber. The adiabatic heating from the deformation also plays a role. The strands that are separated just prior to the bonding—and with the exclusion of

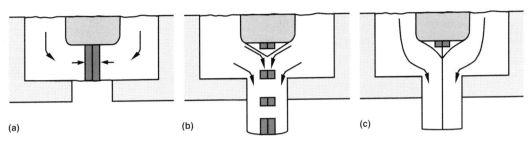

Fig. 4.54 Breakup of the surface layer in longitudinal welds in the production of aluminum hollow sections. (a) Meeting under the leg. (b) Breaking apart. (c) Clean longitudinal weld [Ake 92]

air—are free of any oxide or lubricant surface coating, assuming a clean die is used, that would hinder the bonding.

Oxide is brought into the welding chambers of the die only during the first filling when the free oxide coated end faces come together (Fig. 4.54a) [Ake 92]. The fractured remains of the oxide surface are mostly carried away with the first part of the section (Fig. 4.54b). The subsequent bonding takes place between material regions that have initially been compressed in front of the legs of the mandrel and have then flowed with extreme shearing along the flanks of the leg and combined at the dead metal zones beneath the legs. The strands that come together are free of any oxide film. The process of welding then consists merely of the initially small contact surfaces being extended over the entire length of the section and thus being increased by several orders of magnitude. Subgrains then form continuously even over the original contact surfaces. This repolygonization is linked to the movement of dislocations but does not require any atom diffusion.

In addition, the material recrystallizes usually in the deformation zone (e.g., copper) or immediately on leaving the die (e.g., AlMgSi0.5) so that the newly formed grains grow away from the contact faces freshly bonded by adhesion and heal them.

The contact faces that equate to a severely distorted grain boundary disappear during this recrystallization and cannot be identified under the microscope (Fig. 4.55).

The suitability for producing hollow sections varies from material to material. There are even differences between aluminum alloys, which appear to be predestined for hollow section production. Numerous precipitates or phase segregations with foreign lattice structures can impair the bonding. The hot strength of the high-strength materials can be so high that the large degree of deformation required to produce sufficient pressure in the bonding chamber is not reached and the use of hollow section dies made difficult or even impossible. Finally, with materials that do not recrystallize at the extrusion temperature, there is no possibility of healing the voids in the bonds by recrystallization [Ake 92a].

There are, however, cases where defects in the bonds occur even with materials well suited for hollow section extrusion. These problems are discussed in more detail in Chapter 5.

With copper and brass, which are extruded in the temperature range 600 to 900°C, the danger of separating oxides flowing in is greater than with aluminum alloys. This is one of the reasons why extrusion of these materials through hollow section dies is usually avoided (see Chapter 7, the section on tooling for copper alloys).

The ability of aluminum alloys to bond by pressure welding is not only utilized in the production of hollow sections but also in billet-on-

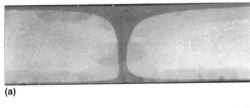

(a)

(b)

Fig. 4.55 Extrusion weld in aluminum. (a) Different etchant attack. (b) Full recrystallization across the weld [Ake 92]

billet extrusion where transverse welds form (Fig. 4.56).

There is—however rarely used—the case where the billet is extruded onto the discard of the previous billet (Fig. 4.56a). This is successful only after careful cleaning of the surfaces of the end faces and the removal of air to avoid blisters and material separation in the extrusion. This process is used in aluminum cable sheathing (see section 3.6 in Chapter 3).

With aluminum alloys, the discard is usually sheared off (solid section dies and porthole dies, Fig. 4.56c) or pulled off (bridge dies, Fig. 4.56d) before the next billet is extruded. If a solid section is extruded through a flat die, then a "feeder chamber" is normally used (Fig. 4.56b). The residue of the first billet remaining in this feeder chamber behaves in the same way as the residue in a hollow section die after removal of the discard. It can bond by adhesion with the subsequent billet. This usually occurs because the different flow conditions between the regions close to the surface and the core of the section result in the material of the next billet flowing as a tongue into the material from the preceding billet so that the contact surfaces are extensively increased.

4.12.3 Composite Extrusion

Composite extrusion is used to produce sections from two or more different materials, usually with a constant cross-sectional distribution over the entire length. The process and practical applications are given in Chapter 5 in the section "Extrusion of Semifinished products from Metallic Composite Materials." This section covers the mechanism of the bonding of two materials during extrusion.

Numerous metals react so severely at the high extrusion temperatures required by adhesion with the extrusion tooling that the latter is immediately destroyed unless protective measures are taken (See section 4.12.5).

This attack of the extrusion tooling and oxidation of the hot billet can be avoided by cladding the billet of the reactive material (Be, Ti, Zr, Hf, V, Nb, Ta) with copper or iron. Even alloy steel can be clad for specific purposes with mild steel, an aluminum alloy with pure aluminum, or even aluminum with copper to give just a few examples.

To ensure that a solid bond forms between the sheath and the billet by pressure welding, both carefully degreased components must undergo such severe deformation in the deformation zone (at least 50%) that any brittle surface coating present (oxide) breaks up and pure metals contact each other.

The diffusion of atoms across the boundary surface can simplify the bonding by transposition processes. On the other hand, these diffusion processes can also result in the formation of undesired alloy layers at the contacting surfaces. In the worst cases, a low-melting-point secondary phase can form from the atoms of the two components. Table 4.1 lists these low-melting-point phases in the corresponding binary system base material-cladding. The extrusion temperature must not exceed these limits [Ric 69].

If intermetallic brittle phases form by diffusion during the pressure welding between the sheath and the base material (e.g., between zirconium and iron), this is not always detrimental because the bond zone can be kept extremely thin.

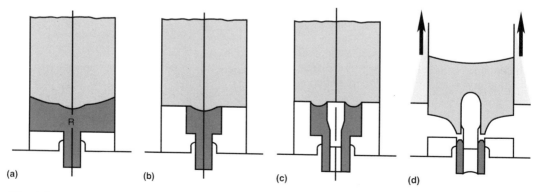

Fig. 4.56 Extrusion of aluminum "billet-on-billet" [Ake 92]. (a) Extrusion of a billet on the discard in the container. (b) With feeder die. (c) In the ports of a porthole die. (d) Pulling off the discard in a bridge die [Ake 92]

Table 4.1 Liquid phases between the cladding and the billet

Element	Melting point, °C	Transformation point, °C	Lowest temperature for the formation of liquid phases (°C) with		
			Copper	Nickel	Iron
Beryllium	1280	. . .	850	1157	1165
Titanium	1720	882	885	942	1085
Zirconium	1860	862	885	961	934
Vanadium	1900	. . .	. . .	1203	1468
Niobium	2410	. . .	1080	1175	1360
Tantalum	3000	. . .	1080	1360	1410

Source: [Ric 69]

It is not only the intermetallic phases that form during extrusion that can damage the surface zone of the extruded base material to such an extent that different properties exist relative to the core after removal of the cladding, e.g., corrosion susceptibility. The formation of a solid solution between the cladding material and the base metal can also result in the same problems. The selection of the cladding material and the extrusion parameters must, therefore, be carefully considered.

Other types of composite materials are produced so that a second or third material in the form of bar is added to the billet. Super conductors or contact wires can be produced by placing suitable bars or wires into holes in a copper billet. This is then extruded.

In certain cases extrusion is carried out with the knowledge that intermetallic phases will form between two adjacent materials, e.g., to achieve a high wear resistance or super conducting properties [Web 82].

There is also composite extrusion between two metals that exhibit extremely different properties and that apparently do not react with each other at the extrusion temperature. One example is the production of a composite of an aluminum section and a steel strip in which the wear resistance of the steel and its high hardness are utilized where the section is subjected to high stresses [Mie 87].

In fiber composite materials, metallic or nonmetallic fibers are embedded in a metallic matrix to improve the mechanical properties. The adhesive bonding between the fibers and the base material is usually low because the lattices are so different and, in the case of nonmetallic fibers, a metallic bond cannot be produced. Stiff fibers are broken into small pieces during extrusion by the elongation of the parent metal—the higher the extrusion ratio, the smaller the pieces. These pieces are mechanically held so tightly in the base material without adhesion that they can withstand tensile forces even during elongation of the extruded section and thus increase the strength. The softer metallic matrix transfers the forces under load into the fibers, which determine the strength [Kel 73].

The behavior of the fiber-reinforced metallic materials at different temperatures can only be explained to a limited extent by the behavior of the base material. At low temperatures, the fibers increase the strength. At high temperatures, in contrast, the base material can shear at the interface with the fibers. This can damage the material in such a way that it fails before a material without fibers [Scu 92].

4.12.4 Powder Extrusion

The process and the application of powder extrusion is described in detail in the section "Extrusion of Powder Metals" in Chapter 5 (see also [Sch 86]). This section covers the metallurgy of this process.

The particles of loose or cold compacted powder have a fill density of 50 to 80%; i.e., depending on the production process the round or angular particles contact each other, at best, incompletely. After cold compaction the particles have to some degree linked together and in some places even adhesively bonded so that the stabilized billet (green compact) can withstand the handling before extrusion without breaking. In the press the particles are initially to some extent plastically deformed so that they contact virtually over the entire surface. A certain amount of relative movement between the particles in this accommodation process results in the particles also rubbing together. This is believed to produce partial friction welding [She 72]. This process is either stopped in front of or at the start of the deformation zone by the plastic elongation corresponding to the extrusion ratio. The approximately round powder particles become elongated fibers. The surface area of the particles is increased to such an extent that brittle surface coatings, usually oxides, break up to free the pure metal. A good lattice match, combined with transposition processes across the boundaries between the individual grains, develops a good adhesive bond by pressure welding [Rob 91].

The extruded section has a fine structure corresponding to the powder grain size that can scarcely be distinguished under the microscope from that of an extruded cast billet. However, the structure of a cast (or preforged) billet is usually coarse grained and exhibits in corresponding materials coarse primary precipitates that have a negative influence on the quality of the extruded section. The fine-grain structure of powder of the same composition is, in contrast, far more homogeneous (e.g., [Asl 81]).

With perfect bonding, the mechanical properties of a material produced from either a cast billet or a powder metallurgical material of the same composition are largely identical.

For dispersion hardening, hard particles of an intermetallic phase or a nonmetal (usually oxides, nitrides, or carbides) are embedded in the base material by powder extrusion. The effect of these particles corresponds exactly to that of precipitates described in section 4.7. They act as barriers to dislocation movement, which increases the yield strength and the work hardening. The number and distribution of the particles and not the size are important: the finer the distribution, the greater the effect.

The particles added by powder metallurgy are resistant to very high temperatures in contrast to precipitates in cast alloys. Coagulation and dissolution are impossible. Therefore, the application of dispersion-hardened materials is mainly attributable to the high-temperature properties. They are still effective at very high temperatures where other strength-increasing methods fail (work hardening, dissolved foreign atoms, precipitated particles), e.g., [Mat 90] (Fig. 4.57).

Very finely distributed dispersoids also hinder grain-boundary migration, which leads to recrystallization. Finely distributed aluminum oxide particles in a copper matrix can, for example, completely suppress recrystallization at 1000 °C, which is just below the melting point. This means that cold work-hardened materials also have a higher strength at high temperatures than the original soft material because of the retention of grain boundaries that hinder dislocation movement [Zwi 57].

The boundary surfaces matrix-hard particles do not usually have good adhesion, similar to fiber materials, because the adhesive effect is weak with different metallic lattices and completely absent with metallic inclusions. With their small size, however, they are embedded so securely in the base material that this is not important. If the hard particles or their material fraction are too large, tearing at the boundary surfaces can result in a decrease in strength. Volume fraction, size, and distribution of the hard particles have to be carefully balanced.

4.12.5 Friction between the Extruded Material and the Tooling

The friction conditions between the billet and the container as well as at the end faces and on the die working faces play a very important role in extrusion. This section discusses only the physical and metallurgical aspects of these processes. The basics of lubrication are also touched on (more information on adhesion is given in [Tyl 68]).

In the absence of lubrication, there is direct contact between the tooling and the extruded material. The roughness of the tool surface is determined by the machining. The high pressure in extrusion smears the plastically deformed material into the depressions and as it glides over the tool, it has to travel over the peaks and into the valleys. This process results in friction.

The adhesion between the tool and the material is more important. It occurs where there is metal-to-metal contact. The partial adhesion and breaking away of the material at the tool increases the friction between both. The adhesion can, however, be larger than the cohesion within the material. Particles of the material torn from its surface adhere to the tool. It is also possible for the pieces of the tool surface to be torn away and to pass out with the extruded section. This increases the roughness of the tool. High pressure and temperature increase the adhesive tendency.

This tendency to adhesion varies with the material/tool combination. It can be assumed that a slight adhesion tendency and thus a low friction force occurs where both partners only slightly dissolve in each other. Aluminum and titanium adhere very strongly with steel tooling. This, naturally, also applies to steel because the adhesion tendency between partners of the same material is particularly marked. On the other hand with copper the adhesion tendency to steel tooling is only half as high as that of aluminum [Czi 72].

The tooling surface is oxidized at the extrusion temperature. The adhesion tendency will be

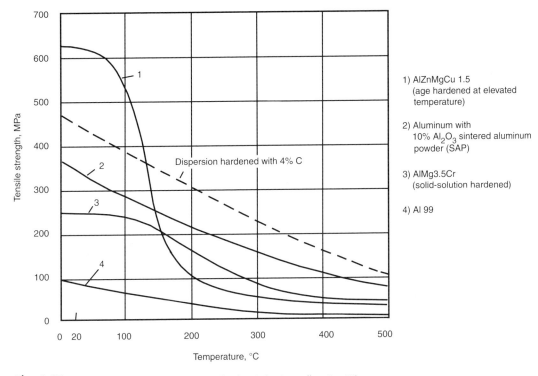

1) AlZnMgCu 1.5
(age hardened at elevated
temperature)

2) Aluminum with
10% Al_2O_3 sintered aluminum
powder (SAP)

3) AlMg3.5Cr
(solid-solution hardened)

4) Al 99

Fig. 4.57 Hot strength of normal and dispersion-hardened aluminum alloys [Jan 75]

reduced by this oxide coating on the hot tool. Its effect has still not been extensively studied. Probably, poorly bonding oxides are partly torn away and carried out with the extruded section so that the clean tool surface comes into contact with the material.

Even without taking into account the adhesion from the relative movement material/tooling, the plastic deformation needed for smearing at the surface structure of the hard tool produces heat. The catching on and releasing of the material caused by the adhesion can also produce local temperature peaks that can approach the melting point of the material. They are, however, immediately reduced by the good conductivity of the metal. Both processes are the cause for the temperature increase due to friction at the material surface.

The thin but firmly bonded oxide layer on aluminum is broken up by a large deformation even at high temperatures. The clean metal comes into contact with the tooling during extrusion. A thin layer of aluminum quickly forms on the bearing surface of the die, and this bonds so solidly because of the adhesion that the profile formed in the bearings largely slides along aluminum and not steel [Ake 83]. A smooth bearing surface thus behaves hardly differently from a slightly rougher one. The roughness measured perpendicular to the section corresponds to the roughness of the aluminum coating on the die bearing surface [The 93] (see also Chapter 6, the section on extrusion of aluminum alloys).

"Crow's feet" or "pickup" are particles that have been torn out within the die opening and have bonded to the tool. They produce grooves in the surface. They continue to grow until the shear force exerted by the extrusion is sufficient to tear them away and to carry them out with the extruded section [Mer 77].

Nitriding, which is usually used to harden the surface of extrusion dies for aluminum alloys, has only a slight effect on the adhesion behavior but does prevent premature wear of the tool surface. Grooves in the tool thus occur later, if at all. The aluminum coating does form later on nitrided tooling during extrusion than on unnitrided tooling. Once it has formed then, as far as the section surface is concerned, there is no longer any difference [The 93].

The container liner surface is coated with solidly bonded aluminum, even after the first extrusion, because of the strong adhesion tendency between steel and aluminum already mentioned.

After this, the billet no longer slides or, more correctly, shears, over steel during extrusion but over aluminum [Ake 83].

Only extrusion without lubrication has been considered so far, which is usual for aluminum. Lubricants—including certain oxides—should separate the material and the tooling and hinder any friction reaction between them (see [Sce 83] for a more detailed discussion).

The lubricant film has to bond both to the tooling and the material. The slip takes place within the lubricant film itself. The selected lubricant film has to be thick enough not to break down and must have the correct viscosity (toughness) at the extrusion temperature. The lubricant on one hand has to be able to follow the severe increase in the surface area in extrusion and, on the other hand, must not be squeezed out under the high extrusion pressure.

Only a few metal oxides act as lubricants and only copper oxide is so ductile at the extrusion temperature and bonds to the tooling and billet solidly enough while retaining the sliding effect that the container does not have to be lubricated at all and the die only slightly. However, an incomplete coating of the billet surface with oxide results in irregularities in the slip of the billet along the container liner wall and to defects in the extruded section (see the section on copper alloys in Chapter 5 for more information).

If nonlubricating oxides in copper alloys dominate, e.g., zinc oxide in CuZn alloys (brass), the lubricating effect of the copper oxide is lost.

The usual lubricants with copper alloys and other materials with moderate extrusion temperatures are graphite containing lubricating oils, which can be classified under the heading "solid lubrication." The hexagonal structure of graphite, the base surfaces of which exert only a weak attraction force between each other, is the reason that graphite plates easily slide over one another. The oil in which the graphite plates are embedded acts as a carrier and ensures that the lubricant bonds to the tooling with a suitable thickness.

If the extrusion temperature is higher than approximately 1000 °C, graphite is unsuitable as a lubricant because it is destroyed by oxidation, as is the carrier oil. Molybdenum disulfide, which exhibits at room temperature and slightly elevated temperatures outstanding lubrication properties—attributable like graphite to its crystal structure—loses its effect by oxidation above 300 °C. It is therefore not suitable for extrusion at higher temperatures.

Glass lubrication in the Séjournet process is the current practice for high-temperature extrusion (stainless steels, nickel alloys, etc.). This is described in detail in the section "Extrusion of Iron-Alloy Semifinished Products" in Chapter 5. It should also be mentioned that the thermal insulation between the material and the tooling plays an important role in addition to the good lubrication properties.

The billet and tooling have to be completely wetted by the glass lubricant. Good adhesion is also a requirement and it should also not attack the metal. The glass film on the extruded section should be approximately 10 to 30 μm thick.

The relative movement between the material and the tooling occurs entirely within the glass film, the viscosity of which corresponds to a first approximation to a Newtonian liquid:

$$\text{Viscosity } \eta = A \cdot \exp(E/RT)$$

The glass film becomes more fluid as the temperature increases. Pressure dependence of the glass viscosity has not been found.

Different glass compositions are recommended to give the correct viscosity, which should be between 10 and 100 Pa · s, at the different extrusion temperatures and extrusion ratios. The table in Fig 4.58 gives the composition of different glasses and shows some viscosity curves.

4.13 Extrudability of Metallic Materials

Good extrudability is a collective term for a low-extrusion load, high extrusion speed, good surface finish, freedom from defects, tight dimensional tolerances, and high tooling throughput. The breadth of the term makes definitions and deductions difficult. In general, a material is described as having a better extrudability than another if it has better hot-working characteristics in extrusion when specific extrusion parameters are held constant. Extrusion materials are classified by this term into high, moderate, and low extrudability.

One material from an alloy family can then have a higher extrudability than another if:

- The maximum extrusion speed before the occurrence of surface defects (roughness, grooves) under otherwise equal conditions (initial billet temperature, container temperature, extrusion ratio, die) is faster.

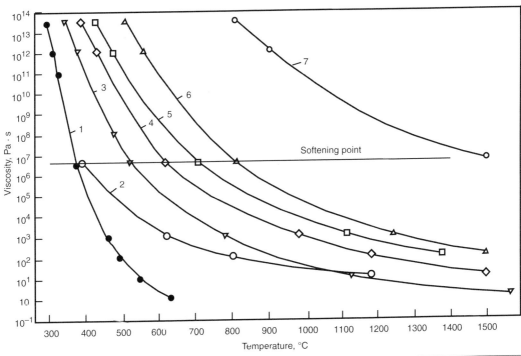

Fig. 4.58 Dependence of the viscosity of glass lubricants on the temperature [Sce 83]

No.	Type of glass	Approximate composition	Recommended temperature range, °C
1	Lead-borate	10 B$_2$O$_3$, 82 PbO, 5 SiO$_2$ 3 Al$_2$O$_3$	530
2	Borate	. . .	870
3	Potassium-lead-silicate	35 SiO$_2$, 7 K$_2$O, 58 PbO	870–1090
4	Potassium-sodium-lead-silicate	63 SiO$_2$, 8 Na$_2$O, 6 K$_2$O, 4 MgO, 21 PbO	1090–1430
5	Boron-silicate	70 SiO$_2$, 1 PbO, 28 B$_2$O$_3$, 1 Al$_2$O$_3$	1260–1730
6	Boron-silicate	81 SiO$_2$, 4 Na$_2$O, 13 B$_2$O, 2 Al$_2$O$_3$	1540–2100
7	Silicate (quartz)	96 + SiO$_2$	2210

- The extrusion load under otherwise equal conditions (initial billet temperature, container temperature, extrusion ratio, die, extrusion speed) is lower.
- The initial billet temperature and the container temperature under otherwise equal conditions (extrusion ratio, die, and extrusion speed) are lower.

The material and its properties influence the extrudability in many ways:

- *The melting point* is a controlling factor for the deformation temperature and thus for the tooling life and for the subsequent processing of the extruded product by calibration or finish drawing.
- *Alloying additions* (type and content) determine the flow stress, extrusion speed, and the tendency to extrusion defects.
- *Large precipitates and inclusions* can result in the formation of surface defects (furrows, flaking, and cracks) and increase the tool wear.

From the practical point of view it is important to be able to use simple criteria before accepting an order and before using an unknown material to estimate whether and at what cost an order can be realized. The size and the type of press available, the tooling, and the dimensions of the extruded product play a role in addition to the material.

The theory of the extrusion load is given in Chapter 3. Reference should be made to section 3.1.1.4 and the calculation example in Fig. 3.18.

The values of k_f or k_w and η_u cannot be obtained from the data obtained from normal tensile tests since the strain that can be attained is too low because of the necking and because the rate of deformation in extrusion is several orders of magnitude higher than the experimental conditions on a tensile testing machine.

The logarithmic principle strain rate $\dot{\varphi}_g$ of 1 to 10 s^{-1} reached in torsion tests falls in the range of the average logarithmic principle strain rate in extrusion. In compression testing on fast presses, φ_g up to approximately 2 and $\dot{\varphi}_g$ up to 1000 s^{-1} are achieved.

The *Atlas of Hot-Working Properties of Non-Ferrous Metals* (Vol 1, *Aluminum Alloys*) [DGM 78] gathers the known data from the literature in a standard format (ordinate: flow stress k_f, abscissa: logarithmic principle strain φ_g with the parameters temperature and principle strain rate). For the extrusion press specialist it is difficult to find the necessary data for the extrusion ratios of $V = 10$ to 300, corresponding to principle strains φ_g between 2 and 6 and the logarithmic strain rates $\dot{\varphi}_g$ between 0.5 and 10 s^{-1} normally used in extrusion.

What helps in practice?

One suggestion made after trials with aluminum alloys was to define the extrusion behavior by using a standard two-hole die [Mon 75] (Fig. 4.59) as follows: The farther the thicker section travels during extrusion, the higher is the extrudability of the material. Tests with this process found it to be too insensitive. Seven-hole dies of a specific design have also been used for experiments [Mis 91].

Scharf estimated the extrudability of aluminum alloys in experimental extrusions from the extrusion time at a constant extrusion load. He therefore used indirectly the extrusion speed as the limiting parameter and could thus differentiate between alloys and their heat treatment [Sca 64].

Castle and Lang [Cas 78] developed a test die and test section with which it was possible to make a meaningful assessment of the material properties of continuously cast material with and without heat treatment (Fig. 4.60). The limiting speed for poor shape or tearing away of the ribs was determined. The necessary extrusion load can also be used as a measure of the extrudability of a material.

Many extrusion plants use similar test dies—even dies for hollow sections with corresponding ribs.

Figure 4.61 shows the various limiting speeds for a range of alloys.

The extrusion speed does not play such a large role with materials that are extruded at moderate and high temperatures (e.g., copper alloys, steels); it is usually very high. In this case the

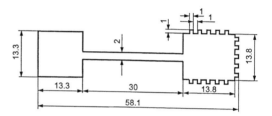

Fig. 4.60 Test section to estimate the extrudability of aluminum alloys using the extrusion speed as the limiting factor [Cas 78]

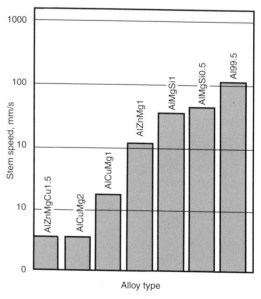

Fig. 4.61 Limiting extrusion speed measured on different aluminum alloys using the test section in Fig. 4.60 [Cas 78]

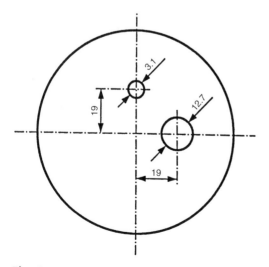

Fig. 4.59 Experimental die to determine extrudability

flow resistance and thus the limiting extrusion load have to be taken into account.

Hot-tearing tests can give a rough comparison between the different materials. The dependence of the strength of different materials on the temperature is in principle correctly reproduced. The k_f values obtained, however, cannot be used to calculate the extrusion load.

The following method is known from the copper alloy processing industry: Equations 3.4, 3.5, and 3.49 given in Chapter 3 in for the variation of the extrusion load during extrusion with and without lubrication are used.

For simplicity, the relevant formulae for the maximum extrusion load F_0 are:

Unlubricated container $F_{St\,max}$
$$= A_0 \cdot k_w \cdot \varphi_g + D_0 \cdot \pi \cdot (l_0 - l_R)\tau$$
(Eq 4.1)

and

Lubricated container $F_{St\,max}$
$$= A_0\{k_w \cdot \varphi_g \cdot e^{4(\mu_0/D_0)\cdot l_c} + k_{f_0}(1 - e^{4(\mu_0/D_0)\cdot l_c})\}$$
(Eq 4.2)

With glass lubrication the friction factor μ_0 is approximately zero. Then:

$$F_{St\,max} = A_0 \cdot k_w \cdot \varphi_g$$

where

$$k_w = \bar{k}_f/\eta$$

and

$$\varphi_g = \ln A_0/A_1$$

where A_0 is the container cross-sectional area; A_s is the section cross-sectional area; D_0 is the container bore; l_0 is the upset billet length in the container; $\bar{k}_f$ is the mean flow stress of the material being deformed in the deformation zone; η_u is deformation efficiency; k_{f_0} is flow stress in the billet outside the deformation zone; and, μ_0 is the coefficient of friction for the friction between the billet and the container.

Successive trials are carried out on the extrusion press in question with a standardized billet size (diameter, length) at the assumed temperature. Using initially large and then increasingly smaller extruded bar diameters, extrusions are carried out up to the maximum press capacity.

A value of k_w can then be calculated from Eq 4.1 (unlubricated container) or Eq 4.2 (lubricated container) using the coefficients η and μ_0 obtained from the practical measurements. It is then possible using Eq 4.1 or 4.2 to deduce possible billet or section dimensions for the material studied on this press [Ret 99].

The very specific test process described to estimate the extrudability reflects the extent of the problem and the complexity of this term. At the same time such tests have become useful aids to determine optimal deformation conditions. Many extrusion plants also use their own test methods.

Other criteria for the extrudability, including freedom from defects, dimensional tolerances, and tooling life do not lend themselves to model investigations and practical experience has to be used.

Appendix: Additional Information for Chapter 4 Metallurgical Principles

Additional Information 1: Miller's Indices to Describe a Space Lattice

Various planes can be drawn through the atomic points of a crystallite, referred to as *crystallographic planes*. Because there are numerous parallel crystallograhic planes, these are referred to as a family of crystallographic planes. The orientation of the crystallographic planes is described by a coordinate system, the axes x, y, and z coincide with the edges of the unit cell (edge length a, b, c) (Fig. 4.62).

The lengths ma, nb, and pc from the origin to the intersection points of the crystallographic planes define their location. The reciprocal values of m, n, p, are taken to give the Miller indices as follows:

$$h{:}k{:}l = 1/m{:}1/n{:}1/p$$

The Miller indices of closely packed planes consist of small whole numbers (in the diagram: m = 2, n = 4, p = 1 gives h:k:l = 2:1:4).

The indices are given in ( ): $(hkl) = (214)$. Negative indices are described with ‾ (overbar)

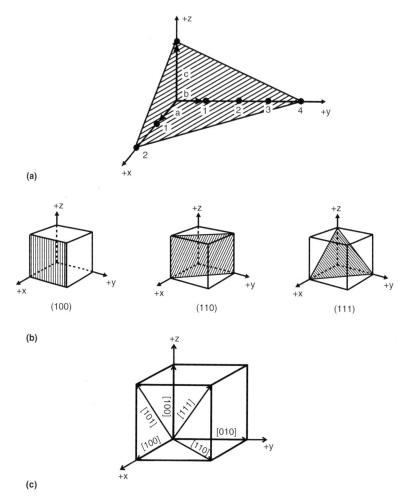

Fig. 4.62 Miller's indices for space lattices. (a) Designation of lattice planes. (b) Examples of planes in the cubic lattice. (c) Examples of directions in the cubic lattice

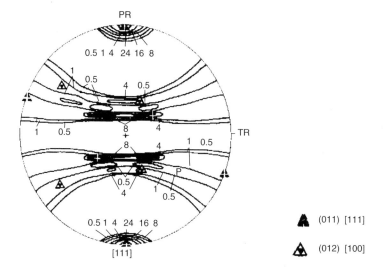

Fig. 4.63 Representation of textures in pole figures. [111] pole figure from the section core of an extruded AlCuMg bar [Moe 75]

over the number: e.g., $-1 = \bar{1}$. Figure 4.62(b) shows some examples of crystallographic planes in a cubic lattice.

Directions in the unit cell are described with the location coordinates of a point on a line going through the origin—also whole numbers but this time within angular brackets. A surface diagonal in the cubic lattice is designated with [011], and a spatial diagonal with [111] (Fig. 4.62c).

Additional Information 2: Representation of Textures in Pole Figures

In general, the orientation distribution in a textured structure is shown on a stereographic projection in which a spherical surface is represented on a plane (known as the projection plane).

The specimen is located in the center of the sphere, and the normals of the crystallographic planes penetrate the surface of the sphere. A texture is described by showing in the pole figure the frequency of the orientations of individual crystallographic planes (e.g., (111) or (100)). The pole plane coincides with a specific projection plane (e.g., the rolling plane in rolled sheets). In extruded or drawn bar the north-south direction of the pole figure is usually orientated along the bar axis (Fig. 4.63).

Additional Information 3: Temperature and Speed Dependence of the Flow Stress in Hot Working [Sel 79, Ake 70, McQ 90]

In the stationary region of the work-hardening curve where work hardening and recovery are in equilibrium, the flow stress is dependent on an exponential function of the temperature as deduced from diffusion. The activation energy is that for self diffusion:

$$k_f \approx f(Q/RT)$$

At the same flow stress there is a simple relationship between the strain rate and the absolute temperature T:

$$\dot{\varphi} = A \cdot \exp(-Q/RT)$$

If deformation is carried out at a higher temperature and higher speed then, according to this relationship, the flow stress is the same as that at a lower temperature and corresponding low speed:

$$k_f = f(\dot{\varphi}\exp(Q/RT))$$

Or, using the Zener-Hollomon parameter Z:

$$k_f = f(Z)$$
$$Z = \dot{\varphi}\exp(Q/RT)$$

There are various expressions for the relationship between the flow stress k_f and the Zener-Hollomon parameter Z that apply depending on the material and temperature-speed situation:

$$Z = a \cdot k_f^a \qquad Z = a \cdot \exp(b \cdot k_f)$$

REFERENCES

Books and Overviews

[Alt 94]: D. Altenpohl, *Aluminium von innen (Aluminum from the Inside)*, Aluminium-Verlag, Düsseldorf, 1994

[Ber 83]: W. Bergmann, *Werkstofftechnik, Teil 1: Grundlagen, Teil 2: Anwendung (Material Technology, Part 1: Fundamentals, Part 2: Application)*, Carl Hanser Verlag, Munich, Vienna, 1983

[Blu 93]: W. Blum, H. Mughrabi, and B. Reppich, *Grundlagen der Werkstoffkunde—Nichteisenmetalle* in *Umformtechnik (Fundamentals of Material Science)*, Verlag Stahleisen, Düsseldorf, 1993

[Dah 93]: W. Dahl, R. Kopp, and O. Pawelski, *Umformtechnik—Plastomechanik und Werkstoffkunde (Non-Ferrous Metals in Deformation Technology)*, Verlag Stahleisen, Düsseldorf, 1993

[Guz 70]: A.G. Guz and G. Petzow, *Metallkunde für Ingenieure (Metallurgy for Engineers)*, Akad. Verlagsges, Frankfurt, 1970

[Hor 67]: E. Hornbogen and H. Warlimont, *Metallkunde (Metallurgy)*, Springer-Verlag, 1967

[Hou 93]: H.P. Hougardy, *Grundlagen der Werkstoffkunde (Fundamentals of Metallurgy)*, Stahl in *Umformtechnik*, Verlag Stahleisen, Düsseldorf, 1993

[Sce 83]: J.A. Schey, *Tribology in Metalworking*, ASM International, 1983

[Sch 81]: W. Schatt, *Einführung in die Werkstoffwissenschaft (Introduction to Material*

Science), VEB Deutscher Verlag für die Grundindustrie, Leipzig, 4, Auflage, 1981

[Tyl 68]: R.F. Tylecote, *The Solid Phase Welding of Metals,* Edward Arnold Ltd., London, U.K., 1968

[Wie 86]: A.G. Wielandwerke, *Ulm: Wieland-Buch Kupferwerkstoffe* (*Wieland-Book Copper Alloys*), Wieland-Werke AG, Ulm, 5, Auflage, 1986

Special Literature

[Ake 66]: R. Akeret and A. Künzli, Ermittlung der Formänderungsfestigkeitkf von Aluminiumlegierungen mit Hilfe von Torsionsversuchen und Vergleich der Er-gebnisse mit denjenigen von Strangpreßversuchen (Determination of the Flow Stress of Aluminum Alloys Using Torsion Tests and Comparison of the Results with Those from Conclusion Trials), *Z. Metallkde.,* Vol 57, 1966, p 7789–7792

[Ake 70]: R. Akeret, "Fließspannung und Struktur bei der Warmumformung (von Aluminium)" ("Flow Stress and Structure in Hot Working [of Aluminum]"), Alusuisse report 220/70

[Ake 83]: R. Akeret, Einfluß der Querschnittform und der Werkzeuggestaltung beim Strangpressen von Aluminium, Teil II: Die Reibung im Preßkanal (Influence of the Cross-Section and Tool Design on the Extrusion of Aluminum, Part II: Friction in the Die Bearing), *Aluminium,* Vol 59, 1983, p 745–750

[Ake 88]: R. Akeret, A. Ried, and J. Theler, *J. Metall,* Vol 42, 1988, p 760–769

[Ake 90]: R. Akeret and M. Textor, *Strangpressen* (*Extrusion*), DGM-Informationsgesellschaft, Oberursel, Germany, 1990

[Ake 92]: R. Akeret, Strangpreßnähte in Aluminiumprofilen (Extrusion Welds in Aluminum Sections), Parts 1 and 2, *Aluminium,* Vol 68, 1992, p 877–886 and 965–973

[Ake 92a]: R. Akeret, "Extrusion Welds—Quality Aspects Are Now Center Stage," presented at International Aluminum Technology Seminar (Chicago, IL), May 20–22, 1992

[Alt 65]: D. Altenpohl, *Aluminium und Aluminiumlegierungen* (*Aluminum and Aluminum Alloys*), Springer-Verlag, 1965

[And 48]: W.A. Anderson and R.F. Mehl, *Trans. AIME,* Vol 161, 1948, p 140

[Ash 79]: M.F. Ashby, C. Gandhi, and D.M.R. Taplin, *Acta Metall.,* Vol 27, 1979, p 699–729

[Asl 81]: C. Aslund, G. Gemmel, and T. Andersson, Stranggepreßte Rohre auf pulvermetallurgischer Basis (Extruded Tubes with a Powder Metallurgy Base), *Bänder Bleche Rohre,* Vol 9, 1981, p 223–226

[Bag 81]: J. Baumgarten, W. Bunk, and K. Lücke, Strangpreßtexturen bei AlMgSi-Legierungen, Teil 1: Rundstangen (Extruded Texture in AlMgSi Alloys, Part 1: Round Poles), *Z. Metallkde.,* Vol 72, 1981, p 75–81

[Bau 59]: M. Bauser, "Einführung in die Physik der plastischen Verformung der Metalle" ("Introduction to the Physics of the Plastic Deformation of Metals"), unpublished manuscript

[Bau 61]: M. Bauser, *Verhalten von Nichteisen-Metallen bei der Warmumformung* (*Behavior of Nonferrous Metals in Hot-Working*), Vortrag Metallfachabend, Düsseldorf, 1961

[Bau 63]: M. Bauser, Verformbarkeit und Bruchverhalten bei der Warmformgebung (Workability and Fracture Behavior in Hot-Working), *Metall.,* Vol 17, 1963, p 420–429

[Bau 64]: M. Bauser, Zeit-temperatur-Auschärtungsschaubilder und die Festigkeit stranggepreßter aushärtbarer Aluminiumlegierungen (Time Temperature Age-Hardening Diagrams and the Mechanical Properties of Extruded Age-Hardening Aluminum Alloys), *Z. Metallkde.,* Vol 55, 1964, p 816–821

[Bux 77]: K. Buxmann, *Metall.,* Vol 31, 1977, p 163–170

[Bux 77a]: K. Buxmann, Fachbericht (technical reports) FB 41/777/100 der Deutschen Gesellschaft für Materialkunde, Oberursel, Germany

[Cas 78]: A.F. Castle and G. Lang, *Proceedings Aluminium Konferencia 78,* Szébesfehérvár, Vol 1, 1978

[Czi 72]: H. Czichos, *J. Appl. Phys.,* Vol 5, 1972, p 1980

[DGM 78]: Deutsche Gesellschaft für Metallkunde: *Atlas der Warmformgebungseigenschaften von Nichteisenmetallen, Aluminiumwerkstoffe* (*Atlas of Hot-Working Properties of Non-Ferrous Metals*), Vol 1, *Aluminum Alloys,* DGM, 1978

[DGM 78a]: Deutsche Gesellschaft für Metallkunde: *Atlas der Warmformgebungseigenschaften von Nichteisenmetallen,* Band 2, *Kupferwerkstoffe* (*Atlas of Hot-Working Properties of Non-Ferrous Metals*), Vol 2, *Copper Alloys,* DGM, 1978

[Die 77]: O. Diegritz, "Preßfehlerkatalog; Fehlererscheinungen beim direkten Strangpressen von Kupferwerkstoffen" ("Defects in the Direct Extrusion of Copper Alloys"), manuscript, AK Schwermetall im Strangpreßausschuß, DGM

[Fie 57]: D.S. Fields and W.A. Backofen, Determination of Strain Hardening Characteristics by Torsion Testing, *Proc. Amer. Soc. Test. Mat.*, Vol 57, 1957, p 1259–1272

[Fle 74]: M.C. Flemings, *Solidification Processing*, McGraw-Hill Inc., 1974

[Fra 50]: F.C. Frank and W.T. Read, *Phys. Rev.*, Vol 79, 1950, p 722–723

[Got 84]: G. Gottstein, Rekrlstallisation metallischer Werkstoffe (Recrystallization of Metallic Materials), Deutsche Ges., *F. Metallkunde, e.V.*, 1984

[Grz 93]: B. Grzemba and J. Hasenclever, *Non-Ferrous Metals Volume Using Aluminum and Copper as Examples,* Umformtechnik, Kopp und Pawelski, Ed., Verlag Stahleisen, Düsseldorf, 1993

[Haa 84]: P. Haasen, *Physikalische Metallkunde (Physical Metallurgy)*, Springer-Verlag, Berlin, 1984

[Hof 62]: W. Hofmann, *Lead and Lead Alloys, Metallurgy and Technology,* Springer-Verlag, 2, Auflage, 1962

[Jan 75]: G. Jangg, F. Kutner, and G. Korb, Herstellung und Eigenschaften von dispersionsgehärtetem Aluminium (Production and Properties of Dispersion Hardened Aluminum), *Aluminium,* Vol 51, 1975, p 641–645

[Kat 67]: T.Z. Kattamis, J.C. Coughlin, and M.C. Flemings, *Trans. AIME,* Vol 239, 1967, p 1504–1511

[Kel 73]: A. Kell, *Werksstoffe hoher Festigkeit (High Strength Material)*, Vol 4, Verlag Vieweg, Wiesbaden, Germany, 1973

[Lan 89]: G. Lang, Warmformverhalten von Aluminiumlegierungen beim direkten Strangpressen (Hot-Working Characteristics of Aluminum Alloys in Direct Extrusion), *Aluminium,* Vol 65, 1989, p 291–294

[Los 77]: E. Lossack, *Erzmetall,* Vol 30, 1977, p 243

[Los 83]: E. Lossack and W. Schneider, *Galvanotechnik,* Jahrg, Vol 74, 1983, p 787–794

[Mat 90]: K.H. Matucha, K. Drefahl, G. Korb, and M. Rühle, Neue oxiddispersionsge-härtete Legierungen für Hochtemperatur-Anwendungen (New Oxide Dispersion Hardened Alloy for High Temperature Application), *VDI-Berichte* (*VDI-Reported*), 1990, Vol 797, p 125–152

[McQ 75]: H.J. McQueen and J.J. Jonas, *Plastic Deformation of Materials. Treatise on Material Science and Technology,* Vol 6, Akad. Press, New York, 1975, p 393–493

[McQ 90]: H.J. McQueen, Micromechanisms of Dynamic Softening in Aluminum Alloys during Hot Working, *Hot Deformation of Aluminum Alloys Proc.* (Detroit, MI), 1990

[McQ 90a]: H.J. McQueen, Effect of Solutes and Precipitates on Hot Working Behavior of Al Alloys, *Hot Deformation of Aluminum Alloys Proc.* (Detroit, MI), 1990, p 105–120

[Mer 77]: G. Merk and S.E. Naess, Pick-Up Formation on Aluminium Extrusion, *Z. Metallkd.,* Vol 68, 1977, p 683–687

[Mie 87]: G. Mier, Verbundstromschienen Aluminium-Stahl für S-und U-Bahnen (Composite Bus-Bars in Aluminum Steel for S and U Trains), *Schweizerische Aluminium Rundschau* (*Swiss Aluminum Review*), 1987, p 12–17

[Mis 91]: W. Misiolek and J. Zasadzinski, Test-Die for Estimation of the Extrudability of Metals, *Aluminium,* Vol 67, 1991, p 85–89

[Möl 75]: M. Möller, "Werkstofffluß, Grobkornbildung und Preßeffekt bei stranggepreßtem Aluminium (AlCuMg)" ("Course Grain Formation and Extrusion Effect in Extruded Aluminum"), dissertation, Technical University of Clausthal, Germany, 1975

[Mon 75]: L.F. Mondolfo, A.R. Peel, and J.A. Marcantonio, *Met. Technol.,* Sept 1975, p 433

[Mor 69]: G. Moritz, *Z. Metallkde.,* Vol 60, 1969, p 742–749

[Mug 84]: H. Mughrabi, Mechanisms and Mechanics of Plasticity, *Rev. Phys. Appl.,* Vol 23, 1984, p 367–379

[Ohm 88]: L. Ohm and S. Engler, *Aluminium,* Vol 64, 1988, p 513–520

[Ohm 89]: L. Ohm and S. Engler, *Metall.,* Vol 43, 1989, p 539–543

[Ray 49]: G.V. Raynor, *Ann. Equilibr. Diagrams*, No. 2, 1949

[Rei 80]: W. Reif and W. Schneider, *Gießereiforschung,* Vol 32, 1980, p 53–60

[Res 92]: O. Reiso, Ph.D. thesis, Norwegian Institute of Technology, Trondheim, Norway, 1992

[Ret 99]: W. Rethmann, Pers Mitteilung KM-Kabelmetall AG (communication from KM-Kabelmetall AG), Osnabrück, Germany, 1999

[Ric 69]: H. Richter, Die Herstellung von Stangen, Rohren und Profilen durch Verbundstrangpressen (The Production of Bars, Tubes and Sections by Composite Extrusion), *Z. Metallkde.,* Vol 60, 1969, p 619–622

[Rie 87]: H. Riedel, *Fracture at High Temperatures,* Springer-Verlag, Berlin, 1987

[Rob 91]: Roberts and Ferguson, Strangpressen von Pulvermetallen (Extrusion of Powder Metals), *Int. Mater. Rev.,* Vol 36, 1991, p 62–79

[San 75]: R. Sandström and R. Lagneborg, *Acta Metall.,* Vol 23, 1975, p 387

[Sca 64]: G. Scharf, Einfluß der chemischen Zusammensetzung auf Preßbarkeit und Festigkeit von AlMgSi0.5 (Influence of the Chemical Composition on the Extrudability and Strength of AlMgSi0.5), *Z. Metallkde.,* Vol 55, 1964, p 740–744

[Sch 86]: W. Schatt, *Pulvermetallurgie (Powder Metallurgy),* Hüthig-erlag, Heidelberg, Germany, 1986

[Scn 85]: W. Schneider, *Aluminium,* Vol 61, 1985, p 338–345

[Scu 92]: K. Schulte, *Metal-Matrix Composites with Aluminium Matrix: Advanced Aerospace Materials,* Springer-Verlag, 1992, p 108–118

[See 85]: A. Seeger, *Kristallplastizität. Handbuch der Physik (Handbook of Physics),* Springer-Verlag, Berlin, VII/2, p 1–210

[Sel 79]: C.M. Sellars, The Physical Metallurgy of Hot Working, *Proc. Int. Conf. Hot Working and Forming Processes* (Sheffield, U.K.), 1979, p 3–15

[She 72]: T. Sheppard and P.J.M. Chare, *Powder Metall.,* Vol 15, 1972, p 17–41

[Stü 69]: H.-P. Stüwe, Einfluß einer plastischen Verformung auf Phasenumwandlungen in Metallen (Influence of a Plastic Deformation on the Phase Transformations in Metals), *Härt.-Tech. Mitt.,* Vol 24, 1969, p 1–5

[The 93]: W.W. Thedja, K. Müller, and D. Ruppin, Die Vorgänge im Preßkanal beim Warmstrangpressen von Aluminium: Reibung im Preßkanal und Matrizenverschleiß (The Processes in the Die Aperture in the Hot-Extrusion of Aluminum: Friction in the Die Aperture and Die Wear), *Aluminium,* Vol 69, 1993, p 524–528 and 649–653

[Web 82]: H.R. Weber, Extrusion of Technical Superconductors, *Extrusion* symposium, DGM, 1982, p 277–296

[Wei 94]: H. Weiland, T.N. Rouns, and J. Liu, The Role of Particle Stimulated Nucleation during Recrystallization of an Aluminum-Manganese Alloy, *Z. Metallkde.,* Vol 85, 1994, p 592–597

[Wev 54]: F. Wever and A. Rose, *Atlas zur Wärmebehandlung der Stähle (Atlas on the Heat Treatment of Steels),* Verlag Stahleisen, Düsseldorf, 1954

[Wie 86]: A.G. Wieland werke, *Wieland-Book Copper Alloys,* Ulm, 5, Auflage, 1986.

[Zwi 57]: K.M. Zwilsky and N.J. Grant, *J. Met.,* Vol 9, 1957, p 1197–1201

CHAPTER 5

The Production of Extruded Semifinished Products from Metallic Materials*

THE HOT-WORKING PROCESS extrusion is, in contrast to other compressive deformation processes used to produce semifinished products, a deformation process with pure compressive forces in all three force directions. These favorable deformation conditions do not exist in other production processes for semifinished products. Even in rolling, which is the most important compressive working process for producing semifinished products, tensile forces occur in the acceleration zone of the roll gap as well as in the cross rolling process used to pierce blanks in the rolling of steel tubes. These tensile forces cause problems in the rolled product if the deformation conditions are not optimized. The benefits of this three-dimensional compression in terms of deformation technology, which have already been discussed in this book, can be clearly seen in Fig. 5.1 based on experimental results for face-centred cubic (fcc) aluminum and zinc with its hexagonal lattice structure.

The extensive variations in the extrusion process enable a wide spectrum of materials to be extruded. After rolling, extrusion can be consid-

ered to be the most important of the hot-working processes.

Extrusion of Materials with Working Temperatures between 0 and 300 °C

Günther Sauer*

5.1 Extrusion of Semifinished Products in Tin Alloys

Tin is a silver-white, very soft metal with a stable tetragonal lattice in the temperature range 20 to 161 °C. The pure metal has a density of 7.28 g/cm^3 and a melting point of 232 °C.

The material can be easily worked with its recrystallization temperature below room tem-

---

*Extrusion of Materials with Working Temperatures between 0 and 300 °C, Günther Sauer
Extrusion of Semifinished Products in Magnesium Alloys, Günther Sauer
Extrusion of Semifinished Products in Aluminum Alloys, Rudolf Akeret
Materials, Günther Scharf
Extrusion of Semifinished Products in Copper Alloys, Martin Bauser
Extrusion of Semifinished Products in Titanium Alloys, Martin Bauser
Extrusion of Semifinished Products in Ziroconium Alloys, Martin Bauser
Extrusion of Iron-Alloy Semifinished Products, Martin Bauser
Extrusion of Semifinished Products in Nickel Alloys (Including Superalloys), Martin Bauser
Extrusion of Semifinished Products in Exotic Alloys, Martin Bauser
Extrusion of Powder Metals, Martin Bauser
Extrusion of Semifinished Products from Metallic Composite Materials, Klaus Müller

perature. Consequently, the softest condition develops rapidly in tin materials after cold working. Work hardening by cold working is not possible.

Tin is very stable at room temperature and is not poisonous. Unlike lead, it can therefore be used in contact with food. The metal is used as the base material for soft solder, anode materials as well as bearing materials and for tin plating steel sheet (tin plate).

Soft solders are the main application for tin. Lead, silver, antimony, and copper are used as alloying elements. Special soft solders also contain cadmium and zinc. Aluminum is used as an alloying component for soft solders used to join aluminum alloys. Bearing metals based on tin contain antimony, copper, and lead as the alloying elements as well as additions of cadmium, arsenic, and nickel.

The production of semifinished products in tin alloys by extrusion is limited today to the production of feedstock for the manufacture of soft and special soft solders on transverse extrusion presses and to the direct extrusion of feedstock for the manufacture of anodes with solid and hollow cross-sectional geometries for electrochemical plating. Tin is also used for the production of rolled strip, as the feedstock for the manufacture of high-capacity electrical condensers, as well as for roll cladding of lead-base strips for organ pipes, wine bottle caps, and Christmas ornaments (tinsel).

In general, tin-base materials have good bearing properties and are consequently used as the base material for bearing metals. Very little friction occurs in direct extrusion between the billet surface and the container inner wall because of these good bearing properties. Tin-base extruded alloys, therefore, tend to flow largely according to flow pattern A (Fig. 3.11) in direct extrusion.

The flow stress k_f that has to be overcome for the deformation of very soft pure tin is significantly higher than that of pure lead, as can be clearly seen in Fig. 5.2. It is, however, extremely low at 20 to 32 N/mm^2 for logarithmic strains φ_g up to 0.7 [Sac 34]. Therefore, a specific press pressure of maximum 400 N/mm^2 is sufficient for the direct extrusion of tin alloys when the low friction between the billet and the container liner surface is taken into account.

Tin-base alloys for the production of soft solders are generally extruded transversely at billet temperatures of 50 to 60 °C and a container temperature of approximately 100 °C. It is often sufficient to heat the front third of the billet to this temperature so that, on one hand, the billet upsets from the front to the back to prevent air entrapment and, on the other hand, the optimal welding conditions for the resultant transverse weld in the extruded product are obtained. This transverse weld in soft solders has to be capable of withstanding the drawing loads during the reduction in diameter of the extruded wires on multispindle drawing machines.

Semifinished products in tin materials including bar, wire, tubes, and sections are produced on direct extrusion presses. For productivity reasons, higher extrusion speeds are desired in this process than those used in the transverse extrusion of soft solders, which are typically 4 m/min. It is therefore advantageous to heat the billets to 100 to 150 °C. Again, it is beneficial to have a temperature profile with the temperature decreasing toward the back of the billet. In automatic fully integrated extrusion plants complete

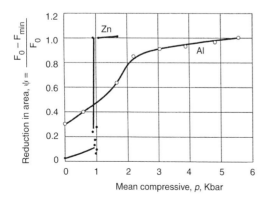

Fig. 5.1 Improving the workability of aluminum and zinc with a hydraulically produced increasing mean compressive stress p measured by the increase in the reduction in area at fracture φ in tensile tests at room temperature

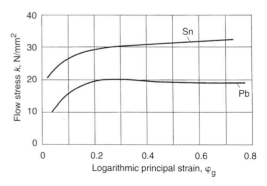

Fig. 5.2 Flow stress k_f as a function of the logarithmic strain of pure lead and pure tin (Source: Rathjen)

with melting furnaces and mold casting machines, as shown in Fig. 5.3, the cast billets retain the heat from the casting process to assist the deformation process. Care has to be taken to ensure that the heat from the casting process, when combined with the deformation heat, does not result in excessive temperatures at high extrusion speeds in the deformation zone of the extrusion tooling. The solidus of the lead-tin eutectic at 183 °C has to be taken into account in the tin alloys containing lead. If melting occurs in the solid tin matrix, transverse cracks will definitely be produced in the extruded products. Controlled cooling of the extrusion tooling improves the situation. In addition, the billet surface is sometimes brushed with a lubricant to improve the product surface.

Tin alloys will weld during the extrusion process under suitable deformation conditions including the extrusion load and temperature. They can, therefore, be used with porthole and bridge dies as well as for billet-on-billet extrusion with feeder chamber dies. These extrusion tools are, in principle, similar to those used in aluminum extrusion. Their design is simpler in detail and the dies are nitrided.

Simple two-column horizontal oil-hydraulic extrusion presses are used. Figure 5.3 shows a typical two-column extrusion press for tin and tin alloys with a maximum press load of 5000 kN.

5.2 Extrusion of Semifinished Products in Lead Materials

Lead is a soft metal, matte blue in appearance with a fcc lattice structure. The pure metal has a very high density of 11.34 g/cm^3 and a melting point of 327 °C. Lead alloys can also be easily worked. Work hardening after cold working at room temperature, for example, from 40 to 120 N/mm^2 disappears within a few minutes because the recrystallization temperature of the base material is about 0 °C. Cold working of lead-base alloys can be approximately compared in its effect to hot working of other metals. Work hardening by cold working is not possible.

Pure lead is very soft and ductile. Soft lead has a very low flow stress k_f as shown in Fig. 5.2. It is, therefore, not possible to draw pure

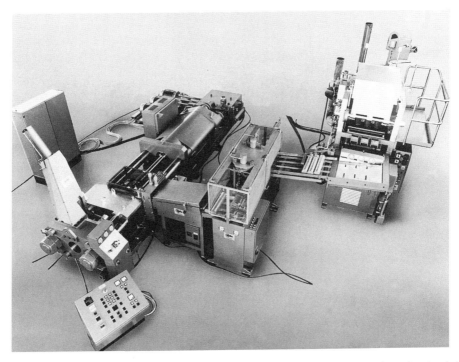

Fig. 5.3 Modern integrated fully automatic 5000 kN extrusion plant for the production of bar, wire, tube, and sections in lead and tin alloys complete with casting oven, triple billet casting plant, hot-billet shear, and oil hydraulic long-stroke extrusion press (Source: Collin)

lead to wire. However, lead alloys have higher flow stresses. Additions of antimony and tin produce solid-solution hardening of the lead, increasing both the base strength and the work-hardening capability. This raises the recrystallization temperature. The loads needed in deformation processes also increase. Antimony and zinc are the main alloying elements for lead, although small amounts of arsenic and cadmium, as well as copper nickel and silver, are also used.

Lead antimony alloys are referred to as hard lead because the antimony significantly hardens the soft lead. Alloys of this type with antimony contents up to 3 wt% also age harden. For example, the Brinell hardness of an alloy with 2 wt% antimony increases from 56 to 130 N/mm^2 within 100 days after quenching from 240 °C. The toughness and the fatigue strength, as well as the corrosion resistance of these alloys, can also be improved by the addition of specific amounts of tin. This is important for the mechanically fatigue loaded sheathed cables on, for example, bridges. Lead forms a eutectic with 11.1% antimony at 253 °C. This has to be taken into account when determining the deformation temperature for the extrusion of PbSb alloys with eutectic, low-melting point phases on grain boundaries.

Lead-tin alloys with their low solidus and liquidus temperatures are particularly suitable for the production of soft solders. Lead forms a eutectic with 38.1% tin at 183 °C. These soft solders can be used to solder steel and copper alloys. Organ pipes are produced from lead-tin alloy strips with similar tin contents. Tin contents from 45 to 75 wt% are used depending on the timbre. Lead-tin-antimony alloys with additives of arsenic, cadmium, and nickel are very important as bearing metals.

Table 5.1 gives recommended lead alloys for the extrusion of rod, wire, tubes, sections, and cable sheathing. Lead alloys are extruded with deformation temperatures in the range 100 to 260 °C, depending on the composition, to obtain economic extrusion speeds of typically 50 to 60 m/min. On the other hand, lead-base soft solders are extruded at significantly lower temperatures of approximately 55 °C and slower speeds of 2 to 4 m/min. When determining the billet and container temperatures, care must be taken to ensure that any eutectics on the grain boundaries do not melt as a result of excessive deformation temperatures in combination with the deformation and friction heat during extrusion. A liquid metal phase on the grain boundaries of a solid metal matrix in extrusion will unavoidably produce transverse cracks in the extruded product. Lubricant is added to the billet surface with a controlled brush stroke.

Lead has even better bearing properties than tin. Lead alloys, therefore, also flow mainly ac-

Table 5.1 Lead-base extruded materials

Material	Abbreviation	German Standardization Institute (DIN)	Alloy constituents and permitted impurities, wt%	Application
Fine lead	Pb 99.99 Pb99.985	1719	Permitted impurities, max 0.01 Permitted impurities, max 0.015	Tube and wire for the chemical industry
Copper fine lead	Pb 99.9 Cu	1719	Cu, 0.04–0.08 Permitted impurities, max 0.015 Pb remainder	Pressure tube
Primary lead	Pb 99.94 Pb 99.9	17641	Sb 0.75–1.25.2006 As 0.02–0.05 Pb remainder Sb 0.2–0.3 Pb remainder	Pressure tube Waste pipe
Cable lead	Kb–Pb Kb–Pb (Sb) Kb–PbSb0.5 Kb–PbSn2.5 Kb–PbTe0.4	17640	. . . Sb 0.5–1.0 Sn ≥ 2.5 Te ≥ 0.035	Standard cable sheath Cable mantle sheath resistant to fatigue failure resulting from severe vibration
Hollow anodes	PbSn10	. . .	Sn 8–12	Anodes for electrochemical coating of bores of bearing shells and bushes for bearing production Anodes for corrosion protection of bearing shells

Source: Laue/Stenger

cording to flow type A in direct extrusion as shown in Fig. 5.4 where the variation of the extrusion load over the container cross-sectional area A_0 is plotted as a function of the stem displacement and the extrusion ratio [Sac 34, Hof 62].

Lead alloys will weld during extrusion at suitable temperatures and extrusion pressures similar to tin alloys and certain aluminum alloys. Tubes and hollow sections can, therefore, be extruded with porthole and bridge dies. Feeder chamber dies have also proved successful for the extrusion of these materials and are required for billet-on-billet extrusion. The tools used for the extrusion of tin and lead alloys are in principle similar to those used for aluminum extrusion, although the designs are simpler because of the significantly lower thermomechanical stresses. All extrusion dies are nitrided.

Extrusion plants consist of integrated automatic complete plants with horizontal, hydraulically operated two-column presses and maximum extrusion loads of 5000 to 10000 kN, as shown in Fig. 5.3. A specific extrusion pressure of 400 N/mm² is similar to tin-base extruded materials, adequate for the extrusion of lead-base alloys.

Large tubes with internal diameters up to 300 mm in lead alloys are sometimes extruded on old vertical indirect extrusion presses over mandrels and charged with liquid metal. These extrusion presses can have loads between 5000 and 15,000 kN. Cable sheathing with lead alloys is carried out on special cable sheathing presses as shown in Table 5.1 (see the section on cable sheathing in chapter 3).

5.3 Extrusion of Tin- and Lead-Base Soft Solders

The standard soft and special tin solders in DIN 1707, as well as nonstandardized special soft solders, are extruded as solid bars, solder threads, solid wire, and hollow wire (tube solder) filled with flux mainly on small hydraulic automatic extrusion presses. The maximum extrusion loads are usually 2500 kN with a maximum specific pressure of 600 N/mm², which is required because of the extreme metal flow. The billet-on-billet process is used on transverse presses. Extrusion is usually followed by drawing to the finished diameter of 5 to 0.5 mm on multispindle drawing machines. The majority of finished diameters fall in the range 1 to 2 mm. Special soft alloys with low cold-working capacities sometimes have to be extruded as multiple strands to the finished diameter using the direct extrusion process. Economic wire solder presses operate completely automatically in the same way as large extrusion plants with automatic billet feed called by the press during the extrusion cycle and automatic removal of the extruded semifinished product. Figure 5.5 shows a fully automatic plant with an integrated melting furnace and a chill mold billet casting machine.

Cored solders are hollow wire filled with flux by a special tool during extrusion as shown in Figures 5.6 and 5.7. The extrusion tool system needed for the extrusion of hollow wire with flux filling, which includes the die head with the hollow mandrel, the extrusion die, and the welding chamber, and, in particular, their relative arrangement is similar to that for cable sheathing. Figure 5.6 depicts the construction of a die head. The application of "transverse extrusion" combined with "billet-on-billet" extrusion is an essential requirement for the production of continuous cored solder. Cored solder has, similar to the cable sheath, both longitudinal and transverse welds from this production method. The billets are usually produced by the chill casting process using casting machines and are normally processed with the cast skin forming the billet surface.

Typical widely used solders are the soft solders L-PbSn40, L-Sn50Pb, L-Sn60Pb and L-Sn60PbCu2, the special soft solders L-SnCu3

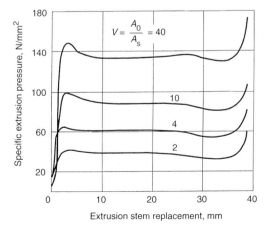

Fig. 5.4 Specific extrusion pressure in N/mm² as a function of the stem displacement and the extrusion ratio $V = A_0/A_S$ in direct extrusion of soft lead (Source: Siebal/Fangmeier)

Fig. 5.5 Modern fully automatic extrusion plant for the production of soft solder with casting oven, chill mold billet casting plant, hot-billet shear, and oil hydraulic 2500 kN extrusion press. The extrusion press is fitted with a fixed dummy block on the stem. (Source: Collin)

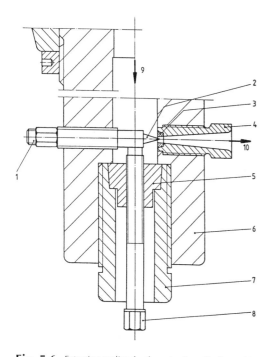

Fig. 5.6 Extrusion tooling for the extrusion of hollow solder. 1, connection to the flux container; 2, hollow mandrel; 3, extrusion die; 4, extrusion die holder; 5, pressure nut; 6, one-piece die head with the container; 7, front nut; 8, hollow mandrel screw adjustment; 9, extrusion stem direction during extrusion; 10, direction of extruded product (Source: Collin)

and L-SnAg5 to DIN 1707 and, as an example of a nonstandard solder, the special soft solder L-SnCd25Zn5.

The easy and moderately difficult to extrude soft solders are usually worked with a temperature of 55 to 60 °C. Heating of the front third of the billet is sufficient. To avoid air entrapment the billet should upset under the influence of the extrusion load and the temperature from the front end to the back and readily weld to the previously extruded billet. The container temperature is set to 90 to 110 °C. With automatically operating integrated extrusion plants for solder wire that include a melting oven and chill mold casting machine, as shown in Fig. 5.3, the cast billet must be transferred with sufficient heat for deformation retained from the casting heat. Equally, an automatic extrusion plant for solder wire need not include a melting oven and chill mold casting machine. Plants with a large number of program changes and small production batches also operate economically without these facilities. The extrusion plant is then equipped with a billet magazine and an induction furnace in line with a hot billet shear. This is used to heat either the entire billet volume or the front third to the deformation temperature.

Special soft solders need to some extent lower the more difficult-to-extrude alloys' higher deformation temperatures, which can be as high as 400 °C. The container temperature has to be set correspondingly high to avoid excessive heat transfer between the billet and the container during extrusion.

The wires are usually extruded to a diameter of approximately 15 mm and then draw on multispindle drawing machines to diameters between 5 and 0.5 mm. The transverse and longitudinal welds formed in the welding chambers of the extrusion die are able to withstand the drawing deformation loads without any problem. Good extruded surfaces are achieved by lightly lubricating the surface of statistically uniformly selected billets with a special lubricant. The quantity applied of this lubricant must be controlled extremely accurately; otherwise, the lubricant can enter the extrusion welds and prevent perfect welding. The wires would then break at the welds during drawing and have to be scrapped.

The extrusion process for the production of feedstock for solder wire commences with the billet call from the extrusion press. The extruded wire passes continuously through a multispindle drawing machine in line with the press corresponding to its capacity. The drawing machine controls the extrusion press. The billet is transferred either directly from the chill molding machine as shown in Fig. 5.8 or from a billet magazine via an induction furnace, depending on the plant specification. The billet end faces are sheared in a hot shear and thus cleaned of any oxide [Lau 76]. This is necessary to ensure perfect transverse welds. After this operation the billets collect in a magazine in front of the container and fall one by one into the centerline of the press when the stem is fully withdrawn. When the stem moves forward, the billet enters the container and is pushed against the previously extruded billet and the contacting material volumes weld together. The extrusion emerging from the die is automatically fed into a multispindle drawing machine and heavily reduced in diameter in one operation using a large number of drawing dies. The extruded wire usually passes through a water cooling system before reaching the drawing machine.

The production plan given subsequently for the manufacture of solder wire with a flux core (hollow solder) explains the solder wire manufacturing process in more detail.

Production of 1000 kg hollow solder with a diameter of 0.8 mm from the soft solder L-Sn60Pb according to DIN 1707 filled with a flux of type F SW32 according to DIN 8511 with 2.5% by weight:

1. Casting in a chill mold casting machine or heating of 168 billets with dimensions: 72 mm diam. × 175 mm long (initial billet weight: 6.05 Kg) using an induction rapid billet heating furnace to 50 °C.

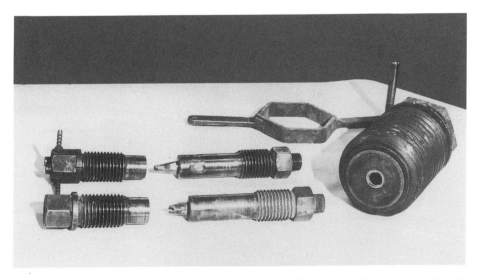

Fig. 5.7 Die holder, left, and hollow mandrel, right, as well as the front nut of the container with the pressure nut for adjusting the hollow mandrel (See Fig. 5.6) (Source: Collin, Alchacht)

2. Shearing of the billet end faces using the double shear visible in Fig. 5.5 during the transfer to the extrusion press.

3. Extrusion into air with subsequent water cooling after the press—one extruded bar per extrusion with the dimensions 14.7 × 6.7 diam. using the billet-on-billet process and transverse extrusion with simultaneous addition of flux using an extrusion tool system shown in Fig. 5.6 from a container: 75 mm diam. on a 2500 kN extrusion press—container temperature: 100 °C; exit speed: 3.02 m/min; extrusion ram speed: 5.5 mm/s; extrusion ratio $V = 32.86$.

4. Drawing to: 6 mm diam. in one operation with 14 drawing dies on a roughing multispindle drawing machine. This drawing machine controls the extrusion press according to the wire requirement via a dancing roll.

5. Drawing to: 1.35 mm diam. in one operation with 40 drawing dies on an intermediate multispindle drawing machine

6. Drawing to: 0.8 mm diam. in one operation with 40 drawing dies on a fine multispindle drawing machine

7. Coiling the wire on bobbins. This operation is frequently combined with operation 6. Quality control of the wire surface is also carried out.

8. Control and labeling

Solder threads are produced by multiple drawing of extruded solid wire approximately 15 mm diam., depending on the final dimensions on the multispindle drawing machines and automatically cut transversely after drawing.

The work hardening of the solder material produced during the cold working is countered by the continuous softening from recrystallization during the multispindle drawing process. The process is helped by the heat of the drawing lubricant in the sump of the drawing machine, in which the entire drawing process takes place. Soft solder usually recrystallizes at room temperature following work hardening. Therefore, intermediate annealing is not needed to achieve the soft, i.e., recrystallized material, state required for further cold working.

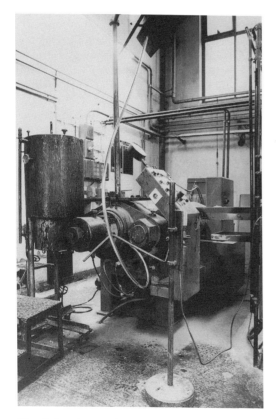

Fig. 5.8 Oil-operated 2500 kN solder wire extrusion press as shown in Fig. 5.5 with extruded hollow solder emerging transverse to the press longitudinal axis. The vessel on the left-hand side is filled with flux and linked by a tube to connection 1 on the hollow mandrel 2 in the extrusion tool in Fig. 5.6. The container is located above the hollow mandrel, and the usually very liquid flux heated to approximately 60 to 120 °C flows under hydrostatic pressure to the hollow mandrel.

5.4 Extrusion of Zinc Alloy Semifinished Products

Pure zinc has a density of 7.13 g/cm^3 and a melting point of 419.5 °C. The metal crystallizes with a hexagonal lattice structure, which, at room temperature only permits material slip on the (0001) basal plane. Consequently, polycrystalline zinc alloys at room temperature and below, in particular, are brittle. Deformation of this material is possible only after heating to temperatures between 150 and 300 °C. Twin formation during the deformation improves the plasticity. Zinc alloys do not have any great work-hardening capacity because the recrystallization temperature of these alloys is at room temperature or just above. The main alloying elements of zinc are aluminum and copper. Aluminum improves the mechanical properties of zinc alloys particularly when combined with hot working by extrusion. Copper also improves the mechanical properties of zinc-base alloys but not to the same extent as aluminum. However, copper improves the fatigue strength and machinability of zinc alloys.

Typical zinc-base extrusion alloys are ZnAl1Cu and ZnAl4Cu1. Bars, wires, tubes, and sections are produced from ZnAl4Cu1. The material can also be drawn. ZnCu is an alloy that is used for the production of sections and hot-stamping components. Car tire valves are produced from the alloy ZnAl15.

After hot rolling, extrusion is the most important deformation process for zinc-base alloys, although the main application of zinc alloys is pressure die castings. The extrusion of these alloys has lost a lot of its importance. Zinc alloys are extruded only to a limited extent mainly because the limited workability associated with the hexagonal lattice structure also affects the hot workability. Zinc alloys are extruded at deformation temperatures of approximately 150 to 300 °C. Only very low extrusion speeds of approximately 3 to 6 m/min can be achieved because of the limited extrudability of the extruded materials at high specific pressures [Sac 34, Lau 76, Schi 77, Schu 69].

Extrusion of Materials with Deformation Temperatures between 300 and 600 °C

Günther Sauer*

5.5 Extrusion of Semifinished Products in Magnesium Alloys

Magnesium is a metal with the low density of 1.74 g/cm^3, which is approximately 40% below that of aluminum. The densities of magnesium alloys fall in the range 1.76 to 1.83 g/cm^3. The modulus of elasticity of pure magnesium is approximately 41,000 N/mm^2 and that of magnesium alloys between 45,000 and 47,000 N/mm^2, i.e., on average about 66% of that of aluminum alloys. Pure magnesium has a liquidus temperature of 650 °C and crystallizes with a hexagonal lattice structure. Metals with the hexagonal lattice structure can only slip on the (0001) base plane at room temperature. Consequently, magnesium alloys are very brittle at room temperature. However, temperatures above 200 °C permit the activation of other slip planes as well as the formation of deformation twins enabling these materials to be hot workable. The narrow temperature range between the brittle and the plastic deformation behavior of magnesium alloys is of interest and is illustrated in Fig. 5.9 for the alloy MgAl6Zn [Sac 34, Bec 39]. Whereas this material clearly has a limited workability at 208 °C as can be seen by the shear stress cracks running at 45°, it can be readily hot worked at 220 °C; i.e., a temperature increase of only 12 °C produces significantly better deformation properties in this alloy. The formation of twin lamellae is associated with the improvement in the plastic workability.

Only magnesium alloys are used as structural materials and in structural applications, the high notch sensitivity has to be taken into account. This also has to be allowed for in the cross-sectional geometry of extruded sections. In addition, magnesium alloys have a very elastic behavior in compression because of their low elastic moduli between 45,000 and 47,000 N/mm^2, but this also increases the sensitivity to buckling.

Specific alloy additions can raise the static and dynamic materials properties of magnesium by a factor of two or three. The principle alloying elements of the wrought alloys are aluminum with contents up to 10 wt%, zinc up to 4 wt%, and manganese up to 2.3 wt%. Zirconium, cerium, and thorium are also added. More recently, lithium has been increasingly used as an alloying element.

| 200 °C | 205 °C | 208 °C | 212 °C | 220 °C |

Fig. 5.9 Deformation behavior of the magnesium alloy MgAl6Zn in hot-compression tests in the temperature range between 200 and 220 °C (Source: Schmidt/Beck)

*Extrusion of Semifinished Products in Magnesium Alloys, Günther Sauer

Aluminum is the most important alloying element for magnesium, which forms a solid solution with aluminum at low contents and the intermetallic phase Al_2Mg_3 at higher contents. A eutectic occurs at 436 °C at an aluminum content of 32.2 wt%. Crystal segregations can occur in wrought alloys at aluminum contents above 6 wt%. They can be dissolved and thus removed by homogenization of the cast in the temperature range of 400 to 450 °C for correspondingly long times. The solid-solution formation at aluminum contents of 2 to approximately 6 wt% increase the fracture toughness and hardness of magnesium alloys as shown in Fig. 5.10. At higher aluminum contents, the fracture strength and, in particular, the hardness can be further increased by the formation of the hard γ phase, but with a reduction in the ductility of the material as can be clearly seen in Fig. 5.10 [Schu 69]. Magnesium-base wrought alloys have aluminum contents up to 9 wt%. Magnesium alloys can be hot rolled at aluminum contents up to 7 wt% and hot worked by extrusion at aluminum contents up to 9 wt%. The magnesium alloy becomes increasingly more brittle at aluminum contents > 9 wt% as shown by the elongation in Fig. 5.10. This also shows that magnesium alloys with contents > 7 wt% can be age hardened after solution heat treatment. At the same time, the alloy suffers a drastic loss in ductility [Schu 69].

Zinc readily dissolves, depending on the temperature, in magnesium by the formation of solid solutions with the phase MgZn. An addition of up to 3 wt% increases the fracture strength and the fatigue strength of magnesium. Zinc contents more than 3 wt%, however, result in a drastic reduction in the elongation to fracture. Zinc containing magnesium alloys can be age hardened. This can increase the fracture strength of magnesium alloys by 30 to 40%.

Manganese dissolves in magnesium by, depending on temperature, up to 3.4% at 645 °C. At this temperature magnesium forms a eutectic with manganese. Manganese is dissolved by magnesium with the formation of solid solutions and the phase MgMn. It increases the strength of magnesium at contents > 1.5 wt%. Manganese containing magnesium alloys have better corrosion resistance than other magnesium-base alloys. Manganese contents of between 0 and 0.5% are therefore added to all magnesium alloys to improve the corrosion resistance.

Additions of zirconium form finely dispersed zirconium oxides that act as the nuclei for a fine-grain structure and thus increases the tensile strength of magnesium alloys with no reduction in the elongation.

Cerium also increases the fine-grain structure and improves the hot strength.

Thorium improves the hot strength even more than does cerium. This has resulted in the development of magnesium-thorium alloys with particularly high resistance to softening. Thorium also significantly improves the fatigue strength and specifically the creep strength [Tech

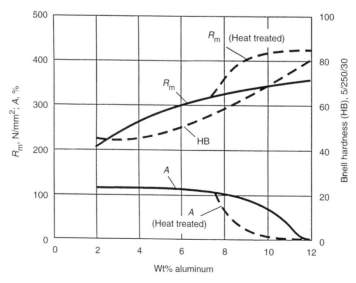

Fig. 5.10 The influence of aluminum on the mechanical properties of extruded magnesium alloys (Source: Spitaler)

96/97/98]. However, in England, alloys with more than 2 wt% of thorium are classified as radioactive. In the United States, use of magnesium-thorium alloys is very restricted because thorium-free magnesium alloys have been substituted.

Magnesium alloys are very susceptible to corrosion compared with aluminum alloys because they are electrochemically less noble. Additions of nickel, iron, copper, and so forth promote the corrosion of the material. Therefore, these additions are held in the range ppm by using purer starting materials as well as improved melt refining processes. This enables the corrosion sensitivity to be significantly reduced. High-purity-based magnesium alloys today have corrosion resistances comparable to aluminum alloys.

This has been one of the factors that has increased the interest of the automobile industry in magnesium-base alloys and provided the in-

centive to improve the existing alloys and to develop new ones with the intention of:

- Improving the static and dynamic materials properties, including elongation and toughness
- Improving the temperature resistance
- Further reducing the density
- The development of alloys with self-healing surface passive films

The coarse cast structure is transformed into a fine grain elongated structure by hot working in the extrusion process. This structural transformation is associated with a significant improvement in the mechanical properties of the magnesium alloys in the same way as aluminum alloys. The mechanical properties that can be achieved improve with increasing extrusion ratio, i.e., with increasing working during extrusion. Figure 5.11 illustrates this process, which is of considerable importance for the supply of

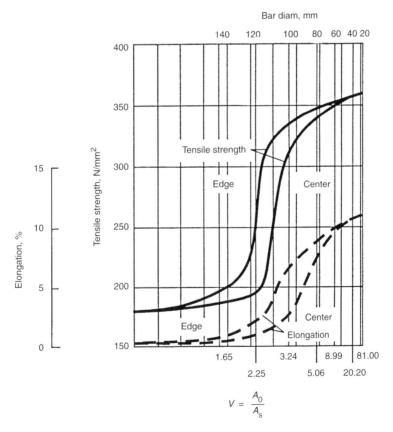

Fig. 5.11 Tensile strength R_M and elongation to fracture A as a function of the extrusion ratio determined on single cavity extruded round bars in the alloy MgAl10. Billets 175 mm diam were used for the experiments with a container diam of 180 mm (Source: Beck)

extruded semifinished products [Bec 39]. The extrusion ratio $V = A_0/A_S$ should not fall below 5, and it is better to specify the minimum at 7. A fine-grained extruded structure with good mechanical properties can be achieved with extrusion ratios of 25 [Har 47].

Magnesium alloys are mainly extruded using the direct extrusion process. Indirect extrusion is possible and is used. Magnesium alloys flow more uniformly in direct extrusion than do aluminum alloys. The discards can be reduced in thickness because of the lower distortion in the region of the billet surface and the resultant flatter dead metal zones in the deformation zone of the container. Magnesium alloys can be welded in the extrusion process. Therefore, porthole dies and bridge dies can be used to produce tubes and hollow sections. Similar to aluminum alloys, large-diameter tubes are extruded over mandrels. It is also possible to use billet-on-billet extrusion with magnesium alloys. However, the weldability is reduced by increasing aluminum contents.

Typical magnesium alloys for hot working by extrusion are given in Table 5.2. There are other wrought magnesium-base alloys in addition to those listed, particularly abroad, for example alloys of the MgAl family. The working temperatures for extrusion are at 250 to 450 °C, depending on the alloy and are higher than those used for hot rolling the same magnesium alloys. Extrusion ratios $V = A_0/A_S$ similar to those for aluminum alloys can be achieved. The extrudable magnesium alloys belong to the category of difficult-to-extrude alloys mainly because of their hexagonal lattice structure. The extrusion speeds fall in the range of moderate- to difficult-to-extrude aluminum alloys. According to [Har 47], the extrudability of magnesium alloys decreases with increasing aluminum content as do the extrusion speeds. Only the alloys MgMn and MgMn2, as well as MgAl1Zn, can be extruded at speeds up to a maximum of 30 m/min [Zol 67]. The predominantly slow extrusion speeds naturally result in long extrusion cycles. Therefore, the extrusion container temperature has to be set so that the billet does not lose any heat to the container during the extrusion cycle; otherwise, the billet will freeze in the container. In

Table 5.2 Extruded magnesium-base alloys

Symbol	No. (DIN standard)	ASTM	Composition, wt%	Billet, °C	Shape and condition	$R_{p0.2}$ N/mm²	R_m N/mm²	A_S/A_{10} %
Mg 99.8H	3.5003 (DIN 17800)	...	Cu: 0.02 Si: 0.10 Mn: 0.10 Ni 0.002 Fe: 0.05	250–450	Bar, wire, tube, section	...	...	...
MgMn2	3.5200 (DIN 1729)	M2	Mn: 1.20–2.00 Mg: remainder	250–350	Bar, tube, section Extruded and straightened Drawn and straightened	150–170	200–230	10–15
MgAl2Zn	...	...	Al: 1.20–2.20 Zn: 0.5 Mn: 0.1 Mg: remainder	300–400	...	...	...	...
MgAl3Zn	3.5312 (DIN 1729)	AZ31	Al: 2.50–3.50 Zn: 0.50–1.50 Mn: 0.05–0.40 Mg: remainder	300–400	Bar, tube, section Extruded and straightened	130–200	240–260	3–12
MgAl6Zn	3.5612 (DIN 1729)	AZ61	Al: 5.50–6.50 Zn: 0.50–1.50 Mn: 0.05–0.40 MG: remainder	350–400	Tube and section Extruded and straightened	180–200	250–280	6–10
MgAl7Zn	...	...	Al: 6.50–8.00 Zn: 0.50–2.00 Mn: 0.05–0.40 Mg: remainder	300–350	Bar Extruded and straightened Age hardened if required	200–230	280–320	3–10 (A_5)
MgAl7Zn	3.5812 (DIN 1729)	AZ81	Al: 7.80–9.20 Zn: 0.20–0.80 Mn: >0.12 Mg: remainder	300–420	Bar and section Extruded and straightened Age hardened if required	200–230	280–320	6–10 (A_5)
MgZn5Zn0.6	3.5161 (DIN 1729)	...	Zn: 4.80–6.20 Zr: 0.45–0.80	300–400	Bar, tube, section Extruded and straightened Age hardened if required	200–250	280–320	4–5 (A_5)
MgTh3Mn2(a)	...	...	Th: 2.50–3.50 Mn: >1.2	...	Bar, tube, section Extruded and straightened	180	270	4 (A_5)

(a) Experimental material Fuchs Metallwerke. Source: Schimpke, Schropp, and Konig

Table 5.3 Dependence of the specific extrusion pressure for the extrusion of tubes 44×1.5 mm in the alloy $MgAl_3$ on the homogenization treatment and the heating conditions of the billet 48×150 mm

Thermal treatment of the cast before heating prior to extrusion	Heating before extrusion		Specific extrusion pressure, N/mm^2
	Temperature, °C	Time, h	
Not carried out	380–350	1	250–300
Not carried out	380–350	3	210–260
Not carried out	380–350	6	180–220
Not carried out	340–300	1	320–400
Not carried out	340–300	3	250–300
Not carried out	340–300	6	200–250
350 °C–12 h	340–300	1	190–250
350 °C–12 h	340–300	3	170–200
350 °C–12 h	340–300	6	150–180
350 °C–12 h	340–300	1	170–220
350 °C–12 h	340–300	3	160–200
350 °C–12 h	340–300	6	130–170

Source: Zubolob and Zwerev

addition, good soaking of the billet during heating is required. Magnesium alloy extrusion billets are normally extruded with the cast skin.

Heat treatment such as homogenizing improves the hot workability of the magnesium-base extrusion alloys. The effect of homogenization on the extrusion loads needed for hot working of the alloy $MgAl_3$ is shown in Table 5.3 [Zol 67, Lau 76].

Extruded magnesium alloy semifinished products exhibit extreme anisotropy because of the hexagonal lattice structure of the metal. For example, tensile tests on extruded semifinished magnesium alloys in the longitudinal direction, i.e., the extrusion direction, have significantly higher values for the 0.2% proof stress, tensile strength, and elongation than in the transverse direction.

If the ratio of the tensile strength transverse/longitudinal is taken as a measure of the anisotropy of a material, magnesium alloys have values in the range 0.6 to 0.7.

The nitrided dies used for the hot working of magnesium extruded alloys have, in principle, the same design features as those used for the extrusion of aluminum alloys. Only the shape-forming regions of the die are matched to the specific properties of magnesium alloys by having longer bearings and larger radii. The typical hollow section die used for aluminum alloys can in principle be used for these alloys because of their ability to weld during extrusion. In addition, in contrast to aluminum alloys, magnesium alloys have a significantly lower affinity for iron alloys [Tech 96/97/98]. This property results in a slower buildup of an intermediate layer of the extruded material on the die bearing surfaces

compared with aluminum alloys, even though the formation of a layer cannot be avoided with magnesium alloys even when nitrided dies are used.

Cold working by drawing to improve the mechanical properties is practically impossible for wrought magnesium alloys because of their limited cold workability associated with their hexagonal lattice structure.

Drawing in the form of a calibration draw is, however, of interest, as a means of improving tolerances.

Extrusion of Semifinished Products in Aluminum Alloys

Rudolf Akeret*

5.6 General

Of all the materials processed by extrusion, aluminum occupies the predominant role in terms of both production volume and value. Based on the annual volume of production of primary and secondary metal, aluminum is placed directly after iron. The majority are al-

*Extrusion of Semifinished Products in Aluminum Alloys, Rudolf Akeret

loyed to produce wrought alloys and formed into semifinished products of which 25% are extruded. The majority of all extrusion plants, three quarters in Germany, for example, process aluminum alloys [Bau 82], 465,000 t in 1995.

The physical metallurgical properties of aluminum alloys make them particularly suitable for the extrusion of products very close to the finished shape and with attractive properties. The face-centered cubic (fcc) structure with 12 slip systems combined with a high stacking fault energy is a requirement for good cold and hot workability. Corresponding to the melting point of 660 °C, the hot-working temperature of aluminum alloys falls in the range of 350 to 550 °C, which can be easily withstood by tools made from suitable hot-working steels. In this temperature range the flow stress is reduced to values that require relatively low specific press pressures for processing. The natural oxide skin gives aluminum an attractive appearance and a good corrosion resistance in the natural state. Increased surface protection is given by anodic oxidation. Aluminum forms age-hardening alloys with low-alloying additions that combine good hot workability with a high strength after a simple heat treatment.

Sections with an extensive range of function specific cross sections can be extruded within narrow tolerances from aluminum alloys. Hollow sections in the form of rectangular tubes and hollow engineering plates offer a high bending and torsional stiffness. The extensive variety of aluminum sections used today in a wide range of technologies is described in detail in Chapter 2.

The selection of the extrusion process is largely determined by the physical metallurgical properties of the aluminum alloys. The high affinity to steel and thus the tendency to adhere to all extrusion tools has to be included in the material properties in addition to low extrusion temperature and the good extrusion weldability.

Direct hot extrusion without lubrication and without a shell is used for the majority of extruded products, including solid and hollow sections from the easily and moderately difficult alloys. Direct extrusion can be used for practically the entire spectrum of products, from the simple round bar to complicated sections with a circumscribing circle close to the container cross section. Flat dies are used for solid sections and porthole dies for hollow sections.

Indirect extrusion comes into consideration for compact cross sections in hard-to-extrude al-

loys. Cold and hot extrusion with lubrication of the container and the die is also used for bars and tubes [Ake 73].

5.7 Extrusion Behavior of Aluminum Alloys

5.7.1 Flow Stress

The extrusion temperature range, the flow stress variations, and the friction across the tooling determine the extrusion behavior of aluminum alloys. Alloy and quality requirements determine the necessary exit temperature for the extruded product and the temperature range for the deformation. In the range 350 to 550 °C, the flow stress of aluminum alloys is very dependent on the temperature and the composition [Ake 70, DGM 78]. The increase in the flow stress with increasing content of the most common alloying elements is shown in Fig. 5.12 [Ake 70].

The dependence of the flow stress on temperature and speed is described in the context of the basics of metallurgy in Chapter 4. Figure 5.13 shows for some non-heat-treatable alloys that reducing the temperature by approximately 100 °C results in an almost doubling of the flow stress providing the alloy additions stay in solution [Ake 70].

With age-hardening alloys similar to Al-MgSi1 the variation of the flow stress is dis-

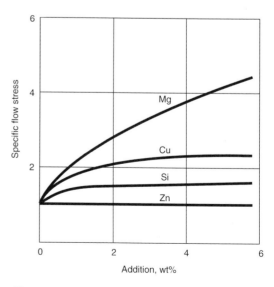

Fig. 5.12 Increase in the flow stress of aluminum in hot working with different alloying additions [Ake 70]

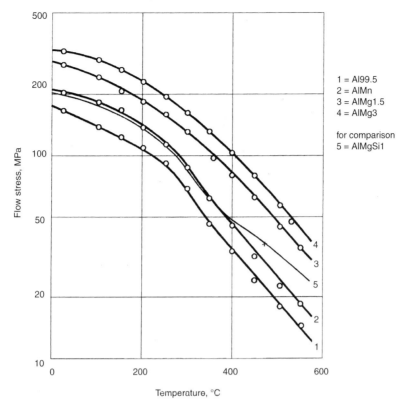

Fig. 13 Flow stress of some non-age-hardening aluminum alloys as a function of the deformation temperature (maximum of the flow curve in torsion tests with $\dot{\varphi}_g = 0.655\ s^{-1}$) [Ake 70]

placed by solution and precipitation processes according to the content of alloying elements in the matrix.

5.7.2 Flow Process

The aluminum alloys are almost always extruded in direct contact with the container and die manufactured in hot-working steel. However, aluminum exhibits a significant chemical affinity and adhesion tendency with iron [Czi 72]. Even in the solid state it tends to adhere to tool surfaces. At face pressures above the flow stress, Coulomb's laws of friction lose their validity if the shear distortion of the peripheral layer requires less force than the slip along the surface of the harder frictional party [Wan 78]. The face pressure at the inner face of the container is of the order of 10 times the flow stress. Therefore, aluminum alloys flow in direct extrusion according to flow type B1 as shown in Fig. 5.14 [Val 96].

5.7.2.1 The Dead Metal Zone

The billet surface is stationary relative to the container inner wall, and the shear distortion is

at a maximum immediately below the surface (Fig. 5.15) [Gat 54].

A dead metal zone forms in front of the face of the flat die. The surface of the extruded section is not formed from the surface of the billet

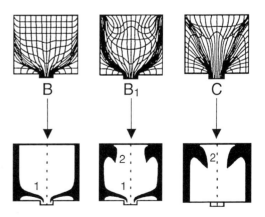

Fig. 5.14 Flow types B, B1, and C and the flow inward of the billet peripheral layer along the dead metal zone (path 1) and from the dummy block edge into the interior of the billet (path 2) [Val 96]

but from the interior of the billet by shearing along the dead metal zone [Ake 88, Lef 92]. The outermost layer of the billet surface initially adheres to the inner wall of the container and is shaved off by the advancing dummy block. The material that is compressed together in front of the dummy block and that contains oxide and exudations from the billet surfaces ends up well below the surface of the extrusion following the path shown in Fig. 5.14, No. 2, and forms an incompletely bonded intermediate layer referred as the piping defect. Material located farther below the surface is compressed at the upper edge of the dead metal zone and follows path 1 of the dead metal zone into the region of the surface of the extruded product. Adhesion of the material also occurs in feeder chambers and in the ports of porthole dies where there is a high pressure [Ake 88].

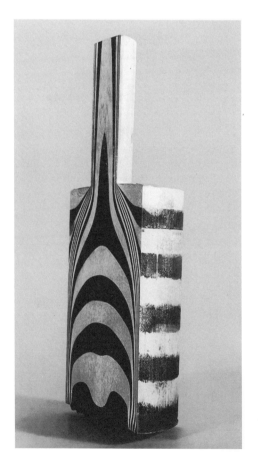

Fig. 5.15 Adhesion of the billet surface to the container wall and the shear deformation of the peripheral layer
[Gat 54]

5.7.2.2 In the Shape-Producing Aperture

The pressure conditions in the die aperture are different. The axial pressure at the exit is zero, or there can be a small tensile stress—if a puller is used.

The face pressure, which determines the friction, cannot be easily calculated because it straddles two boundary cases. If the section can slide as a solid body through the die aperture, the face pressure, and thus the friction, is low. If the section undergoes a reduction in thickness through a narrowing die aperture, the face pressure is at least equal to the flow stress. The large adhesion affinity of aluminum increases the friction stress to the same order of magnitude as the shear stress [Ake 88, Ake 85].

The friction in the die opening is responsible for the increase in the axial pressure against the flow direction.

Slip with Coulomb friction is impossible in the extrusion of tubes over a mandrel because of the high radial pressure between the billet and the mandrel. If the extrusion is carried out over a stationary mandrel, relative movement with shear friction takes place between the billet and the mandrel from the start of extrusion over the entire billet length. The relative speed is therefore of the order of magnitude of the stem speed. The billet material is only accelerated to the exit speed of the tube as it crosses the deformation zone and at the same time the pressure on the mandrel surface falls rapidly. The transition to slipping friction of the finish extruded tube over the mandrel tip takes place in the region of the die aperture.

When a moving mandrel is used, the zone in which relative movement occurs between the billet and the moving mandrel is only the length of the deformation zone. The shear zone moves toward the back of the billet as the extrusion progresses [Rup 82].

5.7.3 *Thermal Balance and Extrusion Speed*

The theoretical background to the thermal balance in extrusion is discussed in chapter 3 (see also Fig. 3.22).

In the direct extrusion of aluminum alloys without lubrication, two to three times the mechanical work is needed than would be required for an ideal loss-free deformation. The work carried out by the press on the material being extruded is practically completely transformed into heat, which is partly transferred into the tooling and partly removed in the emerging extrusion. In the adiabatic limiting case, each MPa of average extrusion pressure corresponds to an average increase in temperature of 0.3 K.

The magnitude involved is shown in Fig. 5.16 for the case of an easily extruded material with a flow stress of 25 MPa in which a billet of length $l_0 = 4D_0$ is extruded as quickly as possible with an extrusion ratio of 30 to avoid any heat losses. When a material volume corresponding approximately to the volume of the deformation zone is extruded, there is initially a steep increase in temperature. With loss-free deformation, which approximately occurs in the core of the extrusion, the material is initially heated by 25 K.

The shearing of the material flowing through the deformation zone along the dead metal zone requires approximately the same amount of work as the pure deformation [Ake 72, Sah 96]. An additional contribution, which cannot be ignored, is the friction in the die aperture, the magnitude of which depends on the angle and the length of the bearings [Ake 85, Moo 96, Mue 96]. The shear takes place in a surface layer approximately 10% of the diameter of the deformation zone, and the friction heats an even thinner surface layer of the section. A peripheral layer approximately one-third of the cross-sectional area is therefore heated to a significantly higher temperature than the core of the section [Ake 72]. This temperature difference is very short lived and is practically completely equalized on the way from the die to the press platen. Experiments with sheathed thermocouples in the die land have shown that the maximum surface temperature can be 60 to 100 K higher than the mean section temperature [Joh 96].

With sections, the maximum temperature, which governs the onset of tearing, occurs during the passage through the die opening usually at an edge where the longitudinal stress is the highest and the temperature probably at the maximum.

The possible working range of the press, i.e., the "window" in the temperature-speed field, is limited by the following thermal and mechanical conditions:

- The surface temperature cannot exceed the maximum value that results in excessive scoring or even transverse cracks at any point (limit curve 1 in Fig. 5.17). The temperature equalizes to some extent during the crossing of the deformation zone.
- The average section temperature has to be high enough to ensure adequate solution heat

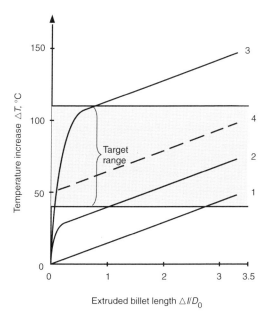

Fig. 5.16 Heating from deformation and shear deformation of the peripheral layer in the adiabatic limiting case (example, AlMgSi0.5: flow stress 25 MPa, billet length:billet $\varnothing = 4$, extrusion ratio 30). 1, temperature increase up to the entry into the deformation zone; On exit from the die: 2, temperature increase of the section core; 3, temperature increase of the section surface; 4, mean temperature increase of the section

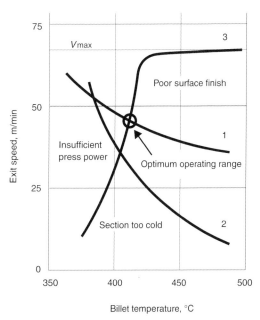

Fig. 5.17 Limit diagram for maximum surface and minimum mean section temperature

treatment with AlMgSi alloys and to reduce the tendency of AlCuMg and AlZnMgCu alloys to recrystallization (limit curve 2).

- The press and its power source, on the other hand, determine the maximum extrusion load and the ram speed. The latter decreases with increasing extrusion load (reduction in billet temperature) because of the increasing slip loss (limit curve 3).

In the literature there are several different proposals for depicting the process limits [Joh 96, Hir 58, Ste 73, She 77].

The range of extrusion speeds that can be practically obtained with aluminum alloys is shown in Fig. 5.18 [Ake 71] plotted against the flow stress at the extrusion temperatures used in practice.

The exit speeds V_A are scattered around a line with a steep negative gradient that can be approximated by the expression:

$$V_A \sim k_f^{-2}$$

This empirical equation [Ake 68] can be explained by the laws of heat penetration [Lag 72].

5.7.4 Section Surface and Surface Defects

In all stages in the production of aluminum extruded sections, the plant and process tech-

nologies are influenced mainly by the need to avoid defects that would impair the mechanical properties or the decorative appearance [Bry 71, Fin 92, Par 96]. The following defects are particularly important:

- Uneven color tone (bands or flecks)
- Coarse recrystallization
- Excessive roughness (scoring or pickup)
- Imperfectly bonded brittle contact areas between material streams flowing together (piping, defective welds)
- Material separation in the form of transverse cracks, blisters, and flaking
- Subsequent mechanical damage or corrosion

The cause of these defects can be found in the structure of the billets, the flow process, and the extrusion temperature, in a subsequent heat treatment or defects in the logistics (handling, transport, and storage of the finished sections).

To determine and eliminate the causes of these defects, correct diagnosis and an accurate knowledge of the process technological relationships are necessary. The results obtained from more accurate analysis of the flow processes and the temperature field contribute significantly to the understanding of these relationships. Mention should also be made of the extrusion defect catalog produced by the "extrusion" working party in conjunction with the Institute for Material Science of the RWTH Aachen University.

5.7.4.1 Section Surface and the Peripheral Layer

Microgeometric surface defects and structural-related tone variations (banding, flecks) are related to the method of formation of the section surface and the additional through working and heating of the peripheral layer compared with the section core. Using high resolution marking and evaluation processes, it is possible to localize the exact source of the peripheral layer in the billet [Val 88, Val 92, Val 92a]. Only a small material volume located between the dead metal zone and the deformation zone is involved in the formation of a 50 μm-thick peripheral layer, and this can be extended by a factor of more than 1000 [Val 92a]. This extreme working of the peripheral layer deforms a cast grain to a strip that is thinner than the subgrain size corresponding to the deformation conditions. The subgrains then grow by recovery through the original grain boundaries, as shown in Chapter 4 in the section on metallurgical basics.

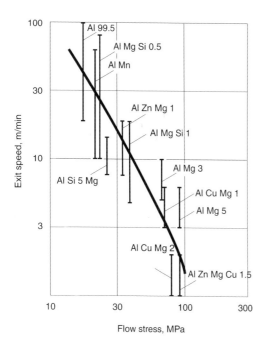

Fig. 5.18 Flow stress and extrudability [Ake 71]

The peripheral layer therefore has a subgrain structure without defined grain boundaries, providing the heat from extrusion or subsequent solution heat treatment does not result in static recrystallization. This high deformation of the peripheral layer does not produce any higher hardness in the as-extruded condition [Moe 75].

An additional feature of the highly deformed peripheral layer is its $\langle 001 \rangle \{211\}$ shear texture, which differs from the $\langle 111 \rangle + \langle 100 \rangle$ double fiber structure of the core zone [Moe 75, Auk 96].

Rows of precipitates are pulled apart by the extreme deformation and moved closer together in the transverse direction so that the particles appear to be irregularly arranged. The recrystallization retarding effect of layers heavily decorated with particles is then lost. This results in undesired coarse grain recrystallization of the AlCuMg and AlZnMg alloys, particularly at the end of extrusion where the peripheral layer forms up to 90% of the cross section.

5.7.4.2 Cast Structure and Anodizing Capability

Knowledge of the relationship between the location of the volume element in the billet and in the section is the key to explaining and overcoming linear and banded tone variations in anodized sections [Ake 88, Bau 71, Lyn 71, Sta 90].

The formation of the cast structure of the billet is discussed in Chapter 4, in the section on metallurgical basics. From the point of view of the uniformity of the anodized surface, the following regions of the billet surface are important:

- The oxide skin (10–100nm)
- The segregation zone (up to $\sim$600 μm)
- The impoverished peripheral zone
- The periodic cold shut (up to several mm)
- The columnar solidified crust (up to 15 mm)
- The primary solidified regions scattered over the entire billet cross section

Differences in the brightness of the oxide layer are primarily caused by differences in the number of depressions from the initial alkaline etching. The etch attack does not occur uniformly but preferentially at all types of particles at grain boundaries. The brightness is affected, in particular, by the depressions that form at all AlFeSi particles. Particularly deep craters develop at the locations where the Mg_2Si equilibrium particles are nucleated on AlFeSi. Experiments on the etching kinetics have shown that it is these craters that have a strong effect on the matte finish [Sta 90]. The number of particles per unit area depends on the average dendrite spacing (cell size) in the cast structure and also on whether a region is normally elongated or highly deformed during extrusion. The impoverished peripheral zones and the primary solidified regions appear bright after anodizing, whereas the oxide skin and the segregation zones matte. The controlling factors for the frequency of nucleation of Mg_2Si and AlFeSi are the temperature changes during billet heat treatment and during cooling or quenching after extrusion.

Pits form during etching along the grain boundaries. The shape of the pits depends on the formation of the age-hardening β-MgSi phase. In general, different cooling conditions (influencing the pit width) as well as different grain size (influencing the pit length) can result in significant variations in brightness.

An orientation-dependent face etching occurs on the surface during etching and this consists of small cube faces with an edge length less than 0.5 μm. The deformation texture of the section with the $\{011\} \langle 211 \rangle$ principle components can form to different extents in different parts of the extrusion die. This results in an inhomogeneous distribution of the cube faces and thus in different reflection properties. This is how some of the undesired leg marks can occur.

Investigations on a hollow section [War 95] have shown that different die designs for the same profile cross section can result in completely different decorative appearances. Feeder chambers and splitting can affect the magnitude and direction of the local strain of the surface layer. The die design therefore has a strong influence on the texture, precipitate distribution, and grain size.

The three mechanisms just described for the roughening of the surface (depressions, pits, texture) have approximately equal importance for the decorative appearance of the anodized section. In addition, precipitates of the base metal, which can neither be dissolved nor removed during etching, end up in the oxide layer, giving it a cloudy or colored appearance.

The external oxide skin in single-cavity extrusion follows path 2 (Fig. 5.14) and finishes in the interior of the sections forming a brittle layer (piping defect). In multicavity extrusion, sections with reentrant angles, and hollow sections, the side adjacent to the center of the die consists of normally elongated material, whereas the external side, particularly at the end of extrusion, can consist of highly deformed material [Ake 88a] (Fig. 5.19).

If the distance between two die openings is large, a dead metal zone can form so that the section surfaces extend into highly deformed material. Within a short distance the central dead metal zone disappears and the section surface extends partly into the normally wrought fibrous material [Ake 88, Val 96a]. In between the oxide and segregation layer of the billet appears on the surface.

Cold shuts, which can extend several millimeters into the billet peripheral zone, can finish up in the peripheral layer of the section following path 1 (Fig. 5.14). If the defects are deep, and if they occur in the front part of the billet, the entire section can be unusable [Bag 81].

In addition, other variations in the material flow and in the through working with subsequent static recrystallization can result in variations in the size and orientation of the recrystallized grains and thus to undesired contrasts in brightness on anodized section surfaces. Known examples include the side opposite to a branch in the profile cross section and the highly deformed material in the area of a weld (see also section 5.7.6.5). In the extreme case variations in the billet structure and in the through working occur as regions with different tones on the same flat polished surface of a section.

5.7.4.3 Surface Roughness

In contrast to most deformed surfaces, extruded section surfaces of aluminum alloys in particular are not formed by the extension and dissipation of the surface of the starting material [Kie 65, Mie 62]. Instead, the section surface is newly formed from the interior of the material by a cutting process between the deformation zones and the dead metal zones.

Two shear zones meet during this cutting process. In one, the flowing material is sheared along the dead metal zone; in the other, it is moved into the exit direction.

The extremely severe deformation of the outermost surface layer in the region of the entry edge can result in cavitation defects in heterogeneous materials. Hollow spaces form by the separation of nonplastic particles from the matrix or by the fracture of these particles without the matrix metal filling the space between the fracture pieces. If the hollow spaces bond together in the direction of extrusion and the hard particles separate from the matrix, microgrooves form on the surface [She 88, Clo 86].

The surface formed in the region of the entry edge undergoes a change by adhesion wear as it passes through the die aperture. The roughness of the section is therefore usually higher than that of the die bearing.

In the same way as the friction load as an integral value is strongly dependent on the

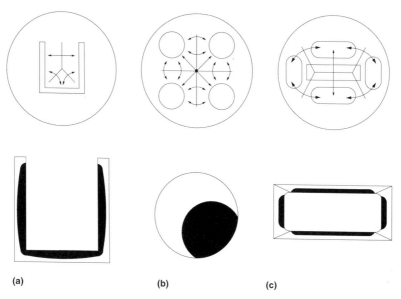

(a)　　　　　　　(b)　　　　　　　(c)

Fig. 5.19 Highly deformed peripheral zone material (light) and normally elongated core material (dark) at the end of extrusion [Ake 88a]

length and the angle of the bearing surface, the locally effective mechanisms of friction and wear of the surfaces of the section and die vary along the die bearing.

The following possibilities have to be considered, as shown in Fig. 5.20:

- Slip of the section as a solid body with a sudden speed increase at the steel surface
- Formation of a coherent layer of aluminum adhering to the bearing surface and slip of the solid section with a sudden speed increase between the section and the bonded layer
- Adhesion of the section peripheral layer on the bearing surface, parabolic speed distribution across the section thickness

Slip exactly corresponding to "the first point" is not seen in hot extrusion of aluminum without lubrication.

A friction "a + b" with adhesion of discrete aluminum particles on the bearing surfaces corresponds most closely to the experience of die correctors and with the nitriding of bearing surfaces. Microscopic investigations on split die inserts confirm that aluminum particles bond to the bearing surfaces to an increasing extent and size in the extrusion direction and determine the microgeometry of the section surface. The aluminum nodules that adhere to the bearing surfaces form grooves on the section surface. The formation of layers of aluminum, which can be interspersed with oxide, increases the number of adhesion points opposing the extrusion direction [The 93]. The nodules are finally torn off with the section and appear as particles ("pickup") on the surface [Tok 88, She 88, The 93, Abt 96].

In the majority of cases, die bearing lengths are less than the section thickness. If the bearing surfaces are parallel, mixed friction occurs over the entire length. The surface roughness of the extruded product is governed by the adhered layer, i.e., by the tendency for the material to adhere to the die [Mue 96, Mie 62, The 93]. This adhesion tendency cannot be completely suppressed by nitriding the bearing surfaces, but the aluminum layer builds more slowly on nitrided die bearings. In the absence of lubrication, the aim for a high surface quality is not the maximum possible undistorted slip of aluminum over steel (slip process (a) in Fig. 5.20) but the most uniform buildup of a thin adhered layer of aluminum on the die bearing surface. This aim is best fulfilled by die bearings ground perpendicular to the extrusion direction. Die surfaces ground or polished parallel to the extrusion direction or polished favor an irregular buildup of the adhered layer in the form of long elongated and correspondingly wide and high ridges. Figure 5.21 [Tok 88] shows the roughness variation over the length of a flat section on a small research press.

The surface roughness of the extruded product decreases as the bearing length increases between $l_k = 0$ and $l_k = 1$ to 3 mm because with increasing back pressure the adhesive layer regresses at the entry edge. As the bearing length increases, the roughness increases again as a consequence of higher temperatures [Wel 96] and possible mechanical activation processes [She 88] (Fig. 5.22). The optimum has been found to be bearing lengths of the order of half the thickness for flat sections [Mie 62, Tok 76, Tok 88, She 88, The 93].

As the number of extrusions increases, the fine aluminum nodules combine to form a layer that ultimately completely covers the die bearing surface. The relationship between the surface roughness of the extruded product and the buildup of the adhesive layer on the slip surface is shown in Fig. 5.23 [The 93].

In the initial region 1, no aluminum adheres to the bearing surfaces so that section roughness is governed by the surface finish of the die. In

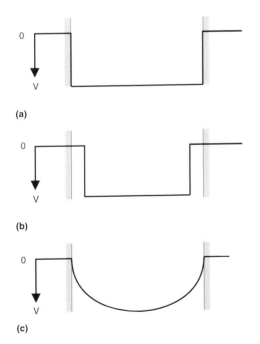

Fig. 5.20 Velocity distribution transverse across the die aperture

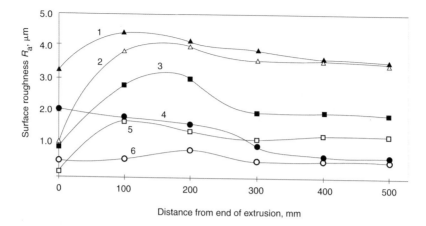

Distance from end of extrusion, mm

No.	Finish	Roughness, μm	Billet temperature, °C
1	Ground parallel in direction of extrusion	1.50–1.75	450
2	Ground parallel in direction of extrusion	0.50–0.75	450
3	Polished	0.50–0.75	500
4	Ground perpendicular in direction of extrusion	1.50–1.75	450
5	Polished	1.50–1.75	450
6	Ground perpendicular in direction of extrusion	0.50–0.75	450

Fig. 5.21 Influence of the finish of the bearing surface on the quality of the section surface [Tok 88]

region 2, the aluminum adhesive layer builds up and the section roughness increases rapidly. When the bearing has been completely covered, dynamic equilibrium develops in region 3 between adhesion and tearing away of aluminum particles so that the surface roughness remains almost constant. The section roughness is significantly lower than the roughness of the adhered layer. A reduction in the section roughness was periodically observed in trials involving 180 extrusions, and this was attributed to a partial or complete detachment of the coating.

The angle of the die bearing has a significant influence on the friction force and results in a different formation of the coating [Mue 96]. However, it has only a small influence on the section roughness. Hand-filed bearing surfaces close up at the entry and open up at the exit. Mixed friction dominates on bearings that are not too long, yet the changes in the face pressure and the angle result in a different formation of the coating. In the opening exit area loose adhesions form and damage the section surface by die lines and pickup [Clo 90].

As the billet temperature increases, the tendency for adhesion between the section surface and the bearing surfaces increases [Mie 62, Tok 88, Clo 90].

For a given billet temperature, the roughness, the degree of pickup, and the scatter of the gray scale (as a measure of the degree of streaking) increase to a maximum with increasing extrusion speed and then decrease at even faster speeds. This is explained by the hypothesis that at higher speeds the section surface slides over a thin layer of almost liquid metal [Par 96].

Alloy type, alloy content, and differences in the thermal pretreatment of the billets can have a significant influence on the extrusion speed that can be achieved for given surface finish re-

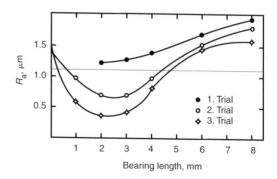

Fig. 5.22 Influence of the bearing length on the roughness R_a of the section surface [She 88]

quirements. Precipitates of alloying constituents have the worst effect.

5.7.4.4 Transverse Cracks and Peeling

The tensile stresses produced in the peripheral layer by the friction on the bearing combined with the considerably higher temperature [Moo 96, Joh 96] and the correspondingly lower flow stress result in defects, which can penetrate deep into the section from the surface. Figure 5.24 (a–d) shows the qualitative variation in the velocity and the stress at the entry to the die aperture.

The material being formed flows from the deformation zone into the die aperture. The profile core flows faster than the surface section, which is retarded by the friction at the surface. The core

remains in compression, but a tensile stress prevails in the peripheral zone. If this stress is too low to produce plastic strain, the section can flow as a solid body through the die aperture (Fig. 5.24a). Higher tensile stresses can result in an elongation of the hotter and at the entry slower flowing peripheral layer. This is seen particularly on thin ribs and internal legs of hollow sections (Fig. 5.24b). The elongation of the peripheral layer after the removal of the dominating high mean compressive stress in front of the die results in various types of material defects, depending on the structure and the peripheral layer temperature. Lubricant residues that inadvertently have reached the inner wall of the container can flow into the section following path 1 in Fig. 5.14 and form an interface parallel to the surface. The surface layer can break away during extrusion (peeling) (Fig. 5.24c). In other cases, the material of the interface can break up during a subsequent heat treatment, and the surface layer bulges out in the form of a row of blisters. Peeling is also caused by the melting of isolated eutectic regions resulting from unfavorable casting and homogenization conditions [Rei 84, Lef 96].

A classic defect process is the formation, growth, and the amalgamation of voids resulting in transverse cracks that penetrate deeply into the section (fir tree) (Fig. 5.24d), The propagation and expansion of the cracks occur at the location of the plastic elongation of the peripheral layer. At the same time the transfer of the tensile stresses into the billet is prevented so that less material flows into the peripheral layer. The volume deficit in the peripheral zone is therefore considerably larger than in the case of plastic elongation as shown in Fig. 5.24(b).

In the common aluminum wrought alloys the melting of individual structural regions, e.g., along grain boundaries, is the defect initiating process (hot shortness). The transient exceeding of the solidus temperature in the peripheral layer is the most common cause of transverse cracks. The average section temperature measured at the exit is naturally well below the solidus temperature.

Another type of transverse crack that can occur well below the solidus temperature occurs in materials with a high fraction (>15%) of nonplastic brittle structural components.

5.7.5 Procedures to Control the Thermal Balance

As a general rule, the optimal productivity and quality with aluminum alloys can only be

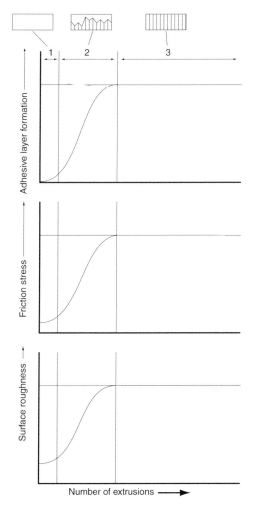

Fig. 5.23 Relationship between adhesive layer formation, friction stress, and surface roughness [The 93]

achieved by taking the thermal balance of the extrusion process into consideration. The temperature control is optimized by measures that either reduce the amount of heat that has to be removed or accelerate the heat transfer [Ake 71, Ake 80]. These measures have been described to some extent along with the extrusion process (Chapter 3). The technicalities of temperature control are described in more detail in Chapter 6.

5.7.5.1 Material

The heat produced during the extrusion process from the transformation of the mechanical work can be minimized by selecting the most easily extruded alloy from those that meet the product specification (see the section "Materials").

The additional fine adjustment covers the optimization of the composition, the solidification conditions, and the thermal treatment of the billet. Small changes appear to result in considerable differences in the extrusion speeds that can be achieved [Ake 71, Sta 90, Rei 84, Sca 69, Lyn 71, Lan 82, Spe 84, Lan 84].

5.7.5.2 Billet Temperature

The exit temperature is higher than the billet preheat temperature because of the deformation induced heating of the material being deformed; therefore, the billet is usually heated to a temperature below the desired average exit section temperature. The material reaches the desired value only as it passes through the deformation zone. This is described in detail in Chapter 3.

A uniform temperature gradient from the front to the rear of the billet can compensate approximately for the increasing heat from the shear deformation of the peripheral layer. Additional heating of the front of the billet reduces the load needed at the start of the extrusion process and ensures that there is sufficient solution heat treatment effect at the front of the section. This method of achieving "isothermal extrusion," however, requires rapid localized heating or cooling because of the good thermal conductivity of the aluminum. The billet then has to be extruded with minimum delay.

In general, the effectiveness of the procedures in this first group increases as the billet cycle time decreases, for example the extrudability of the alloy improves.

5.7.5.3 Heat Removal

The opposite applies to the following procedures, which require heat flow into the tooling and which are most effective for slow extrusion speeds and long cycle times.

Container. The most important heat sink is the container, which plays an important role in the productivity in the extrusion of aluminum alloys. The container is basically heated to a

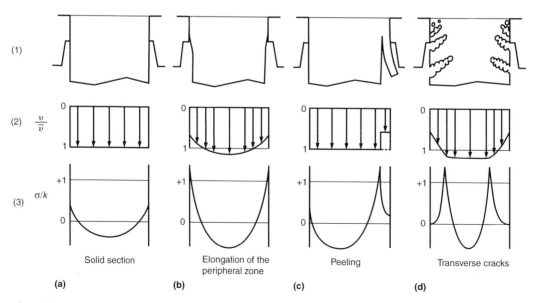

(1)

(2) $\dfrac{v}{\bar{v}}$

(3) σ/k

| Solid section | Elongation of the peripheral zone | Peeling | Transverse cracks |
| (a) | (b) | (c) | (d) |

Fig. 5.24 Influence of tensile stresses in the section peripheral layer. 1, appearance of the extrusion; 2, velocity variation across the section; 3, variation of the longitudinal stresses across the section

temperature below that of the specified billet preheat temperature. The temperature difference is usually limited to 50 K in order to avoid the billet sticking in the container because of inadequate press power ("sticker"). The thermal balance in the system container-billet is described in Chapter 3.

The temperature set or recorded on the container heater controller applies only to the hottest location, where, from experience, overheating of the tool steel has to be avoided. The actual temperature field in the container is shown in the example in Fig. 3.19. There are temperature differences of the order of 100 K in the axial and radial direction. The temperature maximum moves during 5 to 10 extrusions from the heating zone to the liner inner face [Ake 71, Ake 72, Sch 79].

The cooling, i.e., the heat flow from the container bore through the wall and into the atmosphere, is determined largely by the thermal conductivity of the container wall. Cooling of the mantle surface by an intensive air blast has only an insignificant effect on the cooling. Blowing onto the container end face has more effect.

Today, combined heating and cooling systems are installed in containers for temperature control (see the section on tooling in chapter 7).

Die. Removing excess deformation heat through the die is helped by the short thermal path from the deformation zone to the location of the cooling channels. Another advantage is that the cooling takes place during the final stage of the deformation so that the load requirement is increased only during the final deformation stage. There is also the possibility of specifically cooling the critical regions, e.g., at the edges prone to tearing.

Because a significant amount of heat has to flow through a relatively small die cross section, it is necessary from the cooling point of view to have an intense heat transfer to a coolant with sufficiently large thermal capacity.

This requirement is more easily fulfilled with liquid coolants than gas. On this basis, the following methods can be differentiated for die cooling:

- Water cooling
- Cooling with liquid-supplied evaporating nitrogen
- Flushing with gaseous nitrogen

Approximate calculations demonstrate that the cooling capacity through a plate 200 mm in diameter is in the range between 2 and 12 kW,

depending on the thickness and the coolant. This can be compared with the drive power of a press of up to 400 kW.

The approximate calculations show that with the fast extrusion of alloys with a high extrudability, only a small amount of deformation heat can be removed through a cooled die. With a plate thickness of 50 mm, an aluminum flow of 1 kg/s can at best be cooled by approximately 6 K with water and by only approximately 2.5 K with liquid nitrogen.

A significant reduction in the exit temperature is achieved only with the slow extrusion of the difficult-to-work alloys. In trials it has been possible to increase the exit speed of an AlCuMg alloy by 30% using water cooling. Approximately 15% of the deformation heat can be removed by the water cooling [Bat 79].

The limited resistance of the die materials to temperature fluctuations makes water cooling of a die difficult.

Liquid nitrogen is usually fed through channels machined either in the die itself [Sca 79] or more commonly in the front face of the backer [Wag, Sel 84, Yam 92]. If a separate feeder plate is used, an additional network of cooling channels can be machined in the rear face so that the die is cooled from the front and the back [Ros].

The aim is for the nitrogen fed in as a liquid to evaporate extensively as it flows through the cooling channels. This gives an approximately constant cooling capability, the effect of which is distributed over a more or less large aluminum material flow, depending on the extrusion speed.

In experiments with nine different alloys, the extrusion speed of AlMgSi0.5 could be increased by approximately 8% by cooling, but with the more slowly flowing alloy AlZn-MgCu1.5, by a significant 80% [Sca 79].

The dwell time of the deformation material in the die region is short so that the peripheral zone of the section is cooled the most. This reduces the temperature peaks, which are largely responsible for the tearing of the section surface at high extrusion speeds (Fig. 5.25) [Sel 84].

This is the reason why even with limited cooling effect the speed can often also be increased considerably with fast-flowing alloys. The evaporated nitrogen emerges from behind the die aperture onto the surface of the newly extruded section to utilize the protective atmosphere effect (see below).

Gaseous nitrogen is fed through channels in the gap between the die and the backer into the space behind the die exit. The mass flow of the nitrogen stream is usually not more than 1% of that of the aluminum stream because of the low density. The nitrogen flow is therefore not sufficient to cause any serious cooling.

The regularly observed improvement in the section surface must therefore be more attributable to an influence on the dynamic equilibrium of adhesion and tearing off of the aluminum particles on the die bearing by the reaction of the newly formed aluminum surface with the atmosphere.

Mandrel. In contrast to heavy metal extrusion where cooling of the mandrel is unavoidable because of the high thermal loading, in aluminum extrusion, mandrel cooling is not required to compensate for high temperatures. In practice, mandrel cooling is therefore not used. However, temperature measurements on the extruded profile have shown that the specific heat removed by cooled mandrels is at least equal to that associated with die cooling with liquid nitrogen so that it appears to be possible to achieve higher maximum extrusion speeds by extruding over cooled mandrels [Rup 82].

5.7.5.4 Optimization of the Extrusion Parameters

Following the discussion of the different means of influencing the thermal balance their application to the optimisation of the extrusion parameters will now be considered. Apart from other limiting additional parameters the extrusion parameters are at an optimum if the exit temperature over the entire cross-section falls within the permitted range for the alloy under consideration, the extrusion speed is as high as possible in the range limited by the equipment, and the extrusion load needed uses the maximum press power of the press within a specific safety factor [Rup 77, Rup 77a, Rup 83].

The parameters that can be set at the press are the ram speed, the initial billet temperature, and the container temperature. The billet temperature and speed can be constant for a heating and extrusion cycle or be decreasing from the front to the back and then be adjusted in subsequent extrusion cycles.

Of all the set parameters, only the extrusion speed can be varied during a single extrusion cycle. The billet temperature and the temperature profile can, in contrast, be set for each cycle before loading into the press. A change in the average temperature or the temperature profile is possible in experimental work and under production conditions in the next billet. The temperature profile in the container with the usual arrangement of heating elements in the container mantle follows a change in the set temperature only after a long delay of several hours. A rapid change in the container temperature can be achieved with heating and cooling systems installed in the liner [Har 94].

The parameter that has to be controlled is the section exit temperature; however, there are numerous difficulties in its continuous measurement, particularly in the case of aluminum alloys:

- The critical maximum temperature occurs in an unknown location in the die aperture that is practically impossible to access for measurements.
- The critical temperature occurs for only a very short time.
- The section surface is soft and easily damaged.
- The radiation is in the invisible infrared range.
- The emissivity of bright aluminum surfaces is very low and also is strongly dependent on the roughness and the wavelength (it is not a "gray" body).
- The measurement area is surrounded by strong sources of additional radiation.

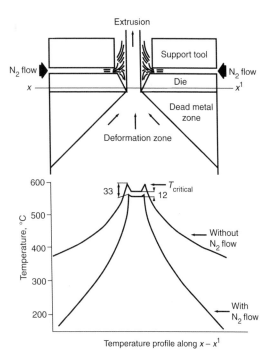

Fig. 5.25 Temperature variation in the die with and without cooling with liquid nitrogen [Sel 84]

- The display of all temperature sensors is associated with definite delays and with significant measurement scatter.

The original concept of isothermal extrusion assumed a continuous control of the speed based on the measured exit temperature [Lau 60]. This concept is difficult to achieve because of the difficulties mentioned previously, as well as the delayed response of the exit temperature to a change in the speed associated with the heat content of the material in the press. Changing the speed with a rapid reacting control system would result in an unstable reaction in the control loop.

The control systems used or proposed and tested today attempt to cope with these problems associated with exit temperature measurement in various ways. All these control systems are based on optimization concepts with the aim of maintaining the exit temperature within the desired range by suitable combinations of the available parameters and simultaneously maximizing the productivity of the press. One factor to take into account is that every change of one parameter changes all heat sources and heat flows, i.e., the factors that combine to give the exit temperature [Ake 80]. This is described in more detail in Chapter 6.

5.7.6 *Joining by Extrusion*

The production of complex sections with one or more cavities plays a particularly important role in aluminum alloys. Approximately half the sections produced in the easy to moderately difficult to extrude AlMgSi alloys are hollow sections such as box beams and hollow engineering plates. Compared with the functional corresponding solid sections (I-beams, plates with T-shaped reinforcements) the hollow sections have the advantage of a much higher torsional and bending stiffness. With the exception of tubes in the strictest sense, the hollow sections have *longitudinal welds* where the metal streams split by the supporting legs of the mandrel reunite in a metallic bond.

The joining of the metal from billets extruded one after the other by *transverse welds* is used for products in long lengths and large coil weights. In addition, having a material residue in the die entry or a feeder chamber provides exact positioning of the front of the section, which is essential for automation of the guiding of the front end. The next billet has to join to the residual material in the die.

Special applications of joining in extrusion are cladding or locally reinforced sections of two different materials (two aluminum alloys) (aluminum-copper, aluminum-steel), the compaction and deformation of powder and granular scrap, and the production of composite materials with a metal matrix. This is described later in this chapter.

5.7.6.1 Extrusion Welding

The general metallurgical principles of bonding by extrusion are discussed in Chapter 4. The following section describes how the extrusion process relevant properties of the aluminum alloys influence the technology of extrusion welding and the quality characteristics of the extruded welds.

Aluminum alloys can be extruded in a temperature range at which the tooling is not overheated so that the stability and service life of even complex hollow section dies are adequate. The high adhesion affinity for steel results in adhesive friction in the die at areas with high surface pressures and to the formation of dead metal zones (Fig. 5.26).

After only a short time in air, newly formed aluminum surfaces are coated with an oxide layer that cannot be reduced by any gas atmosphere or removed by diffusion of the oxygen into the parent metal. Aluminum therefore belongs to the group of metals that cannot be joined without macroscopic shape change, i.e., not by mere pressure and heat (diffusion welding) [Jel 79, Bry 75].

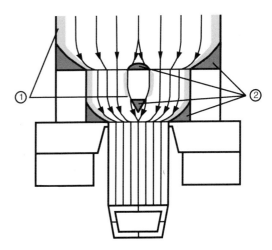

Fig. 5.26 Laminar material flow [Ake 92]. 1, adhesive friction; 2, dead metal zone

In order for two aluminum bodies to join in the solid state, these brittle separating oxide layers require a significant combined deformation to break up the oxide skin and to bring nonoxidized metal to the joint. The generic term *deformation welding* includes roll cladding, composite impact extrusion, and powder extrusion, as well as extrusion welding. It is possible from observations of these processes using general metallurgical basic principles to draw conclusions on the processes (previously studied only to a limited extent) that occur during bonding by extrusion.

The influence of the initial unevenness of the surfaces is also important [Ast 75]. The adhesion process is the result of the plastic flow of the metal in the contact zone, the deformation of the rough tips, the formation of slip and shear bands in the region of the contact surfaces, and the movement of the dislocation fields of the individual contacts. Uneven contact areas, however, rarely occur in longitudinal welds and then in conjunction with cavities under the support legs of the mandrel system.

5.7.6.2 Longitudinal Welds in Hollow Sections

When applying these thoughts on deformation welding to extrusion welding, it is assumed that the latter consists of three sequential extrusion processes and the associated transport and deviation processes (Fig. 5.27). In the first stage (Fig. 5.27a), the billet is divided into two or more streams that flow together under the legs (Fig. 5.27b, c). In the deformation final stage (Fig. 5.27d), the hollow section forms by the metallic bonding of the streams.

The processes at the contact areas are related to the material flow (Fig. 5.26). The conditions on the exit side of the leg are critical where either a dead metal zone or a cavity can form.

Normally, the pressure in the welding chamber is so high that the space under the legs is completely filled and a dead metal zone forms. The conditions for the formation of a dead metal zone and for a good weld have been expressed by several authors in the form of ratios that can be deduced from the die geometry and provide a reference point for the magnitude of the total deformation. As well as the size of the welding chamber, the ratio of the welding chamber cross section to the profile cross section is important [Gil 75].

The pressure applied at the point of formation of the longitudinal weld is composed of components for the reduction in cross-sectional area from the welding chamber to the section, for the deviation in the flow of the metal stream and for overcoming the friction in the die aperture.

Oxide can only enter the welding chamber with the first filling of the die when the free oxide coated front faces of the streams meet (Fig. 5.28a) [Ake 92]. The fractured residues of these

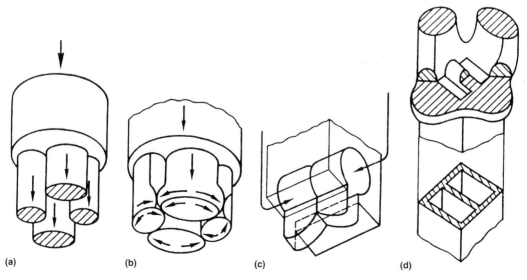

(a) (b) (c) (d)

Fig. 5.27 Extrusion of hollow sections. (a) Straight into the ports. (b) At an angle under the legs. (c) At an angle between two mandrel heads. (d) Emergence of the section [Ake 92]

oxide films are largely removed with the front part of the section (Fig. 5.28b). Further bonding occurs between material regions that initially have been upset in front of the legs and mandrels and have then flown along the flanks of the leg with severe shear distortion to collect in the dead metal zone under the legs. The streams that meet together have no free surface and, therefore, no roughness and no oxide film. The welding process then merely consists of the initially small contact area being extended over the total length of the section and thus being enlarged by several orders of magnitude, whereby the subgrains also continuously reform over the original contact areas. This repolygonization is associated with the movement of dislocations but does not require diffusion of atoms.

Die geometries where the cross section of the material flow path is too narrow should be avoided because these result in inadequate feed into the weld chamber and in an inadequate pressure buildup. This can result in cavities

forming on the exit side of the leg (gas pockets) [Val 95].

Two-dimensional numerical simulation and experimental semiplanar extrusion both showed the formation of cavity with a section thickness of 25 mm and a dead metal zone with a section thickness of 12.5 mm for the same welding chamber height (Fig. 5.29) [Wel 95].

The contact with the leg is lost under the conditions where a cavity is formed, and it is the free more or less roughened surfaces of the streams that meet in the welding chamber.

The bonding is then restricted to the rough crests [Val 95, Val 96], has little ductility, and is above all very brittle [Ake 92]. Voids in the joint are recognizable in the fracture as bands without fracture dimples and they are preferentially etched in the cross section by alkaline etchants.

Transverse cracks can also occur in the region of the longitudinal welds. In principle these are no different to the surface and edge cracks that occur on solid sections when the peripheral layer

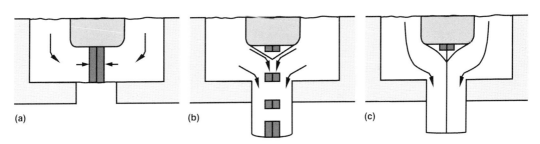

Fig. 5.28 Breakup of the surface layer in longitudinal welds. (a) Meeting under the leg. (b) Breaking apart. (c) Clean longitudinal weld [Ake 92]

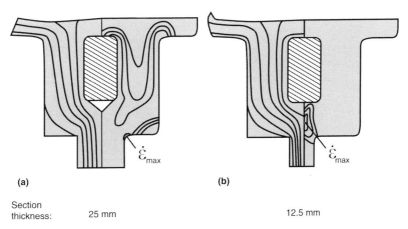

Section thickness: 25 mm   12.5 mm

Fig. 5.29 Formation of a hollow space (gas pocket) under the mandrel support leg at a low extrusion ratio (a) and a dead metal zone at a higher extrusion ratio (b). On the left, flow lines; right, lines of equal strain rate [Wel 95]

reaches the hot-shortness temperature [Val 96a]. The fact that the transverse cracks occur preferentially next to the longitudinal welds can be attributed to the severe heating of the peripheral layers of the metal streams, particularly under the legs [Ska 96].

5.7.6.3 Transverse Welds

Transverse welds are usually the severely curved surfaces where the material of the next billet bonds with the residue of the previously extruded billet. This residue can be located in the container, in the feeder chamber of a die for a solid section, or in the entry ports of a hollow die (Fig. 5.30a–c).

The process where the residue is left as a thick discard in the container (Fig. 5.30a) is usually used for the extrusion of cable sheaths and electric conductors in large coil weights. Special measures have to be taken to avoid smearing of the contact surfaces.

The process shown in Fig. 5.30(b) and (c) in which the discard is removed in front of the feeder chamber or in front of the entry ports is common for aluminum sections. Stripping of the discard (Fig. 5.30d) is also possible with aluminum but increases in difficulty with more complex sections.

The originally flat contact surface between the residue and the next billet is deformed to a tongue because of the adhesion of the aluminum to the tool surface. The outline of the tongue approximates to the contour of the corresponding material stream. In the region of the tips of these tongues the contact surface can contract by as much as 50% so that the fractured residues of the oxide layer are more likely to slip over each

other than be pulled apart. In the most unfavorable case, there is no bonding [Ake 72], particularly with the current practice considered to be unavoidable of lubricating the dummy block and the discard shear [Joh 96a].

With highly stressed sections, a length long enough to contain the tongue of the transverse weld is removed as scrap from the stop mark. This section usually includes one to two times the content of the entry zones and the welding chambers.

In most of the transverse weld the fractured residues of the oxide layer are extensively pulled apart. These profiles can be supplied with the transverse weld for noncritical applications providing the material surrounding the tongues, which originates from the previously extruded billet, can withstand the stresses from the stretching of the section.

When the method of formation is considered, it is easy to understand that there is a greater risk of transverse welds being impaired by surface coatings than longitudinal welds. When material separations apparently occur in longitudinal welds, usually the transverse welds running along both sides are involved [Val 95].

The most important sources of defects in extrusion welds are [Wei 92]:

- Lubricant or corrosion on the dies
- Impurities on the billet front surface or dirt on the billet surface
- Incorrect die design

Basically, all parts that come into contact with the material being extruded must be clean and, in particular, be free of oil, grease, or graphite. The requirement for perfect separation of the

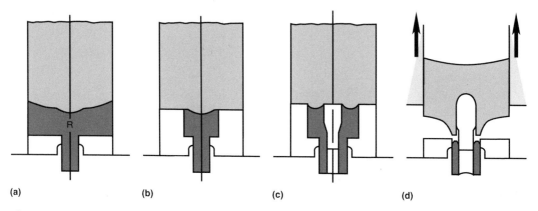

(a) (b) (c) (d)

Fig. 5.30 Extrusion of aluminum "billet on billet." (a) Extrusion of a billet on the discard R in the container. (b) With feeder die. (c) In the ports of a porthole die. (d) Pulling off the discard in a bridge die to avoid transverse welds [Ake 92]

dummy block and the discard, however, results in practice in compromise solutions in which specific lubricants are considered to be indispensable but have to be used as little as possible and accurately applied.

5.7.6.4 Testing of Extrusion Welds

The extrusion weld has to be considered as a surface of which a fraction f_D is covered with fragments of the original surface coating [Ake 92]. The remaining fraction f_1 consists of metallic ligaments with the same flow stress as the parent material. These ligaments are very short in relationship to their width and can therefore withstand a high three-dimensional tensile stress under tensile loading.

In a tensile test perpendicular to an extrusion weld the specimen can completely neck outside the weld. In the plastic region where the limit of elastic deformation is exceeded many times over, failure in the extrusion weld can still occur. The concentration of fragments of the surface coating on the contacting surfaces facilitates the damage with increasing deformation, i.e., the formation, the growth, and the combination of pores to form microcracks and, finally, failure.

The usual parameters of 0.2% proof stress and the tensile strength from the tensile test have limited relevance to the quality testing of extrusion welds. The increased sensitivity to damage in the region of the extrusion weld compared with the parent material is best expressed by a decrease in the reduction in area at fracture. The quicker the extrusion weld is damaged, the lower is the strain to fracture [Ake 92]. With decreasing extrusion weld quality, the elongation and, in the extreme case, the tensile strength, are also impaired as well as the reduction in area.

Structural Investigation. Because the information from tensile tests is limited, numerous other testing procedures are used for testing the quality of extrusion welds. The location of the longitudinal and transverse welds can be seen in the macrostructure. If a section is cut from an extrusion at an externally visible interface between two billets, it is possible to identify from the structure between neighboring transverse welds whether sufficient material has been cut out to achieve sound material. An extremely intensive etch attack will reveal the inclusion of a lubricant or the peripheral layer.

Ultrasonic Testing, Fatigue Investigations. Ultrasound enables both hidden material separations and laminar enrichments of noncoherent particles to be detected. For example, the tongues of transverse welds can be localized. In fatigue studies the quality of the extrusion welds does not have a significant influence on the total number of cycles but does on the rate of growth of a crack in the extrusion weld at the end of the endurance.

Various Mechanical Tests. A critical mechanical test for extrusion welds requires that the strain is reached at which failure will occur in the parent material or in the weld. This critical strain is strongly material dependent because the energy released from the material separation ("the damage potential") grows with the square of the elastic limit. Various technological testing procedures [Gil 75] enable the controlled transverse of strains that correspond in tensile tests approximately to the region of uniform elongation up to fracture necking:

- Bending tests on samples taken transverse to the extrusion welds. The limiting bending angle is measured at a section dependent specified bending radius.
- Folding tests along and between the welds up to an internal radius ≈ 0 and elongation of the outer surface of $\approx 100\%$
- Axial compression of a tube section to the point of folding
- Bending of tubes with a roll bending system under longitudinal loading of the extrusion weld
- Expansion with a conical mandrel and measurement of the strain in the circumferential direction

These technological testing procedures are suitable for following quality variations along and between profiles with the same cross section and the same material and for monitoring the maintenance of tolerance limits that have been specified for the individual application. However, they do not supply any characteristic values that could be used for numerical validation of the safety of a design. The "calibration" of a technological testing process from the point of view of a fracture mechanics test value is still an unresolved problem.

5.7.6.5 Influence of the Extrusion Weld on the Surface Appearance

Although it is only a few atomic spacings thick, an extrusion weld can affect the appearance of the anodic film on a visible surface in the form of a band several times wider than the wall thickness [War 95]. Depending on the incidence angle of the light, the area of the same extrusion weld can appear to be lighter or darker than the rest of the surface. The primary cause of this optical contrast between the region of the extrusion weld and the residual material is the heavier working of the peripheral zones of the split streams compared with the core zone. In the region of the weld the section consists of heavily deformed material throughout its full thickness, which results in variations in the size and orientation of the grains and thus the reflection behavior.

5.7.6.6 Suitability of the Material for Hollow Section Extrusion

The selection of the material and the extrusion temperature as well as the die geometry and the avoidance of impurities play an important role in determining the practical applicability of extrusion welding. As a basic rule, all wrought aluminum alloys can be extrusion welded [Ake 72a]. The extrusion pressure, which is already increased by the flow through narrow angled channels, increases with increasing flow stress to values that overload the mandrel. However, hinge sections with a small core (the hole for the pivot) are extruded with bridge dies in the high-strength AlCuMg1.5 and AlZnMgCu alloys [Cre]. Engineering sections with large cores are usually produced in the alloys of the group AlMgSi0.7, AlMgSi1, and AlZnMg.

Only the strength and toughness of the parent metal in the thickness direction is achieved in the transverse direction across the weld because of the fiber orientation in the region of the extrusion weld. In alloys that have a high manganese content to obtain the extrusion effect, transverse sections frequently exhibit lamellar tears along surfaces parallel to the extrusion weld, which are enriched with eutectically precipitated particles. The mechanical properties in the region of the weld can also be impaired by coarse-grain recrystallization of heavily worked material regions. There are alloys available for hollow engineering sections that recrystallize completely and that include peritectically solidifying transition elements instead of manganese [Scw 84].

With the more easily extruded alloys, mainly AlMgSi0.5, a complete fine-grain recrystallization is desired to give the decorative appearance.

Materials

Günther Scharf*

The selection of the alloy for extrusion is usually based on achieving a given property range with specific surface properties at the lowest possible cost. These include the costs for the billet; the actual extrusion; the heat treatment; and the additional operations including stretching, detwisting, and cross-sectional correction.

In contrast to rolling where the strength is increased significantly by cold working, extruded products are hot worked and, therefore, the material condition is practically soft. Cold working can be considered for wires and tubes, which are drawn to their final dimensions. However, aluminum alloys are usually extruded to the final dimensions and the optimal mechanical properties are produced by a suitable heat treatment.

With the exception of the isolated use of silver, the usual alloying additions to aluminum alloys have only a slight effect on the cost of the billets. However, the influence on the cost of extrusion, heat treatment, and correction is much higher.

The influence of the most common alloying additions, magnesium, copper, silicon, and zinc, on the flow stress can be found in section 5.5 and in Fig. 5.12 in section 5.7.

Magnesium increases the flow stress the most followed by copper, whereas silicon only has a small influence and zinc, practically no increase [Ake 70]. The influence of intermetallic phases, in particular of Mg_2Si, has also been extensively studied. This has shown that it is not only the amount of the alloying constituents that increases the flow stress and thus reduces the extrusion speed, but also that the microstructure in which the alloying constituents occur plays an important role [Sca 69, Gru 66, Sca 69b]. Supersaturated dissolved or fine dispersions of precipitated Mg_2Si increase the flow stress and thus make deformation more difficult, whereas coarse precipitates of Mg_2Si phases reduce the flow stress.

The influence of the structure has a particularly significant effect on those alloying elements that tend to supersaturation during solidification and later precipitate during subsequent

---

*Materials, Günther Scharf

billet heat treatment as a reversible fine dispersion. The influence of manganese, in particular, is strongly dependent on the precipitate state and on the number and fineness of the intermetallic particles [Gru 66]. Intermetallic phases including Al_6Mn, MnFeSi, Al_3Zr, and $FeAl_3$ reduce the extrudability significantly [Sca 67, Sca 69a].

Figure 5.31 shows the product strength of the most common aluminum alloys as a function of the flow stress at the extrusion temperature. The majority of extruded products therefore are produced in heat treatable alloys with the lowest possible alloy content. The desire to reduce the magnesium content by a tenth or even a hundredth of a percent is due to the strong influence of the flow stress on the cost of extrusion as well as the downstream processes. The extrusion load required is proportional to the flow stress as is the deformation work converted into heat. Another important consideration is that the time needed for this heat to penetrate into the tooling increases with the square of the flow stress, and the extrusion speed decreases accordingly. Apart from the dead cycle time, which is largely independent of the material, the machine costs of the extrusion process alone increase to the cube of the flow stress. The heat

treatment costs and correction processes also increase with higher alloy contents.

The heat treatment of age-hardening alloys basically consists of the processes (see also Chapter 4):

- Dissolution of the alloying constituents
- Quenching to retain in metastable solution
- Age hardening, usually hot, in one or more temperature stages

An important simplification is possible if the product leaves the press with a temperature in the region of solution heat treatment and can be immediately quenched to achieve the desired result. This requires that the interval between the solution temperature and the start of melting is greater than the unavoidable temperature error and differences along the length of and across the section. In other cases an optimum solution heat treatment can be achieved only by a separate operation in a very accurately controlled oven. In this case, the material cannot be "press quenched."

As the alloy content is reduced, the precipitation pressure decreases. The section does not have to be quenched so quickly but can be cooled using less drastic means. This has the advantage that distortion resulting from excessive localized temperature differences is avoided. Thin AlMgSi0.5 sections can be adequately cooled in static air or under fans. A more intensive heat transfer is necessary for thick wall sections and higher alloy contents (e.g., AlMgSi0.7). This can be obtained with high air velocities (nozzles) or air water mixtures (mist nozzles) [Kra 93, Str 96]. The cooling requirements provide an additional material-dependent cost factor partly related to the cost of the cooling system but mainly because of the correction costs that rapidly increase with increasing cooling rate.

Because the extrusion load depends mainly on the flow stress k_f, the wrought aluminum alloys are classified according to the flow stress into the groups easy to extrude, moderately difficult, and hard to extrude. Thus

Easy to extrude	$k_f \leq 30$ N/mm^2
Moderately difficult	k_f 30 to 45 N/mm^2
Hard to extrude	k_f 45–57 N/mm^2

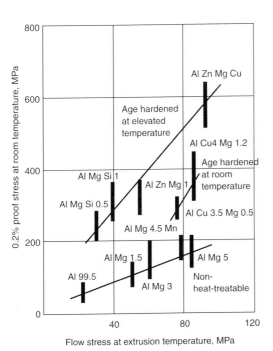

Fig. 5.31 0.2% proof stress of extruded aluminum alloys in the standard as-supplied condition as a function of the flow stress at the usual extrusion temperatures [Ake 71]

On top of this, there is the increasing investment in equipment and the cost of heat treatment and correction as well as the quality control.

The material behavior during plastic working can be derived from high-temperature torsion flow curves. These show the deformation load k_f as a function of the logarithmic principal strain φ. It should be emphasized here that the flow curve is a material parameter for the ideal deformation and depends on the working temperature and, in particular, the rate of deformation.

Figure 5.32 shows the torsion flow curves for the extrusion alloy AlMgSi0.5 at 450 °C and a

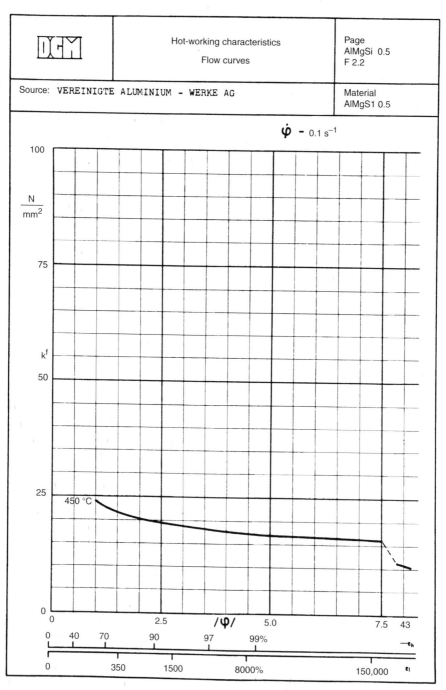

Fig. 5.32 Torsion flow curves of AlMgSi0.5 [DGM 78]

logarithmic strain rate of $d\varphi/dt = 0.1 \text{ s}^{-1}$ as a function of the logarithmic principal strain φ_g between 1 and 7.5.

The flow stress of the most important extrusion alloys is shown in Table 5.4 at a logarithmic principal strain of $\varphi_g = 2.7$. This corresponds to an extrusion ratio of 15:1. The k_f values listed illustrate the different deformation properties of the individual extruded alloys. These were obtained from torsion flow curves taken from both the DGM *Atlas of Hot-Working Properties,* Volume 1 [DGM 78], and internal investigations at VAW Aluminium, Bonn, Germany.

The aluminum alloys are designated below by the chemical symbols, which was the custom until recently. Table 5.5 compares the material designation of the old DIN 1712 T and 1725 T with the new DIN EN 573-3.

5.8 Easily Extruded Alloys

Alloys with low k_f values ($k_f \leq 30 \text{ N/mm}^2$) are usually classified as easily extruded. To a first approximation, the lower the required flow stress the better is the workability. Normally the possible exit speed increases with the workability [Ake 68].

5.8.1 Aluminum Alloys

In addition to aluminum, the naturally hard alloys AlMg1 and AlMn1, as well as AlMgSi0.5

Table 5.4 Flow stress of different aluminum alloys

Experimental material: homogenized cast billets. Test: torsion flow curves; test temperature 450 °C. Logarithmic principal strain $\varphi_g = 2.7$; deformation rate (log principal strain rate) $\dot{\varphi}_g = 0.1 \text{ s}^{-1}$

DIN EN 573-3(a)		Flow stress k_f, N/mm^2
Symbol	No.	
Easy-to-extrude alloys		
Al99.5	1050A	17.9
AlMgSi	6060	19.8
AlMn1	3103	23.6
AMg1	5005A	28.2
Hard-to-extrude alloys		
AlSiMgMn	6082	41.5
AlMg3Mn	5454	43.8
AlZn4.5Mg1	7020	44.2
Difficult-to-extrude alloys		
Al4.5MgMn0.7	5083	46.7
AlCuMg2	2024	48.2
AlCuMgFeNi	2618	51.5
AlMg5	5056A	55.9
AlZn5.5MgCu	7075	56.3

(a) The prefix "ENAW" has been omitted from the DIN EN 573-3 designations. A199.5 is ENAW-Al99.5; 1050A is ENAW-1050A.

and AlMgSi0.7, are considered to belong to the easily extruded alloys. Because AlMg1 and AlMgSi0.5 are frequently used for anodizing or bright finish applications, care must be taken to ensure that the Mg and Mg$_2$Si components are dissolved in the solid solution in the as-extruded state. Also, none or, if necessary, very small additions of insoluble or supersaturated dissolved elements such as manganese, chromium, zirconium, or iron may be used. For this reason, AlMg1 and AlMgSi0.5 are produced from a base metal of a higher purity for bright finish qualities. In DIN EN 573-3 the individual alloys are shown based on 99.85, 99.9 and 99.98 Al. If this is not taken into account, secondary precipitates can form during billet heat treatment and these can impair the surface quality of the extruded sections by streaking.

The billet heat treatment—referred to as *homogenization*—of AlMg1 is mainly to reduce crystal segregation and dendritic residual melt-

Table 5.5 Comparison of the aluminum alloys according to DIN and DIN EN

DIN 1712 T3/DIN 1725 T1	DIN EN 573-3(a)	
Symbol	Symbol	No.
Easy-to-extrude alloys		
Al99.5	Al 99.5	1050A
Al99.8	Al 99.85	1085
Al99.98R	Al 99.98	1098
E-Al	E Al 99.5	1350
AlMg1	AlMg1	5005A
AlMn1	AlMn1	3103
AlMgSi0.5	AlMgSi	6060
AlMgSi0.5	AlMg0.7Si	6063
AlMgSi0.7	AlSiMg	6005A
Moderately difficult-to-extrude alloys		
AlMg2.5	AlMg2.5	5052
AlMg3	AlMg3	5754
AlMg1Mn1	AlMn2Mg1	3004
AlMg2.7Mn	AlMg3Mn	5454
AlMgSi1	AlSiMgMn	6082
AlMgSiCu	AlMg1SiCu	6061
AlMgSiPb	AlMgSiPb	6012
AlZn4.5Mg1	AlZn4.5Mg1	7020
AlCuLi(b)	AlCu2LiMg1.5	2091
AlLiCuMg1(b)	AlLi2.5Cu1.5Mg1	8090
Hard-to-extrude alloys		
AlMg5	Al Mg5	5056A
AlMg4.5Mn	AlMg4.5Mn0.7	5083
AlCuMg2	AlCu4Mg1	2024
AlCuSiMn	AlCu4SiMg	2014
AlCuMgPb	AlCu4PbMgMn	2007
AlCuMgFeNi(b)	AlCu2Mg1.5Ni	2618
AlZnMgCu0.5	AlZn5Mg3Cu	7022
AlZnMgCu1.5	AlZn5.5MgCu	7075
AlZn8MgCu(b)	AlZn8MgCu	7049A

(a) The prefix "ENAW" has been omitted from the DIN EN 573-3 designations. A199.5 is ENAW-Al99.5; 1050A is ENAW-1050A.
(b) Not standardized in DIN

ing and to produce an easily worked cast structure. In contrast, in AlMn1 the manganese exits in a supersaturated solid solution. This nonequilibrium state is activated by the thermal treatment and tries to attain equilibrium by the formation of secondary precipitates. The size of the precipitated particles depends on the temperature and the heat treatment time. The higher the temperature and the longer the heat treatment time, the coarser are the particles. It is known that the degree of dispersion influences the recrystallized grain structure and the workability. It is therefore important with AlMn1 to heat treat at a high temperature of 590–620 °C in order to produce a fine grain during extrusion.

The most common easily extruded alloy is AlMgSi0.5. It differs from the materials described so far in that it achieves its properties by age hardening. AlMgSi0.5 is characterized by good mechanical properties as well as by outstanding workability combined with an excellent surface quality.

As already mentioned, the temperature range for the hot-working process coincides with that for solution heat treatment. In this case, separate solution heat treatment and quenching of the extruded section—as required for the high-strength materials—is not required.

AlMgSi0.5 extruded sections only need to be cooled with moving air because of the low quench sensitivity in order to retain the age-hardening phase Mg_2Si in α-solid solution. A characteristic of this alloy is that Mg_2Si can be retained in supersaturated solution with a cooling rate of only 2 K/s. The desired increase in strength can be obtained by subsequent cold or warm age hardening.

The important requirements for AlMgSi0.5 and AlMgSi0.7 type alloys are small fractions of the principle alloying elements dissolved in the α-solid solution at the press exit temperature and the avoidance of large additions of the recrystallization retarding elements of manganese, chromium, and zirconium because, in the form of fine secondary particles, these significantly increase the flow stress and thus reduce the extrudability. In addition, they act as foreign nuclei for the age-hardening phase. Mg_2Si is deposited at the Al(Mn,Fe)Si containing crystals and in this form can no longer contribute to the age hardening [Sca 64].

The quality of the continuously cast billets has a not insignificant influence on meeting the high quality and productivity requirements of the extrusion plant. It is known that the formation of

a smooth billet surface goes hand in hand with the improvement of the internal structure. A fine-cellular dendritic cast structure with little variation in the cell size across the billet diameter is desired [Sca 78] (see also the section "Melting and Casting Processes" in Chapter 4).

During the billet heat treatment (homogenizing), the plasticity of the cast structure can be significantly improved. This occurs by the reduction in grain segregation and the formation of the intermetallic AlFeSi cast phases during the billet heat treatment just below the solidus line. These effects are the more marked the finer the dendritic structure of the cast billet because the initial conditions are then more favorable for the thermally activated processes.

The billet heat treatment cycle involves not only the heat treatment temperature of 560–580 °C and the holding time of 6 to 8 hours, but also the heating and cooling of the billets. The rate of heating is not limited for any metallurgical reasons. With AlMgSi0.5, rapid cooling from the heat treatment temperature is recommended because with slow cooling ($\leq$ 50 K/h), the Mg_2Si is precipitated in a coarse format. With rapid billet heating to the extrusion temperature—in an induction furnace—the heat treatment time can be too short to redissolve the coarse particles. This reduces the mechanical properties after age hardening. In addition, coarse precipitates reduce the surface quality, particularly in anodizing.

5.8.2 Extruded Products

Extruded products are classified as bar, tube, and extruded sections and are standardized in DIN 1746, 1747, and 1748 (See The Aluminum Association, ANSI H35.1).

The range of profile cross sections is almost inexhaustible for the easily extruded aluminum alloys. Profiles with asymmetric cross sections and considerable wall thickness variations can be produced. Reference should be made to Chapter 2, which covers the wide range of applications.

Aluminum and the easily extruded AlMgSi types also have excellent extrusion welding properties. Hollow sections can therefore be produced with extruded longitudinal welds using special dies (bridge, porthole, and spider dies). The wall thickness that can be held with extruded sections is determined by the following parameters:

- Material
- Specific pressure

- Dimensions and type of section
- Degree of difficulty

The problems and limits of hollow section production are covered in section 5.7.6.1.

Extruded AlMgSi0.5 sections are used for façades in high-rise buildings because of their good surface quality, particularly after anodizing. Particular attention has to be given to the design of the die and the location of the extrusion welds. Texture and grain variations in the location of the welds can occur as a result of the material separation as it flows into the die and the bonding of the metal streams in the welding chamber by pressure welding resulting in a different appearance to the other visible surfaces. This is covered in detail in section 5.7.6.5.

With high demands on the brightness of the extruded sections, for example, for trim on household goods, furniture, or automobiles, chemical or electrochemical brightening has to be carried out before anodizing. Because particles of AlFeSi phases impair the brightness alloy variations based on Al99.85, Al99.9 or Al99.99 are used for both AlMg1 and AlMgSi0.5.

Large extruded sections are preferred for rail and road vehicles. It is possible to produce profile cross sections with a circumscribing circle of a maximum of 540 mm and a weight per meter up to 80 kg on presses in the range 72 to 100 MN installed for this application.

Round and flat bars as well as tubes and sections are used as conductors in electrical engineering. The mechanical and electrical properties are standardized in DIN 40501 parts 1 to 4 for the product shapes mentioned. E-Al and E-AlMgSi0.5, which are mentioned in DIN EN 573-3 are used (ASTM Internation Standards for aluminum bus conductors are B 236 and B 317). A special heat treatment in the range of overaging increases the conductivity of E-AlMgSi0.5 without any loss in mechanical properties [Ach 69].

Extruded products are standardized according to the product shape, material, and material condition, the technical delivery conditions, and the dimensional tolerances. Table 5.6 summarizes the standards for bar, tube, and extruded sections.

5.8.3 Extrusion and Materials Properties

The interaction of a suitable alloy, the quality of the cast billet and the correct billet heat treatment, the optimal tool design, the extrusion conditions and the cooling of the extruded section, and the subsequent age hardening is needed to produce a high-value product that completely fulfills all the geometric, chemical, physical, and metallurgical requirements of the extruded section.

The alloys AlMg1 and AlMn are naturally hard alloys in which the mechanical properties are obtained mainly from the solid-solution hardening. Therefore, the extrusion conditions are determined by the material deformation parameters. The extrusion is selected to give the optimal hot-working parameters. This, however, depends on the cast quality and the billet heat treatment (homogenizing), which forms the basis for improving the plasticity. The heating of the homogenized extrusion billets is usually carried out in induction or gas-fired continuous ovens to a temperature that can be found in Table 5.7.

In general, the billet temperature should be as low as possible in order to obtain a smooth section surface at a high extrusion speed. It also depends on the degree of difficulty of the section and the extrusion ratio. With the easily extruded alloys, the extrusion ratio should be between $V = 20$ and $V = 100$, but, if possible, a value of $V = 40$ to $V = 60$ is preferred.

The container temperature is usually approximately 50 °C lower than the billet preheat temperature.

Table 5.6   Comparison of standards for extruded products

Product format	Material/material condition	Technical delivery conditions	Dimensions, permitted deviations	Other comments
Round tube	DIN 1746, part 1 Board 4.6	DIN 1746, Part 2	DIN 9107	. . .
Round-, rectangular-, square-, and hexagonal bar	DIN 1747, Part 1 Board 4.6	DIN 1747, Part 2	DIN EN 755-3 DIN EN 755-5 DIN EN 755-4 DIN EN 755-6	. . .
Extruded section	DIN 1748, Part 1	DIN 1748, Part 2	DIN 1748, Part 4	Cross-sectional shape DIN 1748, Part 3
Rectangular tube	Board 4.7	DIN17615, Part 1	DIN17615, Part 3 Board 4.1	Board 5.17

With alloys that do not age harden, the exit temperature and the rate of cooling of the extruded section are not critical for the mechanical properties. Nevertheless, cooling with fans is recommended for economic reasons and to prevent precipitation and grain growth. The guidelines for the extrusion parameters discussed for the individual alloys are given in Table 5.7.

In the production of extruded sections in the age-hardening alloys AlMgSi0.5 and AlMgSi0.7, the combination of special metallurgical and process technological measures enables not only the economic production of complicated profile cross sections but also simultaneously the attainment of favorable mechanical properties. This is possible because with these alloys the temperature range for hot working and solution heat treatment largely coincide. A further positive characteristic of these alloys is that the age-hardening phase Mg_2Si can be retained supersaturated in solution even with a cooling rate of only about 2 K/s and the mechanical properties subsequently improved by precipitation during age hardening.

It is important to set the process parameters to meet both the metallurgical and production requirements. In many cases a compromise has to be found. The exit temperature is determined by two opposing criteria. The lowest possible exit temperature is needed to obtain a smooth surface finish. This is also desired from an eco-

nomic point of view because higher extrusion speeds are achieved with lower extrusion temperatures. This, however, conflicts with the metallurgical requirement of the exit temperature ≥ 500 °C in order for the age-hardening phase—in this alloy family approximately 1% Mg_2Si—to dissolve in the α-solid solution. If this does not occur, the section cannot be age hardened to the desired values.

The exit temperature depends on the optimized flow stress of the material produced by the billet heat treatment, the billet temperature and the heating conditions before extrusion, the extrusion ratio, and the rate of deformation.

The billet heating in an induction oven requires approximately 4 to 6 minutes. This is significantly faster than a gas-heated continuous oven where approximately 45 to 50 minutes are needed. These differences influence the diffusion-controlled solution processes. It is easy to understand that rapid heating of the billet before extrusion is advantageous where rapid cooling from the billet heat treatment temperature prevents the formation of coarse Mg_2Si particles. If preheating is carried out in a gas-fired continuous furnace, then the opposite applies because the cooling from the billet heat treatment does not play the decisive role.

It should be pointed out here that in the United States in particular, one method of operation is to heat the billets to a temperature above the

Table 5.7 Typical values for billet high-temperature heat treatment and extrusion conditions of aluminum alloys

Alloy	Homogenization, °C	Holding time	Preheat, °C	Container temperature, °C	Typical exit speeds, m/min
Al99.8–99.99	580–600	6	380–450	330–350	50–100
AlMg1	530–550	6	400–460	350–380	30–70
AlMn	590–620	12	400–460	350–400	30–70
AlMgSi0.5	560–580	6	450–500	400–450	30–80
AlMgSi0.7	560–580	6	470–510	420–450	25–65
AlMg2.5	520–540	6	430–490	360–380	5–15
AlMg3	510–530	6	460–490	360–380	5–15
AlMg1Mn1	540–560	16	450–500	380–400	10–30
AlMg2.7Mn	510–530	16	480–510	380–400	10–20
AlMgSi1	480–570	12	500–540	400–420	15–35
AlMgSiCu	540–570	12	500–540	380–400	10–40
AlMgSiPb	470–480	12	450–530	400–420	10–30
AlZnMg1	460–480	12	420–480	370–430	10–40
AlCuLi	520–550	12	400–450	350–400	5–25
AlLiCuMg	520–550	12	400–450	350–400	5–20
AlMg5	500–520	12	440–480	360–410	1.5–3
AlMg4.5Mn	500–520	12	430–480	410–430	2–5
AlCuMg2	480–490	12	400–460	370–400	1.5–3
AlCuSiMn	475–485	12	400–460	380–400	1.5–3
AlCuMgPb	450–480	12	380–440	360–400	1.5–3
AlCuMgFeNi	520–530	24	400–440	360–380	1.5–3
AlZnMgCu0.5	475–485	12	420–480	360–410	1.5–3
AlZnMgCu1.5	475–485	12	420–480	360–410	0.8–2.5
AlZn8MgCu	475–485	12	420–480	360–410	0.8–2.5

subsequent extrusion temperature to achieve complete dissolution of the Mg_2Si phase. The billet is cooled outside the oven to the desired lower production temperature before extrusion. Higher mechanical properties can then be achieved [Sca 64, Rei 88].

As mentioned previously, a wide range of extrusion ratios from $V = 20$ to $V = 100$ can be used for the easily extruded alloys. The selection usually depends on the container diameter. From the point of view of the grain formation, it can be advantageous to change to higher extrusion ratios because the recrystallized grain size depends on the degree of deformation as well as the temperature.

Obviously, the deformation rate should be as high as possible for economic reasons. High deformation rates are also desired for metallurgical reasons because the deformation temperature has a significant influence on the exit temperature, which in turn determines the hardening behavior. Limiting factors are again the specific pressure (stem load over the container cross-sectional area) and the roughening or tearing of the section surface. The effect of die cooling with nitrogen can be found in section 5.7.5.3.

As a guideline, exit speeds of 30 to 100 m/min can be expected with AlMgSi0.5, depending on the degree of difficulty. With AlMgSi0.7, the values are approximately 15 to 20% lower because of the higher amounts of magnesium and silicon, as well as small manganese additions.

Immediately after leaving the press, the sections are cooled with air or an air water mist mixture to a temperature ≤ 200 °C. This procedure avoids deformation or twisting of the sections. A cooling rate of 2 K/s is sufficient to retain the Mg_2Si in solid solution.

The extruded sections are finally stretched by 0.5 to 1.5% to achieve the straightness specified.

The final operation after cutting to the finished length is age hardening. With the AlMgSi alloys, the mechanical properties are usually reached after 4 to 12 hours at 160–180 °C, depending on the selected temperature (Table 5.8).

Preaging at room temperature has a favorable influence on the properties that can be achieved with alloys with low contents of the main alloying elements [Dor 73].

5.9 Moderately Difficult Alloys

Aluminum alloys with flow stresses >30 to 45 N/mm^2 are classified as moderately difficult. The relative extrudability of these alloys in this category is only 40 to 60% of AlMgSi0.5 if the extrudability of this easily extruded alloy is set at 100% [Hon 68]. This reduction is due to the increase in the main alloying elements, which are added for alloy technical reasons to increase the material properties as well as the addition of manganese to produce the desired hot-working structure.

5.9.1 Aluminum Alloys

The naturally hard materials include the AlMg alloys with higher magnesium contents as well as the AlMgMn alloys. The magnesium contents vary between 1.8 and 3% and the manganese content between 0.3 and 0.8%. The billet heat treatment temperature has to be lowered compared with the easily extruded alloys AlMg1 and AlMn to avoid melting because the solidus line in the phase diagram has a strong temperature dependence (Table 5.7).

Table 5.8   Typical values for heat treatment of age-hardening aluminum alloys

Material	Temper(a)	Quenching at the press exit temperature, °C	Separate heat treatment, °C	Cooling method	Age-hardening temperature/time
AlMgSi0.5	T5	≥ 500	...	Moving air	160–180 °C/12–6 h
AlMgSi0.7	T5	≥ 510	...	Moving air	160–180 °C/12–6 h
AlMgSiCu	T5	≥ 520	...	Moving air	160–180 °C/12–6 h
AlMgSiPb	T5	≥ 520	...	Moving air	160–180 °C/12–6 h
AlMgSi1	T6	...	530–540	In water	...
AlCuMg2	T3	...	495–502	In water	...
AlCuMgPb	T4	...	480–485	In water	...
AlCuSiMn	T4	...	500–505	In water	...
AlCuMgFeNi	T6	...	525–535	In water	...
AlZn4.5Mg1	T5	≥ 460	...	Air	185–195 °C/18–20 h
AlZnMgCu0.5	T6	...	475–480	In water	90 °C/10–12h + 120 °C/18–20 h
AlZnMgCu1.5	T6	...	475–480	In water	90 °C/10–12h + 120 °C/18–20 h
AlZn8MgCu	T6	...	475–480	In water	120VC/20–24 h

(a) Material temper condition according to DIN EN515

The heat treatable materials that belong to the moderately difficult alloys include the alloy AlMgSi1 that is frequently used in Germany and the alloy AlMgSiCu preferred in the United States, the free-cutting alloy AlMgSiPb and the readily weldable alloy AlZn4.5Mg1, as well as the more recent lithium-containing alloys AlCuLi and AlCuMgLi.

AlMgSi1 does not only differ from the AlMgSi0.5 alloy in the higher Mg_2Si content but also in the addition of about 0.4 to 1.0% manganese. From the metallurgical point of view, this results in the recrystallization temperature being increased to a significantly higher temperature and higher strain. It is important to note that both the manganese dissolved in the α-solid solution as well as the precipitated manganese-containing phases have a recrystallization retarding effect and increase the deformation resistance. The size of the manganese-containing phases can be controlled by the temperature of the billet heat treatment [Sca 69a] (see also the section "Extrudability of Metallic Materials" in Chapter 4). Coarse particles that form at a temperature of 560 to 580 °C have a lower recrystallization retarding effect than fine particles that are produced at a heat treatment temperature of 460 to 480 °C.

AlMgSi1 extruded sections do not have a recrystallized grain structure like AlMgSi0.5 because of the recrystallization retarding effect of the manganese additions but an elongated hot-worked structure with deformation texture components (Fig. 5.33). This formation of the grain structure is referred to as the extrusion effect. It is characterized by an increase in the mechanical properties over those of the recrystallized extruded structure, particularly in the direction of extrusion [Die 66]. The formation of a coarse grain recrystallized peripheral layer and an unrecrystallized core is well known in these alloys after age hardening.

The same observations are made in the copper-containing AlMgSi alloy where manganese is partly replaced by chromium, which metallurgically functions in a similar way. The low-copper addition favorably affects the grain formation and the mechanical properties as well as the general corrosion resistance [Sca 65].

Both the alloys AlMgSi1 and AlMgSiCu are significantly more quench sensitive than AlMgSi0.5 because of the manganese addition. Sections in these alloys have to be rapidly cooled immediately after extrusion with a water mist or in a standing water wave. A separate solution heat treatment with water quenching is recommended with thick-walled tubes and bars to maintain the strength and the toughness. The manganese-containing phases of the order of 0.05 to 0.7 µm obtained from low-temperature billet heat treatment and which are uniformly and densely distributed in the matrix have a positive effect on the toughness behavior [Sca 82]. The particle arrangement described displaces the fracture from the grain boundary into the matrix by cavity formation. Manganese-containing AlMgSi alloys therefore are less susceptible to intercrystalline facture and thus have significantly higher toughness values.

Another moderately difficult-to-extrude alloy that should be mentioned is AlZn4.5Mg1. Mechanical properties even higher than AlMgSi1 can be achieved and a structure with the extrusion effect is also needed for this alloy to achieve high mechanical properties. Figure 5.34 shows that only a small recrystallized fraction is to be expected if the billet heat treatment is carried out at 460 to 480 °C and the extrusion ratio is not high. With this alloy a higher billet heat treatment temperature should not be used as otherwise recrystallized grains occur, and there is a tendency toward stress-corrosion cracking (SCC), and the values in the standard are not reached [Sca 73].

AlZn4.5Mg1 is characterized by a significantly lower quench sensitivity than AlMgSi1. Maintaining a cooling rate of 0.5 K/s is not only recommended for process technology reasons but has to be held for metallurgical reasons to avoid SCC.

Since the middle of the 1980s, intensive attempts have been made worldwide to develop

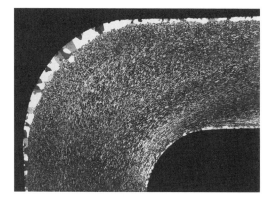

Fig. 5.33 Extruded section (extrusion effect with thin recrystallized peripheral zone) of an AlMgSi1 bar (cross section, Barker anodized, micrograph in polarized light)

new aluminum alloys with improved materials properties. The specific aims for the aerospace industry are a higher component stiffness and weight reduction. Lithium was considered as an alloying element because of its density of only 0.534 g/cm³ and because it is one of the few elements that increase the modulus of elasticity of aluminum alloys. In addition, the Al-Li phase diagram shows a temperature-dependent solubility so that the requirement for an increase in strength by age hardening is also fulfilled [Web 89].

Age-hardening lithium-containing alloys based on AlCu and AlCuMg have been developed with a 10% lower density and a 15% increased modulus of elasticity. The lithium content has to be approximately 3%. Special melting and casting technology is required because of the high reactivity of lithium-containing melts with oxygen and moisture and the aggressive attack of the lining of the melting furnaces.

The age hardening of the AlLiCuMg alloys is, in contrast to the conventional aluminum alloys, characterized by the partly coherent Al_2CuMg particles that occur in addition to the coherent Al_3Li precipitates during further hardening. These cannot be cut by dislocations and there is an increase in cross slip, which has a positive effect on homogeneous slip distribu-tion. With extended age-hardening, this results in an increase in the elongation to fracture with a simultaneous increase in the flow stress.

Mechanical property variations across the cross section are found in lithium-containing alloys because of the nonuniform texture formation [Tem 91].

5.9.2 Extruded Products

With their outstanding corrosion resistance to seawater, the naturally hard alloys are particularly suitable for industrial atmospheres and for pipe systems in the chemical industry. The seamless tubes extruded over a mandrel are further processed by drawing.

The age-hardening materials with their favorable mechanical properties are mainly used for superstructures in rolling stock and as hollow girders for bedplates as well as the manufacture of processing plants.

The moderately difficult alloys can be produced as either solid sections or hollow sections whereby the wall thickness has to be set 20 to 40% higher than the easily extruded alloys, depending on the alloy, for the same circumscribing circle because of the higher deformation stress. The AlZn4.5Mg1 alloy is often used for highly stressed welded structures because of its good weldability and the rehardening in the heat-affected zone. In the "age-hardened" condition (2-stage aging), this alloy has a good resistance to general corrosion and SCC (Table 5.7).

Lead-containing alloys such as AlMgSiPb are available for chip forming machining. They are particularly suitable for the machining on automatic drilling, milling machines, and lathes because they enable fast cutting speeds to be used.

The alloy AlMgSiPb has good mechanical properties, is corrosion resistant, and can be decoratively anodized. The extruded or extruded and drawn products are primarily supplied as round, hexagonal, and octagonal bars. The tolerances are standardized in DIN1769–1799 and DIN 5000-59701 (Aluminum Association H35.2).

Extruded sections in the lithium-containing aluminum alloys are used as stringer sections and floor plate supports in the aerospace industry because of their lower density and increased modulus of elasticity compared with the conventional high-strength alloys. Further applications are limited by the present high billet production costs.

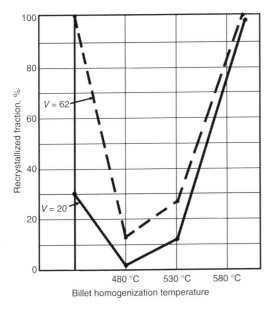

Fig. 5.34 Recrystallized structural fraction as a function of the billet heat treatment temperature and the extrusion ratio (extrusion temperature, 550 °C) [Sca 73]

5.9.3 Extrusion and Materials Properties

The flow stress of AlMg and AlMgMn increases with increasing magnesium content, and the melting point decreases. To compensate for the lower extrudability of, for example, AlMg3, the preheat temperature can be set to 30 °C higher than for AlMg1. However, the exit temperature should not significantly exceed 500 °C to avoid the surface turning brown because of increased oxidation. As mentioned earlier with naturally hard alloys, the cooling from the extrusion temperature to room temperature is not that critical. The process parameters for the individual alloys are summarized in Table 5.7.

Higher mechanical properties are obtained with AlMgSi1 and AlMgSiCu by age hardening. However, some compromises have to be made for extrusion. The metallurgical procedures that improve the extrudability (e.g., higher billet heat treatment temperature) have an unfavorable effect on the grain formation and thus on the mechanical properties [Sca 67].

In the production of AlMgSi1 sections, the decision has to be taken in the selection of the metallurgical conditions whether the solution heat treatment and quenching are coupled with the extrusion process or whether these should be carried out as separate operations. For economic reasons it is better if additional operations can be avoided. From the metallurgical point of view, there are advantages in the formation of the grain structure if no additional heat treatment in the shape of solution heat treatment has to be carried out. The decisive factor is whether the age hardening producing Mg_2Si is extensively dissolved at the exit temperature and can be retained in solution during the cooling. AlMgSi1 and AlMgSiCu sections have to be cooled quickly with water because they are quench sensitive due to the manganese content [Sca 64]. Whether this requirement can be fulfilled depends on one hand on the section shape to be produced, in particular, the wall thickness, and on the other hand, on the cooling system installed on the extrusion press. As a general rule, the rate of cooling of AlMgSi and AlMgSiCu in the temperature range 530 to 150 °C has to be a factor of 10 faster than with AlMgSi0.5; i.e., it should be at least 10 to 20 K/s. The required cooling rate can only be achieved with water. Quenching with water after the die can, however, result in uncontrolled distortion of the section that must be kept to a minimum by pullers.

If the solution heat treatment and quenching are to be carried out simultaneously with the extrusion process, care should be taken to ensure that the exit temperature is at least 530 °C. The preheat temperature should, accordingly, be 500 to 520 °C because there is no significant temperature increase from the heat of deformation. On the other hand, with a separate solution heat treatment a lower preheat temperature should be selected, and there is no demand on the exit temperature. The exit speed that can be achieved with AlMgSi and AlMgSiCu is approximately only half that of AlMgSi0.5. The extrusion ratio on the other hand does not differ significantly from that with AlMgSi0.5.

The increase in the mechanical properties of the section is achieved by age hardening for 6 to 8 hours at 160 °C or 4 to 6 hours at 180 °C. However, it should be pointed out that with AlMgSi1, the maximum achievable mechanical properties decrease with increasing room temperature intermediate storage. The damaging influence of an intermediate room temperature aging can be largely overcome by a preventative heat treatment. The sections have to be heated to 180 °C and held for 3 minutes, which eliminates the cold aging that would otherwise take place by approximately 1 day [Koe 61].

The alloy AlMgSi1 is suitable for sections that have to be color anodized because the manganese content that is embedded in the metallic form in the oxide layer produces the brown tone. Attention must be paid to the grain structure because different microstructures can result in bands on the surface after anodizing. In this case it has proved advantageous to try and obtain a completely fine-grain recrystallized structure. This can be achieved when the recrystallization retarding influence of the manganese is largely excluded by the formation of coarse secondary precipitates and thus the rate of nucleation accelerated and recrystallization promoted [Sca 69]. Billet heat treatment at 570 to 590 °C has proved successful in this respect. The associated simultaneous reduction in the mechanical properties is not important for applications in buildings.

The copper-free age-hardening AlZn4.5Mg1 alloys are very suitable for the production of hollow sections and flat sections because with this material the working temperature in extrusion coincides with the solution temperature range, and this alloy has a low quench sensitivity so that air cooling suffices.

Also, the mechanical properties that can be achieved are higher than AlMgSi1. However, with incorrect treatment, a tendency to SCC cannot be completely excluded. Today it is generally recognized that the danger of SCC of extruded sections can be excluded if the production conditions are strictly maintained. These conditions are [Sca 73]:

- The billet heat treatment must be carried out at a low temperature (12 h at 460–480 °C) to suppress the recrystallization by fine manganese, chromium, or zirconium phases.
- The extrusion temperature should be as low as possible (450–490 °C).
- The cooling with air in the temperature range 350–200 °C should be in the range 0.5–1.5 K. Water quenching should be avoided at all costs.
- The age hardening—after an intermediate room temperature aging of at least 3 days—has to be carried out in stages (12 h at 90 °C plus 12–24 h at 120–130 °C) to produce an overaged structure.

The extrusion behavior of the alloy AlZn4.5Mg1 from the point of view of the extrusion speed is comparable to the alloy AlMgSi1. The advantages of AlZn4.5Mg1 are the relatively low solution heat treatment temperature and the use of air even with thick-wall sections to achieve the necessary slow cooling rate.

The extrudability of the alloy AlLiCuMg is comparable with that of the moderately difficult alloys AlMgSi1 and AlZn4.5Mg1. The flow stress of AlCuMgSi is approximately 10 to 15% lower than that of AlMgSi1. The maximum extrusion speed that can be obtained is reduced to a value of only 60% of that of AlMgSi1 because of the low-melting-point copper phase. It is beneficial with the lithium-containing alloy as with the other high-strength materials to pass the section through nitrogen as it leaves the die to avoid oxidation of the surface [Sca 79].

The age hardening of the lithium containing alloys is carried out by solution heat treatment at 530 to 540 °C and quenching in water. Cold working (stretching) of 1.5 to 2% before aging at 185 °C has proved to be beneficial to both the magnitude of the strength and the elongation [Tem 91].

5.10 Difficult-to-Extrude Alloys

The highest mechanical properties in the aluminum alloys can be achieved with the age-hardening alloys of the AlCuMg and, in particular, the AlZnMgCu systems. Alloy technological procedures have to be followed, however, that can be disadvantageous from other perspectives. The addition of up to a few percent copper results in the formation of low-melting-point intermetallic phases. They also have an unfavorable effect on the general corrosion resistance. Recrystallization retarding elements, including manganese, chromium, and zirconium, also have to be added in order to obtain a hot-worked structure in the extruded sections that contains elongated grains in the longitudinal direction. The mechanical properties in the longitudinal direction are higher than in the transverse direction. This is referred to as the *extrusion effect* [Sca 69c]. The alloy technological measures described do fulfill the mechanical property requirements but have serious hot-working disadvantages. The additions of the main alloying elements magnesium and copper and the additions of manganese and chromium increase the flow stress significantly so that AlCuMg2 and AlZnMgCu1.5 have to be classified among the difficult-to-extrude alloys. The difficulty is increased by the low-melting-point phases, which severely limit the extrusion temperature range, and if the latter is exceeded, hot cracking occurs. These alloys have a marked quench sensitivity and a severely limited solution range so that in most cases they have to be solution heat treated and quenched in a separate operation.

In addition to these alloys, the AlMg and AlMgMn alloys with 4 to 5% magnesium are included in the difficult-to-extrude alloys. The flow stress of 47 to 56 N/mm^2 is attributable to the high magnesium content and the manganese secondary precipitates, particularly if these occur in a fine format and a high density in the matrix.

It should be pointed out here that new production processes are being used to develop new aluminum alloys for extruded sections with improved materials properties. These include alloys produced by powder metallurgy and particle reinforced conventional alloys [Web 89] (see the section "Extrusion of Powder Metals" in this chapter).

5.10.1 Aluminum Alloys

There are various types of alloys with copper as the main alloying element. They differ in special material properties. These alloys are usually cold age hardened to give the most favorable properties. AlCuMg2 has the highest mechanical properties and a good toughness. It is very important in the aerospace industry. The alloy AlCuMgFeNi has the best high-temperature mechanical properties of all the conventional alloys. The alloy AlCuSiMn is characterized by high mechanical properties at room temperature and elevated temperatures. Because this alloy also has excellent forging properties, preforms are extruded and then forged in dies. Bars for drilling, milling, and turning are made from the alloys AlCuMgPb and AlCuBiPb.

The billet heat treatment of these alloys is usually carried out at 480 ± 5 °C. Only AlCuMgFeNi is heat treated at 525 ± 5 °C because of the additions of nickel and iron. The heating should not significantly exceed 50 °C/h to avoid melting. After the heat treatment, slow cooling to approximately 360 °C is recommended, preferably in the homogenizing furnace. The cooling can then be carried out in air. These measures help avoid quenching stresses, which can produce cracks in the billets in these alloys.

The following AlZnMgCu alloys are the most common: AlZnMgCu0.5 and AlZnMgCu1.5, which are both standardized, as well as alloys with higher zinc contents in which manganese and chromium are replaced by zirconium. This reduces the quench sensitivity of these alloys. The highest mechanical properties measured on extruded sections are typically $R_{p0.2}$ 580–610 N/mm^2 and R_m 610–640 N/mm^2 and approximately 8–10% for A5.

The billet heat treatment of these alloys is particularly important because of the complexity of the cast structure. Structural rearrangements occur during heating, holding at temperature, and cooling, and these have a significant influence on both the mechanical properties and the extrudability. Cast billets have a lower melting point than homogenized billets. The melting point is increased by 70 to 90 °C by reducing the residual melt bands and segregations as well as dissolution during the billet heat treatment. On the other hand, the supersaturated dissolved fractions of the peritectic phases are precipitated in a fine form in the matrix by thermal activation. In the billet heat treatment—usually 12 h at 480 ± 5 °C —the cooling of these alloys has a decisive influence on the extrusion speed [Fin 96]. If the cooling is not fast enough, coarse particles can form during the cooling. These do not dissolve completely during heating and then melt in the extrusion process, resulting in surface cracks in the section.

The high-alloyed alloys AlMg5 and AlMg4.5Mn are particularly suitable for low temperature applications. The mechanical properties increase as the temperature falls; this also applies to the elongation to fracture. If the magnesium content exceeds 3%, some of the magnesium exists preferentially as intermetallic phases on the grain boundaries and some in the matrix. This applies in particular if the material is held for a long period in the temperature range 250 to 150 °C. Intercrystalline corrosion susceptibility can occur under unfavorable conditions if the application temperature is >80 °C. The magnesium phase can be precipitated by suitable thermal treatments during production so that no coherent precipitates form and intercrystalline corrosion can be practically eliminated.

5.10.2 Extruded Products

The high-strength materials are mainly used in the aerospace industry, military applications, and machinery. The products include solid sections, bars, and seamless extruded tubes. AlCuMg2 and AlZnMgCu1.5 are normally not suitable for the production of hollow sections with extrusion welds because of the low-melting-point phases and the high extrusion pressures required [Wei 78]. Simple, thick-wall tubular components are, however, occasionally extruded with bridge or porthole dies.

Whereas AlCuMg2 is usually used in the room temperature age-hardened condition for high-stress applications, AlCuSiMn and AlCuMgFeNi as well as AlZnMg alloys are mainly used after hot age hardening. AlCuSiMn is used in the as-extruded or annealed state for subsequent processing to forged components.

Only the alloy AlMg4.5Mn of the difficult-to-extrude naturally hard alloys can be extruded as a hollow section with extruded welds. However, this is possible only with a large wall thickness because of the high deformation loads. The applications are primarily chemical equipment and machinery.

5.10.3 Extrusion and Materials Properties

Only extrusion ratios of $V = 10$ to $V = 40$ are used for the difficult-to-extrude alloys because of the high flow stress of over 45 to 57 N/mm^2. The extrudability is less than 10% of the easily extruded alloys.

Indirect extrusion of high-strength alloys has been used to an increasing extent in recent years. This has clearly confirmed the advantages of the indirect extrusion process for the high-strength and difficult-to-extrude alloys AlCuMgPb, AlCuSiMn, and AlZnMgCu1.5 [Eul 75]. Indirect extrusion has a higher productivity compared with direct extrusion. Significant advantages include the higher extrusion speed at lower temperatures (340–360 °C) and the use of longer billets (3–7 times the container diam). The different material flow in indirect extrusion produces a homogeneous structure and thus more uniform properties. However, indirect extrusion places higher demands on the casting quality. Only defect-free turned or scalped billets give a good extruded surface finish. The distance between the die and the cooling section at the press exit is greater because of the design of indirect extrusion presses. This makes the quenching of quench-sensitive alloys at the press more difficult. In addition, quenching at the press requires a sufficiently high exit temperature to achieve complete age hardening. In direct extrusion, the extrusion speed of difficult-to-extrude alloys is increased by 20 to 40% by die cooling with nitrogen. This is demonstrated with the copper-containing alloys, which have a relatively low melting point. Die cooling enables some of the deformation heat to be removed so that the critical melting temperature, which results in section cracking, is reached at a higher exit speed [Sca 79].

The solution heat treatment of the high-strength alloy AlZnMgCu1.5 is usually carried out separately after extrusion. The reason for this has already been discussed. This is then followed by age hardening. Room temperature intermediate aging for 3 to 5 days has proved beneficial. The age hardening is carried out in one or two stages (Table 5.8) and depends on the customer specifications. If the maximum mechanical properties are required, age hardening is carried out at only 120 °C to the maximum of the age-hardening curve. However, a slightly overaged condition is recommended because this significantly improves the stress-corrosion resistance for only a slight loss in mechanical properties. A two-stage age hardening is used to achieve the T73 designated properties. The sections are initially aged for 12 to 24 hours at 120 °C and then for 3 to 5 hours at 170 °C [Dah 93].

The alloy AlCuMg2 is usually aged at room temperature after quenching in water as hot age hardening has a negative influence on the corrosion properties; a tendency toward intercrystalline corrosion can be detected. Hot age hardening is the standard process for the AlCuSiMn

and the AlCuMgFeNi alloys to achieve the desired high mechanical properties. The age-hardening parameters are given in Table 5.8.

Finally, the difficult-to-extrude alloy AlMg 4.5Mn is a naturally hard alloy where the increase in mechanical properties is not obtained by heat treatment but by solid solution and work hardening. For this reason, the extrusion ratio should not be too high; otherwise, the fraction of recrystallized structure increases to such an extent that the specified values are not reached. This occurs, in particular, when a higher extrusion temperature has to be used because of the limited specific pressure of the extrusion press.

Extrusion of Materials with Deformation Temperatures of 600 to 1300 °C

5.11 Extrusion of Semifinished Products in Copper Alloys

Martin Bauser*

5.11.1 General
5.11.1.1 Copper, Bronze, and Brass— A Long History

The knowledge and application of copper and some of its alloys extends back into prehistory (Bronze Age). They were used up to the beginning of our technical era mainly for jewelry and household goods. The good workability of copper and copper-zinc alloys combined with the attractive appearance is responsible today for their use for metal wares, including containers, lamps, and trays as well as brass instruments.

5.11.1.2 Advantageous Physical and Chemical Properties

Copper is the commercial metal with the highest electrical conductivity (58 m/Ω mm^2 at 20 °C). The additions to some low-alloy copper ma-

*Extrusion of Semifinished Products in Copper Alloys, Martin Bauser

terials only reduce the conductivity slightly but significantly improve the mechanical properties. The high thermal conductivity corresponds to the high electrical conductivity. Copper is located close to the noble metals in the electrical chemical series and has a natural resistance to numerous corrosive effects.

The good corrosion resistance and the ease of working make copper one of the most important materials for water supply pipes. It is also particularly suitable for heat exchangers because of its good thermal conductivity. The property of copper used most is the excellent electrical conductivity, which secures its very wide application in electrical engineering and electronics—naturally also in the form of rolled products.

5.11.1.3 Importance of Extrusion in the Processing

Pure copper melts at 1083 °C. The melting point is only increased by the addition of nickel (continuous solid solution). All other element additions lower the melting point, sometimes to less than 900 °C (Table 5.9). The recrystallization temperature falls in the range 350 to 650 °C depending on the composition. Copper alloys are extruded at temperatures between 550 and 1000 °C corresponding to the melting temperature. Along with aluminum alloys, they belong to the group of materials where long semifinished sections are mainly produced by extrusion.

According to the statistics in Europe in 1988, 1.4 million tonnes (metric tons) of extruded

Table 5.9 Extrusion data for copper alloys

Material	Melting interval, °C	Billet temperature, °C	Maximum extrusion ratio	Maximum extrusion speed, m/min
Copper				
E-Cu	1080–1083	780–950	250	300
Low alloyed copper				
CuCrZr	1070	930–980	100	150
CuNi2Si	1040–1070	750–900	75	100
CuNi3Ni	1030–1050	850–950	50	75
CuZn (tombac and brass)				
CuZn10	1015–1035	825–875	150	100
CuZn20	950–990	750–850	60	100
CuZn30	910–935	720–800	150	150
CuZn37	900–920	710–790	200	150
CuZn38Pb1	880–900	650–750	250	250
CuZn40Pb2	875–885	650–750	300	300
Special brass				
CuZn28Sn2	890–930	750–780	75	100
CuZn31Si1	930–950	720–760	150	150
CuZn35Ni2	880–890	700–800	200	300
CuZn40Al2	880–890	600–700	250	250
CuZn40Mn2	880–890	650–700	250	250
CuSn (tin-bronze)				
CuSn2	1020–1070	800–900	100	150
CuSn6	910–1040	600–700	100	50
CuSn8	860–1015	650–720	80	30
CuAl (aluminum-bronze)				
CuAl5As	1050–1060	750–850	75	150
CuAl8	1030–1035	740–780	100	150
CuAl10Fe3Mn2	1030–1050	750–900	100	200
CuAl10Ni5Fe4	~1050	750–900	50	100
CuNi (copper-nickel)				
CuNi10Fe1Mn	1100–1145	850–950	80	50
CuNi30Mn1Fe	1180–1240	900–1000	80	50
CuNi30Fe2Mn2	1180–1240	900–1000		
CuNiZn (nickel-silver)				
CuNi12Zn24	~1020	900–950		
CuNi12Zn30Pb	~1010		80	50
CuNi18Zn20	~1055	850–920		
CuNi18Zn19Pb	~1050		50	30

Source: Lau 76, Moe 80

products were produced in copper alloys by 70 companies and approximately 120 presses [Zei 93]. In Germany there are 14 companies with 37 presses in the range 10 to 50 MN press power.

Sixty percent of all extruded products are bar, wire, and section of which the majority are produced in copper-zinc alloys (brass). The remaining 40% are tube—usually in copper.

5.12 The Groups of Extruded Copper Alloys—Their Important Properties and Applications

5.12.1 Alloy Groups

The DIN standards cover 81 wrought alloys in seven groups that can be extruded under specific conditions (Table 5.10).

The conversion to European standards had not been completed at the time of publication. Only product standards and not individual alloy groups, as is the case in DIN, are included in the European standards. Each EN then usually applies to all alloy groups (Table 5.11). ASTM International Standards cover alloys, product shape, and specific applications.

In addition to these alloys produced from cast billets there are a few composite materials and powder metals discussed in the sections "Extrusion of Powder Metals" and "Extrusion of Semifinished Products from Metallic Composite Materials."

5.12.2 Tooling Temperatures in Extrusion

With extrusion temperatures between 500 and 1000 °C, the tooling is subjected to significantly higher temperatures than with aluminum alloys. However, as copper alloys can usually be extruded at much higher speeds than aluminum, the contact time with the tooling is so short that heating of the tools over the limit of 500 to 600 °C can be avoided. The tooling wear is, however, naturally much higher than with aluminum alloys (see the section "Tools for Copper Alloy Extrusion," in Chapter 7).

5.12.3 Structure

Copper and numerous copper alloys, e.g., copper-tin (up to 8% Sn) and copper–zinc (up to 37% Zn) have a pure face-centered cubic (fcc) α structure up to the melting point and therefore have good cold workability but only moderately good hot workability. On the other hand, the body centered cubic (bcc) β phase, e.g., copper-zinc over 40% zinc, has excellent hot workability but is difficult to cold work.

5.12.4 Typical Extruded Semifinished Products and Applications

The section "Copper Alloy Extruded Products" in Chapter 2 describes typical extruded semifinished products and their applications.

Whereas bar and wire are produced over the entire alloy range, tubes are mainly in SF-Cu for water supply, brass for plumbing fittings, and in special brasses and copper-nickel alloys for corrosive media. Large quantities of free-machining brass are machined to fittings and turned components, including bolts.

In contrast to aluminum, the production of sections is no longer important. The higher extrusion temperature results in higher die temperatures and thus greater wear and more severe tool defection than with aluminum alloys. The

Table 5.10 Copper alloy groups and the associated composition DIN standards

Alloy groups	No. of DIN standardized alloys	ASTM standard
DIN 1787: copper	6	B 133
DIN 17666: copper wrought alloys—low alloyed	20	E 478
DIN 17660: copper-zinc alloys (brass, special brass)	31	B 371
DIN 17662: copper-tin alloys (tin bronzes)	4	B 505(a)
DIN 17665: copper-aluminum alloys (aluminum bronzes)	8	B 150, B 359
DIN 17664: copper-nickel alloys	6	E 75
DIN 17663: copper-nickel-zinc alloys (nickel-silver)	6	B 151

(a) For continuous casting

Table 5.11 Euro standards for extruded copper alloy semifinished products

Standard	Designation
EN 1057	Seamless round copper tubes for water and gas supplied for sanitary installations
EN 12735	Seamless round copper tubes for air conditioning
EN 13348	Seamless round copper tubes for medicinal gases
EN 12449	Seamless round tubes for general applications
EN 12451	Seamless round tubes for heat exchangers
EN 12163	Bar for general application
EN 12164	Bar for machining
EN 12165	Feedstock for forged components
EN 12166	Wire for general applications
EN 12167	Section and rectangular bar for general applications
EN 12168	Hollow bar for machining

extrusion tolerances of copper alloys are wider than with aluminum and it is also not possible to produce thin profile cross sections (see DIN 17 674, page 3). With few exceptions the sections have to be subsequently drawn. Section production is usually limited to copper and low-alloy copper materials as well as the easily extruded α-β brasses.

The most economic production of readily cold-worked alloys to tubes, bar, and section depends on the equipment available at the individual companies. Depending on the type of press, the size, and the number and size of the drawing machines, the most suitable extruded dimensions vary for the same finished product.

5.13 Extrusion Properties of Copper Alloys

Numerous authors have covered the extrusion of copper alloys [Tus 80]. Only the work relevant to practical applications is included here.

5.13.1 Extrudability of Different Materials

Table 5.9 gives the extrusion temperatures, the maximum extrusion speeds, and the maximum extrusion ratios. The data were obtained from practical experience in various extrusion companies. These can differ from plant to plant.

5.13.2 Temperature and Speed—Structure of the Extrusion

The temperature dependence of the workability of different copper alloys is shown in the following section in the form of hot-strength curves. Data obtained from tensile tests only have limited application in calculating the forces needed for extrusion. However, if they have all been measured using the same method on soft specimens, they are suitable for comparing the materials (see also Chapter 4). Values of the flow stress k_f obtained from torsion tests, which are often described in the literature, are more suited to calculating the load. Strains comparable to those in extrusion can be achieved. The *Atlas of Hot-Working Properties of Non-Ferrous Metals,* Volume 2, *Copper Alloys* [DGM 78] gives these k_f values as a function of the logarithmic principal strain φ_g and the logarithmic principal strain rate $\dot{\varphi}_g$. Unfortunately, not all the important alloys are included. In addition, as different

authors have used various methods of measurement these data are not suitable for comparison.

Up to the extrusion temperature, copper and low-alloy copper materials have the face centered α-structure, which does not have good hot-working properties.

Brass in the α-β range (free-machining brass) has very good hot workability. The extrusion of brass bars was the first large-scale application of this process (A. Dick, 1890, see the section "Historic Development of Extrusion" in Chapter 1).

With difficult-to-extrude alloys, the flow stress, depending on the press size and the extrusion ratio, places a lower limit on the extrusion temperature and an upper limit on the susceptibility to hot shortness [Lau 76]. Aluminum bronzes and lead-containing nickel silvers are particularly susceptible to hot shortness. The cracks can range from light surface cracks to fir tree defects (Fig. 5.35). It is not only on eco-

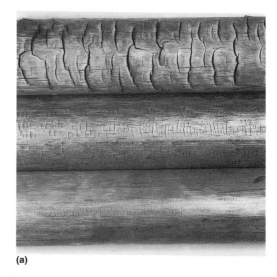

(a)

(b)

Fig. 5.35 Hot shortness cracking at excessive extrusion temperature. (a) CuSn8 extruded tube with coarse, moderate, and fine hot shortness cracks. (b) Extruded round bar in CuSn6 with gaping hot shortness cracks [Die 76]

nomic grounds that the extrusion speed should be as high as possible and the initial billet temperature as low as possible. The output is higher and the thermal stressing of the tooling during extrusion shorter. The material itself also cools less during extrusion by the conduction of heat into the container, which is at a maximum of 500 °C, which results in a more uniform section exit temperature and structure over the length of the extrusion.

The age-hardening copper-chromium and copper-chromium-zirconium alloys represent a special case where it is possible to quench small sections from the extrusion temperature, which is also the solution heat treatment temperature. In this case, extrusion is carried out at the highest temperature possible (900 to 1000 °C).

The maximum extrusion speed is frequently limited by the equipment, e.g., by the puller system for sections or by the speed of the down coilers for wire.

The extrusion temperature and the deformation are normally so high that the extruded section completely recrystallizes as it leaves the die, usually with a fine-grain structure. However, it is possible to have structural variations from the front of the extrusion to the back. At the start of extrusion the deformation is lower than in the middle and at the end. Depending on the extrusion ratio, the extrudability, and the extrusion speed, the exit temperature can fall or even increase. With multiphase structures the quantity and distribution of the second phase can vary over the cross section and the length of the extrusion. Details are given in the material-specific sections 5.16 to 5.16.9.

5.13.3 Extrusion to Finished or Close-to-Finished Dimensions

Because the α-β brasses are difficult to cold work, brass bar and sections in these alloy groups are extruded close to the final dimensions and then brought to the desired finished dimensions and mechanical properties by a subsequent cold-working operation (usually by drawing). In contrast, the alloys that have good cold workability (copper, low-alloy copper materials, α-brasses) are extruded well above the finished dimensions and then cold worked in several stages. Cold working of sections can be difficult and requires considerable experience in deciding the extruded dimensions, the tool design, and the drawing parameters.

5.13.4 Lubrication

Lubricants based on graphite oil mixtures are well suited for the temperature range in which copper alloys are extruded.

There have been many attempts to introduce other lubricants for the extrusion of copper alloys. These have largely been disappointing. Usually, viscous oil blended with graphite flakes is used. If automatic lubrication systems are used, which is increasingly common on modern equipment, the lubricant has to have a low viscosity. "Lubricant sticks" of graphite containing wax are available for die lubrication. The container is usually unlubricated so that only the die and the mandrel in the case of tubes have to be regularly lubricated. To reduce graphite inclusions and banding on the surface of the section, the minimum of lubricant should be accurately applied. However, too little lubrication will result in wear between the tooling and the extruded material.

5.13.5 Extrusion with a Shell

Materials that are oxide free or have a limited amount of oxide usually bond to the tooling in the absence of lubrication. Brasses, aluminum bronzes, and copper-nickel alloys have to be extruded with a stable shell. At the end of each extrusion the dummy block is pushed out and the shell removed with a cleaning disc. The shell thickness is usually about 1 mm. If it is too thick there is the risk that the material will flow back between the dummy block and the container over the stem. This can occur in particular with alloys that are easy to extrude. An incomplete shell can form if the shell is too thin. A fixed dummy block, which is used for the easily extruded aluminum alloys, cannot be used for copper alloys.

Copper and low-alloy copper materials, as well as bronzes, tend to oxidize. The oxide layer adhering to the hot billet acts as a lubricant [Bla 48, Bei 76, Vat 70]. However, because the billet surface is generally not uniformly oxidized, partial adhesion to the container can occur and extrusion has to be carried out with a shell.

The thin shell in the extrusion of copper and low-alloy copper materials can be easily removed from the container and squashed so that it is possible to operate with a combination dummy block and cleaning pad (see Chapter 7). The front ring of this block has the diameter of the dummy block and the rear the diameter of the cleaning block. In between there is a deep and wide circular recess into which the thin shell folds. Extrusion with a shell is still carried out with the combination dummy block and cleaning pad but the additional cleaning operation is eliminated.

5.13.6 Different Material Flow Behavior

In the direct extrusion of copper alloys with a shell and unlubricated container, flat dies are used. Differences in the hot-working properties and the flow behaviors of different material groups result in different types of material flow. The material flow patterns can be found in Chapter 3.

5.13.6.1 Flow-Type C—Piping Defect

Aluminum bronzes and α-β brasses adhere to the container because of the minimal oxide formation and flow according to type C because the layer close to the surface cools during extrusion and does not flow as readily as the billet core. The danger of the piping defect (see Fig. 5.46) is countered by restricting the billet length. However, the end of the extrusion has to be regularly tested using a fracture test.

It is advantageous with these alloys to change to the indirect extrusion process where there is no friction between the billet and the container and the risk of the piping defect is removed. The material then flows according to type B. Longer billets can then be used, providing the other conditions allow it, and the discard length is reduced [Zil 82].

5.13.6.2 Flow-Type B—Shell Defect

Copper and low-alloyed copper alloys similar to CuCrZr or CuNiSi but also CuNi, CuNiZn, α-brasses as well as CuSn are frequently extruded at temperatures so high that, depending on the material, a more or less thick oxide layer forms that in turn can result in extrusion defects including shell defects and thus blisters on the extruded section (see Fig. 5.39). The material flows according to type B. The dead metal zones when flat dies are used hold back the oxide. Nevertheless, the billet length has to be limited or the discard thickness correspondingly increased to avoid shell and blister defects. This is covered in more detail in Fig. 5.38.

The risk of shell defect is somewhat less in indirect extrusion than in direct extrusion.

5.13.6.3 Back End Defect

If the extrusion ratio is too low (heavy sections), there is the risk of the "back end defect" forming particularly with material that flows according to type C in direct extrusion. The accelerating material in the center of the billet can form a funnel at the end of extrusion. Short billet lengths and large discard lengths can be used to reduce this (see Fig. 5.47).

Back end defect is seen less in indirect extrusion than in direct extrusion and only when the extrusion ratio is too small and the discard too thin.

5.13.7 Discard Length

Discard lengths between 20 and 40 mm are used for copper, α-brasses, and tin bronzes, which also flows according to flow pattern B in direct extrusion.

For α-β brasses and special brasses, which flow following flow pattern C, discard lengths are between 30 and 50 mm.

The lengths should be 40 to 70 mm with the hard-to-extrude aluminum bronzes—also flow pattern C.

These are not always valid. Sometimes—independent of the material and the container—30 to 50 mm discard lengths are used in direct extrusion and the possible defective section ends removed by careful control of cross sections (fracture tests).

The discard length can be significantly smaller in indirect extrusion.

5.13.8 Direct Extrusion with Lubrication and without a Shell

Extrusion is rarely carried out with internal lubrication of the container, which reduces the extrusion load because the friction between the billet and the container is largely eliminated. This process was adopted for the vertical extrusion presses that used to be used when high extrusion ratios were required from relatively low-powered presses. Even today thin-walled tubes and small hollow sections are produced on vertical presses with lubricated containers. On horizontal presses it can be necessary to process difficult-to-extrude alloys, e.g., copper nickel, at higher extrusion ratios than would be possible taking into account the friction between the billet and the container. Lubrication of the container can help in this case.

Blisters on the surface of the extrusion can be avoided on susceptible alloys by extruding with a lubricated container. It is necessary to use a conical entry in the die and to machine the billet surface. The billet surface forms the surface of the section because of the laminar flow and every defect on the billet surface appears on the section.

5.13.9 Extrusion into Water or Air

Alloys that tend to oxidation are often extruded into a water bath or through a water wave. This ensures that the extruded product does not have to be pickled before subsequent further processing. It is also possible with copper tube to restrict the secondary recrystallization observed when extruding into air and thus a coarse grain on the exit from the die [Gre 71]. A fine grain is often required for further processing.

Water cooling should, as a general rule, be avoided for α-β materials because otherwise, as the material leaves the die, the structure consisting mainly of the β-phase is undercooled and it is possible for some of the α-phase to precipitate as needles. Both reduce the workability and increase the strength of the extrusions [Bro 73]. If more rapid cooling than air cooling is required (e.g., with brass wire), the material can only come into contact with water after air cooling (to 500–300 °C, depending on the material) if it is to remain soft. Direct slower cooling with a water-air mixture is possible.

5.14 Extrusion Processes and Suitable Equipment

Whereas earlier extrusion plants were mainly multipurpose plants capable of producing rod and sections as well as wire and tube, today extrusion plants are designed specifically for the production of large quantities of one product [Ste 91]. Specific design details are given in Chapter 6.

5.14.1 Extrusion Presses for Brass Wire and Sections

There are some presses on which large quantities of brass are produced where only wire is extruded onto down coilers and others that are equipped with pullers (up to 4 sections) for the production of rod and sections. In contrast to the extrusion of aluminum sections where several strands can be pulled with a single puller, with copper alloys a specific puller device must be provided for each strand. The exit speeds of the individual sections are not exactly equal so that the slower section would be severely stretched at the high exit temperature.

Indirect extrusion is often used for brass wire and rod because this avoids the piping defect and long billets can be used.

A rod and section press—usually the direct process—has a section cross-transfer system as well as the puller system and frequently a water trough in which the sections can be quickly brought to room temperature after crossing the critical temperature of approximately 300 °C. Wire is also cooled in water after a specific cooling time in air.

If a wide range of materials and dimensions have to be processed, a multipurpose press is still the correct choice.

5.14.2 Tube Extrusion

Tube presses today obviously have a piercer system. Water-cooled mandrels are used that usually move with the stem (moving mandrel). The mandrel that is stationary in the die during extrusion is subjected continuously to a high temperature. The "stationary mandrel" is therefore used only for the extrusion of tubes with small internal diameters and suitable hollow sections.

Copper sections are extruded under water (or occasionally in a protective atmosphere).

In the 1950s and 1960s a large range of vertical tube presses were installed. They were built because the vertical axis simplified the alignment of the mandrel to the container and the die giving a better tube concentricity. On today's horizontal presses the tools can be so easily adjusted and guided that this advantage no longer applies. Horizontal presses need simpler foundations and enable larger section weights to be produced and have therefore almost completely displaced the vertical tube presses.

5.14.3 Drive

Whereas water and accumulator driven extrusion presses were previously exclusively used for copper alloys giving high ram speeds (up to 150 m/s), these are used today only for copper tube and thick sections.

In other cases direct oil drives are used, although these allow only a maximum ram speed of approximately 50 mm/s at an economically acceptable investment; this is usually adequate. The advantages of oil drive (good speed control and regulation over the billet length, simpler maintenance, and smaller footprint) predominate. Exact speed control is particularly advantageous for a linked puller and synchronously operating wire coilers. Variable oil drive also simplifies the automation of the extrusion process.

5.14.4 Die Changing

It must be possible to easily change dies and to control them on copper alloy presses: the high thermomechanical stresses result in such severe wear and deformation of the shape forming dies that dressing can be required after only a few extrusions. Chapter 6 describes suitable die changing systems (rotating arm, slide).

Quick container changing is more important than in aluminum extrusion because of the wear of the liner.

5.14.5 Discard Separation

The discard is normally removed with the saw, in contrast to aluminum extrusion where it is usually sheared. It is important that good swarf extraction prevents damage of the product from swarf.

In indirect extrusion and direct extrusion of small solid sections a powerful shear is, however, preferred [KM 77].

5.15 Billet Production and Heating

5.15.1 Continuous Casting and Homogenizing

Chill cast molds were still used up to the 1960s. They were completely replaced by the continuous casting method developed circa 1930 (see the section "Systems for the Production of Copper Billets" in Chapter 6). Horizontal or vertical casting is used depending on the billet cross section and alloy and usually on continuous plants. Homogenization of the billets is not normally required apart from tin bronze, which is susceptible to severe segregation, where the risk of cracking is reduced.

5.15.2 Billet Length

The length of the extrusion billet is usually determined by the extruded length of the section with rod, sections, and tubes. With coiled wire this is obviously not necessary. In this case the maximum billet length is selected. Alloys that are susceptible to piping are usually limited to 2.5 to 3.5 times the diameter in direct extrusion.

For extruded tubes the traditional rule of thumb is that the billet should not be longer than 5 times the mandrel diameter because of the increasing risk of wall thickness eccentricity as the billet length increases. The billet length also has to be restricted because of the occurrence of shell defects (e.g., with low-extrusion-ratio copper tubes).

5.15.3 Billet Processing

In the case of lubricated extrusion or if the billet surface is defective (particularly with flow type B), the billet has to be skimmed. This expensive operation is, naturally, avoided as much as possible by preferably extruding with an unlubricated container and a thicker shell that collects the casting defects.

In indirect extrusion without a shell and a conical die, the billet surface forms the section surface similar to direct extrusion with a lubricated container. All billets then have to be skimmed. To avoid this, extrusion with a shell and a flat die is also carried out with indirect extrusion so that a dead metal zone forms. Both hinder the flow of the billet surface into the surface of the section. The risk of defects is, however, significantly greater than in direct extrusion and particular emphasis has to be placed on a good, smooth billet surface.

If large-format tubes are extruded from large-diameter billets, the piercing load of the press may not be large enough and the billet has to be prebored. The general rule is that the bore diameter should be approximately 5 mm larger than the mandrel diameter so that the lubricant is not wiped off as the mandrel enters the billet.

5.15.4 Billet Quality Control

The billet quality must in any case be carefully checked before extrusion. This includes porosity and crack monitoring of sensitive material as well as visual inspection of the billet surface.

5.15.5 Billet Heating

Billet heating is described in detail in the section "Billet Heating Systems" in Chapter 6.

The most economic heating in a gas furnace is adequate to heat materials with a relatively low extrusion temperature (e.g., free-machining brasses), even though in terms of the final temperature it is less accurate and less reliable. A temperature profile can be applied, if needed, by subsequent heating in an inline induction furnace with several heating zones and, in any case, the billet temperature can be more accurately controlled. There are also cases in which gas furnaces are used even with higher billet heating temperatures (e.g., copper). In these cases induction furnaces are more common because the risk of overheating is reduced. High billet preheating temperatures are simultaneously close to the solidus temperature and thus there is a risk of the billet melting.

To reduce costs with high billet heating temperatures, the first heating step can be carried out in a gas furnace and the second in an induction oven.

In every case an inline electrically heated equalization chamber can be used in which temperature variations between the billet front and back can be removed and in which billets can be maintained at temperature during press downtime.

5.16 Copper Extrusion

5.16.1 General

Unalloyed copper is mainly extruded to tubes and, to a small degree, to bar and sections. Copper wire is, in contrast, usually cast, hot rolled, and drawn.

5.16.1.1 The Different Grades of Copper, Their Properties and Applications

The different copper grades are standardized in DIN 1787 (see Table 5.11 for the Euro standards). Pure copper with a low oxygen content (less than 0.04%), which bonds the residual impurities, giving the maximum electrical conductivity, is used in electrical technology under the designation E-Cu. In North America a designation beginning "OF" indicate oxygen free. Extruded and drawn sections as well as flat bar are used. Another high-conductivity copper grade that is oxygen free by deoxidation is referred to as SE-Cu in Europe. In North America deoxidized grades, DLP and DHP, are used for no-nelectrical purposes. The STP and ETP designations are used for electric bus. The most expensive variation is OF-Cu that is oxygen free without a deoxidation agent.

Oxygen-containing copper is sensitive to heating in a hydrogen-containing atmosphere. The oxygen forms water vapor in the pores of the annealed material with the diffused hydrogen, and this can burst open the structure. If the material has to be suitable for welding, brazing, or annealing, the oxygen has to be bonded, which is carried out by phosphorus in SF-Cu (0.015–0.04%). Water supply tubes are the main application of this copper grade.

5.16.1.2 Hot Workability, Extrusion Temperature

The hot workability of copper is limited by the fcc structure up to the melting point (see the hot-strength curve in Fig. 5.36). The extrusion temperature is accordingly very high (800–950 °C), and a high extrusion ratio is possible only on powerful extrusion presses.

5.16.2 Copper Tube

5.16.2.1 Application

SF-Cu is used exclusively for domestic water pipe, the most common use of copper tubes, because these need to be welded or soldered. However, SF-Cu is also used for underfloor heating or for industrial applications (heat-exchanger tubes in air-conditioning units, for chillers, etc).

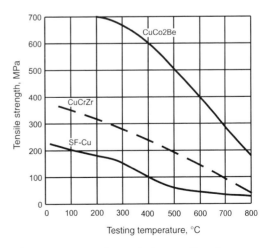

Fig. 5.36 Hot tensile strength of SF-Cu and low-alloy copper materials [Wie 86, Gra 89]

Whereas water supply pipes are available as hard or half-hard pipes or annealed coiled tubes (DIN 1786/EN 1057), industrial tube is usually supplied in annealed multilayered coils (coil weight 60–120 kg). Internal and external finned tubes for heat exchangers are also produced in SF-Cu because of the good thermal conductivity of copper and its excellent cold workability.

5.16.2.2 Production Methods

Numerous modern copper tube plants have been installed specifically for the production of SF-Cu tubes. The combination of the very good cold workability with the reduced hot workability enables hot working to be used to produce a tube larger than the finished dimensions followed by cold working to the finished size by cold pilgering and drawing machines without intermediate annealing. Soft tubes are given a final anneal. Half-hard tubes are lightly drawn after annealing.

Three processes compete for the production of copper tubes [Tus 70]:

- *Production using a piercer, cold pilger machine (tube rolling), and drawing machines:* Heated billets are rolled with inclined rolls over a mandrel to tube blanks. A straight tube up to 150 m long is then produced on a multistage cold pilger machine with a reduction ratio of 10:1 followed by redrawing.
- *Production on an extrusion press, cold pilger machine, and drawing machines:* The usual dimensions of the extruded tube are 80 × 10 mm with a piece weight of more than 400 kg. As in the first process, the extruded tube is then further processed with cold pilger machines and drawing machines. Schumag machines and spinner blocks are used.
- *Production on an extrusion press and drawing machines:* A so-called thin tube, e.g., 73 × 4 mm and a length of approximately 50 m but a lower piece weight, is extruded. Without the need for a cold pilger operation these tubes go directly to the drawing machines.

In the first process (with no extrusion press) there is the risk of cracks and thus laps and oxide inclusions, which impair the quality of the tubes if the high demands of the casting process are not fulfilled. In the production of gas and water supply pipe with a minimum wall thickness of 1 mm this does, however, play a minor role. This very economic process is used almost exclu-

sively in the production of gas and water supply pipes.

In the production of industrial tubes with wall thickness down to 0.35 mm and finned tubes, the demands on the starting tube are very high so that only the second and third processes with extrusion are used.

5.16.2.3 Extrusion

The press and the tooling have to be accurately aligned so that a low tube eccentricity (±7% and under) can be achieved. In spite of careful alignment of the centerline of the container, stem, and mandrel as well as the die, movement of the mandrel during extrusion is almost impossible to avoid. Therefore, to achieve a low eccentricity it is usual to limit the length of the unmachined billet to 5 (up to 8) times the mandrel diameter.

The tube is usually extruded at high speed under water within a few seconds, which reduces the risk of mechanical damage and produces the fine grain needed for extensive cold working.

Only direct extrusion presses are used.

To avoid water getting inside the tube, controlled mandrel movement is used at the start and the end of extrusion to give a tube closed at both ends (Fig. 5.37). The extruded tube is then oxide free internally and externally and can be passed to the cold pilger machine or drawing machine without pickling.

5.16.2.4 Oxide on the Billet Surface, Shell and Blister Defect

As mentioned previously, there is the risk with copper flowing according to type B that the oxide produced on billet heating acts as a lubricant between the billet surface and the container and flows along the dead metal zone that forms in front of the flat die: extrusion shell defects are the consequence (Fig. 5.38). They produce blisters when drawn tubes are annealed (Fig. 5.39).

Fast induction heating is recommended (at least as the final stage) to ensure that the minimum of oxide forms on the billet surface. The oxide on SF-Cu copper does not adhere strongly to the surface—in contrast to the oxide on oxygen-rich qualities. It can be largely removed by a strong water spray at the furnace exit. At the same time the billet hardly loses any heat. Hot scalping of the oxidized billet surface, which is mentioned in the literature, is now rarely used [Vat 70].

In conventional extrusion with a shell, the aim is for the oxide layer to be retained on the container liner. This does not occur completely. Because, as shown in Fig. 5.38, the oxide first arrives at the die toward the end of extrusion, the

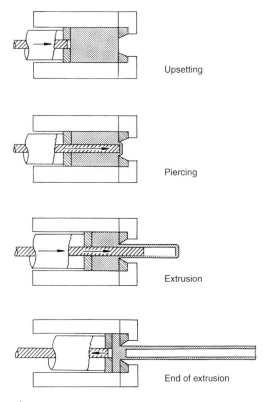

Upsetting

Piercing

Extrusion

End of extrusion

Fig. 5.37 Extrusion of copper tubes [Bau 93]

risk of lines of blisters is reduced by the selection of a large extrusion ratio, which increases the distance between the billet surface and the surface of the extrusion. If the billet is short enough, the flow of the oxide is stopped in time in front of the die.

As already mentioned, the extruded shell is so thin and ductile that a combination dummy block and cleaning block can be used in extrusion.

5.16.3 Copper Rod and Section

5.16.3.1 Dimensions and Shape, Further Processing

The high extrusion temperature of copper prevents the production of thin-wall complex and sharp-edged sections. Extruded shapes therefore have to be brought to the finished dimensions by one or more cold deformation steps—on draw benches. The good cold workability of copper makes this relatively simple. This also produces the preferred hard state. Figure 5.40 shows examples of extruded and drawn copper sections.

As described in section 5.16.2.3 for copper tubes, rods and sections in copper are also extruded underwater to achieve oxide-free, damage-free products with a fine grain. Small cross-sectional areas can be extruded in long lengths through a water wave and then coiled.

5.16.3.2 Hollow Sections

Hollow copper symmetrical sections for internally cooled bus bars in electrical engineering

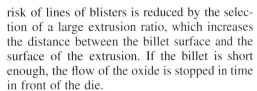

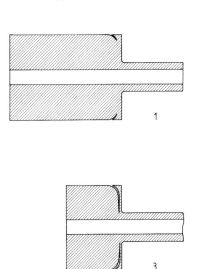

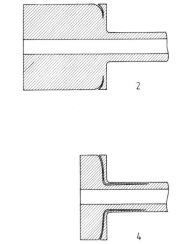

Fig. 5.38 Extrusion shell formation in the extrusion of copper tubes [Bau 93]

are, if possible, extruded from large billets pierced in the press and, for small openings, over the mandrel tip (fixed mandrel). With difficult shapes, prebored billets can be necessary. The shape of the mandrel tip and the exact location in the die require considerable experience.

Hollow sections have to be extruded through bridge dies if the openings are asymmetrical or if the section has several openings. This process is similar to that for aluminum alloys. However, with copper, deformation and cracking of the very expensive dies can occur along with the oxide flowing into the weld seam. This can be avoided only by good technical knowledge and experience. The extrusion of copper through bridge dies is therefore rarely used.

5.16.4 Extrusion of Low-Alloy Copper Materials

5.16.4.1 The Materials, Properties, and Applications

Low-alloy copper materials are covered by the standard DIN 17666 (UNS C-10100–

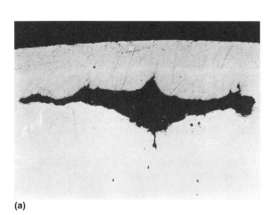
(a)

(b)

Fig. 5.39 Blisters on the tube surface of a SF-Cu-tube after annealing. (a) Transverse section. (b) External surface with line of blisters [Die 76]

(a)

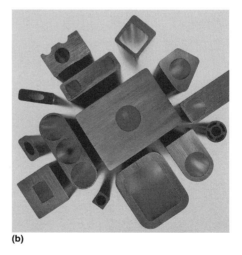
(b)

Fig. 5.40 Example of extruded and drawn copper sections. (a) Solid section. (b) Hollow section (Source: Kabelmetal Osnabruck)

C15815). The composition, properties, and applications of the different alloys are described in detail in the DKI information sheet 8 [DKIa].

In the non-age-hardening alloys, additions of silver, cadmium, magnesium, and iron increase the mechanical properties and, in particular, the softening temperature without reducing the conductivity significantly. Tellurium and lead improve the machinability. Additions of beryllium, nickel, silicon, chromium, and zirconium produce age-hardening alloys that have high mechanical properties and simultaneously high electrical conductivity after solution heat treatment and age hardening.

Application examples of the low-alloy copper materials are found mainly in electrical technology and chemical plant construction, e.g., contacts and spring elements as well as (CuCr, CuCrZr) welding electrodes (see also the section on copper alloy extruded products in Chapter 2).

Alloy development in recent years has resulted in some nonstandard age-hardening materials for elements of electrotechnology and electronics. The majority are used only in the form of strip, and extruded and drawn products are rarely used.

5.16.4.2   Extrusion

The low-alloy copper alloys have similar extrusion properties to unalloyed copper. The risk of flaking and blister formation by the inflow of oxide into the funnel behind the dead metal zone is usually even higher than with copper because of the greater tendency to oxidation [Moi 89]. The oxide thickness also increases when a higher extrusion temperature has to be used for the same extrusion ratio because of the higher hot strength. It is advisable in such cases to blow off the oxide from the hot billet using a water spray.

Figure 5.36 shows some hot-strength curves. Extrusion data are given in Table 5.9.

5.16.4.3   Solution Treatment at the Press

The mechanical and electrical properties of the age-hardening alloys are obtained by solution heat treatment followed by hot age hardening. If the cross section is not too high, the solution heat treatment of CuCr and CuCrZr can be carried out on the press. This process is well known from the low-alloy aluminum materials. Because, however, in this case the solution heat treatment has to be carried out at approximately 1000 °C, the stresses in the container and the die

are extremely high as is, as described previously, the risk of flaking and blistering [Hes 82]. As a general rule, only relatively short billets can be extruded (length:diameter = 1 to 1.5:1). The billet heating time in the induction oven can sometimes be too short to completely dissolve the second phase and to achieve the maximum mechanical properties.

The section has to be cooled in water to freeze the solid-solution state. Above a specific section thickness (60–70 mm diam) water quenching at the press is no longer sufficient. In this case the section has to be solution heat treated after extrusion in a special oven and then quenched. In this case a lower extrusion temperature can be used because the extrusion process and the solution heat treatment are not combined.

The hot age hardening following solution heat treatment (e.g., 475 °C for CuCr) is carried out before or after the cold working, depending on the properties required.

5.16.5   Extrusion of Copper-Zinc Alloys (Brass and Tombac)

5.16.5.1   Binary Copper-Zinc Alloys

Properties, Structure. Brass alloys are the most commonly used of the copper alloys and long sections are almost completely produced by extrusion. All copper-zinc alloys with a copper fraction more than 50% are referred to as brasses. More than 72% copper, the copper-zinc alloys are also referred to as "tombac." These are alloys with a reddish color. As the copper content is reduced corresponding to an increase in the zinc content, the color changes more and more to yellow, and at the same time the hardness increases.

The copper-zinc phase diagram is described first because of the marked variations in mechanical properties and structure with the zinc content.

As shown in Fig. 5.41, three alloy groups can be clearly differentiated:

- Single-phase α-alloys with a copper content above 61%
- Binary-phase α/β-alloys with a copper content of 54 to 61%
- Single-phase β-alloys with a copper content of 50 to 54%

The single-phase α-alloys have a fcc lattice similar to pure copper. They can correspond-

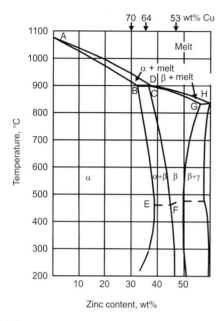

Point	Temperature, °C	Zinc content, wt%
A	1083	0
B	902	32.5
C	902	36.8
D	902	37.6
E	454	39.0
F	454	45.0
G	834	60.0

Fig. 5.41 Copper-zinc phase diagram [Ray 49]

ingly be easily cold worked (see structure in Fig. 5.42).

The single-phase β-structure is body centered cubic (bcc) and has very limited workability at room temperature. Between these limits (shown by the lines BE and CF on the phase diagram) there is a region in which the α-phase and the β-phase can coexist. The greater the zinc content, the lower is the α-content. The cold workability reduces in this region corresponding to the increasing zinc content (see Fig. 5.43, α-β-structure).

The Materials, Properties, and Applications. DIN 17660 covers the commercially used copper zinc alloys (See also ASTM B455 for Copper-Zinc-Lead [leaded brass] extruded shapes). The DKI information sheets i.5 and i.15 [DKIb, DKIc] cover these CuZn alloys in detail (See also Copper Development Association web site www.copper.org).

The brasses with a pure α-structure as well as the tombac (low-alloy CuZn) alloys are used predominantly in the form of sheets and strip, less as tubes, and rarely in the form of bar and section. The producers of jewelery and metal ware, brass instruments, lamp bodies, and light-bulbs use α-brasses. Tubes are used for air brake pipes in goods vehicles and for manometers.

The alloys in the α-β field with a β-fraction between 20 and 40% can be readily machined and are therefore widely used as rod material.

Chip forming additions—usually between 1 and 3% lead—that are embedded as droplets in the matrix further improve the machinability.

Materials with only a low β-content (Cu Zn36Pb1.5) can be readily machined and cold worked. They are used where stamping or bending is required. The free-machining brasses (mainly CuZn39Pb3) are used in large quantities as hard drawn rods for processing on automatic lathes to turned components of all kinds (e.g., bolts). They can be cold worked only to a limited extent (see Table 5.11, EN 12164). Pure β-brass

Fig. 5.42 Structure of α-brass, etched. Image width is 0.5mm [Wie 86]

(e.g., CuZ44Pb2) is almost brittle at room temperature but is used for extruded sections that do not have to be subsequently cold worked because of its excellent hot workability. Sections in α-β brass can, on the other hand, be cold drawn to a limited extent and therefore be supplied to tight finished tolerances. Figure 5.44 shows some examples of extruded and drawn brass sections. They are covered by the DIN 17674 standard (EN 12167).

Extrusion. At the normal extrusion temperature of more than 600 °C, the β-structure has a significantly lower flow stress than the α-structure. The α-β brasses and especially pure β-brasses therefore have a high extrudability. Figure 5.45 illustrates this by hot flow stress curves.

The workability of the CuZn alloys decreases initially in the normal extrusion temperature range of 600 to 800 °C with increasing zinc content and then increases again from approximately 30% zinc when β-phases occur during extrusion.

The low flow stress of the β-phase at the extrusion temperature enables high extrusion speeds and extrusion ratios to be attained. With free-machining brass extrusion ratios up to $V = 900$ and exit speeds up to 8 m/s can be reached.

Table 5.9 gives extrusion data on copper-zinc alloys.

Because the phase boundaries α/α-β and α-β/β are displaced to higher zinc contents on cooling, the α-phase fraction extends into the α-β field on cooling (see Fig. 5.41). The α-precipitation can be partially suppressed by quenching (frozen) so that the β-fraction remains higher than would be the case in the equilibrium state. If quenching is carried out after cooling to 500 to 300 °C, depending on the composition, the α-precipitation has stabilized and the structure no longer changes.

By quenching from the deformation heat and aging at temperatures approximately 200 °C, α-β-brasses can be given a substantial hardness increase by the fine precipitation of the second phase [Bro 73]. This is rarely used in practice because it is difficult to maintain the extrusion

Fig. 5.43 Brass with acicular α-β-structure, etched. Image width is approximately 0.275mm [Wie 86]

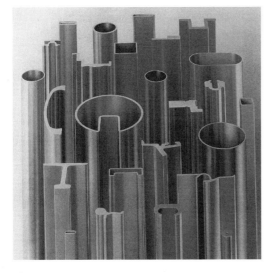

Fig. 5.44 Extruded and drawn brass sections (Source: Wieland-Werke, Ulm catalog)

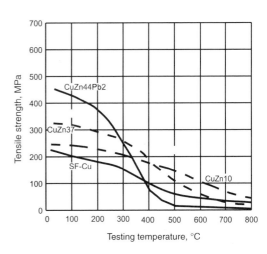

Fig. 5.45 Some hot tensile strength curves for copper-zinc alloys and SF-Cu [Wie 86]

conditions constant from billet to billet, and at the same time the cold workability is restricted.

Possible Extrusion Defects and their Prevention. The high deformation resistance of low-alloy α-brasses requires a high extrusion temperature for a given extrusion press power. This increases the danger of coarse grain formation and in the extreme case, hot shortness. Low initial billet temperatures as well as low extrusion speed reduce the risk of coarse grain formation and hot shortness, as with all materials. However, at the lower extrusion temperature the deformation resistance is higher and the possible minimum extruded cross section for a given press power larger.

With copper-zinc alloys containing more than 80% copper, copper oxide forms on the billet surface during heating in air. With alloys with less than 80% copper, zinc oxide mainly forms and this has no lubrication properties in contrast to copper oxide. Whereas the CuZn alloys with more than 80% copper can still have shell and blister defects, this risk does not occur with higher-zinc-containing materials because the adhesion between the billet and the container is so large that a closed shell is formed when extruding with a shell. On the other hand, the combination dummy block and cleaning disc that can be used in copper extrusion is not suitable because of the large shell thickness. A separate cleaning cycle has to take place after extrusion.

As the zinc content increases, the thermal conductivity of brass decreases and the peripheral cooling of the billet in the container is no longer equalized. Because the β-rich hotter billet core flows more easily than the β-impoverished peripheral zone, the typical flow pattern type C forms (see Fig. 3.11 in Chapter 3) with the risk of the piping defect. Figure 5.46 shows an example.

The billets should have a perfect surface quality to avoid extrusion defects. The difference between the container diameter and the billet diameter should also not be too large to avoid folds forming as the billet is upset in the container. With a good quality liner surface, the shell from the previous extrusion can be completely removed with the cleaning disc [Lot 71].

In direct extrusion, the length of the billet is limited to reduce the risk of the piping defect. As a general rule the billet should not be longer than 2.5 to 3 times the diameter. Routine fracture testing of the end of the sections can remove any sections containing the extrusion defect and ensure that the remaining length is defect free.

Indirect extrusion is recommended for α-β-brasses where there is the risk of the extrusion piping defect forming in direct extrusion because the different material flow excludes this defect. Significantly longer billet lengths can then be used [Sie 78].

As mentioned elsewhere, in direct extrusion, if the extrusion ratio is too low, particularly with brass, the acceleration of the center of the billet can be so severe that cavities can occur toward the end of the section (Fig. 5.47). Their formation in the section can be prevented only by limiting the billet length and leaving a sufficiently long discard.

A further defect, particularly with α-brasses with a low zinc content, is the formation of zinc flakes on the surface of the extruded product. Zinc vaporisation from the newly formed surface immediately behind the die condenses onto cooler parts of the tooling in the form of fine drops, which can be picked up by the passing section. The droplets form zones of high zinc content, containing β phase, on the section surface. These are brittle and can result in defects. These zinc flakes can also be found on the inter-

Fig. 5.46 Extrusion defect (piping) in α-β-brass [Die 76]

nal surface of tubes. In order to prevent them forming it is necessary to ensure that the hot section does not contact the tooling behind the die.

Handling the Section. Because the α-β-brasses and the β-brasses are very soft at the exit temperature and sensitive to mechanical contact, good guiding out of the die (possibly lined with graphite) is needed to avoid damage of the section surface combined with careful handling on the runout table.

Whereas thick bars from single-cavity dies are extruded into air on graphite or steel-lined plates, or onto a freely rotating roller conveyor and then cross transferred until they can be cooled—possibly in a water trough—and cut to length, pullers are usually used for sections and thinner bar. Up to four sections can be simultaneously pulled using independent jaws. The ma-

terial emerging from the die is very soft and it is necessary to use a defined low puller force to avoid undesired stretching of the sections.

If the cross-transfer conveyor is not large enough, water cooling has to be used at the end before the sections can be cut to length. Figure 5.48 shows the principle of the extrusion of brass sections.

Cu-Zn wires, usually in free-machining brass, are extruded from one or two cavity dies into down coilers, the speed of which are synchronized with the ram speed. Periodic oscillations of the rotation speed (wobble) ensure that the individual layers on the drum are not directly above each other. To avoid damage, the strands are usually extruded into pans, which at the end of extrusion are removed from the coilers and transported on a roller conveyor until the brass

Fig. 5.47 End cavities in a brass bar [Die 76]

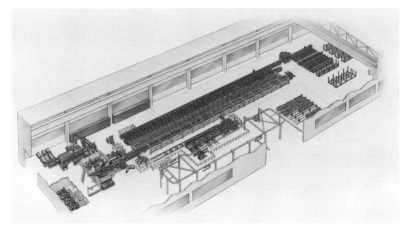

Fig. 5.48 Schematic of a section and wire brass extrusion plant (SMS Hasenclever catalog)

wire has cooled sufficiently and can be lifted out. Further processing is carried out after pickling by a combination of drawing, straightening, and cutting to length.

Straightness—β phase distribution—Further Processing of Bar. The straightness of the bar is very important for machining on automatic lathes with high cutting speeds. Bars that are not clean or straight chatter in the bar feed. If the β-phase fraction and its distribution in the cross section vary over the length of the extrusion, the rectification effect in the combination drawing, straightening, and cutting to length machine changes from the first bar to the last of an extruded coil.

The indirect extrusion process again offers advantages over the direct process. The variation in the size and distribution of the β-phase in the α-β mixed structure between the start of extrusion to the end in indirect extrusion is less than in direct because of the uniform material flow over the length of the extrusion.

In multicavity extrusion the billet no longer flows symmetrically in one strand because the die apertures are arranged asymmetrically. One side of the section surface stems from the outer region of the billet and the other side from the inner region. It is therefore particularly important to ensure a uniform cast structure and good through heating; there are then no disadvantages for the quality of the section and, in particular, for the straightness of the finished bars.

In order to obtain uniform mechanical properties and good straightness, care must be taken to ensure that the degree of deformation in the individual drawing operations is held within narrow limits requiring that the dimensional tolerances of the extruded bar are within tight limits. Suitable selection of the hot-working materials for the die and its design are discussed in detail in the section on tooling for the extrusion of copper alloys in Chapter 7.

5.16.5.2 Copper-Zinc Alloys with Alloy Additions (Special Brasses)

The Different Materials and Their Properties. If additional elements, including aluminum and tin, are added to copper-zinc alloys, properties such as the β-phase fraction, the corrosion resistance, and the strength change significantly. These materials are referred to as special brasses. They are also covered by DIN 17660 copper-zinc-aluminum alloys are known as aluminum bronzes and copper-zinc-tin alloys are tin brasses.

Again, as with brass there are single-phase materials with a fcc α-structure and two-phase materials with an α-β structure. In both groups additional intermetallic phases can occur depending on the type and amount of the additions.

The β-phase fraction in the α-β-mixed structure, which has a strong influence on the extrudability and the cold workability, can be controlled by these additions of alloying elements (see Table 5.12, Fig. 5.49).

Semifinished Products and Applications. The alloys CuZn20Al2 and CuZn28Sn1 are resistant to seawater and corrosion. They are used in heat exchangers and condensers. Because they have a pure α-structure and consequently are difficult to extrude but have good cold workability, the tubes are extruded with large cross sections and brought to the finished dimensions on cold pilger machines and draw benches with intermediate annealing.

CuZn31Si1 is a material with an α-β-mixed structure. Tubes for bearing bushes are produced

Table 5.12 Influence of element additions on the β-phase fraction and the extrudability of special brasses

Alloying element	β-portion	Zinc equivalent(a)	Extrudability
Silicon	Is improved	10	Is improved
Aluminum	Is improved	6	Is improved
Tin	Is improved	2	Is improved
Manganese	Is improved	0.5	Is improved
Nickel	Is improved	−0.9−−1.5	Is improved

(a) 1% the alloying element corresponds to one in the effect on the structure condition one as "zinc equivalent" of indicated multiples of the effect of zinc. Source: Lau 76

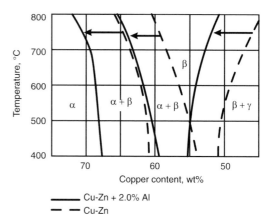

Fig. 5.49 Displacement of the phase limits in the copper-zinc system using aluminum additions as an example [Bar 32]

in this alloy. Other nonstandardized special brasses (with additions of Mn, Ni, Si, and Pb) have proved themselves as wear-resistant bearing materials in special cases.

High-zinc-containing special brasses are construction materials with moderate and high mechanical properties used in the manufacture of chemical plants.

Casting and Extrusion. Casting defects, including porosity and cracks, have to be assumed in special brasses, particularly with aluminum and manganese additions. Careful testing of the billet quality (e.g., using a penetrant such as the Met-L check testing on the cut surface) is necessary. Billets with defects on the mantle surface have to be machined.

In the same way as with pure brasses, the extrudability depends on the amount of the β-phase present at the extrusion temperature. This is shown by the hot tensile test curves in Fig. 5.50. The possible defects and their avoidance follow those described in section 5.16.5.1.

5.16.6 Extrusion of Copper-Tin Alloys (Tin Bronzes)

5.16.6.1 The Different Alloys, Their Structures, Properties, and Applications

The tin content of tin-bronzes can extend to 20%. However, the higher-alloyed materials (more than 10% tin) are extremely difficult to deform and are, therefore, usually used only as cast materials. Complex tin-bronzes can contain additions of zinc and lead.

DIN 17662 describes the composition of the common alloys suitable for extrusion with a maximum tin content of 8%. The DKI information sheet i.15 [DKId] describes the copper-tin alloys in detail (See also Copper Development Center. These tin bronzes are also called phosphor bronzes).

Tin-bronzes belong to the oldest known copper alloys. They are still today very important in the chemical industry and ship construction because of their good electrical and thermal conductivity with simultaneous high-strength and favorable corrosion properties. In electrical technology, significantly more tin-bronze strip is used than wire and sections.

CuSn4 and CuSn6 tubes are used for manometers or suction pipes. Highly stressed components, including gear wheels, bolts, and bearings, are made from CuSn8.

The phase diagram in Fig. 5.51 shows that the wrought materials in the equilibrium state have a pure fcc α-structure and therefore behave like copper in hot and cold working.

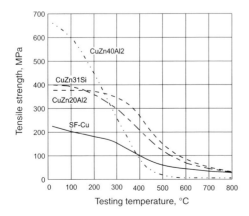

Fig. 5.50 Hot tensile strength curves of special brasses and SF-Cu [Wie 86]

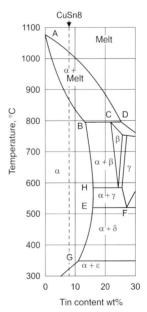

Point	Temperature, °C	Tin content, %
A	1083	0
B	798	13.5
C	798	22.0
D	798	25.5
E	520	15.8
F	520	27.0
G	320	11.0
H	586	15.8

Fig. 5.51 Copper-tin phase diagram [Ray 49]

5.16.6.2 Casting of Copper-Tin Alloys

Because the cast structure—particularly at the higher tin contents—tends toward segregation because of the wide solidification interval and the billets can exhibit tin sweating as a result of inverse billet segregation, turning of the billets is advised. Homogenization of the billets (630 to 700 °C for several hours) reduces the risk of extrusion defects in the form of longitudinal and transverse cracks in the higher-alloyed materials. With more than 6% tin, the brittle α-β eutectoid that forms on solidification is partly retained in the cooled billet; it can be dissolved only by this homogenization. Some phosphorous is added to the 8% tin-bronze to suppress the tin-oxide formation in melts that have not been completely deoxidized. These tin-bronzes are referred to as phosphor-bronzes.

5.16.6.3 Extrusion of Copper-Tin Alloys

The flow stress of the tin-bronzes is higher than that of copper as shown in the hot tensile strength curves in Fig. 5.52 and increases with increasing tin content. Tin-bronzes are best worked between 700 and 750 °C. The extrusion data can be found in Table 5.9.

Tin-bronzes containing up to 6% tin are moderately difficult and those with 8% difficult to extrude. High-alloyed tin-bronzes are very susceptible to cracking and can be extruded only with slow speeds [Moe 80].

Bars smaller than 25 mm diameter are extruded as several strands and coiled. There is the risk of the billet "freezing" in the container because of the low speed and the large difference between the initial billet temperature and the container temperature. Only short billets can therefore be used.

With the good cold workability of the fcc lattice the section can be extruded above the final dimensions and then worked to the final size in several stages—including where necessary intermediate annealing—by section rolling and drawing. This also produces the frequently required high mechanical properties.

5.16.6.4 Flow Type and Shell Defects

Because tin-bronzes tend to oxidize and this oxide exhibits good lubrication properties, flow type A occurs in the direct extrusion of these alloys, giving the risk of shell and blister defects—particularly with low extrusion ratios, i.e., thick bars [Vat 70]. With large extrusion ratios—thin bars—this risk is reduced. Extrusion is normally carried out without container lubrication and with a thin shell. Care has to be taken in the cleaning cycle to ensure that no residues of the shell from the previous extrusion remain.

5.16.6.5 Competition from Wire Casting

As mentioned previously, only short billets can be used in wire extrusion giving low coil weight. The extrusion process and subsequent downstream processing is correspondingly expensive. Direct continuous casting of wire in large coils has grown in competition to the extrusion of thin bar from which tin-bronze wire is produced by rolling and drawing.

The production of tin-bronze wire today is mainly by this continuous casting process [Bau 76].

5.16.7 Extrusion of Copper-Aluminum Alloys (Aluminum Bronzes)

5.16.7.1 The Different Alloys, Their Properties, and Applications

The composition of copper-aluminum alloys, usually referred to as aluminum-bronzes, is covered by DIN 17665 (see Table 5.11 for the Euro standard). The DKI information sheet i.6 [DKIe] describes aluminum-bronzes in detail (see Copper Development Association).

Binary aluminum-bronzes up to approximately 9% aluminum have a homogeneous structure with the fcc α-phase, as can be seen

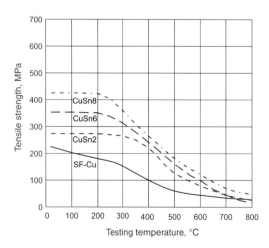

Fig. 5.52 Hot tensile strength curves of copper-tin alloys and SF-Cu [Wie 86]

from the phase diagram in Fig. 5.53. In contrast, complex aluminum-bronzes with aluminum contents of approximately 10% and additions of iron, nickel, manganese, and silicon individually or together usually have a heterogeneous structure.

Aluminum-bronzes are corrosion- and oxidation-resistant alloys because of the formation of Al_2O_3-containing surface layers. They are also very resistant against erosion-corrosion and cavitation and are particularly suitable for seawater applications. Aluminum-bronzes are also found in the chemical industry and in highly stressed machine components.

5.16.7.2 Binary Copper-Aluminum Alloys

Materials and Extrudability. The two standardized alloys CuAl5 and CuAl8 have a fcc α-phase structure. They can be readily cold worked. Their hot workability depends on the aluminum content. Figure 5.54 shows the temperature dependence of the hot tensile strength of the aluminum-bronzes.

The poor extrudability is revealed by the extrusion data in Table 5.9.

The phase diagram in Fig. 5.53 shows that the boundary line α/α-β is displaced to higher aluminum contents with decreasing temperature. The β-content thus decreases during cooling from the extrusion temperature. Even with normal cooling to room temperature from the extrusion temperature, residues of the bcc β-phase are retained with the 8% aluminum-bronze so that only limited cold working is possible. If smaller final cross sections are to be produced

from larger extruded cross sections by cold working, then only the 5% aluminum bronzes can be considered.

Extrusion and Extrusion Defects of Copper-Aluminum Alloys. The oxidized billet surface, mainly with Al_2O_3, does not act as a lubricant in the container in contrast to copper oxide. The friction resistance is so high that it is possible to extrude with a stable shell. Because the cast billets frequently have surface defects, machining is recommended. Testing the cross section for cracks and cavities is also advisable.

If the billet heated to more than 750 °C cools during extrusion—it can only be extruded relatively slowly—variations in the α-β-ratio occur over the length of the extrusion along with various forms of the α-phase, resulting in differences in the mechanical properties.

As with all difficult-to-extrude materials, a higher extrusion ratio for the same press power can be attained with the aluminum-bronzes by extruding with a lubricated container without a shell through a conical die. This process is used only in exceptional cases.

If the aluminum content is 8% or more, then the structure at the high extrusion temperature above 900 °C consists of an α-β mixed structure, the flow stress of which is less than the pure α-structure. However, in the direct extrusion of these alloys, there is the risk of flow type C occurring and the formation of the piping defect at the end of extrusion in the same way as with brass. The countermeasures are the same as those mentioned previously; the piping defect can be controlled by a suitable short billet and

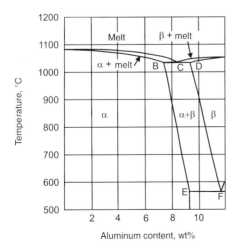

Fig. 5.53 Copper-aluminum phase diagram [Ray 49]

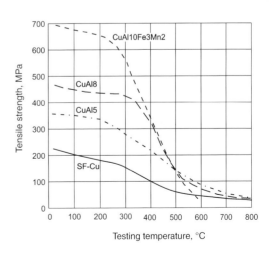

Fig. 5.54 Hot tensile strength curves of copper-aluminum alloys and SF-Cu [Wie 86]

long discard. Fracture tests of the ends of the extrusion are recommended in any case.

5.16.7.3 Copper-Aluminum Alloys with Additions (Complex Aluminum-Bronzes)

Materials, Structure, and Properties. The properties of alloys CuAl8Si, CuAl9Mn, CuAl10Fe, CuAl10Ni, and CuAl10Fe3Mn2 are given in the standards.

The mechanical, physical, and chemical properties of the complex aluminum-bronzes depend on the composition. The aluminum-bronzes with iron, manganese, and silicon additions are usually extruded in the β-phase where they have a lower flow stress than CuAl8 (see Fig. 5.54). On the other hand, CuAl10Ni has an extremely high flow stress (about 70% higher than CuAl8 at 700 °C). This alloy is extremely difficult to extrude.

Extrusion of Complex Aluminum-Bronzes. Complex aluminum-bronzes have a strong tendency to stick to the container wall. In contrast to brass, the shear stress needed to shear away the shell is very high at the extrusion temperature of 600 to 700 °C. The related high stem load needed to shear the shell and the high flow stress result in the complex aluminum-bronzes being very difficult to extrude in spite of the high β-phase component. Often, if small cross sections have to be extruded there is no alternative to working with a lubricated container without a shell and with a conical die entry.

A special case in the complex aluminum-bronzes is the copper-aluminum-nickel-shape memory alloy (about 13% aluminum, 4% nickel) in which the composition, billet pretreatment, and the extrusion conditions have to be exactly maintained to obtain the desired shape memory properties [Don 92].

The sticking of complex aluminum-bronzes to the extrusion tooling can sometimes cause problems in tube extrusion if the mandrel lubrication or the mandrel taper is insufficient. The internal surface of the tube can then exhibit cracks or flaking.

Another almost typical defect with the complex copper-aluminum alloys is the "wood grain fracture" attributable to severe gas porosity of the billet or the inclusion of aluminum oxide films. The billets therefore have to be carefully checked (e.g., by penetrant check) for soundness.

The complex aluminum-bronzes in direct unlubricated extrusion usually flow according to type C similar to CuAl8, so that allowance has to be made for the piping defect.

Further Processing. The cold workability of the complex aluminum-bronzes is very restricted compared with the binary alloys because of the high β-phase component. They are, therefore, normally supplied as extruded.

Similar to special brasses, the complex aluminum-bronzes can be heat treated [Ben 93]. Higher mechanical properties can be obtained with CuAl10Fe and CuAl10Ni by solution heat treatment in the α-β-region followed by quenching and age hardening at 500 to 650 °C. On quenching a β′-martensite forms that partly breaks down on aging. The quenching can take place at the press, but better values are obtained by a separate heat treatment after extrusion.

5.16.8 Extrusion of Copper-Nickel Alloys

5.16.8.1 Materials, Structure, Properties, and Applications

The copper-nickel alloys contain between 4 and 50% nickel, usually approximately 5 to 30%. Nickel forms a continuous solid solution with copper (see Fig. 5.55) so that all copper-nickel alloys are single phase and have a fcc α-structure.

The most important copper-nickel alloys are covered by DIN 17664 (ASTM E 75). They are CuNi10Fe, CuNi20Fe, CuNi30Fe, and CuNi30 Mn1Fe.

The most important alloy technically is CuNi30Fe, which is used for tubes in ship heat exchangers, seawater desalination plants, and air

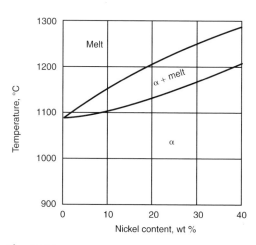

Fig. 5.55 Copper-nickel phase diagram [Han 58]

and oil coolers. However, CuNi10Fe alloys also find applications here. Whereas pure binary alloys are used primarily for the production of coins, the extruded alloys used for other applications, e.g., condenser tubes, have additions of iron and manganese to improve the properties. These elements increase the corrosion and erosion resistance and raise the strength as well as the recrystallization temperature. The DKI information sheet i.14 [DKIf] describes the copper-nickel alloys in detail. (See UNS C/70100 to C/72950 and ASTM B 151.)

5.16.8.2 Extrusion of Copper-Nickel Alloys

The melting point and recrystallization temperature increase with increasing nickel content, and the cold and hot workability decrease. As can be seen in Table 5.9, the extrusion temperature increases with increasing nickel content. The range is between 850 and 1000 °C and is the highest of all the copper extruded alloys. Figure 5.56 shows the hot strength of the copper-nickel alloys as a function of the temperature. It does fall within reasonable limits at the high extrusion temperatures mentioned, but when determining the extrudability, the service life of the tooling plays the decisive role.

Copper-nickel alloys should and can be extruded as quickly as possible because of the high extrusion temperature and the associated thermomechanical stressing of the tooling. Usually, relatively thick-walled tubes are extruded and then further processed on cold pilger machines and by drawing with intermediate annealing because the copper-nickel alloys have good cold-working properties as a result of their fcc lattice.

Extrusion is usually carried out with a shell and without container lubrication through flat dies. This is not possible if small cross sections, i.e., a high extrusion ratio, have to be extruded in these difficult-to-extrude alloys. Container lubrication is then recommended with extrusion through conical dies and without a shell. The resultant significantly lower friction between the billet and the container enables higher extrusion ratios to be produced or lower extrusion temperatures to be used. However, attention has to be paid to having a high-quality container bore and a good billet surface to avoid defects on the surface of the extrusion.

The increase in hydrogen solubility with increasing nickel content and thus the risk of gas porosity with inadequate melt treatment has to

be taken into account when casting the billets into water-cooled molds or by continuous casting.

A homogenization heat treatment of the billets is not considered to be necessary in spite of the nickel concentration variations resulting to some degree from the casting process. The billets often have to be machined to remove the cast skin.

5.16.9 Extrusion of Copper-Nickel-Zinc Alloys (Nickel-Silver)

5.16.9.1 Material, Structure, Properties, and Applications

Alloys of copper, nickel, and zinc are referred to as nickel-silver because of their silver color. The copper content of the technically most common alloys can range from 45 to 62% and the nickel content 7 to 26%, with zinc forming the remainder. Alloys suitable for turning and drilling with an α-β-phase contain up to 2.5% lead as a chip breaker similar to brass. Small additions of manganese are usual to reduce the risk of cracking at high temperatures ("annealing cracking").

The copper-nickel-zinc alloys are covered by DIN 17663 (see ASTM B 151).

Figure 5.57 shows the copper corner of the copper-nickel-zinc system. The solid lines in the phase diagram show the room temperature state; the dashed lines apply at 850 °C.

In the majority of the commercial nickel-silver alloys, the fractions of nickel and zinc are

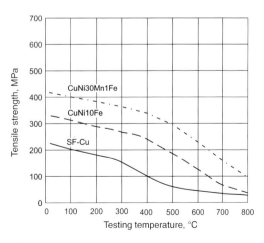

Fig. 5.56 Hot tensile strength curves of copper-nickel alloys and SF-Cu [Wie 86]

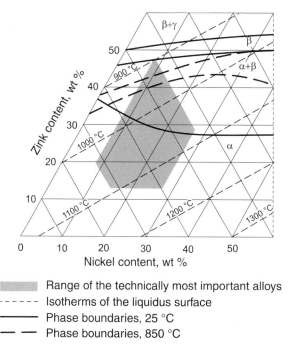

Range of the technically most important alloys
- - - - - Isotherms of the liquidus surface
——— Phase boundaries, 25 °C
— — Phase boundaries, 850 °C

Fig. 5.57 Copper corner of the copper-nickel-zinc system [Sch 35]

completely dissolved in the copper so that only α-solid solution exists. As with brass, only the high-zinc-containing alloys are heterogeneous and consist of α-β mixed crystals.

Tableware and spring elements are produced from lead-free nickel silver. It is also used for frames of glasses and zippers.

The α-β-nickel silvers, also with lead additions, are used for all kinds of turned components and for fine mechanical fittings. The DKI information sheet Nr i.13 [DKIg] describes the nickel-silver alloys in detail (Also refer to ASTM B 151).

5.16.9.2 Extrusion of Nickel-Silver Alloys

The extrusion data for the nickel-silver alloys is also given in Table 5.9. As with the brasses the β-component determines the hot and cold workability of the different alloys. A lead addition hardly reduces the hot workability of the β-containing nickel-silvers but reduces it significantly in the α-alloys. The hot tensile strength can be obtained from Fig. 5.58 for some Cu-Ni alloys. These alloys can be readily extruded in the temperature range between 600 and 700 °C. In principle, the lowest possible extrusion temperature should be used to avoid oxidation, hot

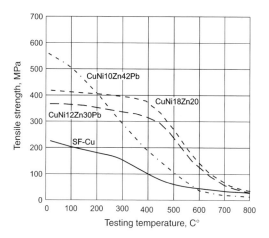

Fig. 5.58 Hot tensile strength curves of copper-nickel-zinc alloys and SF-Cu [Wie 86]

cracking, and a structure with an excessive grain size.

The billet surface of the nickel-silver alloys is usually turned off and extrusion is carried out with a thin shell. Because a defect-free section surface requires the lowest possible extrusion temperature, it is frequently possible to extrude only with a large cross section, i.e., a low-extrusion ratio. Further processing is then carried out by rolling and drawing.

5.16.9.3 Competition from Wire Casting

Lead-free nickel-silver is—similar to tin-bronze—occasionally cast in wire format and then cold worked without hot working. This process is economically superior to the manufacture of wire by extrusion but frequently produces defects in the strand, which reduce the quality [Bau 76].

Extrusion of Semifinished Products in Titanium Alloys

Martin Bauser*

Titanium with a melting point (T_s) of 1668 °C is one of the high-melting-point metals. Although it is the fourth most abundant metal in the earth's crust after aluminum, iron, and magnesium, the high cost, in particular, of the reduction to the pure metal but also of casting and further processing, makes titanium products expensive [Sib 92]. Its low density of 4.5 g/cm^3 compared with iron and, simultaneously, the very high strength of some of its alloys makes it particularly useful where a favorable ratio of strength to density is required, i.e., in the aerospace industry. The very good corrosion resistance against numerous media is attributable to the strongly adhering oxide film that forms even at room temperature. It therefore finds numerous applications in the chemical and petrochemical industries. Titanium alloys can be classified as one of the exotic extruded metals because of the high cost. Because its industrial application only started in the 1950s, all production and application possibilities have certainly not been exhausted.

Special mention should be made of superconductors of titanium-niobium alloys, shape-memory alloys with titanium and nickel as the main constituents, as well as intermetallic phases of titanium and aluminum for high-temperature applications. The book *Titanium and Titanium Alloys* by U. Zwicker gives an overview [Zwi 74].

---

*Extrusion of Semifinished Products in Titanium Alloys, Martin Bauser

With extrusion temperatures of 850 to 1150 °C, the extrusion process largely corresponds to that of iron and nickel alloys. Titanium alloys are, therefore, usually extruded on steel extrusion presses. An analogous technology is used.

Similar to steels and nickel alloys forging, hot and cold rolling are preferred when possible to the more expensive extrusion process for the production of bar material of titanium. Thin-wall tube in unalloyed titanium is also usually made from strip with longitudinal welding. Extrusion is, however, the most suitable method of production for thick-wall titanium tubes, titanium-alloy tubes, and for sections.

5.17 Materials, Their Properties, and Applications

5.17.1 The Structure and Its Influence on the Properties

The example of the phase diagram for titanium with aluminum (Fig. 5.59) shows that pure titanium has a close-packed hexagonal lattice up to 882 °C, the so-called α-phase. Above this there is the bcc β-phase. In alloys there is a more or less wide field within which the α- and β-phases can coexist.

Titanium alloys are classified into three groups according to the structure at room temperature after the most common deformation and heat treatment processes: α-alloys, α-β-alloys, and β-alloys.

β-alloys in general have a lower strength and elongation as well as an inferior fatigue performance compared with the α-β-alloys. However, the β-alloys are superior to the α-β-alloys in terms of creep strength and fracture toughness [IMIa 88].

The α-alloys are relatively difficult to work at room temperature [Mec 80], whereas β-alloys can still be readily deformed.

The alloying constituents of the technically most important materials are aluminum, which increases the strength and stabilizes the α-phase, as well as chromium, manganese, molybdenum, vanadium, copper, tin, and zirconium. Most of these elements stabilize the β-phase and reduce the α/β transformation temperature and are contained in the precipitates after age hardening. Tin as an alloying element, which slightly stabilizes the α-phase, and zirconium have a high solubility in the α-phase and harden it [Mec 80]. Zirconium increases the hot and creep strengths.

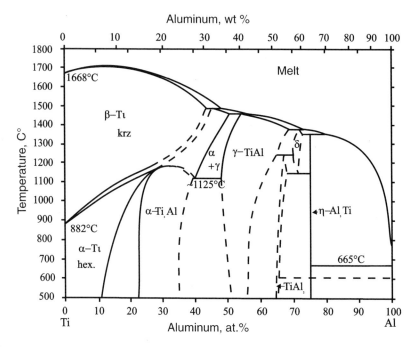

Fig. 5.59 Titanium-aluminum phase diagram [Kum 92]

The undercooling capability of the β-phase and the reducing solubility with the decreasing temperature of numerous alloying elements result in interesting hardening and tempering possibilities. Solution heat treatment is usually carried out in the β-region or just below followed by rapid cooling so that the α-phase or other precipitates can form only in a finely distributed manner after subsequent age hardening. Age hardening cannot be carried out on α-materials [Lam 90].

The often complicated transformation kinetics of the α-β alloys are represented in time-temperature-transformation diagrams similar to steel [Zwi 74].

The lowering of the transformation temperature by β-stabilizing additions is important for hot working because the body-centered cubic β-phase has better forging and extrusion properties than the hexagonal α-phase.

The niobium-titanium alloy with 52% Nb and 48% Ti used for superconductors has a relatively low transformation temperature and can therefore be extruded at approximately 900 °C.

5.17.2   The Most Important Titanium Alloys and Applications

Table 5.13 shows the most important titanium alloys with their properties and application areas.

The strength is not a decisive criterion for thin-wall tube for liquid transport in the chemical or petrochemical industry and, for example, in water desalination plants and power station cooling towers. The requirement is far more for the outstanding corrosion resistance of titanium against a range of media and its oxidation resistance at normal temperatures. In these applications different grades of pure titanium are used that differ from each other only in their oxygen content (Table 5.13).

As with iron alloys the move is away from the production of soft tubes by extrusion, cold pilger mills, and tube drawing. This area has had to be conceded to the more economic longitudinal welding of cold-rolled strip.

Bar and section in commercially pure titanium can be extruded and is produced by this route but the demand is small.

The aerospace industry is the main user of semifinished products in titanium alloys apart from special products, including racing wheels and sports cars. In aircraft, they are used for engine components, fuselage, and wing elements [Pet 92] (Table 5.13). Wherever the strength and mechanical properties of aluminum alloys are insufficient, titanium alloys are used for lightweight fabrications.

Extruded sections, tubes, and bars are produced from the higher-strength materials as well

Table 5.13 Some titanium alloys suitable for extrusion, properties, and applications (IMIa 88, IMIb 88, and personal communication)

Low-temperature alloys

Material	Composition	Structure at room temperature	Strength R_m, N/mm²	Elongation, A_5, %	Properties	Application
Ti1–Ti3(a)	Unalloyed titanium with min 99–99.5% Ti	α-phase	290–590	30–8	Corrosion resistant, readily worked	Tubes and components for the chemical and petrochemical industries
TiPd–Ti3Pd(a)	Addition of 0.12–0.25% Pd	α-phase	250–590	30–8	Very corrosion resistant	The same areas

Intermediate temperature alloys

Material	Composition Cu	Al	V	Sn	Mo	Si	Structure at room temperature	Strength R_m, N/mm²	Elongation, A_5, %	Properties	Application
TiCu2.5 (IMI 230)(c)	2.5	...	...	...	...	...	α-Phase Age-hardening	630–790	>30	Used up to 350°C, soft readily worked	Gas turbines Aircraft components
TiAl6V4(b) (IMI 318)(c)	...	6	4	...	...	...	α-β-mixed structure Quenched and tempered Fine α in β structure	950–1080	>12	Used up to 500°C Creep resistant up to 300°C Suitable for hot-working	Most common alloy, turbines, jet engines, implants
TiAl4Mo4Sn2 (IMI 550)(c)	...	4	...	2	4	0.5	α-β-mixed structure used heat-treated and tempered	1000–1250	>9	Creep resistant up to 400°C	Jet engines Aircraft components
TiAl6V6Sn2(a)	...	6	6	2	...	...	α-β-mixed structure	1000–1300	>8	Creep resistant up to 500°C	Aircraft components

Materials for High-temperature alloys

Material	Composition Al	Sn	Zr	Mo	Si	Nb	Structure at room temperature	Strength R_m, N/mm²	Elongation, A_5, %	Properties	Application
IMI 679(d)	2	11	5	1	0.2	...	α-β-mixed structure with precipitates; high-temperature heat treatment; β with precipitates	>1100	>8	Creep resistant up to 450°C, still suitable for hot working	Aerospace
6242(d) (USA)	6	2	4	2	...	...	Almost α	>900	>10	Creep resistant up to 500°C	Aerospace
IMI 829(d)	5.5	3.5	3	0.25	0.3	1	Almost α		>9	Creep resistant up to 940°C	Gas turbines

(a) DIN 17850/17861/17862. (b) DIN 17851/17861/17862. (c) IMI brochure: *Titanium Medium Temperature Alloys.* (d) IMI brochure: *Titanium High Temperature Alloys.*

as sheet and strip. The alloy TiAl6V4 is the most common not only as a construction material because of its high strength, but also in surgery for implants because of its good biocompatibility.

5.17.3 Titanium Alloys Produced by Powder Metallurgy

Titanium alloys produced by powder metallurgy (P/M) are being offered to an increasing extent. This occurs on one hand when high-alloy materials, e.g., with intermetallic titanium aluminide, cannot be produced by melting metallurgy or cannot be or only to a limited extent be hot worked and, on the other hand, if it is dispersion-hardened material in which the dispersoids can only be added to the metal using P/M. These materials are described in Chapter 4.

5.18 Billet Production, Extrusion

5.18.1 Casting, Billet Preparation, Billet Heating

The billet pre-material is usually obtained from vacuum arc furnaces with melting electrodes of titanium foam and recycled material [Kra 82]. If the ingot diameter is too large, it has to be forged to the final billet diameter. This has the advantage that an originally coarse grain structure with low hot workability can be recrystallized with a fine-grain structure by careful selection of the forging temperature intervals.

Mechanical surface processing is the final stage: a smooth billet surface is the requirement for a good product surface in the same way as with steel extrusion because in direct extrusion without a shell, with lubrication and a conical die entry, the billet surface becomes the product surface.

The billets have to be rapidly heated in an induction furnace or a protective atmosphere (argon) because titanium easily oxidizes above

700 °C and can become brittle in hydrogen-containing atmospheres. Very fast heating is opposed by the poor thermal conductivity of titanium. Heating in a salt bath (e.g., with barium chloride as a deoxidant) is less environmentally friendly and is therefore rarely used.

5.18.2 Extrusion, Lubrication

Table 5.14 shows the important data for the extrusion of titanium alloys produced by melting metallurgy.

Titanium alloys are preferentially extruded in the β-phase region where the flow stress is significantly lower than in the α-β mixed region (or in the pure α-phase). The uniform structure, which is obtained by the recrystallization that occurs during extrusion in the β-region, is also advantageous. If the temperature in the β-region is too high, there is the risk of coarse grain formation, which has to be avoided at all costs. With some alloys it is possible to obtain a martensitic structure if the section is not cooled slowly enough from the β-phase. Subsequent annealing is then required.

Because titanium becomes brittle not only in hydrogen but also nitrogen and oxygen atmospheres, the extrusion temperature should be as low as possible without crossing the α/β temperature limit.

If, on the other hand, deformation is carried out just below the α/β phase boundary, the variations in heating during extrusion over the cross section and along the length of the section result in a changing mixed structure that produce variations in materials properties over the cross section and along the length.

Titanium alloys are extruded in the temperature range 850 to 1150 °C. Above 1000 °C, which is in the β-region, it is necessary to use glass lubrication similar to steel and nickel alloys.

The glass film hinders the contact between the titanium material and the extrusion tooling and

Table 5.14   Data for the extrusion of some titanium alloys (Lau 76, Zwi 74, IMI personal communication)

Alloy	β-phase boundary	Extrusion temperature	Structure at extrusion temperature	Deformation at extrusion temperature
Ti 1–Ti	882 °C	700–900 °C	α-phase	
TiAl6V4	995 °C	900–950 °C	α-β-phase	~120 N/mm^2
		1050–1100 °C	β-phase	~80 N/mm^2
TiAl6VSn2	945 °C	800–1040 °C	α-β or β-phase	
TiAl4Mo4Sn2	975 °C	~900 °C	α-β-phase	~160 N/mm^2
		~1100 °C	β-phase	100 N/mm^2
TiAl6Sn3Zr3MoNbSi	1015 °C	1050–1150 °C	β-phase	~100 N/mm^2

thus the destruction of the bearing surfaces by corrosion, to which titanium tends in contact with steel. The molten glass also acts as a thermal insulation barrier and hinders the heat flow from the hot material into the colder tooling. The glasses 4 and 5 for the lower temperature range are preferred from the recommended glass mixtures for stainless steel tubes (see Table 5.18 and [Mar 74]).

The extrusion technology with titanium alloys differs slightly from that for iron-base alloys: titanium alloys are, if possible, coated with a glass powder suspension at 80 to 150 °C. During the subsequent heating to the extrusion temperature, the glass coating can act as a barrier against the reaction of the billet surface with air constituents [Mar 74].

However, the method described for stainless steels, rolling the billet heated to the extrusion temperature over a table in glass powder is common, particularly with tube extrusion and when induction furnaces are available for heating.

Extrusion is usually carried out quickly, directly through a die with a conical entry with a glass disc in front to minimize the cooling of the material during the extrusion process and to ensure that the tooling is subjected to the high temperatures for only a short time. At a high speed the temperature of the emerging section can even increase from the front to the back.

If the speed is too high, in particular with sections, there is the risk that the glass film will tear. The instantaneous failure of the tool working surfaces is the result [Mar 74]. The extrusion speed is in the range 0.5 to 5 m/s.

There are also alloys that have to be extruded in the α-β-mixed region with temperatures between 700 and 950 °C, especially if subsequent cold working is not carried out and a fine-grain structure is needed in the as-extruded condition [Zwi 74]. The turned billet is then wrapped in a thin copper sheet and extruded with a lubricated container, in this case, a graphite grease mixture, through conical dies. At the upper temperature range of 850 to 950 °C, an iron foil is recommended as an intermediate layer to avoid a reaction between the copper and the titanium.

With adequate lubrication the friction between the billet and the container is, similar to glass lubrication, so low that a quasi-stationary deformation with laminar material flow occurs, and the surface copper layer at the start and end of the section has an approximately constant thickness. This would be even better with indirect extrusion, but usually only direct extrusion presses are available.

The pickling away of the copper film in a mixture of nitric and hydrofluoric acid is unpleasant and is the reason why cladding in copper is avoided as much as possible. It has been reported that an extrusion in the α-β-mixed region is possible without a copper cladding in spite of the severe adhesion tendency between titanium and the tooling surface if a special graphite grease lubrication is used [Boy 89].

5.18.3 Flow Stress, Extrusion Defects

Compared with many stainless steels, the titanium alloys have a high flow stress at the extrusion temperatures mentioned, and they are therefore difficult to extrude (see Fig. 5.60). This means that on a press usually used for extruded semifinished products in steel, titanium can be extruded only with a low deformation. Extrusion ratios of $V = 10$ to $V = 100$ are used.

The flow stress is—particularly in the α-β-mixed region—very temperature dependent: It increases rapidly with falling temperature as shown in Fig. 5.60. Care must therefore be taken to ensure that the billet is not given time in the container to cool, producing a large radial temperature gradient. Otherwise, the material from

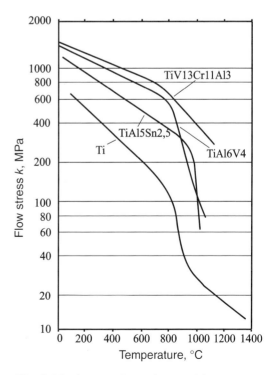

Fig. 5.60 Flow stress k_f as a function of the temperature [Zwi 74]

the billet interior will flow first producing a piping defect at the end of the section. If the extrusion is too slow there is also the risk of the billet's "sticking."

The dependence of the flow stress on the rate of deformation is higher for titanium than for steel. Nevertheless, extrusion has to be carried out quickly for the reasons just mentioned.

5.19 Tooling, Further Processing

The tooling is discussed in Chapter 7 in the section on tooling for the extrusion of titanium alloys.

The tooling loading is similar to the extrusion of stainless steels. When extruding in the β-region with glass lubrication—particularly in section extrusion—only one or two billets can be extruded before the die has to be reworked. The die service life is significantly longer with copper sheathed billets and lower extrusion temperatures. Chapter 7 describes coated section dies that are much more expensive but have a significantly longer service life.

Normally, the lowest limit for the wall thickness of sections is 2 mm. Sections used in aircraft construction often have to have thinner walls (down to 1 mm wall thickness). Because cold working of the common alloys is possible only to a limited extent, drawing and stretching of the extruded sections at a higher temperature is utilized [Mar 74]. However, 350 °C should not be exceeded to avoid undesired structural changes.

Extrusion of Semifinished Products in Zirconium Alloys

Martin Bauser*

5.20 Materials, Properties, and Applications

Pure zirconium and, in particular, zirconium alloys with tin (ZrSn1.5 = zircaloy) and nio-

*Extrusion of Semifinished Products in Ziroconium Alloys, Martin Bauser

bium (ZrNb2.5) are used as construction materials in nuclear reactors, especially for the casing material for the fuel rods because of the low absorption of thermal neutrons, good heat transfer, good corrosion resistance, and high hot strength. The chemical industry also uses zirconium-alloy semifinished products for specific critical corrosion conditions.

The production of the very pure metal necessary for processing is costly, and zirconium alloys are therefore correspondingly expensive.

Zirconium melts at 1852 °C and has a density of 6.5 g/cm^3. Pure zirconium has a hexagonal α-lattice up to 862 °C. Above this transformation temperature, there is a bcc β-phase. With alloys—also with small quantities of element additions—there occurs a more or less wide temperature interval with the simultaneous presence of the α- and the β-phases [Web 90]. The structure is similar to that described for titanium alloys, and the properties during hot and cold working are comparable.

5.21 Billet Production, Extrusion

5.21.1 Casting, Billet Preparation

Similar to titanium production, the starting material is melted from zirconium sponge in vacuum or protected atmosphere furnaces with self-consuming electrodes. After forging or rolling the large-diameter cast ingots, the billets for the extrusion of tubes have to be turned on the outside to remove surface defects and also be prebored. Because zirconium has the same property as titanium of readily welding to the tooling during deformation and also reacts with oxygen, hydrogen, and nitrogen at high temperature, the billets are normally externally and internally clad. Copper sheet material is usually used sometimes with an intermediate steel layer when the temperature is high to prevent diffusion of the copper into the zirconium base material. The copper cladding can, however, be applied by plasma spraying. To avoid an expensive zirconium discard, a copper disc can be attached to the back of the billet to form the discard, at the end of extrusion. The cladding of the billet can be avoided by using special lubricants.

5.21.2 Extrusion, Influence of the Structure

If zirconium, for which there is no great demand, is processed on presses installed for steel or copper alloys, then the technology used follows that for the corresponding main material.

The flow stress of most zirconium alloys is not very high at the extrusion temperature, and the dependence on the temperature is tolerable so that the extrusion temperature and speed can be varied within relatively wide boundaries with no risk.

Because the β-phase has the best hot workability, it makes sense from the deformation point of view to extrude in the temperature range 800 to 1100 °C, where the flow stress is relatively low. This, however, rarely occurs because the billets would then have to be clad in steel. In this case, lubrication is carried out with a glass powder mixture similar to steel and titanium.

In practice zirconium alloys are extruded preferentially in the temperature range 675 to 800 °C to reduce the risk of gas absorption, which severely impairs the toughness of the extruded semifinished product. Just below the α/β transformation temperature and (in the case of alloys) in the α-β mixed phase region the workability is very good [Sch 93].

The best method, but also the most expensive, is cladding the billets in copper. Clad billets can be heated in an induction furnace and lubrication with oil-graphite suffices similar to standard copper alloys. Dies with conical entries are necessary to obtain a predominantly laminar flow and thus to obtain a uniform cladding thickness over the length of the extrusion.

If extrusion is carried out without cladding, it is important that the billets are brought rapidly to temperature and protected as far as possible from atmospheric influences during heating. Salt bath heating is, therefore, preferred over other methods (75% BaCl, 25% NaCl is referred to in [Lus 55]).

Special glass mixtures are used as lubricants when extruding without cladding at approximately 800 °C. They have a low viscosity even at this low temperature and substantially protect the billets from gas absorption.

5.22 Tooling, Further Processing

When selecting the tooling materials and the tooling design, the experience gained from the extrusion of copper alloys and—when extruding at high temperatures—of steels can be utilized.

As a general rule, conical dies ($2\alpha = 140$ to 90 °C) are used to produce tubes and round bars.

If extrusion is carried out with copper cladding, the cladding material has to be removed from the extruded product either mechanically or with nitric acid. Zirconium is not attacked by nitric acid. Coarse grain billet material leaves an orange peel effect on the pickled surface as an image of the grain structure. A fine-grain starting material is therefore preferred.

The subsequent processing of zirconium alloy tubes is carried out on precision cold pilger machines [Jun 93]. Drawing requires careful preparation by bonderizing and lubrication because the material has a tendency to weld to the tooling. More recently, drawing has been carried out using an ultrasonic vibrating mandrel, which improves the internal surface. Zircalloy cladding for fuel rods can be produced from extruded tubes without drawing by multiple cold pilger operations with intermediate annealing (70% reduction per cycle can be achieved).

Extrusion of Iron-Alloy Semifinished Products

Martin Bauser*

5.23 General

5.23.1 Process Basics

The high melting point of iron alloys (pure iron: 1535 °C, density 7.9 g/cm^3) corresponds to a high recrystallization and hot-working temperature. Hot working usually is carried out in the fcc austenite region, depending on the alloy, between 1000 and 1300 °C. This is associated with high tool wear because of the high thermal and mechanical stresses and, depending on the composition, a more or less severe oxide formation. As a result, it was relatively late before these alloys could be successfully extruded.

The oil graphite lubricants known from copper alloys, and which were used for steel extrusion around 1930, were not really suitable. They were initially replaced with mixtures of oil, graphite, and cooking salt, which could be ef-

---

*Extrusion of Iron-Alloy Semifinished Products, Martin Bauser

fective only with very short contact times between the hot material and the shape-forming tooling. This method of lubrication is used only rarely today for the production of mild steel tubes on vertical mechanical presses (see section 5.24).

A significant extension to the application of the extrusion process followed the development of the Ugine-Séjournet process in 1950 in which glass of a specific composition was used for lubrication [Séj 56]. The molten glass not only protects the heated billet from oxidation and acts as a lubricant between the material and the tooling, but also acts as thermal insulation so that the die and container heat more slowly than with the lubricants previously used. It was now possible to produce alloy steel tubes and steel sections on horizontal extrusion presses with a lubricated container.

Steels are extruded using the direct extrusion process with lubricated containers without a shell. With this process it is possible to achieve short contact times with fast extrusion speeds—important for the necessary high extrusion temperatures. The use of conical dies result in a material flow in which the billet surface forms the surface of the extruded product (see Chapter 3, the section on material flow in direct extrusion, Fig. 3.31).

5.23.2 Importance of Steel Extrusion Today

The growth in the extrusion of steel in the 1950s and 1960s was followed by a continuous decline. The production of seamless tubes in mild steels and low-alloy structural steels on vertical presses has largely been replaced by more economic continuous rolling processes. Seamless tubes in these steel grades are now replaced whenever possible by the less-expensive longitudinally welded tubes.

Today, the extrusion of stainless steel tubes and steel sections is used only when the material, the section shape, or the low volume required cannot be produced by other processes or only with significant expense.

The reasons for extruding steel tubes are:

- Crack-free production of long products even in materials that are difficult to hot work and that tend to crack during rolling
- Production of small volumes. If unusual dimensions or materials are involved, then frequently the setting and operation of rolling processes designed for mass production is

uneconomic. The tooling costs can also be very high. In contrast, extrusion can be viable for quantities as low as three billets.

- Experimental or pilot production of tubes and sections that will later be produced in large quantities more economically by rolling

Approximately only 30% of all steel tubes are produced as seamless and of these, less than 10% are produced by extrusion [Bil 79].

Three product groups are described in detail subsequently:

- Mild steel tubes
- Alloy steel tubes
- Steel sections

5.24 Mild Steel Tubes

5.24.1 Use of Mechanical Presses

The numerous vertical mechanical presses previously used in the technically highly developed countries are no longer in operation. Carbon steel tubes are usually produced on continuous production lines that have a significant higher productivity. However, these mechanical presses are still used in other countries.

Carbon steels, free cutting steels, low alloy hot and cold working steels and high speed steels can be processed on mechanical presses.

5.24.2 Application of Mechanical Presses

Mechanical extrusion presses are similar to the machines used in the drop-forging industry.

The billets are pierced and extruded in one operation on vertical mechanical presses. The billets are first heated to 1100 to 1300 °C and loaded into the vertical lubricated container. Then, at the upper top dead center the crankshaft is connected to a continuously operating electrically driven flywheel with a horizontal axis. In one revolution the stem and piercing mandrel fall and the billet is extruded down into a curved channel and the stem and mandrel retracted. The discard is sheared with a shearing tool and removed from above.

The high deformation temperature and the extrusion time, which lasts for only a few seconds on the mechanical press, enables extruded tubes in mild and free-cutting steels to be hot reduced directly after extrusion on a stretch reducing mill without reheating.

The glass lubrication used on horizontal presses to protect the tooling (see section 5.25.4.2) is not really applicable for vertical presses because the glass powder does not adhere securely to the billet surface in the vertical position.

The older method of lubrication with a viscous oil-graphite salt mixture has to be used. This partly evaporates and can even burn during extrusion. Today's environmental requirements are difficult to fulfill even with careful extraction.

5.24.3 Dimensional Range and Throughput

Mechanical tube presses are restricted in their press loads because there is a limit to the load that can be economically transferred mechanically. They are, therefore, used only for extrusion loads up to a maximum of 17 MN. Because the upper limit of the billet weight naturally depends on the extrusion load that can be developed, the maximum billet weight that can be deformed is 120 kg with a diameter of 200 mm.

The entire extrusion process lasts no longer than 3 s so that it is possible to have up to 200 working cycles in one hour (average 120 to 130). The mandrel length is restricted to 5 to 7 times the mandrel diameter because longer mandrels can deflect sideways within the press during piercing.

The dimensional range of the extruded tubes extends from 40 to 120 mm external diameter and 2.5 to 5 mm wall thickness [Sar 75].

5.25 Seamless Alloy Steel Tubes

5.25.1 Extrusion in Competition with Other Hot-Working Processes

There has also been a large reduction in the extrusion of seamless alloy steel tubes over the last few decades and numerous presses have had to be closed down. The extrusion of seamless alloy steel tubes has to compete with a range of more economic rolling processes, the production capacity of which can be seen in Table 5.15.

Economic analysis has shown that extrusion is inferior in output to the continuously operating rolling processes because of the low billet weight and the long dead cycle times. The dies

Table 5.15 Production ranges for the different methods for producing seamless steel tubes (Man 86)

Process	Tube diameter, mm
Extrusion	35–250
Tube continuous rolling	20–180
Diagonal rolling and Pilger process	160–660
Plug rolling procedure	180–400

for extrusion can be produced relatively inexpensively but wear much more rapidly than the tooling in the rolling process.

The most important method of producing seamless alloy steel tubes in the same dimensional range as the extrusion press is the continuous tube-rolling process in which a forged round ingot formed to a hollow billet in a piercing mill is hot rolled over a mandrel through numerous profiled roll pairs and then brought to the finished size on a stretch reducing mill after reheating. This process has at least 4 times the throughput of an extrusion press [Bil 79].

The extrusion process today is restricted to:

- High-alloy stainless ferritic and austenitic steels
- Heat-resistant high-chromium ferritic and austenitic alloy steels
- High-temperature austenitic alloy steels

The dimensional range of these tubes is between 35 and 250 mm external diameter and a wall thickness of 5 to 50 mm with a minimum internal diameter of 30 to 40 mm [Ric 93]. The extruded tubes are usually processed further by rolling and/or drawing.

To produce the infrequently required dimensions over 200 mm external diameter, an alloy steel tube extrusion press would have to be so massive that the high cost would generally prohibit the use of the extrusion process [Bil 79]. A 55 MN press designed for this purpose was supplied to Russia several years ago.

Horizontal water-driven tube presses and only the direct process without a shell are used. Figure 5.61 shows the extrusion principle.

Alloy steel tubes produced by extrusion are sold as hot finished or further cold worked. Applications are in the chemical industry, plant manufacture, nuclear technology, and the petrochemical industry.

5.25.2 Alloys and Extrusion Properties

5.25.2.1 Alloy Groups, Structure, Properties, and Applications

Table 5.16 shows a selection of the alloy steels currently extruded.

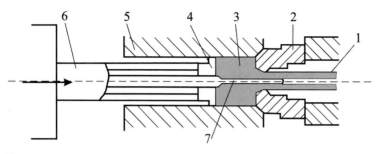

1) Extruded tube
2) Die with support
3) Billet
4) Dummy block
5) Container
6) Extrusion stem
7) Mandrel

Fig. 5.61 Extrusion of alloy steel tubes on a horizontal press [Sar 75]

Table 5.16 Examples of stainless heat-resistant and high hot strength steels that are processed by extrusion (Ric 93)

| Material No. | Chemical composition, % | | | | | Similar UNS No./Common Name |
	C	Cr	Ni	Mo	Other	
Stainless steel						
Ferritic	. . .	. . .	. . .	. . .	. . .	. . .
1.4016	<0.08	16.5	. . .	. . .	. . .	S43000/430
1.4510	<0.05	17.0	. . .	. . .	Ti>4 × (C + N) < 0.8	S43036/430Ti
Austenitic						
1.4301	<0.07	18.0	9.5	. . .	. . .	S30400/304
1.4306	<0.03	19.0	11.0	. . .	. . .	S30403/304L
1.4401	<0.07	17.5	12.0	2.2	. . .	S31600/316
1.4404	<0.03	17.5	12.5	2.2	. . .	S31603/316L
1.4571	<0.08	17.5	12.0	2.2	Ti>5 × %C < 0.7	S31635/316Ti
Heat-resistant steels (austenite)						
1.4845	<0.15	25.0	20.5	. . .	. . .	S31000/310
1.4841	<0.20	25.0	20.5	. . .	Si 2.0	S31400/314
1.4876	<0.12	21.0	32.0	. . .	+ Al + Ti	
High-temperature steels (austenite)						
1.4910	<0.04	17.0	13.0	2.5	N 0.14	S31653/316LN
1.4961	<0.10	16.0	13.0	. . .	Nb 10 × %C ~ 1.20	S34700/347
1.4959	0.07	20.0	32.0	. . .	Al + Ti, V 0.07	. . .

The heat-resistant materials are covered by DIN EN 10095, the other materials by DIN EN 10216-5 and DIN 17456 (the European standard [EN] has replaced the previous DIN standards).

The following material groups are classified by the hot-working temperature range [Ric 93]:

- *Ferritic steels* with bcc α-iron structure. All ferritic chromium steels over 12% Cr content as well as the steels alloyed with molybdenum and/or titanium belong to this group and have a bcc α-iron structure. They are characterized by a flow stress that decreases rapidly with increasing temperature so that they can be readily hot worked.

  However, this alloy group tends to brittleness due to precipitated phases and to grain coarsening during the hot working of the starting material by rolling or forging before extrusion. The embrittlement reduces the notch impact values. Suitable billets for extrusion are therefore difficult to produce free from cracks in the high-chromium-containing materials.

  Hot-brittle lead and sulfur-containing free-machining steels can only be hot rolled with difficulty. Only piercing and rolling over a mandrel are suitable for processing these alloys apart from extrusion, which is still the most common process used for this material group.

- *Austenitic steels* have chromium contents over 16% and nickel contents exceeding 8%. At the extrusion temperature the structure of these alloys is the fcc γ-iron lattice. The austenite is, therefore, usually characterized by very good hot workability as well as a low tendency to embrittlement. The undesirable coarse grain formation found with the ferritic steels does not occur with the austenitic ma-

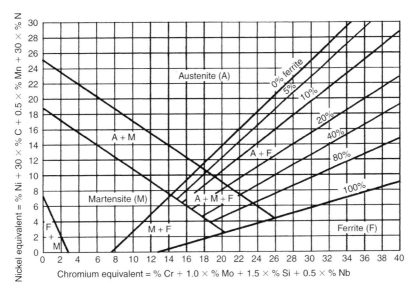

Fig. 5.62 Phase diagram according to Schaeffler-DeLong [Ric 93]

terials so that they can also be readily welded.

The good workability and the good corrosion resistance against many media provide the austenitic materials with a wide range of applications in chemical plant manufacture and in energy production.

The higher the nickel content, the higher is the hot strength of austenitic materials and the more difficult they are to extrude. High-nickel-containing materials can consequently be extruded only at low extrusion ratios.

- *Austenitic–ferritic alloys* with chromium contents of 18–25% and nickel contents of 4–7% are used for a range of applications. They combine to some extent the advantages of both the alloy groups described previously. They have a lower susceptibility to embrittlement than do ferritic materials and are more easily worked than the austenitic materials and also offer advantages in specific types of corrosion attack. The most well-known representative of this group is the material 1.4462 with 22% Cr, 5.5% Ni, and 3% Mo, which is an alloy steel with many applications in the petrochemical industry.

An overview of the structure of the three material groups is given by the phase diagram according to Schaeffler-DeLong (Fig. 5.62), which shows the structure as a function of the chromium and nickel content. The effect of other alloying elements is determined from their chromium or nickel equivalent.

In austenitic steels, δ-ferrite is particularly dangerous because its occurrence limits the extrusion temperature; otherwise, transverse cracking occurs in the extruded section.

5.25.2.2 Extrusion Properties, Defects

The extrudability and extrusion temperature range of the different materials are given in Table 5.17.

The fewer the precipitates, the better the extrudability of ferrite and austenite. Single-phase materials—particularly in the γ-range with a fcc structure—are particularly easy to extrude [Bur 70, Ben 73].

At the normal extrusion temperatures of 1100 to 1350 °C, the flow stress is in the range 150 MPa (materials with high extrudability) to 400 MPa (materials with low extrudability) for austenite and ferrite. The extrusion ratio (V) is usually 8 to 40.

Examples of the relationship of the flow stress and the deformation capability on the composition and the temperature are shown by the curves for different steels in Fig. 5.63.

Whereas the workability of homogeneous structures always increases with increasing temperature, a marked decrease can occur with Cr-Ni steels as a result of the formation of δ-ferrite above approximately 1200 °C. This results in a risk of transverse cracking during extrusion. The limit is considered to be 2 to 3% δ-ferrite at room temperature (corresponding to approximately 8% at the extrusion temperature).

The calculation of the extrusion load is discussed in detail in Chapter 3.

The high extrusion temperature produces a large temperature difference between the material and the container and a rapid loss of heat. It is necessary to extrude quickly to prevent the billet freezing during the extrusion process. This also aids the die life.

In the deformation zone immediately in front of the die, an adiabatic temperature increase of up to 150 °C occurs during extrusion. The higher the flow stress of the material and the faster the extrusion speed, then the higher the temperature increase will be, i.e., the closer the process approaches adiabatic conditions. It is therefore necessary to carefully match the temperature and speed for materials with low-melting-point constituents to avoid melting and thus cracks in the extruded section.

Because the extrusion temperature is above the solution heat treatment temperature of constituents that can form precipitates, the extruded section usually has a fully recrystallized structure.

At low extrusion ratios, i.e., large tube cross-sectional areas, the core region tends to accelerate. The resultant internal longitudinal stresses can result in lamination such as internal cracking within the extruded section that cannot be detected externally. These defects can only be discovered using ultrasonic testing.

In contrast, in thin-wall tubes, these stresses result in cracks originating at the surface.

5.25.3 Billet Production

5.25.3.1 Melting, Casting, Hot Working

Alloy steels are melted today by the following processes [Ric 93]:

- Electric arc melting process with downstream argon-oxygen-decarburization (AOD) or vacuum-oxygen-decarburization [VOD]
- Induction melting in air or in a vacuum
- Remelting using the electroslag refining process (ESR)

Table 5.17 Extrudability of different material groups (examples) (Ric 93)

Group	Characterization	Nominal flow stress k_f MPa	Example, alloy (DIN No.)	Billet preheat temperature, °C
1	Easily extruded	150	410 (1.4006) 430 (1.4016) 439 (1.4510)	1000–1200
2	Good extrudability	200	304 (1.4301) 304L (1.4306) 316 (1.4401) 316L (1.4404) 316Ti (1.4571)	1050–1250
3	Difficult to extrude	250	314 (1.4841) 310 (1.4845) . . . (1.4876)	1100–1300

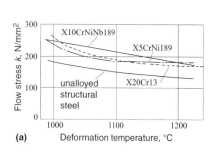

(a) Deformation temperature, °C

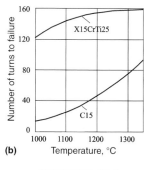

(b) Temperature, °C

Homogenous structure

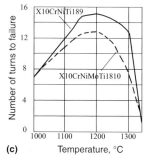

(c) Temperature, °C

With ferrite components (austenitic)

Fig. 5.63 Flow stress and workability of steels measured from the number of turns to failure in torsion tests as a function of temperature. (a) Flow stress. (b) δ. (c) Deformation capacity [Ben 73]

The latter guarantees a high cast purity and an extensively homogeneous distribution of the elements that tend to segregation such as niobium and molybdenum.

Continuous casting is carried out if the charge size permits; otherwise, mold casting is used. Only pure and low-alloy carbon steels can be directly extruded without previous hot working. Higher-alloyed materials have to first be forged or hot rolled to destroy the columnar cast structure and produce a homogeneous structure [Man 91, Bil 79, Bur 70].

5.25.3.2 Homogenizing, Billet Preparation

Homogenizing of the rolled or forged billets is rarely carried out and only when the homogeneity or grain distribution is inadequate for defect-free extruded bars [Ric 93]. The need for homogenization increases with increasing content of the elements molybdenum, niobium, and titanium, which result in the formation of segregations.

Because the billet surface in direct extrusion with lubrication without a shell and using conical dies becomes the surface of the extrusion, the 8- to 12-m-long forged or hot-rolled round bars have to be cross sectioned and carefully machined by turning or peeling. Coarse turning marks result in fish-bone patterns on the extruded tube surface. A chamfer on the front face of the billet simplifies the uniform flow of the glass lubricant during extrusion (see below).

Billet diameters from 200 to 300 mm and billet lengths up to 700 mm are standard.

Whereas in the extrusion of copper alloy tubes large billets are pierced in the press, this process is not possible with alloy steels, which are also processed on hydraulic horizontal presses. The mandrels cannot withstand the severe thermomechanical stresses and would rapidly wear because of the absence of the lubricating film. The billets are therefore bored, although for diameters up to 60 mm, a deep hole without expansion is sufficient. The billet length to bore ratio should not exceed the value of 7:1; otherwise, the bore will deviate. With larger bore diameters, the predrilled billet is expanded in a separate piercing press [Bil 79]. The hole diameter is always larger than the mandrel diameter so that the lubricant spread in the bore is not stripped off by the mandrel.

5.25.4 Billet Heating, Lubrication

5.25.4.1 Billet Heating

Apart from the uniform through heating of the billet, it is important during heating to avoid oxidation and surface decarburization of the heat treatable steels.

Billet heating to the required temperature of 1100 to 1300 °C is carried out in rotary hearth furnaces with protective atmospheres, in induction furnaces, or in a combination of both with a gas furnace for preheating to approximately 700 °C and final heating in an induction furnace.

The slower heating in the rotary hearth furnace with its more uniform through heating can have a homogenizing effect on the structure of some steels.

The cost advantage of gas heating also plays a role, particularly with infrequent alloy changes. The possibility of a rapid temperature change with small batch sizes of different steels is an argument for induction heating.

Induction furnaces are more expensive to operate but heat more quickly, and the temperature can be more accurately controlled, which is the reason why induction furnaces are used in particular for high-alloy steels with exactly specified preheat temperatures. Complex alloy steels often have only a narrow extrusion temperature range. The upper limit is determined by the solidus temperature and the lower limit by the press power.

The temperature of the billet core lags behind during the rapid induction heating, which can result in core cracking in crack-susceptible steels, e.g., heat-resistant ferrites with high chromium contents. In this case the preheating in rotary hearth furnaces mentioned previously is recommended.

Although induction furnaces with the shorter heating times of 5 to 15 minutes largely heat free of oxidation, a protective atmosphere is often passed through the induction coil with the oxide-susceptible steels. This can be necessary, in particular, with furnaces with a vertical axis in which the billets oxidize more severely because of the larger air throughput from the chimney effect.

Salt bath ovens for billet heating are rarely used. Their advantage is the capability of exact temperature control and the avoidance of oxidation. They are, however, unwieldy and expensive and the salt carryover presents a large environmental risk [Sar 75, Lau 76, Kur 62]. The diffusion of nitrogen damages the surface zones of austenite and, as a result, the extruded tubes sometimes have to be ground over.

If the turned billet has to be pierced before extrusion, this process is carried out in vertical piercing presses linked to a vertical single-billet furnace in order to balance out the heat losses and to exactly control the extrusion temperature. In the piercing press, for example, the existing bore diameter is expanded from 35 mm to a range of 53 to 74 mm, increasing the billet length by up to 20%.

Carbon steels and low-alloy steels can oxidize so severely that removing the thick oxide layer with a strong jet of high pressure water after billet heating is recommended. This process is so quick that hardly any heat is lost.

The high billet temperature of high-alloy steels necessitates a fast transport from the oven to the press. Otherwise, the material would cool too quickly, particularly with small billet diameters where there is a large surface to volume ratio.

The use of radiation protective sheaths has been reported in the United States. These have to be removed just before extrusion when the billet is loaded into the container [Lau 76]. However, a thick glass layer, which surrounds the hot billet as a lubricant, also acts as insulation.

5.25.4.2 Lubrication

Similar to other difficult-to-extrude materials, e.g., the nickel alloys, the development of lubrication technology was an important requirement for the economic extrusion of alloy steel tubes. The graphite and salt containing oil suspensions initially used as lubricants would carburize the surface of low-carbon steels, among other disadvantages. Glass lubrication technology was rapidly adopted and had to meet numerous requirements [Ben 73]:

- The lubricant with its good slip properties has to form a closed lubricant film that does not break up even when being extruded through the die aperture. It should prevent contact with the tool working surfaces as well as reduce the load.

- It should form an insulating layer between the billet and the extrusion tooling and thus increase the ability of the tooling to withstand the thermomechanical stressing. A low thermal conductivity is desirable.

- The lubricant applied to the billet surface immediately after heating should protect this and the emerging extrusion from oxidation with a thick film. Thin oxide coatings that have already formed should as far as possible be removed or absorbed by the lubricant.

- Glassy lubricants have a larger volume contraction on solidification and cooling than steel, and the lubricant can readily break off, particularly with rapidly cooled extrusions.

Glasses that are optimally suited for all steels with their different extrusion temperatures and flow resistances do not exist. Therefore, glasses with different compositions and thus a different viscosity temperature dependence are recommended for the various material groups (Table 5.18).

The criterion for the upper limit of the temperature application of glasses in extrusion is the so-called "hemispherical" temperature (see footnote in Table 5.18). The viscosity is then approximately 2×10^4 poise. The lower limit is characterized by the compressive softening temperature (CST) where the glass is extremely tough (approximately 10^{10} poise) but no longer breaks in a brittle manner. The extrusion temperature should be at least 200 to 300° above the CST.

Standardized glasses are available from various manufacturers. Today only a few types are used in extrusion with SiO_2 as the main constituent. They contain oxides of sodium, potassium, calcium, magnesium, aluminum, and boron. Barium oxide is also sometimes added. These

Table 5.18 Glasses used successfully as lubricants for extrusion (Deg 74)

| No. | Composition | | | | | | | | Extrusion temperature | |
	Na_2O	K_2O	MgO	CaO	BaO	Al_2O_3	B_2O_3	SiO_2	Maximum HK(a), °C	Minimum DET(b), °C
1	…	…	…	+	+	+	+	+	1300	765
2	+	+	…	+	…	+	+	+	1220	690
3	+	+	+	+	+	+	…	+	990	645
4	+	+	+	+	+	+	+	+	710	510

(a) Hemispherical temperature (HK) is the temperature at which a specific quantity of the glass powder melted in a heated microscope forms a hemisphere. Viscosity is approximately 2×10^4 poise, i.e., highly fluidic. (b) Compressive softening temperature (DET) is the temperature at which the glass has a viscosity of approximately 10^{10} poise and is extremely tough but no longer brittle.

additions lower the melting point and stabilize the glasses.

The billet from the preheating furnace is rolled over a sloping table covered in the glass powder and also has powder spread in the bore using a spoon. The powder immediately melts and protects the billet from further oxidation and can even dissolve any oxide that has formed. If the billet is not pierced before it is loaded into the press, the procedure for applying the glass powder has to be repeated (after the reheating). Different glasses are sometimes used for internal and external application. The grain size of the glass also plays a role because fine grain-size powder melts more quickly than coarse grain.

In front of the die there is a pressed disc of the same glass powder or fiber glass (with water glass as the binding agent) that slowly melts during the extrusion process and encloses the front of the extrusion. The thickness of the glass layer is of the order of 10 μm.

Careful matching of the type of glass, the extrusion temperature, and the extrusion speed, as well as the quantity of glass is important to produce a perfect glass, coating on the extrusion. If too little glass flows through the die, grooves form; if the quantity is too high, the surface of the section exhibits bulges or a so-called "orange peel surface" corresponding to the individual grains [Bur 70].

It should be mentioned that the removal of the glass film from extruded tubes is expensive and did not have to be carried out with the previous graphite-containing lubricants.

5.25.5 Extrusion Process

A high extrusion speed is possible for the majority of iron alloys. Depending on the material and the extrusion ratio, ram speeds in the range of 20 to 300 mm/s are attained so that the billets are extruded within a few seconds. High extrusion speeds are necessary to keep the stresses on the tooling to a minimum. The tooling temperature should not exceed 500 °C. The melting properties of the glass used for lubrication prevents the use of the maximum extrusion speeds so that in practice, the minimum ram speed is 50 mm/s and the upper limit is 200 mm/s.

High extrusion speeds can be achieved only with hydraulic accumulator drives. In the steel industry, direct oil operating systems are not used.

The construction of the horizontal hydraulic tube extrusion presses are basically similar to those used for copper tube extrusion.

The stem loading is, as usual, restricted to a maximum of 1200 N/mm^2. In order to achieve this, there are presses with several hydraulic cylinders that can be individually switched off to avoid overloading with small billet diameters. The press capacity of these presses is 35 to a maximum of 50 MN. Extrusion ratios (V) of 10 to 40 are standard.

Because extrusion is carried out without a shell the dummy blocks used have to be matched as closely as possible to the container bore; a cleaning pad is not required.

A laminar quasi-stationary material flow is achieved by using dies with a conical entry inlet angle of 120 to 150° or dies with a curved inlet. A fast die-change system is needed to avoid overheating of the dies and to enable die reworking after every extrusion. If a die has to be reused, it is cooled to approximately 250 °C in a water bath.

The container is not heated during extrusion because the heat transferred from the hot billet is sufficient to keep it warm. The container only has to be maintained at approximately 500 °C before starting extrusion and during production interruptions. There are extrusion presses with rotating container devices in which two containers are used in turn: while one container is being used for extrusion, the other can be cooled and cleaned.

The extrusion mandrel moves with the stem during extrusion so that no mandrel cross section has to have prolonged contact with the hot deformation zone in the die. The mandrel is cooled internally as with copper materials or sprayed externally with water between extrusions.

In order to remove the glass lubricant from the tooling, the following operations have to be carried out between extrusions:

- The mandrel is sprayed externally with water.
- The container is cleaned with a steel brush.
- The die is quenched in a water bath.

The discard and tube are separated with a hot saw or a shear between the opened container and the die. The extruded length is restricted to a maximum of 20 m for steel tube extrusion to ensure that the contact time between the material and the die is not too long. Runout tables up to 50 m, which are used for aluminum and copper alloys, are not possible with steel. The runout trough for steel can also be fitted with powered rollers.

In the majority of cases, quenching with water is carried out directly behind the die because most of the alloys produced have to be cooled as quickly as possible to avoid precipitates of carbides and intermetallic phases such as the σ- and χ-phases. Precipitated phases result in embrittlement and in numerous cases, unfavorable corrosion behavior. Water quenching also has the advantage that the glass film breaks up so that it can be easily removed. Quenching should be avoided only with materials where there is a tendency for cracking with rapid cooling and with ferrites where martensite can form [Ric 93].

5.25.6 Tooling

Tooling design and other details are covered in Chapter 7.

The shape-forming tools—die and mandrel—are usually made in steel 1.2343 (H11, UNS T20811). The die with the conical entry is usually located in a die holder with a truncated shaped external face, which mates with the conical container seat. Container liners are also frequently manufactured in the steel 1.2343.

Dies that are removed and cooled can last between 20 and 40 extrusions and can then be opened up to another dimension. The mandrel life is around 400 extrusions and that of the container about 4000 extrusions, with the possibility of reworking.

The use of high-alloy materials for dies and liners in the extrusion of alloy steels has been tried but for economic reasons is not used [Ben 73].

5.25.7 Further Processing, Testing

5.25.7.1 Further Processing

Steel, ball shot blasting (VacuBlast) is used, followed by pickling in nitric acid with hydrofluoric acid additions to remove residual glass lubricant from the internal and external surfaces of the tube. Hot molten sodium and calcium salts are used to some extent for surface cleaning, but they are expensive and environmentally unfriendly because salt carryover is difficult too avoid.

Heat treatment after extrusion is necessary if it is not possible to arrange the cooling of the hot extrusion so that a precipitation-free structure is obtained. The heat treatment after extrusion then has the nature of a homogenization or a solution heat treatment.

Extruded and metallic clean semifinished products can be directly used as hot-finished semifinished products after finishing (straightening and cutting to the finished length). If necessary, the surface has to be ground.

In other cases, the extruded tubes are further processed by cold pilgering and/or cold drawing.

5.25.7.2 Testing

In order to prevent δ-ferrite occurring in austenitic steels, the billets are tested randomly by a magnetic balance. The permitted upper limit is 3%. Crack testing of the billet surface (penetrant testing) is required only occasionally.

As well as the standard visual inspection of the tube surface, ultrasonic testing is required, particularly with high-alloy materials and for some critical applications. This is carried out with either fixed test heads and rotating tubes or with static tubes and rotating test heads. Water is used as the coupling agent.

The danger of internal cracks occurs only with the highest-alloyed materials (molybdenum-containing). Internal inspection with an endoscope is specified only for these.

5.26 Steel Sections

5.26.1 General

5.26.1.1 Extrusion Process, Materials

As with alloy steel tubes, only horizontal hydraulic extrusion presses are used for steel sections. The laminar extrusion takes place with glass lubrication and without a shell. In this case the competing processes, which are economically more competitive for suitable quantities and specific sections, again have a higher market share than the extrusion process.

In principle, all steel grades that can be hot worked can be extruded to sections. Nevertheless, the tool wear increases drastically with increasing extrusion temperature. The higher the flow stress at the extrusion temperature, the lower the possible extrusion ratio will be and also, as a rule, the length of the extrusion.

5.26.1.2 Competition with Other Deformation Processes

The processes used to produce sections are:

- *Hot rolling:* The dimensional range falls within a circumscribing circle of 250 mm diameter. The possible weight per meter is 1 to 7 kg with minimum wall thickness of 3 mm. The minimum wall thickness tolerance is ±0.3 mm. In the hot-rolling process, cross-sectional undercuts are impossible and hollow sections cannot be produced. A relatively large tonnage is required to justify the cost of the manufacture of the profiled roll pairs needed for the sequential tools.

- *Machining from solid material:* The high material loss and the expensive process ensure that this process usually follows a non-machining deformation and only when other methods of producing the final shape have to be excluded.

- *Cold profile forming from steel strip:* This process requires material that can be cold bent and the section must have a uniform wall thickness. The final shape is produced from the flat sheet using several roll sets in the bending machine. The form-shaping tool pairs are expensive, so the process is economic only for large quantities.

- *Joining of part sections by longitudinal welding, riveting, or bolting:* Extruded sections are frequently used to produce more complex sections or larger cross-sectional areas.

- *Extrusion:* The possible dimensional range falls within a circumscribing circle of approximately 250 mm diameter with a weight per meter of 1.5 to 100 kg/m and a wall thickness of at least 3.5 mm. The thickness tolerance that can be achieved is ±0.5 mm. Complicated sections and also hollow sections can be produced (Fig. 5.64).

Obviously, given the severe thermal stressing of the form-producing tooling, the degree of complexity and the range of sections that can be produced cannot be compared with aluminum sections. Sharp edges are impossible because of the risk of tooling failure and the thermomechanical localized stresses. External edges should, therefore, have a minimum radius of at least 1.5 mm and internal edges on hollow sections a minimum of 4 mm (Lin 82). Tolerances that are too wide for the application can often be reduced by subsequent cold drawing.

Extrusion is used even for sections that can be produced by hot rolling when it is not economical to produce the roll sets needed for the multistand mills because of the small volume required. Extrusion can then be used for the production of prototypes and first series.

Fig. 5.64 Extruded steel profiles [Hoe 90]

Extrusion is also preferred for sections that can be more economically produced by welding but which cannot have any weld for safety reasons.

The average lot size is 10 billets per order and is therefore generally small. If larger quantities are required, an alternative method of production is usually sought for cost reasons, e.g., hot rolling, even if the shapes have to be slightly modified and simplified.

Of the steel sections produced in a section mill, only 8 to 10% are extruded. Approximately 65% of sections are hot rolled and the others are produced using other processes.

5.26.2 Materials, Starting Material, Process

Extrusion produces the same mechanical properties as hot rolling. In both processes the hot-working temperature is higher than the recrystallization temperature, and a fine-grain recrystallized structure is produced.

Structural steels are processed along with heat treatable steels and alloy steels (stainless, heat resistant as well as tool grades), as well as nickel-base alloys and, more rarely, cobalt-base alloys and titanium alloys.

The starting material for carbon steels is continuously cast and supplied in approximately 10 m lengths from the foundry cleaned by pickling or shot blasting.

The starting material for alloy steels has to be hot rolled or forged in the same way as for tube production for homogenizing and to achieve a fine-grain, crack-free structure.

The extrusion process with a lubricated container and without a shell resembles that described for tube production. The large billets used for heavy sections and, in the case of hollow sections, prebored billets also have to be chamfered on the end surfaces to achieve the uniform flow of the glass lubricant.

5.26.3 Billet Production, Extrusion, Further Processing

5.26.3.1 Billet Preparation, Heating, Lubrication

As soon as an order is passed to production, the bars delivered to billet production are crosscut, peeled, turned or ground and chamfered. The billets for hollow sections have also to be bored. The hole is larger than the circumscribing circle of the mandrel cross section. The billets are heated to 1000 to 1300 °C in a rotary hearth furnace with a reducing protective gas burner or in an induction furnace similar to steel tubes. Salt bath heating is also used.

After the billets have been removed from the furnace, they are rolled down a table with glass powder. The glass film formed from the molten powder prevents high thermal losses and oxidation of the billet surface and can even dissolve the oxide that has formed. A 4 mm-thick glass powder disc bonded with water glass is placed in front of the conical die. The type of glass used is the same as for the extrusion of steel tubes (e.g., type 3 in Table 5.18 for carbon steels).

Extrusion. The tube and solid extrusion presses used have a capacity of 15 to 25 MN. The diameter of the billets varies from 150 to 250 mm, depending on the section cross-sectional area, and the length can extend to 900 mm. Extrusion ratios up to 100 are possible but rarely used.

Hollow sections are extruded over round or profiled mandrels that are not internally cooled and that move with the stem during the extrusion process. The thickness should be at least 20 mm to be able to withstand the large thermal stresses. It is not possible to use bridge dies as with aluminum and copper because of the high extrusion temperature, the relatively high flow stress, and the resultant thermomechanical stresses on the tooling.

The billet loaded into the container is extruded to a discard length of 10 to 20 mm. After the container has been opened, the discard is cut from the section with a hot saw. The section is pulled back through the die and then removed on a powered roller conveyor. After pushing out the discard together with the dummy block, the die is changed for a new or reworked die using a rotating arm or a slide. The die has to be checked for the dimensional tolerances after each extrusion and, if necessary, reworked because of the high thermomechanical stresses.

The length of the section that is extruded as quickly as possible has a maximum length of 20 m so that the die that is deformed by the temperature effect during the extrusion does not exceed the extrusion tolerances toward the end of the extrusion.

The required high ram speeds of up to 300 mm/s can only be achieved by a water hydraulic system.

The sections cool in free air but bend and twist significantly in the longitudinal direction and deform in the transverse direction because of the different flow behaviors of different cross-sectional areas in the die and the faster cooling of thin legs after extrusion. To avoid accidents from moving sections, the runout table is occasionally covered to form a tunnel.

In multihole extrusion, the extruded sections usually have varying lengths because of the different amounts of lubricant in the die openings.

5.26.3.2 Further Processing

The extruded sections have to be straightened and detwisted by stretching 2 to 3% on stretchers with rotating stretcher heads and capacities of up to 3000 kN. Hot stretching is also used for the higher-strength alloys (alloy steels, Ni, and Ti alloys). This stretching process is sufficient with carbon steels to break off the 10 to 20 μm-thick glass film from the lubrication. Alloy steels, however, have to be pickled and sometimes first shot blasted.

After stretching, it may be necessary to carry out further straightening on a roller correction machine or even on a straightening press with profiled tools. This straightening process adds significantly to the costs of producing steel extruded sections [Lin 82].

If a coarse grain structure or, in the case of alloy steels, excessive mechanical properties are detected, a subsequent annealing treatment is required.

Tight tolerances are obtained by bright drawing. If necessary, sections can also be ground.

5.26.4   Tooling

Information on the tooling for steel sections can be found in Chapter 7 in the section on tooling for the glass-lubricated extrusion of titanium, nickel, and iron alloys.

Extrusion of Semifinished Products in Nickel Alloys (Including Superalloys)

Martin Bauser*

5.27   General

Nickel alloys are used for many applications in machinery, chemical engineering, industrial furnaces, electrical engineering, electronics, and in power stations. Extrusion is used to produce tubes and wire as well as bars for feedstock for the manufacture of turned, forged, and impact-forged components.

High-alloy nickel materials (in particular with iron, cobalt, and molybdenum) are referred to as superalloys and are suitable for applications at temperatures of more than 1000 °C. They are used in gas turbines and jet engines. These multiphase alloys can often hardly be referred to as nickel alloys, but they do not belong to any specific alloy group. Extrusion is important for the production of bars and rods in these high-strength alloys because they are almost impossible to forge [Vol 70].

The extrusion process is largely identical to that described for alloy steel tubes.

Pure nickel melts at 1453 °C and has a density comparable to iron and copper of 8.9 g/cm^3. Nickel and many technically important nickel alloys have a fcc lattice up to the melting point and therefore have good hot and cold workability. The flow stress varies considerably depending on the alloy.

The high-alloy superalloys are very difficult to extrude because of both the high extrusion temperature (up to 1300 °C) as well as the high extrusion loads needed.

Copper forms a continuous solid solution with nickel. Molybdenum increases the strength by the formation of a solid solution. Intermetallic phases (mainly Ni_3Al) increase the strength as do carbides and carbon-nitrides in conjunction with titanium, niobium, molybdenum, and chromium.

5.28   Materials, Properties, and Applications

Table 5.19 refers to the nickel alloy DIN standards. Table 5.20 shows some important and typical nickel alloys that are processed by extrusion.

Pure nickel and low-alloy nickel materials have properties that are particularly suited to chemical processes and electronic applications. Nickel alloys are corrosion resistant to many reducing chemicals and cannot be bettered for resistance to strong alkalis. The food industry is an important application. Nickel also has a high electrical conductivity, a high Curie temperature, and good magnetostrictive properties. Battery components and spark electrodes are application examples.

Low-alloy nickel materials are often used in heat exchangers because of the good thermal conductivity. Good workability and good weldability mean they can be readily worked.

Monel, i.e., nickel-copper alloys, are the most widely used high-nickel-containing alloys and have been used for over a hundred years. Their strength is higher than pure nickel, but in spite of this, they can be easily worked and possess good corrosion resistance against many environmental factors. Their good resistance to acids is utilized in the chemical industry and the good thermal conductivity relative to other nickel alloys in heat exchangers. The seawater resistance of Monel is useful in ship construction.

Certain nickel-iron alloys have a special coefficient of expansion property, which makes them suitable for use with glasses. The soft magnetic behavior of nickel-iron alloys is also utilized.

Nickel-chromium alloys and nickel-iron-chromium alloys are characterized by their good corrosion resistance, good mechanical properties, and excellent oxidation resistance at high temperatures. Combined with their good workability, these alloys have a wide range of applications in heat treatment furnaces, incineration

---

*Extrusion of Semifinished Products in Nickel Alloys (Including Superalloys), Martin Bauser

Table 5.19   German Standardization Institute (DIN) standards for nickel alloys

Standard	Designation	Comments to DIN	Similar ASTM standard	Title
DIN 17740	Nickel in semifinished products	Composition	B39	Standard Specification for Nickel
DIN 17741	Low-alloyed nickel wrought alloys	Composition	. . .	. . .
DIN 17742	Nickel wrought alloys with chromium	Composition	B167	Standard Specification for Nickel Chromium-Iron Alloys (UNS N06600, N06690, N06025) Seamless Pipe and Tube
DIN 17743	Nickel wrought alloys with copper	Composition	B164	Standard Specification for Nickel-Copper Alloy Rod, Bar, and Wire
DIN 17744	Nickel wrought alloys with molybdenum and chromium	Composition	B335	Standard Specification for Nickel Molybdenum-Alloy Rod
DIN 17745	Wrought alloys of nickel and iron	Composition	B407	Standard Specification for Nickel-Iron-Chromium Alloy Seamless Pipe and Tube
			B408	Standard Specification for Nickel-Iron-Chromium Alloy Rod and Bar
DIN 17751	Tubes in nickel and nickel wrought alloys	Dimensions, mechanical properties	B161	Standard Specification for Nickel Seamless Pipe and Tube
DIN 17752	Bar in nickel and nickel wrought alloys	Dimensions, mechanical properties	B160	Standard Specification for Nickel Rod and Bar
DIN 17753	Wire in nickel and nickel wrought alloys	Dimensions, mechanical properties	B473	Standard Specification for UNS N08020, UNS N08024, and UNS N08026 Nickel Alloy Bar and Wire
			B475	Standard Specification for UNS N08020, UNS N08024, and UNS N08026 Nickel Round Weaving Wire

plants, steam generators, and resistance heating elements.

The superalloys contain cobalt, molybdenum, iron, titanium, and aluminum, in addition to chromium and nickel. A wide range of applications are possible at high and very high temperatures. These include gas turbines, jet engines, and nuclear power stations. Hot-working tooling is also produced from these alloys.

There are high-strength dispersion-hardened nickel alloys that have to be produced by powder metallurgy. These alloys are discussed in the section "Extrusion of Powder Metals."

5.29   Billet Production

Depending on the composition and the material requirements, various routes are used to produce the starting material and these have been described in section 5.41.5 [Ric 93].

High-alloy materials are melted in an electric arc furnace and, if a specific purity is required, subjected to the Vacuum-oxygen-decarburization (VOD) process in an evacuated ladle. This removes the carbon and nitrogen and reduces the sulfur content drastically.

Nickel alloys can be continuously cast. If the charge size is insufficient for continuous casting, chill mold casting with all its disadvantages (coarse, radial columnar, and frequently crack-susceptible structure) is preferred. For this reason, as well as reducing the large chill mold casting to the billet dimensions, they are usually broken down by forging or rolling. This aligns the grains axially and frequently produces a fine-grained recrystallized structure. It is then necessary with the high-alloy materials to follow this with a homogenization heat treatment to minimize the segregation.

The feedstock material supplied to the press as long bars is sawn to length, turned, and chamfered. If tubes are being produced, the billets usually have to be bored. A good billet surface is necessary as is the case with alloy steels because it will form the surface of the extrusion as a result of the glass lubrication (see below) and the resultant laminar material flow.

5.30   Billet Heating

The billets have to be heated in a low-sulfur furnace atmosphere because of the sensitivity of nickel and its alloys to intercrystalline attack by sulfur. It should be weakly reducing in gas-fired furnaces because nickel and nickel-copper alloys in particular tend to intercrystalline corrosion and thus embrittlement in an oxidizing atmosphere even without sulfur [Vol 70].

Because the oxide layer of severely oxidizing nickel-iron and nickel-copper alloys also reduces the effect of the lubricant in extrusion and produces a poor surface quality, these materials should be heated as quickly as possible—at best, in an induction furnace.

With high-alloy, crack-sensitive alloys on the other hand, and with coarse grain cast billets, a slow heating rate is important because if the heating is too rapid the thermal stresses can result in grain-boundary cracking. Some nickel-chromium-cobalt alloys cannot be directly charged into the hot-gas-fired furnace if they exhibit coarse grain or severe segregation but have to be slowly heated from a low temperature to the extrusion temperature so that the temperature gradient remains low in all phases of heating [Pol 75]. Reducing continuous, chamber or rotary furnaces are used for this.

High-alloy materials that are not crack sensitive and those that have been well homogenized and have a fine-grain structure can, however, be heated in an induction furnace that guarantees the exact final temperature. With complex alloys, the exact setting of the final temperature is very important if a low-melting-point eutectic has formed (e.g., with niobium).

To save energy and to ensure the slow heating of crack-sensitive materials mentioned above, a gas furnace can be used for the base heating (up to 1000 °C) and an induction furnace for the final stage [Ric 93]. Salt bath heating cannot be used because of the risk of the diffusion of embrittling elements.

5.31 Extrusion

5.31.1 Billet Preparation, Lubrication

As with alloy steels, prebored or pierced billets are used for the production of tubes to avoid high mandrel wear and to obtain a low eccentricity [Eng 74]. With large internal diameters the billets are again expanded on a separate piercing press and then reheated in an induction furnace.

Whereas nickel, low-alloy nickel materials, NiCu, and NiFe can be lubricated with graphite

oil for low extrusion ratios and thus low extrusion temperatures, higher-alloyed material billets are only lubricated with glass using the Séjournet process similar to alloy steels [Pol 75]. Suitable glasses for the corresponding temperature are selected from Table 5.18. The glass with the highest melting point is used for the high-alloy materials with extrusion temperatures of almost 1300 °C. The glass powder is applied even with two-stage heating (gas furnace-induction furnace) only after the billet has left the induction furnace.

5.31.2 Deformation Behavior and Extrusion Data

Figure 5.65 shows the tensile strengths of various nickel alloys as a function of temperature.

The flow stress of pure nickel is low enough for extrusion even below 1000 °C. Similarly, the soft alloys of nickel with copper or with up to 20% Cr have a relatively wide temperature range for hot working. The complex alloys on the other hand have narrow deformation temperature ranges, in particular, the molybdenum-containing and the high-strength nickel-chromium alloys, and these must be accurately maintained to avoid cracking.

The addition of strength-increasing elements to improve the mechanical properties at high

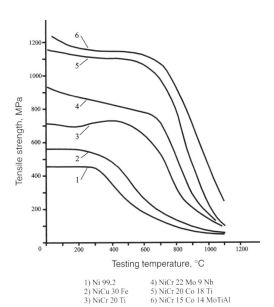

Fig. 5.65 Tensile strength of nickel alloys as a function of the temperature [Inc 88]

Table 5.20   Some important typical nickel alloys that are extruded

(a) Nickel and low-alloyed nickel materials

Material	Standard	British/U.S.	Ni	Fe	Mn	Al	Other	Semifinished product	Strength	Properties	Application
Ni 99.2	DIN 17740 2.4066	NA 11 Alloy 200	>99.2	<0.4	<0.35	...	...	R, S, D	370–590	High electrical and thermal conductivity, corrosion resistant	Corrosion-resistant components, lightbulbs, electrode tubes
NiMn2	DIN 17741 2.4110	...	>97.0	...	1.5–2.5	...	...	S, D	...	...	Lightbulbs, electrotubes, spark plugs

(b) Nickel-copper alloys (Monel)

Material	Standard	British/U.S.	Ni	Cu	Fe	Al	Other	Semifinished product	Strength	Properties	Application
NiCu30Fe	DIN 17743 2.4360	NA 13 Alloy 400	>63	28–34	1.5–2.5	...	<2.0 Mn	R, S, D	450–700	Good strength, best high-corrosion resistance	Corrosion resistant construction units, ship construction, chemical industry
NiCu30Al	DIN 17743 2.4375	Na 18 Alloy K500	>63	27–34	0.5–2.0	2.2–3.5	0.3–1.0 Ti	R, S, D	600–800	Age hardening	Chemical industry, petrochemical industry

(c) Nickel iron alloys

Material	Standard	British/U.S.	Ni	Fe	Other	Semifinished product	Strength	Properties	Application
Ni 42	DIN 17745 1.3917	Alloy 42	40.0–43.0	Remainder	...	R, D	...	Low temperature expansion	Glass/metal ceramic bonds, e.g., for integrated circuits
Ni 48	DIN 17745 1.3922/26/27	Alloy 48	46.0–49.0	Remainder	...	R, S, D	...	Best coefficient of expansion, slightly magnetic	Relay components, transformers

(d) Nickel-chromium (iron) alloys

Material	Standard	British/U.S.	Ni	Cr	Fe	Ti	Other	Strength	Semifinished product	Properties	Application
NiCr20Ti	DIN 17742 2.4951	Alloy 75	>72	18–21	<5	0.2–0.5	...	650	S, P, R, D	High oxide and corrosion resistance	Furnace components, heating conductor, gas turbines
NiCr15Fe	DIN 17742 2.4816	NA 14 Alloy 600	>72	14–17	6–10	...	...	550	S, R, D	Heat resistant, corrosion resistant	Furnaces, chemical industry, spark plugs
NiCr20TiAl	DIN 17742 2.4952	Alloy 80A	>65	18–21	...	2.3	1.0–1.5Al 1.9Ti	1100	S, P, R, D	Age hardening, high hot strength	Components subjected to creep loading

(e) Nickel alloys with chromium, molybdenum, and/or cobalt super alloys

Material	Standard	British/U.S.	Ni	Cr	Fe	Co	Mo	Other	Strength	Semifinished product	Properties	Application
NiMo16Cr16Ti	Din 17744 2.4610	Alloy C4	Remainder	14–18	<3	<2	14–17	...	690–850	S, R, D	Excellent corrosion properties	Chemical industry, paper industry
NiMo16Cr15W	DIN 17744 2.4819	Alloy C276	Remainder	14.5–16.5	4.0–7.0	<2	15–17	3.0–4.5W	690–850	S, R, D	Excellent corrosion properties	Chemical industry, paper industry
NiCr22Mo9Nb	DIN 17744 2.4856	Alloy 625	Remainder	20–23	...	...	8–10	3.15–4.15Nb	690–830	S, R, D	High strength without age hardening, corrosion resistant	Chemical industry, aircraft
NiCr23Co12Mo	DIN 17744 2.4663	Alloy 617	Remainder	20–23	...	10–15	8–10	Al, Ti	~700	S, R, D	Stable up to high temperature, resistant to oxidation	Gas turbine, petrochemical industry, chemical industry
NiCr20Co18Ti	2.4632	NA19 Alloy 90	58	20	<1.5	18	...	2.5 Ti1.5Al	~1100	S, P, R	Creep resistant up to 900 °C	Gas turbine, hot-working tools
NiCr15Co14MoTiAl	2.4636	Alloy 115	51	15	...	14	4	4Ti5Al	~1200	S, P	Creep resistant up to 1010 °C	Jet engine

temperatures results, on one hand, in a reduction in the liquidus temperature and, on the other hand, an increase in the flow stress.

These difficult-to-extrude alloys require a high degree of homogeneity in the starting material (see section 5.29), uniform billet heating (see section 5.30), correct lubrication conditions, and exact maintenance of the extrusion conditions. Economic production is, therefore, not possible without an extrusion plant with a correspondingly high extrusion power [Inc 86].

Table 5.21 gives data for the extrusion of some nickel alloys.

In the high-strength nickel alloys, there are some with a low-melting-point eutectic (e.g., with niobium) that can only be extruded with a maximum of 1150 °C and thus with a low extrusion ratio (e.g., Inconel 625).

Some superalloys, for example, the high-molybdenum-containing alloys, have to be extruded above 1400 °C to obtain low flow stresses. Preferably, extrusion is carried out below 1300 °C because of the high tool wear and the low viscosity of the glasses used, and the resultant low extrusion ratio is accepted. This naturally means more expensive further processing.

5.31.3 Defects and Their Prevention

Narrow limits are placed on the extrusion speed, particularly for the complex molybdenum-containing nickel alloys. If the extrusion speed is too slow, the lubricant film breaks up, resulting in a rough surface on the extruded product and/or the extrusion process "freezes." If the extrusion speed is too high, the exit temperature can increase to such an extent that transverse hot cracking occurs or—particularly with thick bars—lap defects occur. Consequently, especially for the slowly extruded complex high-alloy steels with extrusion speeds below 10 mm/s, the extrusion speed has to be controlled to ensure that the exit temperature remains between the two limits. In other words, if the plant is capable, "isothermal extrusion" is required. Extrusion presses built especially for nickel have a suitable speed control system. Oil hydraulic presses are preferred to water hydraulic ones [Lau 76]. A high press power (up to 60 MN) simplifies the extrusion of the high-alloy nickel materials with high flow stresses [Eng 74]. Because the billet rapidly cools at this slow speed with the risk of freezing, only short billets can be used.

Ultrasonic testing of extruded products is recommended for the crack-sensitive materials.

5.32   Tooling, Further Processing

Information on the tooling used and the tooling design is given in Chapter 7.

The dies are, as described for alloy steel tubes, conical to obtain a laminar flow with the glass lubrication.

The further processing is also similar to that described for alloy steel. The glass lubricant film is removed by shot blasting with steel grit followed by pickling. If the glass skin is broken up by quenching at the press (to suppress precipitation), shot blasting and pickling may not be required. Cold pilgering or drawing is then carried out, possibly with intermediate annealing.

Extrusion of Semifinished Products in Exotic Alloys

Martin Bauser*

All the materials described in this section are rarely used in long lengths and are therefore not

Table 5.21   Data for the extrusion of some nickel alloys (see Table 5.20 for examples indicated by (b), (c), (d), and (e) (Lau 7, Vol 70, Ric 93)

Group	Characterization	Approximate K_f value, N/mm^2	Billet preheat temperature	Examples
1	Easily extruded	150	900–1100 °C	All nickel and the low-alloyed nickel materials
2	Good extrudability	200	1050–1150 °C	Monel(b)
				Nickel iron(c)
3	Difficult to extrude	250	1100–1250 °C	Ni-Cr materials(d)
4	Very difficult to extrude	320	1150–1280 °C	Ni-Cr-Mo materials
				Super alloys(e)

*Extrusion of Semifinished Products in Exotic Alloys, Martin Bauser

extruded in Germany. However, they are included for completeness.

5.33 Beryllium

5.33.1 Properties and Applications

There are special areas of application for beryllium in optical components, precision instruments, and space travel because of its unusual combination of physical and mechanical properties. Selection criteria are the low weight (density 1.85 g/cm^3), a high E-modulus, and low radiation absorption.

Beryllium melts at 1283 °C and has a hexagonal lattice. It is characterized by a high thermal capacity and heat resistance combined with good corrosion resistance and high strength and is therefore used in reactor technology. The very poisonous metal can only be melted and processed under the strictest conditions [Sto 90].

5.33.2 Billet Production

Cast beryllium has a coarse grain, is brittle, and tends to porosity. It can consequently be further processed only with difficulty. For this reason, plus the importance of a fine grain for the properties, beryllium is usually prepared by powder metallurgy.

This also applies to extrusion (see the section "Extrusion of Powder Metals"). Usually, beryllium powder with the minimum possible oxygen content is consolidated to billets by hot-isostatic compaction in vacuum [Sto 90].

If extrusion has to be carried out at a high temperature (approximately 1000 °C), a billet clad in a steel jacket has to be used. The compaction of the beryllium powder directly into the jacket with a ram, the subsequent welding of the jacket and the evacuation (to prevent oxidation) has been described [Kur 70].

5.33.3 Deformation Behavior, Extrusion

According to Fig. 5.66, beryllium exhibits two maxima in the elongation to fracture, one at 400 °C and another one at approximately 800 °C. From experience, the elongation to fracture can be taken to be a measure of the workability. Consequently, it is possible to differentiate between "warm" extrusion with billet temperatures from 400 to 500 °C and "hot" extrusion with billet temperatures from 900 to 1065 °C. In the first case, no recrystallization takes place during

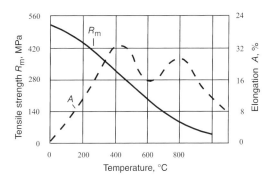

Fig. 5.66 Elongation to failure and tensile strength of compacted beryllium as a function of the temperature [Sto 90, Kau 56, Lau 76]

extrusion and a texture favorable for the mechanical properties is formed. In "warm" extrusion, the compacted and possibly sintered billet can be lubricated with graphite or molybdenum sulfide. Warm extruded bars and tubes can be drawn to the finished sizes.

The "hot" extrusion process is selected for large extrusion ratios because of the lower extrusion loads. The billets sheathed in steel are extruded like alloy steel with glass lubrication. The sections leave the press fully recrystallized and largely texture free.

5.34 Uranium

5.34.1 Properties, Applications

The best-known application is the extensive use of uranium in the form of oxide powder as nuclear fuel in nuclear power stations. Uranium is also sometimes used in other areas as a pure metal and dilute alloys because of the very high density (19.1 g/cm^3, which is 68% higher than lead) and the good radiation absorption. Typical nonnuclear applications are radiation protective shields and counterweights [Eck 90].

Natural uranium contains up to 99.3% of the weakly radioactive isotope U238 and only up to 0.7% of the nuclear fuel U235. Whereas this low radioactivity has little effect on the workability, the poisonous nature and the ease of oxidation of uranium necessitates special measures.

Uranium melts at 1689 °C. It has a rhombic lattice up to 665 °C (α-phase) and a tetragonal lattice (β-phase) above this temperature. At 771 °C this lattice transforms into the body-centered cubic (bcc) γ-phase. Because the tetragonal β-phase is difficult to deform, extrusion cannot be carried out between 650 and 790 °C because of the risk of cracking.

5.34.2 Deformation Behavior, Extrusion

The billets are melted in induction furnaces under a vacuum and cast in molds.

The deformation behavior of uranium is shown in Fig. 5.67. The extrusion in the lower α-region (between 550 and 650 °C) avoids the difficulties of high-temperature extrusion described subsequently but does require a high press power because of the higher flow stress. The extruded sections are fine-grain recrystallized. It is possible to work in this temperature range without cladding with the usual graphite-grease lubrication. Preheating the billets in a salt bath prevents oxidation. They should, however, be subjected to the atmosphere for only a short time at the extrusion temperature.

In the γ-region (between 800 and 1000 °C), where significantly higher extrusion ratios can be used, uranium reacts very rapidly with iron, nickel, and other metals and is very susceptible to oxidation. The billets for this hot extrusion are usually clad in copper, evacuated, and then extruded using graphite grease as a lubricant.

Only a few low-alloy-content uranium alloys with higher mechanical properties and better corrosion resistance are known (with titanium, zirconium, molybdenum, and niobium) that can

be melted in vacuum induction melting furnaces or in vacuum arc furnaces. Because the structure is similar, the extrusion is the same as for pure uranium [Eck 90]. Because the β/γ phase boundary is displaced to lower temperatures by these alloying additions and because in the γ-region secondary phases are held in solution, the extrusion of alloys is easier.

5.35 Molybdenum, Tungsten

5.35.1 Molybdenum

Molybdenum is usually used as an alloying element in steels and high-alloyed materials. However, it is also important as a pure metal and a low-alloy material. Tools in TZM (Mo-0.5 Ti-0.17Zr), for example, can withstand temperatures well over 1000 °C. Further application areas are cathodes, electric resistance elements (up to 2200 °C), and high-temperature components in space travel and for rockets. The highest application temperature is 1650 °C. Molybdenum's good resistance to hydrochloric acid is of interest to the chemical industry. The density of molybdenum is 10.2 g/cm^3 [Joh 90].

The high melting point of 2622 °C permits only powder metallurgical processing. The powder is obtained by hydrogen reduction of molybdenum oxide and then cold compacted and sintered. These sintered billets can then be either directly extruded or melted in a vacuum arc furnace.

The bcc lattice of molybdenum is the reason behind the excellent deformation characteristics. This can be deduced from the hot tensile strength curves in Fig. 5.68.

Pure molybdenum is extruded in the range 1065 to 1090 °C and the most common alloy TZM (Mo-0.5Ti-0.1Zr) at 1120 to 1150 °C. The billets are heated in conventional gas or oil-fired furnaces or by induction. Above 650 °C, molybdenum oxidizes as a gas with a weight loss of 1 to 5% without an oxide layer forming. Rapid heating obviously reduces the loss from oxidation. Similar to steel, glass has to be used for extrusion. Bar, tube, and simple shapes can be produced by extrusion [Joh 90]. The glass applied as powder after the billet has left the furnace melts and protects it from oxidation.

5.35.2 Tungsten

Tungsten melts at the extremely high temperature of 3380 °C. The structure and properties

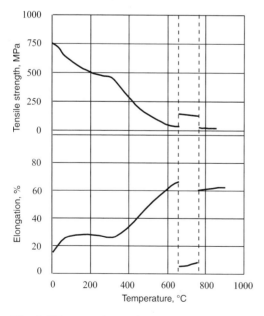

Fig. 5.67 Hot tensile strength and elongation of uranium as a function of the temperature [Eck 90]

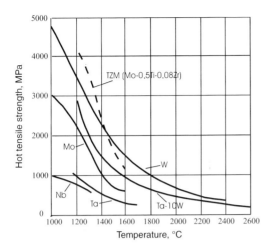

Fig. 5.68 Hot tensile strength of some high-melting-point metals and alloys as a function of temperature [Kie 71]

are similar to molybdenum. With its high density of 19.3 g/cm³, it dominates where high weight is a main requirement. The high melting point combined with its high electrical resistance makes it the most common material for heating conductors and filaments in lamps [Joh 90a].

In contrast to molybdenum, a significantly higher hot-working temperature of 1500 to 1800 °C is required, as shown in Fig. 5.68, which makes tungsten unsuitable for extrusion. Hot forging of sintered powder billets is preferred [Par 91].

5.36   Niobium and Tantalum

Niobium melts at 2468 °C and at room temperature has a bcc structure with a density of 8.4 g/cm³. It can be readily worked at room temperature. Niobium alloys have a wide range of applications in space travel because of their relatively low weight and high hot strength. Niobium and its alloys are also in demand in the chemical industry because of the resistance to specific corrosive media [Ger 90].

Similar to other high-melting-point metals, the extrusion billets are made by a powder metallurgical route.

Figure 5.68 shows for niobium a relatively low hot-working temperature. Extrusion temperatures between 1050 and 1200 °C with extrusion ratios of $V = 4$ to $V = 10$ have been described for niobium alloys with zirconium, hafnium, and tungsten [Ger 90]. However, niobium oxidizes severely above 425 °C so that the billets have to be protected from oxidation by cladding and evacuating.

Niobium forms a continuous solid solution with titanium. Niobium with 46.5% titanium is the alloy most commonly used as a super conductor [Kre 90]. Fine wires of this niobium alloy are embedded in a copper matrix (see the section "Extrusion of Semifinished Products from Metallic Composite Materials"). The niobium-titanium starting material is extruded to bars using glass as a lubricant in the same way as steel and titanium. These are then clad with copper and further processed in several stages.

5.36.1   Tantalum

Tantalum has similar structure and properties to niobium. It also has a bcc structure but first melts at 3030 °C and is twice as heavy with 16.6 g/cm³.

The widest application of tantalum—apart from an alloying element in steel like niobium—is as an anode material in electrolytic cells. In the chemical industry it is known for its resistance to nitric acid, hydrochloric acid, and sulfuric acid. The high melting point ensures applications in the high temperature region [Pok 90].

Processing usually follows a powder metallurgical route. Electron beam cast tantalum is usually too coarse grained for further processing and has to be forged before it can be extruded.

The extrusion of compacted and sintered powders has been mentioned but does not have any great importance because the recrystallization temperature, and thus the extrusion temperature, is very high [Pok 90].

Extrusion of Powder Metals

Martin Bauser*

5.37   General

Oxide-containing aluminum powder was extruded in the 1940s under the name sintered alu-

*Extrusion of Powder Metals, Martin Bauser

minum powder (SAP). In the 1950s the advantages of the extrusion of powder was known for reactor materials and beryllium. This process has only recently found a wide application, particularly with aluminum alloys but also high-alloyed and dispersion-hardened materials.

A good overview of powder metallurgy (P/M) can be obtained from the textbook on powder metallurgy by W. Schatt [Sch 86]. The work of Roberts and Ferguson gives detailed information on the extrusion of powder metals [Rob 91].

5.37.1 Main Application Areas of Powder Metallurgy

Processing by extrusion plays an important role compared with other processes in P/M. The most important is the processing of metal powders to near final shape and thus the economic production of molded components with a piece weight below 2 kg, and mainly in iron alloys. The powder is compacted on vertical compaction presses in dies by a stem and then sintered at a high temperature, during which the particles form a solid bond. For large pieces with simple geometries (e.g., forging billets), the compaction is carried out by fluid pressure applied on all sides (cold isostatic pressing, or CIP) before they are sintered. Compaction and sintering carried out in a single operation by hot isostatic pressing (HIP) is also used occasionally.

5.37.2 Advantages of Metal Powder Extrusion

Where long semifinished products can be conventionally produced by casting and extrusion, powder extrusion is usually less favorable because the production of suitably mixed and sieved powders is usually too expensive.

The production of extruded semifinished products by the powder route is worthwhile when:

- The material cannot be processed conventionally by melting and casting.
- An extremely fine grain size and finely distributed precipitates have to be achieved. Rapidly quenched powder can have a significantly extended solid-solution range [Tus 82].
- A uniform distribution of very small inclusions to achieve specific properties is required (dispersion hardening).

This last-mentioned processing of metal powders with mixed or reaction produced nonme-tallic particles as dispersions by extrusion is also discussed in this chapter (metal matrix composites, or MMCs). Chapter 4 discusses the physical properties, in particular those at high temperatures, and the processes in the deformation of dispersion-hardened materials. Frequently, metallic or nonmetallic fibers are mixed with the metal powder to achieve certain properties and then extruded [Boe 89]. The resultant so-called fiber composite materials are described in the section "Extrusion of Semifinished Products from Metallic Composite Materials."

5.37.3 Powder Production

Atomization of the melt using water or gas streams is the most common of all the different casting, mechanical, and chemical processes used to produce metal powders. Water gives the fastest cooling rate, but the powder particles are coarser (approximately 500 μm) and in a spattered format. If, however, atomization is carried out in an air or protective gas jet, more rounded shapes and smaller particles are produced (down to a few μm, depending on the process parameters) (Fig. 5.69). The output per hour of atomization plants is relatively low. Because a restricted particle size is usually required and the powder usually falls in a wide particle spectrum, the particles of different sizes have to be separated by sieves. The powder costs are correspondingly high. A desired material composition can be obtained by mixing powders if it does not exist in the atomized melt.

"Reaction milling" in ball mills is a new process that enables the mechanical alloying of metal components. Nonmetallic particles can also be finely dispersed by this method. The powder particles are repeatedly broken down and welded between steel balls. A fine structure is obtained after a certain milling time [Inc 86].

5.37.4 Spray Compaction

In the new process of spray compaction developed by the company Osprey [Cra 88], the gas-atomized material from the melt is sprayed onto a rotating block with a vertical axis ([Man 88] (Fig. 5.70). The slowly sinking block grows layer by layer. This process saves precompaction, encapsulation, and evacuation.

Hard particles can be blown into the spray by an injector and form a dispersion in the finished billet.

The disadvantage of spray compaction is that a considerable part of the spray droplets miss the

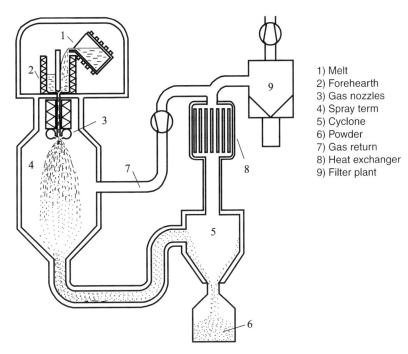

1) Melt
2) Forehearth
3) Gas nozzles
4) Spray term
5) Cyclone
6) Powder
7) Gas return
8) Heat exchanger
9) Filter plant

Fig. 5.69 Example of a gas atomization plant for metal powder [Wei 86]

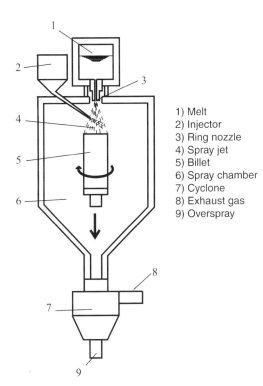

1) Melt
2) Injector
3) Ring nozzle
4) Spray jet
5) Billet
6) Spray chamber
7) Cyclone
8) Exhaust gas
9) Overspray

Fig. 5.70 Schematic of spray compaction [Arn 92]

block and fall to the bottom as powder "over spray," which can be remelted or used as a powder.

The powder particles cool on the solidified block so slowly in spray compaction that a structure similar to casting forms, but with significantly better homogeneity and with finely distributed particles and dispersed particles.

Because the billet diameter varies slightly, it has to be turned to the extrusion dimension. The spray-compacted billets can be extruded like cast billets—also to tubes with piercing mandrels. Plants are in operation producing aluminum, copper, and steel.

5.38 Powder Extrusion Processes

5.38.1 General

The individual powder particles are plastically deformed in the extrusion direction during the extrusion of metal powders, usually at the same temperature as cast billets, and the surface area increases. Oxides and other films on the particle surface break up and release new reactive metallic surfaces. The powder is compacted during extrusion and the newly formed surfaces bonded by pressure welding. Even with low-density powders, a complete compaction and porous-free material is obtained by extrusion if the particles can be sheared sufficiently. This assumes that no gas porosity can form, e.g., from moisture.

Several types of powder extrusion are known, including (a) the rarely used shaking of the loosed powder into the vertical container of an extrusion press, (b) the precompaction outside the press, and (c) the encapsulating of the powder before extrusion (Fig. 5.71). The new process of spray compaction is described above.

5.38.2 Shaking of Loose Powder into a Vertical, Heated Container and Direct Extrusion (Version a)

The loosely filled powder has a low bulk density (maximum 50% of the theoretical density), because the large number of interstitial space. Therefore, a relatively long container is necessary. The stem first compacts the powder before the actual extrusion process commences. This apparently economic process has a low throughput if the powder first has to be heated in the container. It can be used only rarely. An example is the extrusion of magnesium-alloy pellets with grain sizes from 70 to 450 μm to rods [Rob 91].

5.38.3 Precompaction of the Powder outside the Press

"Green" compacts can be produced by cold isostatic pressing (CIP in autoclaves), particularly from angular particles or flakes. These are so stable that they do not break up during handling before extrusion. The powder filled into a plastic container is subjected by a pressurizing liquid to a uniformly applied high pressure (2000 to 5000 bar max), which increases the original powder density of 35 to 50% of the density of a cast billet to 70 to 85%. The risk of the fracture of the precompacted billet during handling can be reduced further if necessary (e.g., with round particles) by sintering before extrusion by heating. An alternative to this two-stage process is to carry out the compaction itself at an elevated temperature (HIP). In this case, the powder has to be filled into a thin-walled metal can that does not melt at the pressing temperature (special case of version c).

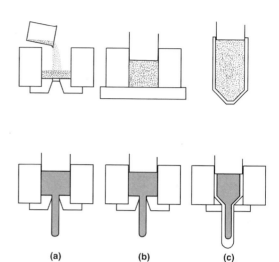

Fig. 5.71 The classic processes for powder extrusion. (a) Addition of loose powder. (b) Precompaction outside the press. (c) Encapsulation before extrusion [Rob 91]

5.38.4 Encapsulation of the Powder before Extrusion (Version c)

Usually the metal powder is compacted in the metal sleeve before sealing. After this it is often evacuated (possibly at an elevated temperature) and then vacuum sealed (Fig. 5.72).

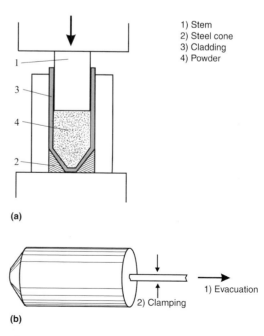

1) Stem
2) Steel cone
3) Cladding
4) Powder

1) Evacuation
2) Clamping

Fig. 5.72 (a) Encapsulation of powder. Cladding sealed at the back and with evacuation tube. (b) Evacuation [Rob 91]

The reasons for encapsulation include:

- Excluding a reactive powder material from air and extrusion lubricants
- Protection from poisonous materials during handling (e.g., Be and U)
- Risk of breaking up of green compacts of round powders or other particles that are difficult to compact in a billet shape
- Improved lubrication and friction behavior and better flow through the die by the correct selection of the container material
- Keeping the base material away from the die and the zone of severe shear deformation. This is important only for materials with low ductility [Rob 91].

With high-purity materials, processing has to be carried out in a clean room with careful cleaning of the can and evacuation at an elevated temperature.

A large disadvantage of this process is that the can material remains on the surface of the extruded product and can be difficult to remove by machining or by pickling. There has been reference to a degassed and hot-compacted aluminum powder in an aluminum capsule, which is removed from the billet before extrusion by machining [Sha 87].

5.39 Mechanism and Flow Behavior in the Extrusion of Metal Powders

If loose powder is extruded (version a), the container first has to be sealed on the die side to ensure good compaction by the stem. The die is then opened.

With precompacted green blanks (version b), a "nose" or a disc of the cast material corresponding to the powder is often placed in front of the die. This compensates for the risk of the surface of the extrusion tearing due to insufficient initial pressure. Indirect extrusion is preferred because of the more uniform material flow. Extrusion with a lubricated container is avoided because of the risk of lubricant penetration of the green blank.

The thermal conductivity in the green blank is relatively low. Too-rapid billet heating therefore results in localized melting with the risk of cracking. Slow heating in a chamber furnace is the most suitable. If heating has to be carried out in an induction furnace, allowance has to be made for an equalization time before loading the billet into the furnace (possibly in an equalization furnace).

Encapsulated powders (version c) are usually extruded with lubricated containers and conical dies (90–120°) or indirectly. This gives a laminar material flow and a uniform cladding material thickness on the extrusion. The selection of the lubricant depends on the cladding material (e.g., aluminum: unlubricated; copper: graphite-oil; iron: glass). Nevertheless, a uniform laminar material flow can be achieved only with round bar or tubes and simple section shapes. Section extrusion is successful only when a suitable die inlet has been developed.

A billet produced from powder usually has a lower density than a cast billet. A longer billet is therefore needed for the same section weight. In extrusion the stem initially pushes together the still not highly compacted powder in the container before the particles are subjected to a shear deformation and friction between each other in the entry (shear) zone to the die and in the die itself. The bonding of the grains on the newly formed surface occurs by friction (or pressure) welding under high pressure and takes place more quickly than the more conventional sintering process used in powder metallurgy.

The extrusion process can produce a better bond between individual particles than sintering. This applies in particular to aluminum alloys, the powder particles of which always exhibit surface films of aluminum oxide because of the high reactivity of the element aluminum. These films are broken up to such an extent in extrusion that the higher the extrusion ratio the greater the number of newly formed surfaces available for particle bonding. An extrusion ratio of at least 20 is often stated to be certain of achieving a perfect bond between the powder particles [Sha 87a]. The resultant structure of the extruded powder corresponds to the structure formed during the extrusion of solid billets.

Encapsulated powder has to be well compacted and degassed. If the strength of the powder material and the encapsulating material differ too severely, or if the can is too thin and the powder inadequately compacted, there is the risk of folds forming during extrusion (Fig. 5.73). Diffusion between the can material and the powder material should be prevented as far as possible, and it should not be possible for a eutectic to form between them. When selecting the can material, consideration should always be given to the fact that it later has to be removed.

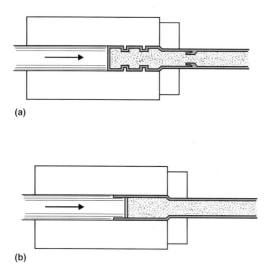

(a)

(b)

Fig. 5.73 (a) Fold formation during extrusion of insufficiently precompacted metal powder. (b) Avoiding fold formation by advance of the capsule back wall [Rob 91]

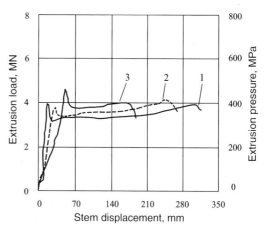

Fig. 5.74 Load variation in the extrusion of powder and spray compacted material compared with cast (Al18SiCuMgNi), indirectly extruded. 1, cast; 2, spray compacted; 3, compacted powder [Mue 93]

An interesting variation of the extrusion of metal powders is the hydrostatic extrusion of silver alloy powders. Presintered billets can be extruded without a can because the pores close during the pressure buildup, preventing the penetration of the pressure medium and the production of defects.

As mentioned previously, spray-compacted billets behave similarly to cast billets—the powder compaction measures then no longer apply.

5.40 Load Variation

The variation in the load in the extrusion of powders differs considerably from that with cast billets because there is a less severe increase in the load during compaction in the first part of the stem movement. The gradient of the load-displacement curve varies with the degree of compaction.

The high load peak often seen with aluminum powders during upsetting can cause problems, and there is still no definite explanation for it (Fig. 5.74).

Additional work also has to be carried out during extrusion to overcome the friction between the grains and for their bonding. It is therefore often assumed that the extrusion load in extruding powders is somewhat higher than in the extrusion of cast billets. In a few cases a lower load has been mentioned [Nae 69]. How-

ever, it is rare for exactly the same material to be extruded as a cast billet or as a powder, which prevents exact comparisons.

The use of indirect extrusion has proved beneficial in the extrusion of powders in order to reduce the extrusion load.

5.41 Examples of Powder Extrusion

In almost every powder metallurgically produced material group there are materials with solid insoluble inclusions (dispersoids). These dispersion-hardened materials can be produced only by powder metallurgical processes.

5.41.1 Aluminum Alloys

It is practically impossible to produce aluminum powder without an oxide skin because of the high affinity of aluminum for oxygen. Normal sintering is therefore hindered or prevented with aluminum alloys. Extrusion, therefore, remains as the only practical possibility of producing defect-free dense materials by P/M of aluminum alloys because the oxide skins on the powder particles are torn away to leave oxide-free, easily weldable surfaces. Pure aluminum powder can be bonded to a metallic dense material with at least 80% cold deformation [Gro 73].

The starting material is usually quenched powder from a gas stream atomization plant that is first compacted in a cold isostatic press or, for small dimensions, in a cylindrical compression die to a green blank with 75 to 80% of the theoretical density. In the extrusion press the green blank is almost 100% compressed with an initially closed die and then extruded using the direct or the indirect process at 450 to 500 °C [Sha 87]. Placing a "nose" or a disc of aluminum in front of the powder billet can promote sufficient compaction during upsetting and also prevent the start of the extrusion from breaking up. The abrasive effect of hard particles in a powder mixture on the shape-forming tools is also reduced. Encapsulation with degassing at 500 °C and hot compaction is required only if absolute freedom from hydrogen is specified. The cladding can be removed by machining prior to extrusion.

In practice, the extrusion of aluminum powder materials is worthwhile only if it produces a material that cannot be produced by casting technology. Most attention is paid to the high-alloy materials with high room temperature strength as well as dispersion-hardened materials that have a much higher strength and better mechanical properties at higher temperatures than naturally hard and precipitation-hardened aluminium alloys (Fig. 5.75).

In the 1940s, a process was developed for producing and working an oxide-containing powder from aluminum powder by a milling process. This product was referred to as sintered aluminum powder (SAP) [Irm 52, Jan 75]. Originally, the extruded aluminum material contained 12 to 15% Al_2O_3; today less than 5% Al_2O_3 is used

because the dispersed particles are finer and better distributed.

Milling aluminum powder with electrographite followed by heat treatment for complete transformation of the carbon into Al_4C_3 produces a dispersion-hardened aluminum material with embedded Al_4C_3 and Al_2O_3 particles marketed under the trade name Dispal [Arn 85]. In variations of the material solid-solution hardening AlMg5 or AlSi12 is used as the base material instead of pure aluminum to achieve better mechanical properties even at lower temperatures. Whereas the solid-solution hardening and precipitation hardening are lost at higher temperatures, the dispersion hardening is retained.

Dispal materials with high silicon content are preferably processed by spray compaction to extrusion billets. As well as saving the cost of cold isostatic pressing of powders, the main advantage is the fine distribution of the embedded particles. After extrusion, rapidly solidified aluminum powder with iron and nickel additions contain finely distributed particles of intermetallic phases of the types Al_3Fe and Al_3Ni (metallic dispersoids) [Sha 87]. Alloys based on AlFeCe, AlFeMo, AlCrMnZr, and AlNiFeMn with additions of copper, magnesium, and titanium, which also form intermetallic dispersoids, are used to achieve high hot strengths. This results in alloys that have an approximately 100% higher hot strength in the temperature range 250 to 350 °C, compared with conventional materials. The fatigue strength of such materials can also be significantly improved. The E-modulus is also increased by 20 to 30%. These improvements in the mechanical properties are, however, obtained with an increase in density to 2.8 to 3.0 g/cm^3 because of the increased content of heavy elements [Sha 87a]. In powder metallurgically produced aluminum alloys with silicon contents of 10 to 30%, the eutectic and the primary phases are very finely formed in the structure (<25 µm). This structure has an advantageous effect on the hot and fatigue strengths [Sha 87a]. The alloys can be readily mechanically worked and are characterized by a low coefficient of thermal expansion. For bearing elements, the extrusion of powder- and spray-compacted materials produces an uneven finer distribution of hard particles than that achieved by casting. The wear properties are significantly improved. Materials that contain other elements in addition to silicon are being tested in engine construction [Arn 92a], where, however, the high manufacturing cost is a major barrier in spite of the sig-

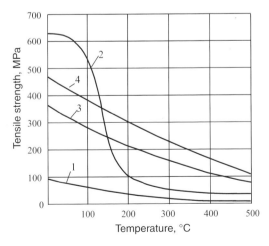

Fig. 5.75 Temperature dependence of the tensile strength of different aluminum alloys. 1, aluminum 99% soft; 2, AlZnMgCu1.5; 3, sintered aluminum powder (SAP) with 10% Al_2O_3; 4, Al with 4% C (as Al_4C_3) [Sch 86]

nificantly better properties compared with conventionally produced components. A breakthrough is high-silicon-containing aluminum tubes for cylinder sleeves that have recently been extruded from spray-compacted billets [Hum 97].

Other aluminum alloys produced by mechanical alloying with oxides and carbides as dispersoids and that contain 1 to 4% copper and magnesium are commercially available. They are hot compacted and then extruded. However, only simple cross sections are available. After extrusion they can be further processed by forging, hammering, rolling, or drawing [Rob 91].

5.41.2 Copper and Noble Metal-Base Alloys

If powders of electrolytic copper and aluminum oxide are cold isostatically compacted, sintered, and extruded to rods, the very fine Al_2O_3 particles (approximately 0.3 µm), which should be finely distributed, prevent recrystallization so that a high strength is retained up to 1000 °C [Zwi 57].

Copper alloys with 1.1% aluminum oxide are supplied as wire and rods and processed to spot welding tips. These tips have a very good electrical conductivity and a high flow stress at the welding temperature. At room temperature the material can be cold worked like copper without intermediate annealing.

The strength-increasing effect up to very high temperatures of the aluminum oxide particles as dispersoids requires extremely fine particles (3–12 nm) and a uniform distance between them of less than 0.1 µm. This is achieved by a so-called internal oxidation of copper-aluminum powders, i.e., an oxidizing annealing in which the oxygen transforms the aluminum to oxide, whereas the more noble copper is retained as a metal.

Dispersion-hardened copper with 0.1 to 0.5 µm large TiB_2 particles (3 vol %) is produced by the following original process.

Two different copper melts are reacted together in a reaction vessel whereby the dispersed phase is produced by a precipitation reaction in situ in the melt. This melt is then atomized to powder, which is filled into a copper can and evacuated [Sut 90]. This material can also be extruded and processed to spot welding electrodes.

CuSn and CuSnNi alloys with high tin contents are known as bearing materials but cannot be extruded because of the coarse δ-phase precipitates. However, with spray compaction, the particles are so finely distributed that the billets can be readily extruded without difficulty to rod and tube. Graphite particles, which improve the slip properties, can be included by an injector during the spray compaction (see Fig. 5.70). A further application of spray-compacted-produced tubes of high-alloy bronze is as super conductors [Mur 96].

Dispersion-hardened silver materials (e.g., with AgNi2 or with cadmium oxide) have better erosion properties, a lower contact resistance, and less tendency to welding than homogeneous materials. Silver and nickel are almost completely insoluble in each other at room temperature. AgNi alloys, therefore, cannot be produced by melting metallurgy but only by powder metallurgy. A uniform distribution of the embedded nickel is obtained by currentless nickel plating of silver powder followed by extrusion [Mue 87].

As described previously for copper, finely distributed particles of cadmium oxide can be formed as a dispersoid in silver by internal oxidation of alloy powders of the noble metal silver, which practically cannot be oxidized, and the base metal additive cadmium. The fraction of cadmium oxide is very high, up to 25%.

Platinum and its alloys, which are used for special heating wires and other high-temperature components, are dispersion hardened whereby they are extruded as powder mixtures with thorium oxide, yttrium oxide, or zircon oxide as dispersoids [Rob 91].

5.41.3 Titanium Alloys

A dispersion-hardened titanium alloy is, for example, a modification of Ti-6242 with 6% Al, 2% Sn, 4% Zr, 2% Mo, 0.1% Si, and 2% Er, which is produced by internal oxidation during the annealing of the powder Er_2O_3, with extremely small particles. Of interest is that the structure obtained by very rapid solidification is not changed by extrusion [Rob 91].

5.41.4 Iron Alloys

The production of chromium-nickel-steels and chromium-aluminum-steels by extrusion of steel powder produced by water atomization was reported in 1969. The process did not go into production [Nae 69] because, normally, even with iron alloys the production, or steels using powder, and compaction is more expensive than by melting and casting.

However, because fewer operating steps are needed than between casting and the production of the bar and a better homogeneity is obtained, powder extrusion is again being promoted for some iron alloys. A Swedish manufacturer offers powder metallurgically produced tubes in stainless chromium-nickel-steels as well as nickel and cobalt alloys [Asl 81, Rob 91]. The melt is atomized under a protective gas and the powder then cold isostatically compacted in an iron can before being extruded over a mandrel. The hollow billet also has to be internally encapsulated to produce tubes. The lubricant is glass, the same as with conventional extrusion, and extrusion is carried out at approximately 1200 °C. The process is supposed to have economic advantages over the conventional one [Tus 82].

Some high-speed and tool steels that are severely segregated when produced by the normal process are extruded as bar from powder to eliminate segregations and to retain elements in solution above the equilibrium value. This is not possible with molten metallurgical production. Because atomization is usually carried out under a protective atmosphere, the round particles that do not readily bond have to be encapsulated for compaction. Water-atomized material can be cold compacted without a can and then sintered before extrusion [Rob 91].

The dispersion hardened iron based alloys MA956 and PM2000 with chromium and aluminium as the main alloying elements and yttrium oxide as the dispersoid are described in the next section.

5.41.5 Nickel and Cobalt-Base High-Temperature Alloys

Alloys with high contents of nickel, chromium, and cobalt are necessary for high-temperature applications, particularly in gas turbines and in the aerospace industries. The high strength is usually obtained by precipitation hardening.

The molten metallurgical production route is the most economic solution when possible. It is, however, accompanied with coarse precipitates and reduced hot workability and is not possible at all with wide melting intervals.

Oxide dispersion strengthened (ODS) alloys are materials in which fine particles, in contrast to precipitates, are also resistant to high temperatures, act as strength increasing dispersions. There is no melting metallurgical alternative to powder metallurgical production. Oxides of yttrium are mainly used [Rob 91].

Table 5.22 summarizes the superalloys produced by P/M.

In the ODS process, the rapidly quenched (more than 10^3 K/s) powder produced by atomization in an inert gas stream after sieving and mixing is encapsulated in a steel can, which has to be evacuated at a high temperature to eliminate micropores. If a particularly uniform precipitation-free structure is required, cooling has to be carried out extremely quickly. Special rapid solidification rate (RSR) processes have been developed (up to 10^6 K/s). Extrusion has proved to be the most suitable compaction method with these materials because the large deformation breaks up oxide films as described for aluminum, disperses impurities present, and provides very good compaction. The encapsulated powder is precompacted by HIP or forging to approximately 85% before it is extruded. The bars extruded at an extrusion ratio of 5–7 with glass lubrication at approximately 1200 °C are further processed by forging and rolling after removal of the can. It is possible with extrusion to significantly reduce the residual porosity and thus the notch impact sensitivity. The extrusion temperature with these alloys has to be very carefully controlled to prevent the risk of coarse precipitates forming at high temperature (e.g., carbide in René 95) [Rob 91].

Table 5.22 Composition of some iron and nickel superalloys produced by powder metallurgy (addition in wt%)

Designation	Fe	Ni	Cr	Co	Mo	W	Ti	Al	Nb	Ta	Zr	B	C	Y_2O_3
MA 956(a)	74.0	...	20.0	...	...	...	0.5	4.5	...	...	...	...	...	0.5
PM 2000(b)	73.0	...	20.0	...	...	...	0.5	5.5	...	...	...	...	...	0.5
MA 754(a)	1.0	77.5	20.0	...	...	...	0.5	0.3	...	...	...	...	0.05	0.6
MA 6000(a)	...	68.5	15.0	...	2.0	4.0	2.5	4.5	...	2.0	0.15	0.01	0.05	1.1
PM 3000(b)	...	67.0	20.0	...	2.0	3.5	...	6.0	...	...	0.15	0.01	0.05	1.1
Renè 95(c)	...	62.0	13.0	8.0	3.5	3.5	2.5	3.5	3.5	...	0.15	0.01	0.07	...
Nimonic AP1(a)	...	55.5	15.0	17.0	5.0	...	3.5	4.0	...	...	...	0.025	0.02	...

(a) Inco Alloys International. (b) High temperature metal GmbH. (c) Nuclear Metals Inc. Source: Sch 86, Rue 92

The alloy René 95 and Nimonic AP1 are precipitation-hardening alloys where solid-solution hardening is also effective at moderate temperatures because of the addition of molybdenum. They are used for gas turbine discs.

In the ODS alloys Ma 965 and PM2000 (Fe-Cr-basis), as well as Ma754, Ma 6000, and PM 3000 (Ni-Cr-basis), the Y_2O_3 is worked into the metal powder by mechanical alloying in high-energy ball mills and finely dispersed. The fiber texture obtained by extrusion is utilized by suitable heat treatment (coarse-fiber crystals from zone recrystallization) to achieve a very good fatigue and creep strength.

MA956 and PM2000 with high oxidation and hot corrosion strength up to 1100 °C are used in combustion chambers, in gas turbines, and other cases demanding maximum resistance at high temperatures.

MA6000 and PM3000 are used in the first and second stages of jet engines and can be hot and cold rolled after extrusion.

5.41.6 Exotic Materials

Beryllium tubes are the ideal construction material in communication satellites because of their low density (1.85 g/cm^3), the high E-modulus, and their considerable elongation. In order to achieve a fine structure, P/M processing is preferred to melting and casting. The material being processed is encased in carbon steel because of the poisonous nature of beryllium and the susceptibility to oxidation. This can be removed by pickling with hydrochloric acid after extrusion with glass lubrication. The workability in the extrusion direction is increased by the texture formed in extrusion of this hexagonal crystallizing material [Rob 91].

Ceramic uranium oxide powder has to be heated to 1750 to 2000 °C for plastic flow. Because no deformation tooling can withstand this high temperature, experiments have been reported in which the hot powder is filled into relatively cold steel cans at approximately 700 °C and then extruded.

This two-temperature process has also been investigated for the production of chromium tube and bar whereby hot chromium powder is filled into a colder steel can and immediately extruded. The aim is to ensure that the very different deformation behaviors of the two materials at the same temperature are matched to each other.

Intermetallic phases such as Ni_3Al_4 or Ti_3Al_4 can only be deformed at approximately 1100 °C.

Because the production of alloy powder would be very expensive, element powders are mixed and cold compacted. The green blanks are encased in aluminum and extruded at approximately 500 °C. This prevents the extreme exothermic reaction from the formation of the intermetallic phases occurring during the extrusion. It takes place—possibly after further deformation steps—in high-vacuum furnaces or in an HIP unit. Another method is "reaction extrusion" at such a high temperature that the phase formation actually occurs during extrusion.

Extrusion of Semifinished Products from Metallic Composite Materials

Klaus Müller*

Metallic composite materials are microscopically heterogeneous, macroscopically homogeneous-appearing materials that consist of two or more components intimately connected with each other and in which at least the component with the highest volume is a metal or an alloy [Rau 78]. Its structure can be matched to the stresses of the component.

Pure metals and alloys have a defined property spectrum so that the determination of a property for a given material also determines all other properties. In composite materials, in contrast, the properties of different components are combined, resulting in a new extended property spectrum. The spatial arrangement of the components in the composite gives rise to typical composite properties, the so-called structural properties. Composite materials can also exhibit properties resulting from interactions between the components, the so-called product properties. Always present are the cumulative properties, i.e., the resultant properties from the addition of the component properties. This is shown in Fig. 5.76 [Sto 86].

The application of metallic composite materials in place of conventional alloys produces in most cases economic as well as technical advan-

*Extrusion of Semifinished Products from Metallic Composite Materials, Klaus Müller

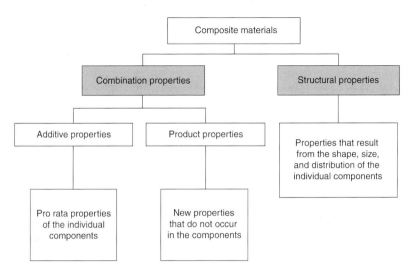

Fig. 5.76 Properties of metallic materials

tages. Composite materials are produced today, the metallic components of which form solid solutions or intermetallic phases corresponding to the phase diagram or are insoluble in each other. The application of the composite materials is determined by the adhesion at the boundary faces of the individual components. The general conditions for a satisfactory boundary surface adhesion with common deformation of heterogeneous materials include:

- Adequate face pressure (compressive stress in the deformation zone)
- Adequate increase in the surface area during the deformation
- A limited inhomogeneity of the flow in the deformation zone that is still sufficient for the structures to conform to each other but, on the other hand, is not so high that the composite material is subjected to unacceptable internal stresses. The composite components have to be capable of flowing together under the process-specific stress conditions.

For longitudinally oriented semifinished products (section, bar, wire, and tubes), the criteria described previously for stresses, surface increase, and flow field formation are fulfilled by the deformation processes rolling, drawing, extrusion, and (to a limited extent) by forging.

However, extrusion provides the most favorable conditions with reference to the three basic requirements:

- Compressive deformation
- Large strains in one operation

- The capability of influencing the deformation zone by die design

Depending on the materials combination, the materials structure, the application, and the extrusion temperature, metallic composite materials can be produced by direct, indirect, or hydrostatic extrusion.

5.42   Terminology and Examples

The metalic composites can be classified according to the spatial arrangement of the components:

- Fiber composite materials
- Particle composite materials
- Penetration composite materials
- Laminated composite materials

Figure 5.77 [Lan 93] shows schematically the geometric structure.

Composite materials in which fibers of the other components aligned or randomly oriented are embedded, aligned, or randomly orientated in the matrix of the predominating component by volume are referred to as *fiber composite materials*. Examples are:

- Directionally solidified eutectics
- Copper-sheathed aluminum conductors for electrotechnology
- Superconducting materials, including NbTi multifilaments in a copper matrix

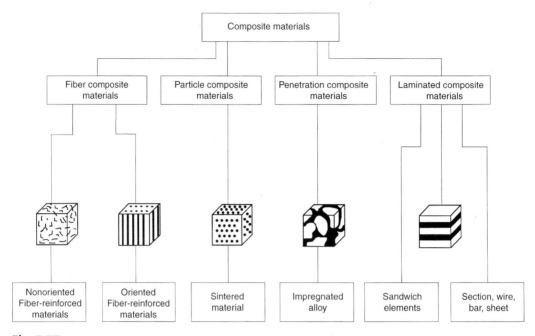

Fig. 5.77 Spatial arrangement of the components in composite materials [Lan 93]

- Electrical contact material, including Ag/C, Ag/Cu/C, and Cu/Pd
- SiC or B fiber-reinforced light metal materials

Composite materials in which the other components are embedded without a marked preferred orientation in the matrix of the predominating component by volume are referred to as *particle composite materials*. They are discussed in the section "Extrusion of Powder Metals."

Composite materials in which the various components form an intermingled structure are referred to as *penetration composite materials*.

Composite materials that have a laminated structure of the composite materials are referred to as *laminated composite materials*.

5.43 Flow Behavior in the Extrusion of Fiber Composite Materials

The following cases can be differentiated from the point of view of the deformation:

- Only one or not all of the components are deformed (aluminum-steel bus bars, metal powder combinations with ceramic additives).

- All the components involved are deformed together whereby different strains can occur within the components.

Because the composite materials produced by extrusion are predominantly metallic fiber composite materials and the production of dispersion composite materials are described in the section "Extrusion of Powder Metals," the basic principles are described using this type of material. The range of possible material combinations, which are not fully utilized today, are illustrated by way of an example in Fig. 5.78 [Mue 91].

Single or multicore wires can be produced as well as wires with solid or powder cores. In some cases, viscous wire fillers (glasses during hot working) can be used. If thermal material influences and diffusion are taken into account as well as the structure along with the associated metallurgical possibilities, the wide range of material technical possibilities is clear [Mue 82].

Metallic fiber composite materials, corresponding to the structure described (outer tube and one or more wire cores), can only be produced, depending on the application, by indirect or hydrostatic extrusion because the outer tube cannot have any distortion relative to the core material resulting from adhesion or friction with the container liner.

Both in indirect extrusion and hydrostatic extrusion there is no friction between the billet and

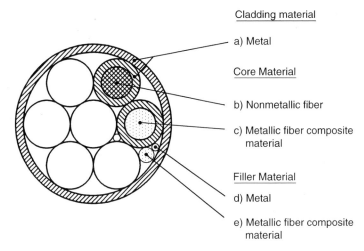

Fig. 5.78 Schematic structure of metallic fiber composite materials

the container. Under comparable stress conditions in the actual deformation zone both processes can be differentiated by the billet upsetting. This is important because the billet used to produce a core filled sheathed tube contains an empty volume of between 15 and 23%. In hydrostatic extrusion, this empty volume is removed by the hydrostatic pressure conditions; in indirect extrusion this occurs by the reduction of the billet length and the increase in the billet diameter. This can result in twisting and buckling processes that can produce defects in the composite material.

The risk of twisting and buckling increases with an increasing length/diameter ratio of the core wire in the tube sheath. The structure can be so severely distorted that further extrusion results in elongated folds and doublings that can initiate cracks and thus render the composite materials unusable [Mue 80].

5.43.1 Criterion for Homogeneous Deformation

In the combined extrusion of metallic materials with different flow stresses k_f, the material flow can take place in different ways. The aim of composite material production by extrusion must be, in addition to pure cladding, to transform the individual components into a compact undamaged material. This requires that the individual components have the same flow stress k_f in the deformation zone. This condition can be achieved by the selection of the following parameters:

- Extrusion ratio
- Volume distribution or volume fraction

- Die opening angle
- Flow stress ratio $k_{f1}/k_{f2}/............/k_{fm}$
- Extrusion speed
- Lubricant (influences the friction conditions in the die in particular)
- Temperature control of the extrusion process
- Bonding quality in the initial billet

These relationships are shown in Fig. 5.79 for the two-component-composite aluminum-copper.

Figure 5.80 represents a homogeneous deformation in which the individual components are subjected to the same reduction for the three-part composite CU/Ni/Cu with the relevant HV 0.1 values in the billet and the extruded section.

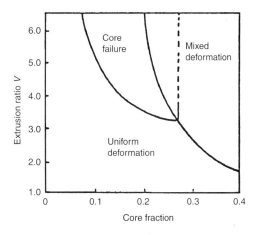

Fig. 5.79 Influence of the extrusion ratio and core fraction on the type of deformation. Material: sheath Al, core Cu, flow stress ratio 2.7, die opening angle 2 alpha (v = 45°). Area for achieving homogeneous deformation [Osa 73]

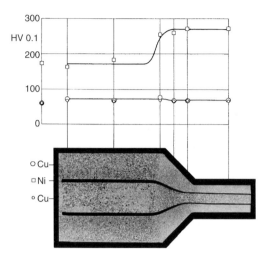

Fig. 5.80 Homogeneous deformation of the composite Cu/Ni/Cu

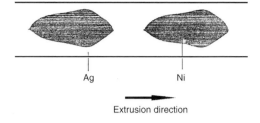

Extrusion direction

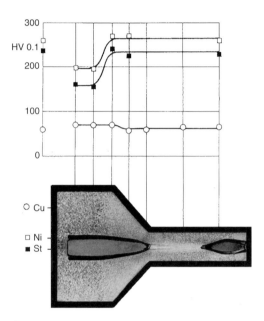

Fig. 5.81 Example of core fracture. The core material used is periodically broken.

A nonhomogeneous deformation in which the individual components are extruded with different reductions can result in the failure of the composite with the pure cladding material not being deformed with the core material.

5.43.2 Deformation with Failure of the Composite Material

The most common failures are core and sheath fracture, if defects from undesired reactions during the deformation are excluded. Examples of core failure are shown in Fig. 5.81 for both a two- and three-component composite. However, there is no external visible defect on the extrusion. This type of failure occurs with the combination of hard core material and soft sheath material. Sheath failure can be seen externally at least for the case of the two-part composite with the material composition hard sheath material and soft core material. In a three-component composite, the damage need not be visible at the surface. The innermost core can have core oscillations, i.e., periodic irregular deformation. Figure 5.82 shows examples. The works of [Ahm 78, Rup 80, Hol 78] give various solutions to avoid these failures for the composite Cu/Al.

5.44 Production of Metallic Composite Materials

Indirect and hydrostatic extrusion offer the following favorable conditions for production:

- It is possible to extrude composite billets with thin casing tubes without the risk of the casing cracking because of the absence of friction between the billet and the container.
- The bonding of the composite components to one another is strongly promoted by the surrounding compressive stress state during the deformation.
- Because the process can be carried out over a wide temperature range, boundary surface reactions can be suppressed by suitable temperature control where they reduce the properties and promoted where they improve the composite material.

Depending on the geometry of the billet used, composite materials with a fibrous, particle and laminated structure can be produced. Figure 5.83 illustrates this for the composite copper-palladium [Sto 87].

The production of a metallic fiber composite material corresponding to the schematic structure shown in Fig. 5.78 and consisting of a cas-

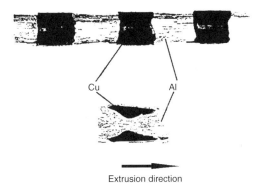

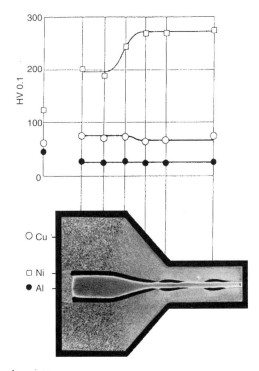

Fig. 5.82 Examples of sheath failure

acceptable handling. Thus, in simple extrusion, the number of fibers in the end product is determined by the maximum possible internal diameter of the casing tube.

The total production is largely determined by the cost of the production of the casing tube. These include casings in the form of closed cups (produced by drawing and redrawing); casings machined with a solid or hollow tip, the angle of which is matched to the angle of the die; and casings that consist of flanged tube sections. The simplest case from the production point of view is shown in Fig. 5.84.

A tube is used for the casing material, the short inlet of which is conically upset outside the press. The upper and lower closure of the core wire packet is made from embedded stamped blanks (indirect extrusion) or from a stamped blank and an embedded radial plug that simultaneously can act as the guide for the billet in the container (hydrostatic extrusion). With suitable materials selection, this component can be reused.

In the application of composite billets that consist of only two components and thus have almost no volume gaps (e.g., copper-clad aluminum bus bar conductor), there are no additional influences resulting from the geometry of the initial material apart from those described.

This is not the case when multicore composite billets are used (simplest billet preparation, no precompaction of the billets). In the case of hydrostatic extrusion, the billet is radially compacted at the start of extrusion because upsetting cannot occur. Twisting and bending of the wire bundle does not occur from experience; however, with thick wires their contour can be seen in the form of corrugations in the encasing tube. With thin wires, the compaction results in the geometry of the billet deviating from a circular shape.

In both cases there is nonuniform flow in the die and explosive lubricant breakdowns in the die aperture, resulting in the extrusion shattering. In the case of hydrostatic extrusion of noncompacted multicore billets, with simple billet preparation, these problems have to be expected if very small core wires (1 mm diam.) are not used [Mue 81].

Under the stress conditions of indirect extrusion, the composite billet is not radially compacted as in hydrostatic extrusion but upsets with a reduction in length and increase in cross section to the diameter of the container. The re-

ing tube and one or more core wires is possible by extruding a number of thin core wires (the number of wires corresponding to the desired number of fibers in the finished product, simple extrusion) or by extruding a less number of thick core wires in a casing to a relatively thick section, a small number of sections of which are then bundled into a common casing and reextruded (repetitive extrusion).

Handling of thin wires can be difficult. It can therefore be assumed that a core wire thickness of approximately 1 mm is the lower limit for

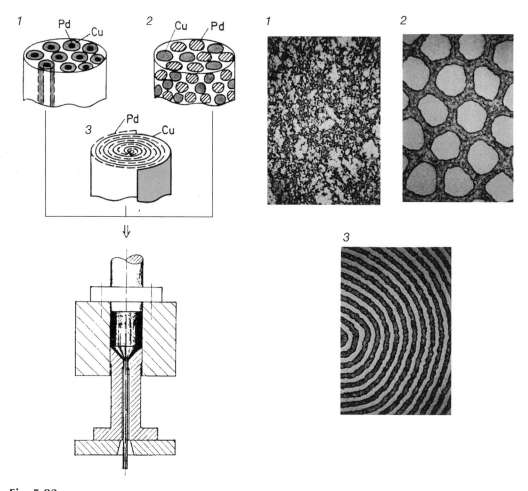

Fig. 5.83 Structure of extruded copper/palladium-composite material. Micrograph image width is approximately 3.6 mm

duction in length of the core wire bundle can take place in three ways:

- Twisting of the core wire bundle

- Buckling of the individual wires or the entire bundle
- Compression of the core wires

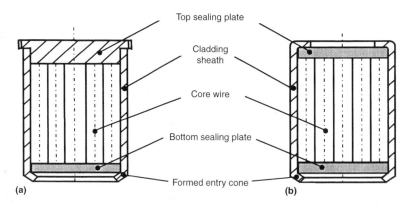

Fig. 5.84 Multicore billet preparation for (a) hydrostatic extrusion and (b) indirect extrusion

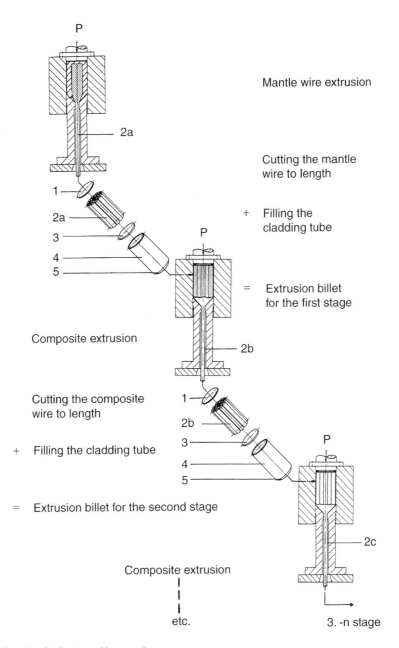

Mantle wire extrusion

Cutting the mantle
wire to length

+ Filling the
cladding tube

= Extrusion billet
for the first stage

Composite extrusion

Cutting the composite
wire to length

+ Filling the cladding tube

= Extrusion billet for the second stage

Composite extrusion

etc.

3. -n stage

Fig. 5.85 Schematic of indirect repetitive extrusion

The first two mechanisms do not initially contain any cross-section increase of the individual wires. There is the risk of the casing buckling or bending giving rise to extrusion defects. The twisting represents energetically the lowest state and can therefore always be expected. Whether compression or buckling occurs after twisting depends on the length-diameter (L/d) ratio of the individual rods as well as their mutual support in the rod bundle, the support of the casing, and the mechanical properties of the material.

[Mue 81] shows that twisting and buckling processes can be identified at an L/d ratio of 20 for a fiber composite material of AlMgSi0.5 wires; however, no material defect occurs. At an L/d ratio of 100, the casing material exhibits folding and a defect-free product cannot be obtained.

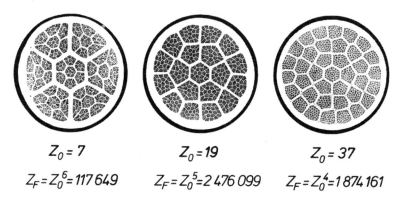

Fig. 5.86 Different structures in Ag/C (billet diam, 30 mm; bar diam, 12 mm). Z_F, number of fibers in sheath tube

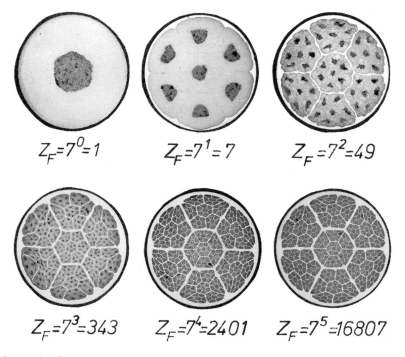

Fig. 5.87 Cross section after progressive extrusion stages (bar diam, 12 mm). Z_F, number of fibers in the sheath tube

Therefore, the so-called indirect repetitive extrusion is a particularly suitable variation of the indirect extrusion for the production of composite materials with complex structures. A billet made from a specific number of core wires (mantle wires) is extruded to a rod, which is then sectioned and the cross sections reextruded. This process can be repeated as often as required to produce the desired structure. The process sequence is shown schematically in Fig. 5.85.

The process for the production of Ag/C and

Ag/Cu/C contact materials is described in more detail in this chapter [Mue 85]. Silver or copper billets were drilled and filled with graphite powder for the production of silver/graphite and copper/graphite composite materials. The diameter of the bores was determined by the graphite content that had to be achieved. The billets were sealed, preheated to extrusion temperature, and indirect extruded to bars. After cutting the sections to length, a specific number of the cross sections was arranged in a thin-walled silver or

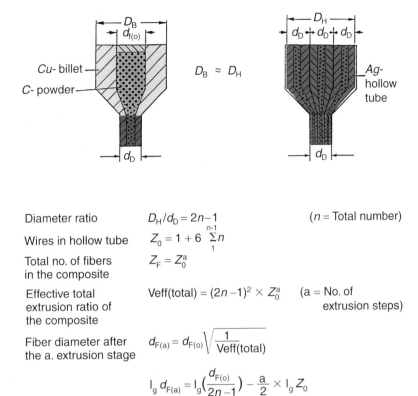

Diameter ratio	$D_H/d_D = 2n-1$	(n = Total number)
Wires in hollow tube	$Z_0 = 1 + 6 \sum_{1}^{n-1} n$	
Total no. of fibers in the composite	$Z_F = Z_0^a$	
Effective total extrusion ratio of the composite	$V_{eff}(total) = (2n-1)^2 \times Z_0^a$	(a = No. of extrusion steps)
Fiber diameter after the a. extrusion stage	$d_{F(a)} = d_{F(o)}\sqrt{\dfrac{1}{V_{eff}(total)}}$	

$$l_g\, d_{F(a)} = l_g\left(\frac{d_{F(o)}}{2n-1}\right) - \frac{a}{2} \times l_g\, Z_0$$

Fig. 5.88 Geometric arrangements in indirect repetitive extrusion

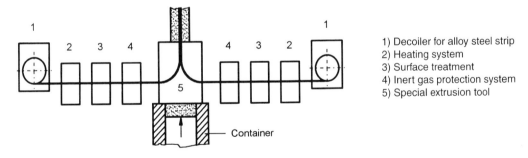

1) Decoiler for alloy steel strip
2) Heating system
3) Surface treatment
4) Inert gas protection system
5) Special extrusion tool

Fig. 5.89 Process principle for the production of Al-alloy steel composite bus bar

copper casing. The number of bar sections depends on the extrusion ratio.

Depending on the extrusion ratio and the number of extrusion stages, different structures can be obtained Fig. 5.86.

The casings were also sealed at both ends and extruded like the powder filled billets. The extruded multicore bars were again cut to length and reprocessed as described previously. The sequential structures can be seen in Fig. 5.87.

The relationship between the casing used, the wire diameter, the extrusion ratio, and the number of fibers in the composite is shown in Fig. 5.88.

5.45 Application Examples

The applications described below subsequently for metallic composite materials produced by extrusion can illustrate only a few areas of the comprehensive range. There has been no attempt to provide a full coverage of all possible and, to some extent, still-experimental materials.

5.45.1 Simple Structures and Coatings

Lead sheathing of electrical cables can be considered as the oldest and also the most well-known example of the production of a metallic composite material. In the mid-1960s, the composite extrusion of bar, tube, and section became technically important [Ric 69], particularly for the processing of reactive metals including beryllium, titanium, zirconium, hafnium, vanadium, niobium, and tantalum. The problem of attack of the extrusion tooling is a major problem in the processing of these metals and their alloys. Technically, this means that the standard lubricants used in extrusion are not able to guarantee reliable separation between the metals being extruded and the extrusion tooling so that localized welding occurs. Billets of reactive metals have to be clad with a metal that provides the lubrication as a "lost shell." Ti/Cu ignition electrodes are produced this way.

The development of suitable lubricants, and of low-melting-point glasses in particular, enables conventional extrusion without a cladding material to be carried out today in many cases. Cladding with, for example, 18/8 chromium-nickel steel, is used today for the extrusion of cast intermetallic materials including NiAl, Ni_3Al, and TiAl to counteract embrittlement by oxygen absorption at the high extrusion temperature of approximately 1250 °C.

Since 1963, laminated composite materials of copper-clad aluminum for conductors have been developed as a substitute for copper [Hor 70, Nyl 78, Fri 67]. The aluminum core consists of EC aluminum, the copper cladding of electrolytic copper. For technical and economic reasons, the copper cladding is 15% of the cross-sectional area. This material is produced only to a limited extent today because of the changes in metal prices.

In contrast, the process developed by the company Alusingen for the production of composite electrical bus bars conductors in aluminum-steel for high-speed and underground trains is commercially important [Mie 87]. The basic process is that two alloy steel strips are fed into an extrusion die. The steel strips are fed from decoilers. They pass through stations for chemical and mechanical pretreatment to apply corrosion protection. They are then fed into the extrusion die and turned through 90°. Both metals bond together in the welding chamber under the influence of the high extrusion pressure and the increased temperature as well as the relative movement between the steel and the aluminum. In this way, two-mirror image, composite bus bars conductor rails are extruded with a metallic bond between the steel and the aluminum. The reason for simultaneously extruding two composite sections is to avoid friction between the steel strip and the die. In this process the steel band does not contact the die surface but emerges with no wear. This is achieved as the steel strips are completely surrounded by the aluminum and never come into contact with the die bearings. Because the steel strips do not stick to each other, the two sections can be easily separated from each other. Figure 5.89 shows the process principles.

Simple composite structures are also found in the area of steel- and iron-alloy composite tubes and sections [Deg 89, Gut 91, Hug 82, Lat 89, Vil 92], as well as aluminum-clad steel wire [Hir 84] that has excellent corrosion resistance even in marine atmospheres and is used as wire cloth and wire netting.

5.45.2 Metallic Fiber Composite Materials with Complex Structures

Outstanding examples in this area are the industrial metallic superconductors NbTi and Nb_3Sn [Web 82, Bre 79, Hil 84]. Very different complex structures of usually three or more individual components are produced depending on the desired current-carrying capacity. The examples in Fig. 5.90 shows examples of niobium wires embedded in a copper-tin matrix.

Copper forms the core of the composite material and is separated from the CuSn of the superconductor by a tantalum barrier. Structures with up to 10,000 individual filaments and a filament diameter between 3 and 5 μm in wire diameter of 0.4 to 2.0 mm are obtained by multiple combination and followed by multiple extrusion, comparable to the repeated indirect extrusion already described but with a packing density of 95 to 98%, followed by drawing.

After the final operation to produce the required dimensions, the material is heat treated to produce the superconducting compound Nb_3Sn by diffusion of the tin from the copper-tin matrix and reaction with the niobium wires. The copper core remains unaltered (protected by the tantalum barrier). Because the superconducting intermetallic phase Nb_3Sn cannot be deformed, this production route has to be used.

The possibility of influencing the material and properties by changing the structure and by

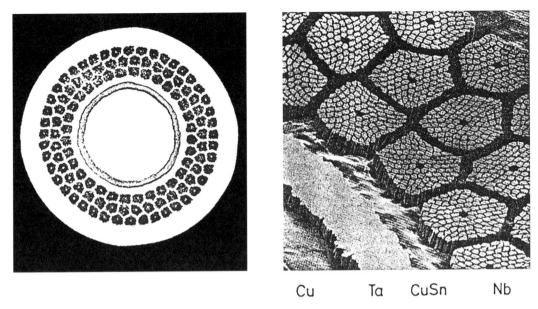

Fig. 5.90 Cross section of a filament super conductor [Web 82]

Cu   Ta   CuSn   Nb

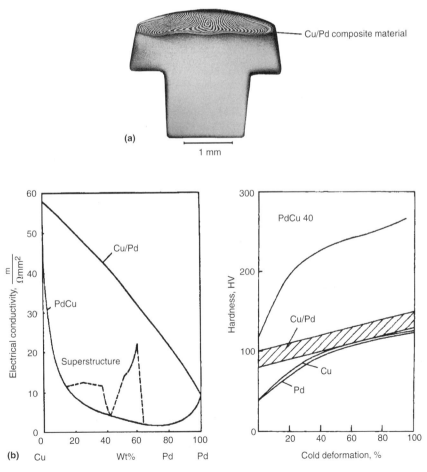

Fig. 5.91 Property comparison between Cu/Pd composite materials (VW) and corresponding Pd/Cu alloys (electrical conductivity and hardness after cold working)

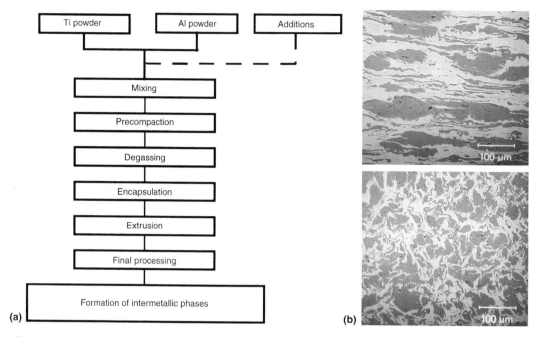

Fig. 5.92 Schematic process for reaction powder metallurgy. (a) Longitudinal and transverse structure of Ti48.5Al, unreacted. (b) Longitudinal and transverse sections in the extruded state

specific heat treatments can be applied to other materials. The work by [Sto 87] and [Mue 86] describes the contact material copper palladium. Palladium-copper alloys with 15 or 40 wt% Cu are used extensively for contact materials for switching direct current because of their high resistance to material movement. Palladium and copper form a continuous solid-solution series with superstructure phases. This governs the electrical conductivity of the alloys. There are significant technical and economic advantages in using Cu/Pd composite materials instead of conventional PdCu alloys. Care should be taken to avoid the formation of solid-solution zones at the boundary surface between copper and palladium in the manufacture of the composite materials. It is possible, by controlling the structure and the temperature in the deformation process, to obtain the microscopic heterogeneous composite structure. The indirect extrusion of coils of copper and palladium strip is particularly suited for this. This produces contact materials that exhibit a completely different property spectrum compared with conventional alloys of the same composition. The electrical and thermal conductivities of Cu/Pd composite materials are up to 10 times higher than the corresponding Cu-Pd alloys. The absence of solid-solution hardening gives the Cu/

Pd composite alloys a high ductility (Fig. 5.91). This provides excellent further processing possibilities, providing savings in the noble metals and economic production processes for complex components.

5.45.3 Metallic Fiber Composite Materials with P/M Structures

This application area includes all those fiber composite materials that can be produced from powder starting materials. These are mainly aluminum-base fiber-reinforced materials [Sch 87, Ros 92, Bei 90, Moo 85], metal matrix composites (MMC) [Sta 88], and materials for electrical contacts [The 90]. The production of fibers [Boe 88] also provides a means of materials strengthening.

Alloys based on the intermetallic phase TiAl have a large potential for use as high-temperature, light structural components. The deformation potential of this phase, which is usually brittle under a conventional stress state, is very limited. Semifinished and structural components can be produced economically by reaction powder metallurgy [Mue 90, Wan 92, Mue 93] (see also the section "Extrusion of Powder Metals"). The production of titanium aluminides by reaction powder metallurgy (Fig. 5.92a) includes the following steps:

1. Mixing the initial powders (element and/or alloy powders)
2. Precompaction of the powder mixture (e.g., by CIP)
3. Production of semifinished product by extrusion
4. Finishing of component
5. Reaction heat treatment

Figure 5.92(b) shows longitudinal and transverse sections in the extruded state. Suitable control of the reaction heat treatment produces the phase TiAl expected from the phase diagram.

In the future, it should be possible for starting materials that have been produced by mechanically alloyed powder particles or by a spray compaction process to be used for the application of new composite materials with excellent properties.

REFERENCES

Extrusion of Materials with Working Temperatures between 0 and 300 °C

[Hof 62]: W. Hofmann, *Blei und Bleilegierungen, Metallkunde und Technologie (Lead and Lead Alloys, Metallurgy and Technology)*, Vol 2, I, Bildsame Formgebund, Springer-Verlag, 1962

[Lau 76]: K. Laue and H. Stenger, Strangpressen: Verfahren, Maschinen, Werkzeuge (Extrusion: Processes, Machines, Tools), *Aluminium*, 1976

[Sac 34]: G. Sachs, Spanlose Formung (Chipless Forming), *Metallkunde*, Springer-Verlag, 1934

[Schi 77]: P. Schimpke, H. Schropp, and R. König, *Technologie der Maschinenbauwerkstoffe (Technology of Materials for Machine Construction)*, Vol 18, S. Hirzel Verlag Stuttgart, 1977, ISBN 3-7776-0312-0

[Schu 69]: M. Schumann, *Metallographie (Metallography)*, Vol 7, VEB Deutscher Vertag für Grundstoffindustrie, Leipzig, 1969

REFERENCES

Extrusion of Materials with Deformation Temperatures between 300 and 600 °C

[Abt 96]: S. Abtahi, T. Welo, and S. Stören, Interface Mechanisms on the Bearing Surface in Extrusion, *ET '96*, Vol II, p 125–131

[Ach 69]: D. Achenbach and G. Scharf, *Z. Metallkd.*, Vol 60, 1969, p 915–921

[Ake 68]: R. Akeret, Untersuchungen über das Strangpressen unter besonderer Berücksichtigung der thermischen Vorgänge (Investigations into the Extrusion with Specific Reinforcement to the Thermal Processes), *Aluminium*, Vol 44, 1968, p 412–415

[Ake 70]: R. Akeret, Untersuchungen über das Umformverhalten von Aluminiumwerkstoffen bei verschiedenen Temeraturen (Investigations into the Deformation Behavior of Aluminum Alloys at Different Temperatures), *Z. Metallkd.*, Vol 61, 1970, p 3–10

[Ake 71]: R. Akeret, Die Produktivität beim Strangpressen von Aluminium-Werkstoffen—Einfluß von Werkstoff und Verfahren (The Productivity in the Extrusion of Aluminum Alloys—Influence of the Material and Process), *Z. Metallkd.*, Vol 62, 1971, p 451–456

[Ake 72]: R. Akeret, Filage de l'aluminium: Analyse des phénomènes thermiques pour différentes conditions opératiores (Aluminum Extrusion: Analysis of the Thermal Phenomenon for Different Operational Conditions), *Mém. Sci. Rev. Mét.*, Vol 69, 1972, p 633–640

[Ake 72a]: R. Akeret, Properties of Pressure Welds in Extruded Aluminium Alloy Sections, *J. Inst. Met.*, Vol 100, 1972, p 202–207

[Ake 73]: R. Akeret, Sonderverfahren zum schnelleren Strangpressen von Aluminium-Hartlegierungen (Special Processes for Faster Extrusion of Aluminum Hard Alloys), *Z. Metallkd.*, Vol 64, 1973, p 311–319

[Ake 80]: R. Akeret, Das Verhalten der Strangpresse als Regelstrecke (Aluminum Extrusion as a Controlled System), *Metall.*, Vol 34, 1980, p 737–741

[Ake 83]: R. Akeret, Einfluß der Querschnittsform und der Werkzeuggestaltung beim Strangpressen von Aluminium (Influence of the Cross-Section Profile and Tool Design on the Extrusion of Aluminum), Teil I: Vorgänge in der Umformzone (Part 1: Processes in the Deformation Zone), *Aluminium* Vol 59, 1983, p 665–669, 745–750

[Ake 85]: R. Akeret, Einfluß des Neigungswinkels und der Länge der Laufflache auf die Reibung im Preßkanal (Influence on the Inclination Angle and the Length of the Bearing Surface on the Friction in the Die Aperture), *Aluminium*, Vol 61, 1985, p 169–172

[Ake 86]: R. Akeret and W. Strehmel, "Heat Balance and Exit Temperature Control in the

Extrusion of Aluminium Alloys," Vol IV, Paper 114 presented at Aluminium Technology '86, The Institute of Metals, London, England, 1986

[Ake 88]: R. Akeret, A. Reid, and J.-J. Théler, Qualitätsanforderungen an AlMggSi0,5-Preßbolzen, (Quality Requirements for ALMgSi 0.5 Billets), *Metall.,* Vol 42, 1988, p 760–769

[Ake 88a]: R. Akeret and W. Strehmel, Control of Metal Flow in Extrusion Dies, *ET '88,* Vol II, p 357–367

[Ake 92]: R. Akeret, Strangpreßnähte in Aluminiumprofilen, Teil I: Technologie, Teil II: Mikrostruktur und Qualitätsmerkmale (Extrusion Welds in Aluminum Sections, Part 1: Technology, Part II: Microstructure and Quality Characteristics), *Aluminium,* Vol 68, 1992, p 877–887, 965–974

[Ast 75]: E.I. Astrov, zitiert in [Gil 75]: (mentioned in [Gil 75]), Lit. 55

[Auk 96]: T.u.M. Aukrust, Texture and Surface Grain Structure in Aluminium Sections, *ET '96,* Vol I, p 171

[Bag 81]: J. Baumgarten, Materialfluß beim direkten Strangpressen von Aluminium (Material Flow in Direct Extrusion of Aluminum), *Aluminium,* Vol 57, 1981, p 734–736

[Bat 79]: A.I. Baturin, Heat Generation and Effectiveness of Heat Removal in Extrusion, *Tekhnol. Legk. Splavov* (No. 5), 1979, p 21–25 (in Russian)

[Bau 71]: M. Bauser and G. Fees, Oberflächenfehler bei stranggepreßten Profilen aus AlMgSi-Legierungen (Surface Defects in AlMgSi Alloy Extruded Sections), *Z. Metallkd.,* Vol 62 (No. 10), 1971, p 705–710

[Bau 82]: M. Bauser and E. Tuschy, State of the Art and Future Development of Extrusion, Extrusion, Scientific and Technical Development, *Deutsche Gesellschaft für Metallkunde,* Oberursel, Germany, 1982, p 7–15

[Bec 39]: A. Beck, *Magnesium und Seine Legierungen* (*Magnesium and Its Alloys*), Springer-Verlag, Berlin, 1939

[Bry 71]: H.J. Bryant, Metallurgical Investigation of Defects in Hot Extruded Aluminium Alloys, *Z. Metallkd.,* Vol 62, 1971, p 701–705

[Bry 75]: W.A. Bryant, A Method for Specifying Hot Isostatic Pressure Welding Parameters, *Weld. J.,* Vol 54, 1975, p 733s

[Clo 86]: M.P. Clode and T. Sheppard, "Surface Generation and the Origin of Defects during Extrusion of Aluminium Alloys," Paper 51 presented at Tagungsbericht Aluminium

Technology '86, The Institute of Metals, London, England, 1986

[Clo 90]: M.P. Clode and T. Sheppard, Formation of Die Lines during Extrusion of AA 6063, *Mater. Sci. Technol.,* Vol 6, 1990, p 755–763

[Cre]: R.A. Creuzet, FP 69 42347, USP 3 748 885

[Czi 72]: H. Czichos, The Mechanism of the Metallic Adhesion Bond, *J. Phys. D. Appl. Phys.,* Vol 5, 1972, p 1890–1897

[Dah 93]: Umformtechnik, Plastomechanik und Werkstoffkunde (Deformation Technology, Plastomechanics and Material Science), W. Dahl and R. Kopp, Ed., Springer-Verlag, 1993, p 707–711

[DGM 78]: *Atlas der Warmformgebungseigenschaften, Bd I, Aluminiumwerkstoffe* (*Atlas of Hot-Working Properties,* Vol 1, *Aluminum Alloys*), Deutsche Gesellschaft für Metallkunde, Oberursel, Germany, 1978

[Die 66]: K. Dies and P. Wincierz, *Z. Metallkd.,* Vol 57, 1966, p 141–150, 227–232

[Dor 73]: R.C. Dorward, *Metall. Trans.,* Vol 4, 1973, p 507–512

[Eul 75]: J. Eulitz and G. Scharf, *Aluminium,* Vol 51, 1975, p 214–218

[Fin 92]: W.-D. Finkelnburg and G. Scharf, Some Investigations of the Metal Flow during Extrusion of Al Alloys, *ET '92,* Vol II, p 475–484

[Fin 96]: W.-D. Finkelnburg, G. Scharf, and G. Tempus, *Proceedings 6th Int. Aluminum Extrusion Seminar* (Chicago, IL), 1996

[Fuc 96]: Otto Fuchs Metallwerke, prospekte (brochure)

[Gat 54]: F. Gatto, "Fondamenti della teoria dell'estrusione Alluminio," Vol 23, 1954, p 533–545

[Gil 75]: M.S. Gildenhorn, W.G. Kerov, and G.A. Krivonos, Strangpreßschweißen von Hohlprofilen aus Aluminiumlegierungen (Extrusion Welding of Hollow Sections in Aluminum Alloys), *Metallurgia,* Moskau, 1975 (Russ., Teilübersetzung durch Forschungszentrum Strangpressen, Berlin, 1995)

[Gru 66]: W. Gruhl and G. Scharf, *Z. Metallkd.,* Vol 57, 1966, p 597–602

[Har 47]: C.S. Harris, Extrusion of Magnesium, Wiederdruck aus Machinery, March 1947

[Har 94]: J.-P. Hardouin, Procédé et dispositiv d'extrusion-filage d'un alliage d'aluminium à bas titre, Franz, Patent 94 14143, Nov 25, 1994

[Hir 58]: J. Hirst and D.J. Ursell, Some Limiting

Factors in Extrusion, *Metal Treatment*, Vol 25, 1958, p 409–413, 416

[**Hob 91**]: *Metallkunde: Aufbau und Eigenschaften von Metallen und Legierungen (Metallurgy, Structure and Properties of Metals and Alloys)*, E. Hornbogen and H. Warlimont, Ed., Vol 2, Springer Lehrbuch, 1991 p 202

[**Hon 68**]: *Aluminium*, Vol III, *Fabrication and Finishing*, third printing, Kent R. van Horn, Ed., American Society for Metals, 1968, p 95

[**Jel 79**]: J.L. Jellison, Effect of Surface Contamination on Solid Phase Welding—An Overview, *Proc. Conf. Surface Contamination: Genesis, Detection and Control* (Washington), 1978, Vol II, Plenum Press, New York, 1979, p 899–923

[**Joh 96**]: V.I. Johannes and C.W. Jowett, Temperature Distribution in Aluminium Extrusion Billets, *ET '96,* Vol I, p 235–244

[**Joh 96a**]: V.I. Johannes, C.W. Jowett, and R.F. Dickson, Transverse Weld Defects, *ET '96,* Vol II, p 89–94

[**Kie 65**]: O. Kienzle and K. Mietzner, *Atlas umgeformter Oberflächen (Atlas of Deformed Surfaces)*, Springer-Verlag, 1965

[**Koe 61**]: K. Köstlin and O. Schaaber, *Härterei-Technik und Wärmebehandlung (Hardening Technology and Thermal Treatment)*, Vol 16, 1961, p 150–156

[**Kra 93**]: C. Kramer and D. Menzel, Konvektionskühlsysteme für Leichtmetallhalbzeuge (Convection Cooling Systems for Aluminum Semifinished Products), *Aluminium*, Vol 69, 1993, p 247–253

[**Lag 72**]: G. Lange, Der Wärmehaushalt beim Strangpressen Teil I: Berechnung des isothermen Preßvorganges (Heat Balance in Extrusion, Part 1: Analysis of the Isothermal Extrusion Process), *Z. Metallkd.*, Vol 62, 1972, p 571–577

[**Lan 82**]: J. Langerweger, Metallurgische Einflüsse auf die Produktivität beim Strangpressen von AlMgSi-Werkstoffen (Metallurgical Influences on the Productivity of the Extrusion of AlMgSi Alloys), *Aluminium*, Vol 58, 1982, p 107–109

[**Lan 84**]: J. Langerweger, Correlation between Properties of Extrusion Billets, Extrudability and Extrusion Quality, *ET '84,* Vol I, p 41–45

[**Lau 60**]: K. Laue, Isothermes Strangpressen (Isothermal Extrusion), *Z. Metallkd.*, Vol 51, 1960, p 491–495

[**Lau 76**]: K. Laue and H. Stenger, *Strangpressen: Verfahren, Maschinen, Werkzeuge (Extrusion: Processes, Machining, Tooling)*, Aluminium Verlag GmbH, 1976

[**Lef 92**]: M. Lefstad, O. Reiso, and V. Johnsen, Flow of the Billet Surface in Aluminium Extrusion, *ET '92,* Vol II, p 503–517

[**Lef 96**]: M. Lefstad and O. Reiso, Metallurgical Speed Limitations during the Extrusion of AlMgSi-Alloys, *ET '96,* Vol I, p 11–21

[**Lyn 71**]: C.V. Lynch, Die Auswirkung der Fabrikationsbedungungen auf die Qualität von Preßprofilen aus der Legieung AlMgSi0,5 (The Effect of the Fabrication Conditions on the Quality of Extruded Sections in the Alloy AlMgSi0.5), *Z. Metallkd.*, Vol 62 (No. 10), 1971 p 710–715

[**Mie 62**]: K. Mietzner, Untersuchungen über die Oberflächenbeschaffenheit stranggepreßter Profile aus Al-Legierungen (Investigations into the Surface Condition of Extruded Al Alloy Sections), *Metall.*, Vol 16, 1962, p 837–843

[**Moe 75**]: M. Möller and P. Wincierz, Grobkornbildung bei Preßstangen aus aushärtbaren manganhaltigen Aluminiumwerkstoffen (Coarse Grain Formation in Extruded Bar in Age-Hardening Manganese Containing Aluminum Alloys), 6, *Internationale Leichtmetalltagung* (Leoben-Vienna), 1975, p 139–141

[**Moo 96**]: H.G. Mooi, A.J. den Bakker, K.E. Nilsen, and J. Huétink, Simulation of Aluminium Extrusion Based on a Finite Element Method (FEM), *ET '96,* Vol II, p 67–73

[**Mue 96**]: K.B. Müller and J. Wegener, Direct Extrusion of AA6060 through Dies with Coated Bearing Lengths, *ET '96,* Vol II, p 147–153

[**Oph 88**]: G.A. Oude Ophuis, The Extrumax System: A New Dimension in the Extrusion Process, A New and Optimal Way to Extrude Section, *ET '88,* Vol 1, p 181–187

[**Par 96**]: N.C. Parson, C.W. Jowett, W.C. Fraser, and C.V. Pelow, Surface Defects on 6XXX Extrusions, *ET '96,* Vol I, p 57–67

[**Rei 84**]: O. Reiso, The Effect of Composition and Homogenization Treatment on Extrudability of AlMgSi Alloys, *ET '84,* Vol l, p 31–40

[**Rei 88**]: O. Reiso, *Proc. 4th Int. Aluminium Extrusion Technology Seminar* (Chicago, IL), Aluminium Association, 1988, Vol 2, p 287–295

[**Ros**]: M. Rossmann, Verfahren zum Strangpressen bzw (Processes for Extrusion and Drawing), Strangziehen. Europ. Pat. 0 210 568 B1

[Rup 77]: D. Ruppin and W. Strehmel, Direktes Strangpressen mit konstanter Austrittstemperatur—Einsatz axialer Blocktemperaturprofile (Direct Extrusion with Constant Exit Temperature—Application of Axial Billet Temperature Profile), *Aluminium,* Vol 53, 1977, p 233–239

[Rup 77a]: D. Ruppin and W. Strehmel, Direktes Strangpressen mit konstanter Austrittstemperatur—Einsatz variabler Preßgeschwindigkeit (Direct Extrusion with Constant Exit Temperature—Application of Variable Extrusion Speed), *Aluminium,* Vol 53, 1977, p 543–548

[Rup 82]: D. Ruppin and K. Müller, Pressen über stehenden Dorn verbessert die Rohrinnenfläche (Extrusion over a Fixed Mandrel Improves the Tube Internal Surface), *Maschinenmarkt,* Würzburg, Germany, Vol 88, 1982, p 2089–2091

[Rup 83]: D. Ruppin and W. Strehmel, Automatisierung des Preßprozesses beim direkten Strangpressen von Aluminiumwerkstoffen (Automation of the Extrusion Process in the Direct Extrusion of Aluminum Alloys), *Aluminium,* Vol 59, 1983, p 674–678, 773–776

[Sac 34]: G. Sachs, *Metallkunde—Spanlosetormung (Metallurgy—Chipless Forming),* Springer-Verlag, 1934

[Sah 96]: P.K. Saha, Influence of Plastic Strain and Strain Rate on Temperature Rise in Aluminium Extrusion, *ET '96,* Vol I, p 355–360

[Sca 64]: G. Scharf, *Z. Metallkd.,* Vol 55, 1964, p 740–744

[Sca 65]: G. Scharf, *VDI-Nachrichten,* Vol 19, 1965, p 6–8

[Sca 67]: G. Scharf, D. Achenbach, and W. Gruhl, *Metall.,* Vol 21, 1967, p 183–189

[Sca 69]: G. Scharf and W. Gruhl, Einfluß von Ausscheidungen auf Warmverformung und Rekristallisationsverhalten von Aluminiumlegierungen (Influence of Precipitates on the Hot-Working and Recrystallization Behavior of Aluminum Alloys), *Aluminium,* Vol 45, 1969, p 150–155.

[Sca 69a]: G. Scharf and W. Gruhl, *Z. Metallkd.,* Vol 60, 1969, p 413–421

[Sca 69b]: G. Scharf and D. Achenbach, *Z. Metallkd.,* Vol 60, 1969, p 904–909

[Sca 73]: G. Scharf and J. Eulitz, *Aluminium,* Vol 49, 1973, p 549–552

[Sca 78]: G. Scharf and E. Lossack, *Metall.,* Vol 32, 1978, p 550–560

[Sca 79]: G. Scharf, Ein Beitrag zum Strangpressen mit gekühltem Werkzeug (A Contribution to Extrusion with Cooled Tools), *Aluminium,* Vol 55, 1979, p 197–201

[Sca 82]: G. Scharf and B. Grzemba, *Aluminium,* Vol 58, 1982, p 391–397

[Sch 79]: H.-E. Scholz, "Werkstoffkundliche, experimentelle und theoretische Untersuchungen zur Optimierung des Strangpressens metallischer Werkstoffe (Verfahren, Thermodynamik, Preßrechnung, Simulation, Gestaltung)," ("Metallurgical, Experimental and Theoretical Investigation to Optimize the Extrusion of Metallic Materials [Process, Thermodynamics, Extrusion Calculation, Simulation, Shape]"), dissertation, RWTH-Aachen, 1979

[Scw 84]: P. Schwellinger, H. Zoller, and A. Maitland, Medium Strength AlMgSi Alloys for Structural Applications, *ET '84,* Vol l, p 17–20

[Sel 84]: R.J. Selines, C. Goff, P. Cienciwa, and F. Lauricella, Extrusion Cooling and Inerting Using Liquid Nitrogen, *ET '84,* Vol l, p 222–226

[She 77]: T. Sheppard, The Application of Limit Diagrams to Extrusion Process Control, *ET '77,* Vol I, p 331–337

[She 88]: T. Sheppard and M.P. Clode, The Origin of Surface Defects during Extrusion of AA 6063 Alloy, *ET '88,* Vol II, p 329–341

[Shu 69]: M. Schumann, *Metallographie (Metallography),* Vol 7, VEB Deutscher Verlag für Grundstoffindustrie, Leipzig, Germany, 1969

[Ska 96]: I. Skauvik, K. Karhausen, M. Melander, and S. Tjötta, Numerical Simulation in Extrusion Die Design, *ET '96,* Vol II, p 79–82

[Spe 84]: P.R. Sperry, Correlation of Microstructure in 6XXX Extrusion Alloys with Process Variables and Properties, *ET '84,* Vol I, p 21–29

[Sta 90]: P. Staubwasser, "Der Einfluß des Gefüges auf das dekorative Aussehen anodisierter AlMgSi0,5 Profile" ("The Influence of the Structure on the Decorative Appearance of Anodized AlMgSi0.5 Sections"), dissertation, Aachen, Germany, 1990

[Ste 73]: H. Stenger, Die maximale Preßgeschwindigkeit beim Strangpressen (The Maximum Speed in Extrusion), *Drahtwelt,* Vol 59, 1973, p 235–240

[Str 96]: W. Strehmel, M. Plata, and B. Bourqui, New Technologies for the Cooling and Quenching of Medium-to-Large-Sized Aluminium Extrusions, *ET '96,* Vol I, p 317–325

[Tech Technische Universität Clausthal/Universität Hannover, 96/97/98]: Sonderforschungsbereich 1515 "Magnesiumtechnologie" (Special Research Report 1515 "Magnesium Technology"), Finanzierungsantrag, 1996/97/98

[Tem 91]: G. Tempus, W. Calles, and G. Scharf, *Materials Science and Technology,* Vol 7, 1991, p 937–945

[The 93]: W. Thedja, K. Müller, and D. Ruppin, Die Vorgänge im Preßkanal beim Warmstrangpressen von Aluminium (The Processes in the Die Aperture in the Hot-Extrusion of Aluminum, Part 1: Surface Roughness and Adhesion Layer on the Die Bearing), *Aluminium,* Vol 69, 1993, p 543–547; Teil II Reibung im Preßkanal und Matrizenverschleiß (Part II: Friction in the Die Aperture and Die Wear), p 649–653

[Tok 76]: M. Tokizawa, K. Dohda, and K. Murotani, Mechanism of Friction at the Interface between Tool Surface and Metals in Hot Extrusion of Aluminium Alloys (1st report); Effect of Dies and Extrusion Temperature, *Bull. Jpn. Soc. Precis. Eng.,* Vol 10 (No. 4), 1976, p 145–150

[Tok 88]: M. Tokizawa and N. Takatsuji, Effects of the Die Condition and Billet Composition on the Surface Characteristics of the Extruded 6063 Aluminium Alloy, *Trans. Jpn. Inst. Met.,* Vol 29, 1988, p 69–79

[Val 88]: H. Valberg, Surface Formation in Al-Extrusion (Direct Extrusion), *ET '88,* Vol II, p 309–320

[Val 92]: H. Valberg, Metal Flow in the Direct Axisymmetric Extrusion of Aluminium, *J. Mater. Process. Technol.,* Vol 31, 1992, p 39–55

[Val 92a]: H. Valberg and T. Loeken, Formation of the Outer Surface Layers of the Profile in Direct and Indirect Extrusion, *ET '92,* Vol II, p 529–549

[Val 95]: H. Valberg, T. Loeken, M. Hval, B. Nyhus, and C. Thaulow, The Extrusion of Hollow Profiles with a Gas Pocket behind the Bridge, *Int. J. Mater. Prod. Technol.,* Vol 10, 1995, p 22–267

[Val 96]: H. Valberg, A Modified Classification System for Metal Flow Adapted to Unlubricated Hot Extrusion of Aluminum and Aluminum Alloys, *ET '96,* Vol II, p 95–100

[Val 96a]: H. Valberg, F.P. Coenen, and R. Kopp, Metal Flow in Two-Hole Extrusion, *ET '96,* Vol II, p 113–124

[Wag]: A. Wagner and J. Hesse, "Vorrichtung zum Kühlen der Matrize einer Strangpresse" ("System to Cool the Extrusion Die"), D. Auslegeschr., DT 22 11 645.6.14

[Wan 78]: T. Wanheim and N. Bay, A Model for Friction in Metal Forming Processes, *Ann. CIRP,* Vol 27, 1978, p 189–193

[War 95]: M. Warnecke and K. Lücke, Einfluß der Werkzeugkonstruktion auf das decorative Aussehen anodisierter Strangpreßprofile aus AlMgSi0,5 (Influence of the Tool Design on the Decorative Appearance of Anodized Extruded AlMgSi0.5 Profiles), *Aluminium,* Vol 71, 1995, p 606–613

[Web 89]: A. Weber, Neue Werkstoffe, VDI-Verlag GmbH, Düsseldorf, 1989, Abschnitt 2.3, p 37–56

[Wei 78]: F. Weitzel, *Aluminium,* Vol 54, 1978, p 591–592

[Wei 92]: F. Weitzel, Gestaltung und Konstruktion von Strangpreßwerkzeugen (Design of Extrusion Tools), *Aluminium,* Vol 68, 1992, p 778–779, 867–870, 959–964

[Wel 95]: T. Welo, A. Smaabrekke, and H. Valberg, Two-Dimensional Simulation of Porthole Extrusion, *Aluminium,* Vol 71, 1995, p 90–94

[Wel 96]: T. Welo, S. Abtahi, and I. Skauvik, An Experimental and Numerical Investigation of the Thermo-Mechanical Conditions on the Bearing Surface of Extrusion Dies, *ET '96,* Vol II, p 101–106

[Yam 92]: H. Yamaguchi, Increase in Extrusion Speed and Effects on Hot Cracks and Metallurgical Structure of Hard Aluminium Extrusions, *ET '92,* Vol II, p 447–453

[Zol 67]: V.V. Zolobov and G. Zwerev, Das Strangpressen der Metalle (The Extrusion of Metals), Übersetzung des Buches, *Presovanie Metallov* (Moscow), 1959, DGM e.V., Frankfurt, Germany, 1967

REFERENCES

Extrusion of Semifinished Products in Copper Alloys

[Bar 32]: O. Bauer and M. Hansen, Sondermessinge (Special Brasses), *Z. Metallkd.,* Vol 24, 1932, p 73–78

[Bau 63]: M. Bauser, Verformbarkeit und Bruchverhalten bei der Warmformgebung (Workability and Fracture Properties in Hot-Working), *Metall.,* Vol 17, 1963, p 420–429

[Bau 76]: M. Bauser and E. Tuschy, *Das Strangpressen in Konkurrenz mit anderen Umform-*

verfahren, Strangpressen (*Extrusion in Competition with Other Deformation Processes Symposium, Extrusion 1*), Bad Nauheim, Germany, 1976, p 228–243

[Bau 93]: M. Bauser, Messingstangen/Kupferrohre, in *Umformtechnik, Plastomechanik und Werkstoffkunde* (Brass Bar/Copper Tube, in *Deformation Technology, Plastomechanics and Material Science*), Verlag Stahleisen, 1993

[Bei 76]: P. Beiss and J. Broichhausen, *Einfluß des Zunders auf den Stofffluß beim direkten Strangpressen von Kupfer Strangpressen* (*Influence of the Scale on the Material Flow in the Direct Extrusion of Copper Symposium*), Bad Nauheim, Germany, 1976, p 92–107

[Ben 93]: G. Benkisser and G. Horn-Samodelkin, Vergüten von heterogenen Mehrstoffaluminiumbronzen (Heat-Treatment of Heterogeneous Complex Aluminum Bronze), *Metall.*, Vol 47, 1993, p 1033–1037

[Bla 48]: C. Blazey, L. Broad, W.S. Gummer, and D.P. Thompson, The Flow of Metal in Tube Extrusion, *J. Inst. Met.*, Vol 75, 1948/49, p 163–184

[Bro 73]: J. Broichhausen and H. Feldmann, Wärmebehandlung einiger Kupfer-Zink-Legierungen aus der Umformwärme (Heat Treatment of Some Copper-Zinc Alloys from the Deformation Temperature), *Metall.*, Vol 27, 1973, p 1069–1080

[DGM 78]: Deutsche Gesellschaft für Metallkunde: *Atlas der Warmformgebungseigenschaften von Nichteisenmetallen*, Vol 2, *Kupferwerkstoffe* (*Atlas of Hot-Working Properties of Nonferrous Metals*, Vol 2, *Copper Alloys*), DGM, 1978

[Die 76]: O. Diegritz, Fehlererscheinungen an Preßprodukten—Schwermetall (Defects in Extruded Products—Copper Alloys), symposium, *Strangpressen*, Bad Nauheim, Germany, 1976, p 278–299

[Dis 67]: K. Dies, *Kupfer und Kupferlegierungen in der Technik* (*Copper and Copper Alloys in Engineering*), Springer-Verlag, 1967

[DKIa]: DKI: "Niedriglegierte Kupferlegierungen—Eigenschaften, Verarbeitung, Verwendung," Informationsdruck i.8 ("Low-Alloyed Copper Alloys—Properties, Processing and Application," Information Sheet i.8), des Deutschen Kupferinstituts, Berlin

[DKIb]: DKI: "Kupfer-Zink-Legierungen—Messing und Sondermessing," Informationsdruck i.5 ("Copper-Zinc Alloys—Brass and Special Brasses," Information Sheet i.5), des Deutschen Kupferinstituts, Berlin

[DKIc]: DKI: "Rohre aus Kupfer-Zink-Legierungen," Informationsdruck i.21 ("Copper Zinc Alloy Tubes," Information Sheet i.21), des Deutschen Kupferinstituts, Berlin

[DKId]: DKI: "Kupfer-Zinn-Knetlegierungen (Zinnbronzen)," Informationsdruck i.15 ("Copper Tin Tough Alloys (Tinbronze)," Information Sheet i.15), des Deutschen Kupferinstituts, Berlin

[DKIe]: DKI: "Kupfer-Aluminium-Legierungen—Eigenschaften, Herstellung, Verarbeitung, Verwendung," Informationsdruck i.6 ("Copper Aluminum Alloys—Properties, Production, Processing, Application," Information Sheet i.6), des Deutschen Kupferinstituts, Berlin

[DKIf]: DKI: "Kupfer-Nickel-Legierungen—Eigenschaften, Bearbeitung, Anwendung," Informationsdruck i.14 ("Copper-Nickel Alloys—Properties, Processing, Application," Information Sheet i.14), des Deutschen Kupferinstituts, Berlin

[DKIg]: DKI: "Kupfer-Nickel-Zink-Legierungen (Neusilber)," Informationsdruck i.13 ("Copper Nickel Zinc Alloys [Nickelsilver]," Information Sheet i.13), des Deutschen Kupferinstituts, Berlin

[Don 92]: P. Donner and P. Körbes, Reversibilität und Langzeitstabilität in Cu-Al-Ni-Formgedächtnis-Halbzeugen (Reversibility and Long-Term Stabilizing in Cu-Al-Ni Shape-Memory Semi-Finished Products), *Metall.*, Vol 46, 1992, p 679–685

[Gra 89]: H. Gravemann, Verhalten elektronenstrahlgeschweißter Kupferwerkstoffe bei erhöhten Temperaturen (Behavior of Electron Beam Welded Copper Alloys at Elevated Temperatures), *Metall.*, Vol 43, 1989, p 1073–1080

[Gre 71]: J. Grewen, J. Huber, and W. Noll, Rekristallisation von E-Kupfer wahrend des Strangpressens und nach Kaitverformung durch Ziehen (Recrystallization of E-Copper during Extrusion and after Cold-Working by Drawing), *Z. Metallkd.*, Vol 62, 1971, p 771–779

[Han 58]: M. Hansen and K. Anderko, *Constitution of Binary Alloys*, New York, 1958

[Hes 82]: H. Hesse and J. Broichhausen, Stoffluß und Fehler beim direkten Strangpressen von CuCr (Material Flow and Defects in Direct Extrusion of CuCr), *Metall.*, Vol 36, 1982, p 363–368

[KM 77]: Kabelmetal Messingwerke GmbH, Nürnberg: Verbesserung von Produktqualität und Wirtschaftlichkeit beim Strangpressen von Messing (Improvement of Product Quality and Economy in the Extrusion of Brasses), *Metall.,* Vol 31, 1977, p 414–417

[Lau 76]: K. Laue and H. Stenger, *Strangpressen—Verfahren, Maschinen, Werkzeuge (Extrusions—Process, Machinery, Tooling),* Aluminium Verlag GmbH, 1976

[Lot 71]: W. Lotz, U. Steiner, H. Stiehler, and E. Schelzke, Preßfehler beim Strangpressen von Kupfer-Zink-Legierungen (Extrusion Defects in the Extrusion of Copper Zinc Alloys), *Z. Metallkd.,* Vol 62, 1971, p 186–191

[Moe 80]: E. Möck, *Preßvorschriften SM,* Taschenbuch Manuskript *(Extrusion Specifications Copper Alloys,* pocketbook manuscript), Wieland-Werke, 1980

[Moi 89]: M. Moik and W. Rethmann, Einfluß der Preßparameter auf die Eigenschaften von Produkten aus Kupfer und Kupferlegierungen (Influence of the Extrusion Parameter on the Properties of Copper and Copper Alloy Products), *Strangpressen,* symposium, DGM 1989, p 197–208

[Ray 49]: G.V. Raynor, *Ann. Equilibr. Diagrams,* No. 2 (1949, CuSn); No.3 (1949, CuZn); No.4 (1944, CuAl)

[Sch 35]: J. Schramm, *Kupfer-Nickel-Zink-Legierungen (Copper Nickel Zinc Alloys),* Würzburg, 1935

[Sie 78]: K. Siegert, Indirektes Strangpressen von Messing (Indirect Extrusion of Brass), *Metall.,* Vol 32, 1978, p 1243–1248

[SMS]: SMS Hasenclever: *Literaturmappe und Referenzliste Strangpressen (Literature Catalogue and Extrusion Reference List),* prospektmappe (prospectus)

[Ste 91]: A. Steinmetz and W. Staschull, Strang- und Rohrpressen von Kupfer und Messing—Gute Chancen mit optimierten Anlagen (Rod and Tube Extrusion of Copper and Brass—Good Opportunities with Optimized Plants), *Metall.,* Vol 45, 1991, p 1104–1107

[Tus 70]: E. Tuschy, Fertigungsverfahren für nahtlose Kupferrohre (Production Processes for Seamless Copper Tubes), *Z. Metallkd.,* Vol 61, 1970, p 488–492

[Tus 80]: E. Tuschy, Literaturübersicht: Strangpressen von Kupfer und Kupferlegierungen (Literature Overview: Extrusion of Copper and Copper Alloys), *Metall.,* Vol 34, 1980, p 1002–1006

[Vat 70]: M. Vater and K. Koltzenburg, Stoffflußuntersuchung beim Strangpressen von Rohren aus Kupfer und Kupferlegierungen (Material Flow Investigation in the Extrusion of Copper and Copper Alloy Tubes), *Bänder Bleche Rohre,* Vol 11, 1970, p 587–595

[Wie 86]: Wieland-Werke AG: *Wieland-Buch Kupferwerkstoffe* (Wieland-Book: *Copper Alloys*), 5, Wielandwerke AG, 1986

[Zei 93]: H. Zeiger, "Marktuntersuchung über Innenbüchsen für Strangpressen für Strangpressen für Kupfer, Stahl und andere schwer preßbare Metalle" ("Market Analysis of Linens for the Extrusion of Copper, Steel and Other Difficult to Extrude Metals"), manuscript, 1993

[Zil 82]: F.J. Zilges, Hauptkriterien bei der Auslegung einer Strangpreßanlage für Schwermetall (Main Criteria for the Layout of a Copper Alloy Extrusion Plant), *Metall.,* Vol 36, 1982, p 439–443

REFERENCES

Extrusion of Semifinished Products in Titanium Alloys

[Boy 89]: R.R. Boyer, E.R. Barta, and J.W. Henderson, Near-Net-Shape Titanium Alloy Extrusion, *JOM,* Vol 41, 1989, p 36–39

[IMIa 88]: "Medium Temperature Alloys," IMI Titanium, England, prospectus, 1988

[IMIb 88]: "High Temperature Alloys," IMI Titanium, England, prospectus, 1988

[Kra 82]: K.-H. Kramer and A.G. Krupp Stahl, Herstellungstechnologien von Titan und Titanlegierungen, Teil I und II (Production Technologies for Titanium and Titanium Alloys, Parts I and II), *Metall.,* Vol 36, 1982, p 659–668, 862–873

[Kum 92]: J. Kumpfert and C.H. Ward, *Titanium Aluminides, Advanced Aerospace Materials,* Springer-Verlag, 1992, p 73–83

[Lam 90]: S. Lampman, Wrought Titanium and Titanium Alloys, *Properties and Selection: Nonferrous Alloys and Special-Purpose Materials,* Vol 2, *Metals Handbook,* Vol 10, American Society for Metals, 1990, p 592–633

[Lau 76]: K. Laue and H. Stenger, *Strangpressen: Verfahren, Maschinen, Werkzeuge (Extrusion: Processes, Machines, Tools),* Aluminium Verlag GmbH, Düsseldorf, 1976

[Mar 74]: M. Markworth and G. Ribbecke, Versuche zur Herstellung von stranggepreßten Profilen aus Titanlegierungen auf Leicht-und Schwermetallstrangpressen (Trials for the

Production of Extruded Sections in Titanium Alloys on Aluminum and Copper Extrusion Presses), *Metall.,* Vol 28, 1974, p 7

[Mec 80]: E. Meckelburg, Eigenschaften und Anwendung von Titan als Konstruktionswerkstoff (Properties and Application of Titanium as a Structural Material), *Maschinenmarkt,* Vol 86, 1980, p 154–158

[Pet 92]: M. Peters, Titanlegierungen in Luft- und Raumfahrt (Titanium Alloys in Aerospace), DGM, Friedrichshafen, Germany, 1992

[Sib 92]: H. Sibum and G. Stein, Titan, Werkstoff für umweltschonende Technik der Zukunft (Titanium, Material for Environmental Beneficial Technology of the Future), *Metall.,* Vol 46, 1992, p 548–553

[Zwi 74]: U. Zwicker, *Titan und Titanlegierungen* (*Titanium and Titanium Alloys*), Springer-Verlag, Berlin, 1974

REFERENCES

Extrusion of Semifinished Products in Zirconium Alloys

[Jun 93]: H. Jung and K.H. Matucha, Kaltgepilgerte Brennstabhüllrohre aus Zirkoniumwerkstoffen in *Umformtechnik* (Cold Pilgered Fuel Rod Cladding Types in Zirconium Alloys in *Deformation Technology*), Verlag Stahleisen, Düsseldorf, 1993

[Lus 55]: B. Lustman and F. Kerze, *The Metallurgy of Zirconium,* McGraw-Hill Book Co., New York, 1955

[Sch 93]: G. Schreiter, "Über das Strangpressen von Sonderwerkstoffen" ("On the Extrusion of Special Materials"), private Mitteilung (private communication), 1993

[Web 90]: R.T. Webster, Zirconium and Hafnium, *Properties and Selection: Nonferrous Alloys and Special-Purpose Materials,* Vol 2, *Metals Handbook,* 10th ed., American Society for Metals, 1990, p 661–669

REFERENCES

Extrusion of Iron-Alloy Semifinished Products

[Ben 73]: G. Bensmann, "Problems beim Strangpressen schwer umformbarer Werkstoffe bei hohen Temperaturen" ("Problems in the Extrusion of Difficult Work Materials at High Temperatures"), manuscript, Krupp Forschungsinstitut (Krupp Research Institute), 1973

[Bil 79]: H. Biller, *Verfahren zur Herstellung nahtloser Stahlrohre* (*Processes for the Production of Seamless Tubes*), Metec, 1979

[Bur 70]: J. Burggraf, Qualitative Einflußmöglichkeiten beim Strangpressen von austenitischen CrNi-Stählen (Qualitative Processes for Influencing the Extrusion of Austenitic CrNi Steels), *Bänder Bleche Rohre,* Vol 11, 1970, p 559–564

[Deg 74]: *Fritten (Gläser) als Schmiermittel zum Heißpressen von Metallen* (*Glasses as Lubricants for the Hot-Extrusion of Metals*), Degussa-Information, Geschäftsbereich Keramische Farben (Ceramic Colors Division), 1974

[Hoe 90]: *Spezialprofile rostfrei* (*Special Profile Stainless*) (brochure), Hoesch-Hohenlimburg AG, 1990

[Kur 62]: E. Kursetz, Die Entwicklung der Strangpresstechnik von Stahl und Sondermetallen in der amerikanischen Industrie (The Development of Extrusion Technology of Steel and Special Metal in the American Industry), *Werkstatt Betr.,* Vol 95, 1962, p 673–677

[Lau 76]: K. Laue and H. Stenger, *Strangpressen: Verfahren, Maschinen, Werkzeuge* (*Extrusion: Processes, Machines, Tools*), Aluminium Verlag GmbH, Düsseldorf, 1976

[Lin 82]: W. Lindhorst, Werkstoff und Bearbeitungskosten sparen durch den Einsatz von Spezialprofilen (Material and Processing Cost Savings by the Application of Special Sections), *Konstruktion und Design,* Vol 9, 1982

[Man 86]: *Verfahren zur Herstellung und Prüfung von Stahlrohren* (*Processes for the Production and Testing of Steel Tubes*), Mannesmann-Röhrenwerke AG, Düsseldorf, 1986

[Man 91]: Mannesmann Remscheid, private mitteilung (private communication), 1991

[Ric 93]: H. Richter, Rohre aus Edelstählen und Nickellegierungen in *Umformtechnik, Plastomechanik und Werkstoffkunde* (Alloy Steel and Nickel Alloy Tubes in *Deformation Technique, Plastomechanics and Materials Technology*), Verlag Stahleisen, 1993

[Sar 75]: G. Sauer, *Strangpressen: Produkte, Verfahren, Werkzeuge, Maschinen* (*Extrusion: Products, Process, Tools, Machines*), Vorlesungsmanuskript (lecture manuscript), TH Darmstadt, 1975

[Séj 56]: J. Séjournet, Glasschmierung (Glass Lubrication), *Rev. Metall.,* 1956, p 897–914

REFERENCES

Extrusion of Semifinished Products in Nickel Alloys (Including Superalloys)

[Eng 74]: J.C. England, Extruding Nickel Alloy Tubing, *Metals Eng. Quart.*, Vol 14, 1974, p 41–43

[Fri 92]: K. Fritscher, M. Peters, H.-J. Rätzer-Scheibe, and U. Schulz, *Superalloys and Coatings, Advanced Aerospace Materials*, Springer-Verlag, 1992, p 84–107

[Inc 86]: Inco Alloys International: Plant Investments for Superalloy Production, *Metallurgia*, Redhill, Vol 53, 1986, p 509–512

[Inc 88]: Inco Alloys International: *Product Handbook*, Inco Alloys International Ltd., Wiggin Works, Hereford, England, 1988

[Lau 76]: K. Laue and H. Stenger, *Strangpressen: Verfahren, Maschinen, Werkzeuge (Extrusion: Processes, Machinery, Tooling)*, Aluminium Verlag GmbH, Düsseldorf, 1976

[Pol 75]: J. Pollock, The Feedstock: Nickel and Nickel Alloy, *Met. Technol.*, Vol 2, 1975, p 133–134

[Ric 93]: H. Richter, Rohre aus Edelstählen und Nickellegierungen in *Umformtechnik, Plastomechanik, Werkstoffkunde* (Tubes in Alloy Steels and Nickel Alloys in *Deformation Technique, Plastomechanics and Materials Technology*), Verlag Stahleisen, 1993

[Vol 70]: K.E. Volk, *Nickel und Nickellegierungen (Nickel and Nickel Alloys)*, Springer-Verlag, Berlin, 1970

REFERENCES

Extrusion of Semifinished Products in Exotic Alloys

[Eck 90]: K.H. Eckelmeyer, Uranium and Uranium Alloys, *Properties and Selection: Nonferrous Alloys and Special-Purpose Materials*, Vol 2, *Metals Handbook*, 10th ed., American Society for Metals, 1990, p 670–682

[Ger 90]: S. Gerardi, Niobium, *Properties and Selection: Nonferrous Alloys and Special-Purpose Metals*, Vol 2, *Metals Handbook*, 10th ed., American Society for Metals, 1990, p 565–571

[Joh 90]: W.A. Johnson, Molybdenum, *Properties and Selection: Nonferrous Alloys and Special-Purpose Metals*, Vol 2, *Metals Handbook*, 10th ed., 1990, p 574–577

[Joh 90a]: W.A. Johnson, Tungsten, *Properties and Selection: Nonferrous Alloys and Special-Purpose Metals*, Vol 2, *Metals Handbook*, 10th ed., American Society for Metals, 1990, p 577–581

[Kau 56]: A.K. Kaufmann and B.R.F. Kjellgreen, Status of Beryllium Technology in the USA., 1. *Intern. Conf. Peaceful Uses of Atomic Energy*, Genf 1955.9, 1956, p 159–168

[Kie 71]: R. Kieffer, G. Jangg, and P. Ettmayer, *Sondermetalle (Special Metals)*, Springer-Verlag, 1971

[Kre 90]: T.S. Kreilick, Niobium-Titanium Superconductors, *Properties and Selection: Nonferrous Alloys and Special-Purpose Metals*, Vol 2, *Metals Handbook*, 10th ed., American Society for Metals, 1990, p 1043–1059

[Kur 70]: E. Kursetz, Das Warmstrangpressen von Beryllium in amerikanischen Halbzeugwerken (The Hot-Extrusion of Beryllium in American Semifinished Product Plants), *Bänder Bleche Rohre*, Vol 11, 1970, p 228–233

[Lau 76]: K. Laue and H. Stenger, *Strangpressen: Verfahren, Maschinen, Werkzeuge (Extrusion: Processes, Machinery, Tooling)*, Aluminium Verlag GmbH, Düsseldorf, 1976

[Par 91]: Y.J. Park and J.K. Anderson, Development of Fabrication Processes for W-Re-Hf-C Wire, *Tungsten and Tungsten Alloys*, Symp. of Refractory Metals Committee of TMS, 1991

[Pok 90]: Ch. Pokross, Tantalum, *Properties and Selection: Nonferrous Alloys and Special-Purpose Metals*, Vol 2, *Metals Handbook*, 10th ed., American Society for Metals, 1990, p 571–574

[Sto 90]: A.J. Stonehouse and J.M. Marder, Beryllium, *Properties and Selection: Nonferrous Alloys and Special-Purpose Metals*, Vol 2, *Metals Handbook*, 10th ed., American Society for Metals, 1990, p 683–687

REFERENCES

Extrusion of Powder Metals

[Arn 85]: V. Arnhold and J. Baumgarten, Dispersion Strengthened Aluminium Extrusions, *Powder Metall. Int.*, Vol 17, 1985, p 168–172

[Arn 92]: V. Arnhold and K. Hummert, Herstellung von Aluminium-Basis-Werkstoffen durch Sprühkompaktieren (Production of Aluminum Based Materials by Spray Compaction), *Pulvermetallurgie (Powder Metallurgy),* DGM-Fortbildungsseminar, Dresden, 1982

[Arn 92a]: V. Arnhold, K. Hummert, and R. Schattevoy, PM-Hochleistungsaluminium für motorische Anwendungen—maßgeschneidete Legierungen und entsprechende Verfahren (High-Strength Aluminum for Motor Applications—Custom Made Alloys and Corresponding Processes), *VDI-Berichte (VDI-Reports),* No. 917, 1992

[Asl 81]: C. Aslund, G. Gemmel, and T. Andersson, Stranggepreßte Rohre auf pulvermetallurgischer Basis (Extruded Powder Metallurgy Tubes), *Bänder Bleche Rohre,* Vol 9, 1981, p 223–226

[Boe 89]: W. Boeker and H.J. Bunge, Verformungsverhalten zweiphasiger metallischer Werkstoffe (Deformation Behavior of Binary Phase Metallic Materials), Verbundwerkstoffe und Stoffverbunde in *Technik und Medizin,* 1989, p 183–188

[Cra 88]: A.W. Cramb, New Steel Casting Processes for Thin Slabs and Strip—A Historical Perspective, *Iron Steelmaker,* Vol 7, 1988, p 45–60

[Gro 73]: J. Grosch, "Kaltpreßschweißen von Aluminiumpulver durch Strangpressen" ("Cold Pressure Welding of Aluminum Powders by Extrusion"), Diskussionstag Strangpressen, 1973

[Hum 97]: K. Hummert, *PM-Aluminium als Hochleistungswerkstoff-Entwicklung, Herstellung und Anwendung. Neuere Entwicklungen in der Massivum-formung (PM Aluminum as High Strength Material—Development Production and Application. New Developments in Massive Deformation),* Verlag DGM Informationsgesellschaft, 1997

[Inc 86]: Inco Alloys International: Plant Investments for Superalloy Production, *Metallurgia,* Redhill, Vol 53, 1986, p 509–512

[Irm 52]: R. Irmann, Sintered Aluminium with High Strength at Elevated Temperatures, *Metallurgia,* 1952, p 125–133

[Jan 75]: G. Jangg, F. Kutner, and G. Korb, Herstellung und Eigenschaften von dispersionsgehärtetem Aluminium (Production and Properties of Dispersion Hardened Aluminum), *Aluminium,* Vol 51, 1975, p 6

[Man 88]: "Mannesmann-Demag: Sprühkompaktieren—Das Osprey-Verfahren" ("Spray Compaction—The Osprey Processes Brochure"), Prospekt Mannesmann Demag Hüttentechnik, Duisburg, Germany, 1988

[Mue 87]: K. Müller, and D. Ruppin, Anwendungsmöglichkeiten des indirekten Strangpressens zur Herstellung metallischer Verbundwerkstoffe (Possible Applications of Indirect Extrusion to the Production of Metallic Composite Materials), *Metall.,* Vol 41, 1987, p 8

[Mue 93]: K. Müller and A. Grigoriev, Direct and indirect Extrusion of Al-18SiCu-Mg-Ni, *Proc. Int. Conf. Aluminum Alloys* (Atlanta, GA), Sept 1993

[Mur 96]: H.R. Müller, Eigenschaften und Einsatzpotential sprühkompaktierter Kupferlegierungen (Properties and Potential Applications of Spray-Compacted Copper Alloys), Universität Bremen, Sonderforschungsbereich 372, "Sprühkompaktieren," Kolliquium, Vol 1, 1996

[Nae 69]: G. Naeser and O. Wessel, Herstellung von Stäben und Rohren aus Metallpulvern durch Strangpressen (Production of Bars and Tubes from Metal Powders by Extrusion), *Arch. Eisenhüttenwes.,* Vol 40, 1969, p 257–262

[Rob 91]: P.R. Roberts and B.L. Ferguson, Extrusion of Metal Powders, *Int. Mater. Rev.,* Vol 36, 1991, p 62–79

[Rue 92]: M. Rühle and Th. Steffens, Legierungsbildung und Amorphisation beim mechanischen Legieren (Alloy Formulation and Amorphization with Mechanical Alloying), *Metall.,* Vol 46, 1992, p 1238–1242

[Sch 86]: W. Schatt, *Pulvermetallurgie—Sinter und Verbundwerkstoffe (Powder Metallurgy—Sintered and Composite Materials),* Vol 2, Dr. Alfred Hüthig,Verlag, 1986

[Sha 87]: G. Scharf and I. Mathy, Entwicklung von Aluminium-Knetwerkstoffen aus schnell erstarrten Legierungspulvern (Development of Aluminum Wrought Materials from Rapidly Solidified Alloy Powders), *Metall.,* Vol 41, 1987, p 608–616

[Sha 87a]: G. Scharf and G. Winkhaus, Technische Perspektiven der Aluminiumwerkstoffe (Technical Perspectives of the Aluminum Alloys), *Aluminium,* Vol 63, 1987, p 788–808

[Sut 90]: Sutec: "New Dispersion-Strengthened Electrodes," prospekt (brochure), 1990

[Tus 82]: E. Tuschy, Literaturübersicht: Strangpressen—Neue Verfahren (Literature Review: Extrusion—New Process), *Metall.,* Vol 36, 1982, p 269–279

[Wei 86]: W.G. Weiglin, *Pulvermetallurgie—eine Zukunftstechnologie im Krupp Konzern Sie und wir—Information der Krupp Stahl AG*

(*Powder Metallurgy—A Technology for the Future in Krupp. You and Us International on Krupp Steel AG*), Jan 1986, p 34–37

[Zwi 57]: K.M. Zwilsky and N.J. Grant, *J. Met.,* Vol 9, 1957, p 1197–1201

REFERENCES

Extrusion of Semifinished Products from Metallic Composite Materials

[Ahm 78]: N. Ahmed, *J. Mech. Work. Technol.,* Vol 2, 1978, p 19–32

[Bei 90]: R. Beier, *Technica, Zürich,* Vol 39, 1990, p 76–80

[Boe 88]: W. Böcker and H.J. Bunge, *Z. Metallkd.,* Vol 42, 1988, p 466–471

[Bre 79]: I. Breme and H. Massat, *Z. Metallkd.,* Vol 33, 1979, p 597–601

[Deg 89]: H.P. Degischer and K. Spiradek, *Verbundwerkstoffe und Stoffverbunde in Technik und Medizin* (*Composite Materials in Engineering and Medicine*), 1989, p 31–39

[Fri 67]: G.H. Frieling, *Wire W. Prod.,* Vol 42, 1967, p 72–76

[Gut 91]: I. Gutierrez, J.J. Urcola, J.M. Bilbao, and L.M. Vilar, *Mater. Sci. Technol.,* Vol 7, 1991, p 761–769

[Hil 84]: H. Hillmann, *Z. Metallkd.,* Vol 38, 1984, p 1066–1071

[Hir 84]: M. Hirato, M. Onuki, and K. Kimura, *Wire J. Int.,* Vol 17, 1984, p 74–81

[Hol 78]: C. Holloway and M.B. Bassett, *J. Mech. Work. Technol.,* Vol 2, 1978, p 343–359

[Hor 70]: N. Hornmark and D. Ermel, *Drahtwelt,* Vol 56, 1970, p 424–426

[Hug 82]: K.E. Hughes and C.M. Sellars, *Met. Technol.,* Vol 9, 1982, p 446–452

[Lan 93]: K. Lange, *Umformtechnik* (*Deformation Technology*), Vol 4, Springer-Verlag, 1993

[Lat 89]: E.P. Latham, D.B. Meadowkroft, and L. Pinder, *Mater. Sci. Technol.,* Vol 5, 1989, p 813–815

[Mie 87]: G. Mier, *Schweizerische Aluminium Rundschau* (*Swiss Aluminum Observer*), 1987, p 12–17

[Moo 85]: T. Mooroka, Ch. Kawamura, et al., *Aluminium,* Vol 61, 1985, p 666–669

[Mue 80]: K. Müller et al., *Z. Maschinenmarkt,* Vol 86, 1980, p 34, 37, 38; K. Osakada et al., *Int. J. Mech. Sci.,* Vol 15, 1973, p 291–307

[Mue 81]: K. Müller and D. Ruppin, *Z. Werkstofftech.,* Vol 12, 1981, p 263–271

[Mue 82]: K. Müller and Ruppin, Extrusion, Scientific and Technical Developments DGM-Tagungsband, *Symposium Strangpressen,* 1982, p 233–245

[Mue 85]: K. Müller, D. Ruppin, and D. Stöckel, *Z. Metallkd.,* Vol 39, 1985, p 26–30

[Mue 86]: K. Müller, D. Stöckel, and H. Claus, *Z. Metallkd.,* Vol 40, 1986, p 33–37

[Mue 90]: K. Müller, *Proc. Third JCTP Kyoto, Advanced Technology of Plasticity,* Vol 1, 1990, p 329–334

[Mue 91]: K. Müller, *Neuere Entwicklungen in der Massivumformung* (*New Developments in the Large Scale Working*), K. Siegert, DGM Informationsgesellschaft, Verlag, 1991, p 369–387

[Mue 93]: K. Müller, X. Neubert, et al., *Proc.Third Japan International Sampe Symposium,* 1993, Vol 2, p 1564–1569

[Nyl 78]: C.G. Nylunal, *ASEA* zeitschrift (periodical), 1978, p 3–10

[Osa 73]: K. Osakada et al., *Int. J. Mech. Sci.,* Vol 15, 1973, p 291–307

[Rau 78]: G. Rau, *Metallische Verbundwerkstoffe* (*Metallic Composite Materials*), Werkstofftechnische Verlagsgesellschaft, Karlsruhe (Material technical publishing house company, Karlsruhe), 1978

[Ric 69]: H. Richter, *Z. Metallkd.,* Vol 60, 1969, p 619–322

[Ros 92]: D. Roß, "VDI Fortschrittsberichte Reihe 5" ("VDI Progress Report Series 5"), No. 282, 1992

[Rup 80]: D. Ruppin and K. Müller, *Aluminium,* Vol 56, 1980, p 523–529

[Sch 87]: G. Scharf and G. Winkhaus, *Aluminium,* Vol 63, 1987, p 788–808

[Sta 88]: M.H. Stacey, *Mater. Sci. Technol.,* Vol 4, 1988, p 227–230

[Sto 86]: D. Stöckel, *Metall.,* Vol 40, 1986, p 456–462

[Sto 87]: D. Stöckel, K. Müller, and H. Claus, *Z. Metallkd.,* Vol 41, 1987, p 702–706

[The 90]: W.W. Thedja and D. Ruppin, *Z. Metallkd.,* Vol 44, 1990, p 1054–1061

[Vil 92]: L. Villar, *Stainl. Steel Eur.,* Vol 4, 1992, p 38–39

[Wan 92]: G.X. Wang and M. Dahms, *PMI,* Vol 24, 1992, p 219–225

[Web 82]: H.R. Weber, Extrusion, Scientific and Technical Developments DGM-Tagungsband, *Symposium Strangpressen,* 1982, p 277–296

CHAPTER 6

Machinery and Equipment for Direct and Indirect Hot Extrusion

Horst Groos*

6.1 Machinery and Equipment for Direct and Indirect Hot Extrusion

THE MACHINERY AND EQUIPMENT required for rod and tube extrusion is determined by the specific extrusion process, as previously discussed in Chapter 3, "Rod and Tube Extrusion Processes."

Ideally, the machinery and equipment should have flexibility but, also, provide specific extrusion process with the optimum quality and economic efficiency. As discussed in Chapter 3, direct hot extrusion is the most widely used process, and the term *extrusion* usually refers to this process. The machinery used is usually based on so-called standard designs.

The other extrusion processes usually require specially developed machines. They are designed accordingly and built to meet the needs of the operator.

6.1.1 Machinery for Direct Extrusion

The design of a direct-extrusion press is determined by the following factors:

- Product
  a. Aluminum and aluminum alloys (light metal) easy to extrude and/or difficult to extrude. Wire, bar, section, hollow section, and wide flat sections
  b. Copper and copper alloys including brass (heavy metal) easy to extrude and/or difficult to extrude. Wire, bar, and section
  c. Steel and high-strength steel alloys easy to extrude and/or difficult to extrude. Section
- Process technology
  a. Extrusion without lubrication and without a shell
  b. Extrusion without lubrication and with a shell
  c. Extrusion with lubrication without a shell
- Tooling
  a. Container, stem, dummy block, and die

The wide range of different designs for extrusion presses has recently been reduced in most extrusion plants to a few high-output types. Therefore, only extrusion press designs that dominate today's market are discussed in this chapter. These are referred to as standard extrusion presses in Table 6.1.

Direct-extrusion presses account for more than 95% of the total volume of all presses. The direct-extrusion press is used for all current extrusion processes.

*Billet Heating Systems, Josef Putz
Handling system, Horst H. Groos
Age-Hardening Ovens for Aluminum Alloys, Willie Johnen
Systems for the Production of Extrusion Billets, Wolfgang Schneider
Systems for the Production of Copper Billets, Adolf Frei
Process Control in Direct and Indirect Hot Extrusion of Aluminum Alloys without Lubrication, Klaus Siegert
Process Control Concepts for Extrusion Plants, Armit Biswas

Machines for the direct hot extrusion of light-metal alloys are mainly used for the extrusion of section (80%), tube (10%), and rod (<10%) in aluminum and aluminum alloys.

The machines for direct hot extrusion of heavy metals, mainly copper and copper alloys, are used for the extrusion of rod, wire, and section (60%) (mainly in brass) and tube (40%) (mainly in copper).

Steel and steel alloys are only produced by extrusion to a limited extent, and then only when rolling is not possible or the volumes are too small.

The following major points must be considered in the construction of extrusion presses:

- *Technology requirements:* This covers the metallurgical aspects of the deformation technology of extrusion. The process technology for the material being extruded has been discussed in detail in Chapter 3, "Rod and Tube Extrusion Processes."
- *Economic factors:* The economic need for rationalization in the construction of extrusion presses is most clearly seen in aluminum extrusion. New extrusion plants are built as integrated production lines. They include billet stores, billet heating, extrusion press, handling equipment with longitudinal and transverse conveyors, section cooling systems, stretcher, cut-to-length saws and stackers, as well as heat treatment equipment and packing lines. Similar developments can be found in heavy-metal extrusion plants. Sophisticated systems for electronic data collection and data analysis

for the economic optimal production are already considered to be standard.

6.1.1.1 Extrusion Press Design Principles

Initial discussions, over 50 years ago, to rationalize the construction of extrusion presses, resulted in the standardization of extrusion tooling in (DIN 24540). Within the last 30 years, the press manufacturing companies have introduced standardized designs onto the market.

Table 6.1 shows the features of extrusion presses for light metals, heavy metals, and steel.

The main feature of the direct-extrusion press is the stationary container during extrusion. The die, which is also stationary, and the support tooling are located at one of the end faces of the container, in front of the container bore. Opposite the die, the dummy block located in front of the extrusion stem pushes the billet through the container bore, and the section emerges through the die (Fig. 6.1).

The geometric proportions for different designs for direct extrusion are shown in Fig. 6.2.

The most common design of extrusion press today is the prestressed four-column press. It is usually built with a standard stroke, which provides good access and easy maintenance.

In a standard-stroke press, the billet is loaded between the container and the stem. The press stroke is determined by the loading stroke and the extrusion stroke. There are no

Table 6.1 Presses for the direct extrusion of aluminum alloys (light metal), copper alloys (heavy metal), and steel

	Direct-extrusion presses(a)				
	Light metal		Heavy metal		Steel
Equipment	Standard press	Special press	Standard press	Special press	Rare
Press					
Discard shear	I, II, III	I, II, III, IV	. . .	. . .	. . .
Discard saw	. . .	. . .	I, II	I, II	I, II
Press drive					
Oil hydraulic drive up to 25 mm/s	I, II, III	I, II, III, IV	. . .	. . .	. . .
Oil hydraulic drive up to 60 mm/s	. . .	. . .	I, II	I, II	. . .
Water hydraulic drive up to 300 mm/s	. . .	. . .	. . .	. . .	I, II
Manipulation systems					
For fixed dummy blocks	I, II, III	I, II, III, IV	. . .	I, II	I, II
For loose dummy blocks without cleaning block	. . .	I, II, III, IV	. . .	. . .	. . .
For loose dummy block and cleaning block	. . .	. . .	I, II	. . .	. . .
For loose combination dummy and cleaning blocks	. . .	. . .	. . .	I, II	. . .

(a) Product: wire, bar = I, section = II, hollow section = III, wide solid section = IV (rectangular container)

specific requirements placed on the quality of the billet geometry; it is not important for the billet loading. Over 95% of extrusion presses in extrusion plants are standard-stroke presses.

Figure 6.3 shows a 75 MN aluminum extrusion press with extrusion tooling for the extrusion of round and flat billets. The moving cross head has X-guiding similar to the container holder. The control and information systems to monitor and optimize the extrusion process can be seen in the foreground.

The short-stroke press is compact and requires less space. The short stroke (approximately 60% of the standard stroke) includes the extrusion stroke and a free stroke for manipulation. There are three different designs. The billet-loading requirements are either:

- Billet loading with a billet loader in the free space between the die and the container, with the billet clamped on the press centerline (the most common design)
- Free space by extrusion stem transverse movement on the moving cross head (billet loading with a billet loader between the moving cross head and the container) [Bri 96]
- Three containers that can be rotated around a column of the press frame (billet loading without a billet loader in one of the three containers outside the press)

Figure 6.4 shows the control desk, movable auxiliary control desk (swinging), hot log shear with the billet loader, and the short-stroke press for aluminum alloys. The container is in the extrusion position. The billet is loaded between the die and the stem when the container has moved back over the stem. The billet must

be held exactly between the die and the stem on the press centerline. This ensures that the clearance between the billet and the container is as uniform as possible, guaranteeing perfect upsetting of the billet in the container.

The tolerance-related diameter variations must be compensated by the billet loader to ensure that the billet can be clamped on the press centerline (Fig. 6.5). This ensures that the upsetting of the billet takes place under optimal conditions because of the equal clearance on all sides to the container bore. Air inclusions are less critical, and transverse forces, even if acceptable to a small degree, are avoided during upsetting.

Short-stroke extrusion presses have been the state of the art for some time. There are various reasons for this. Schloemann built two 125 MN rod-and-tube extrusion presses for aluminum around approximately 1950. These were manufactured as short-stroke presses for production reasons, with billet loading between the die and the container. The stem transverse movement was used before the end of the last century. The length of expensive press components, including columns and the main cylinder, can be kept to a minimum.

The company Loewy built a steel tube extrusion press in 1960, with three containers that could be rotated around a column. The aim was high-throughput extrusion with fast press cycles. In practice, this was unsuccessful. The manipulation of the heavy heated containers was only possible with expensive technology. Temperature variations within the container holder as well as in adjacent press components could not be avoided during production. Accurate location of the rotating con-

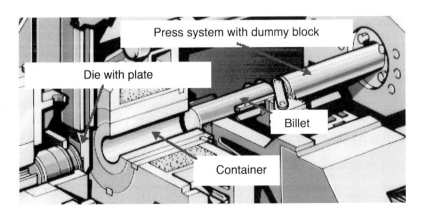

Fig. 6.1 Tool arrangement for direct extrusion

tainers on the press centerline and in line with the stem and the die could not be guaranteed to the necessary reproducibility. The continuous movement of the large containers, three rotations of 120° within an extrusion cycle, required extensive maintenance and regular repair. Only a few presses were built to this design and actually used for production. In

Direct extrusion press designs

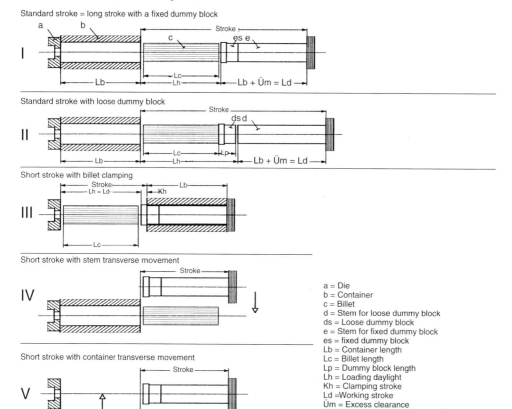

Standard stroke = long stroke with a fixed dummy block

Standard stroke with loose dummy block

Short stroke with billet clamping

Short stroke with stem transverse movement

Short stroke with container transverse movement

a = Die
b = Container
c = Billet
d = Stem for loose dummy block
ds = Loose dummy block
e = Stem for fixed dummy block
es = fixed dummy block
Lb = Container length
Lc = Billet length
Lp = Dummy block length
Lh = Loading daylight
Kh = Clamping stroke
Ld = Working stroke
Üm = Excess clearance
Working stroke = container length + excess clearance
Container length = 0.3 to 0.5 discard length + max billet length
Loading stroke = max billet length + clearance

I   Stroke = Loading stroke +working stroke. Application for aluminum alloys and for lubricated extrusion without a shell; no billet length restriction; no manipulation of the dummy block; fast extrusion cycle; not suitable for extrusion with a shell

II Stroke = Loading stroke + Working stroke.   Universal application for all extrusion processes; no billet length restrictions; dummy block manipulation necessary

III Stroke = Working stroke + clearance (clamping stroke). Application to aluminum extrusion; press appoximately two billet lengths shorter; billet must be clamped on the press centerline; billet length depends on the dimension of the loader

IV Stroke = Working stroke + clearance. Press approximately two billet lengths shorter; universal application; no billet length restrictions; can be used with loose or fixed dummy blocks; stem must move sideways, billet pusher required

V   Stroke = Working stroke + clearance. Press approxmately two billet length shorter; no billet length restrictions; used for steel tube extrusion fast press cycle; used with a fixed dummy block; container must move sideways

---

Fig. 6.2 Geometric relationships for different designs for direct extrusion

general, short-stroke presses are more expensive than standard-stroke presses because of the manipulation needed for billet loading and the mechanical design.

6.1.1.2 Main Subassemblies of the Direct-Extrusion Press

All extrusion presses consist of the following main subassemblies:

- Press frame, consisting of the following subassemblies:
    a. *Main cylinder:* One or two piece; housing and main cylinder
    b. *Platen:* One piece with or without a discard shear and/or with a discard saw
    c. *Columns:* Round columns with inboard and external nuts, round columns with compression sleeves (tubular) and external nuts, lamellar tension elements with compression members
    d. *Bed plate:* Standard with round columns

- Moving crosshead, consisting of stem holder, return cylinders, and, if necessary, advance cylinders
- Container holder with container-moving cylinders
- Die slide or short die carrier, rotating die carrier, or stationary tool carrier acting as the die holder
- Discard shear and/or discard saw

The function of the press frame is to withstand the extrusion load. A prestressed stiff press frame provides:

- Low press extension
- Low deflection of the die support [Stt 96]
- Short decompression time

The press frame consists of a cylinder housing with the main cylinder and ram, a platen, and, if the four columns are not designed as tension and compression elements, a bed plate and guide.

The elastic behavior of the press frame under production conditions is an important character-

Fig. 6.3 Standard stroke extrusion press. Location: Alusuisse in Chippis, Switzerland

istic of the extrusion press. The stiffness of the machine influences the accuracy of the guiding and the die support during extrusion.

In many respects, the quality of the press frame plays an important role in the extrusion process. The operational reliability must first be guaranteed. Failures in the column threads must be avoided at all costs. The notch effect at the root of the thread can increase the normal stress by a significant factor. In practice, only the first threads can transfer the forces. This disadvantage is avoided with hammer head lamellar columns. The geometry of the hammer head can be optimized by finite element analysis. In the area of the cylinder housing and the platen, prestressing with round columns is carried out, using inboard and external nuts. There is no prestressing between the housing and the platen, resulting in a relatively large elongation of the press during extrusion. If hollow compression members are located between the housing and the platen in-

stead of the inboard nuts, then this is referred to as a fully prestressed press frame.

With prestressed columns designed so that the tension elements are more highly stressed and the compressive elements subjected to lower stresses, the elongation can be reduced to 50% or less of that of non-prestressed columns with normal dimensions.

For example, for a 35.5 MN rod-and-tube press with a column length of 12 m and an extrusion load of 30 MN, the elongation for a prestressed press frame is approximately 2.5 mm and approximately 5 mm for a non-prestressed press frame. Figure 6.6 compares the load elongation diagrams for both tension and compression elements and columns with nuts for this press frame.

It is correct that larger column diameters result in a lower stress and thus reduce elongation of non-prestressed frames. However, from the machine design point of view, this approach

Fig. 6.4 Short-stroke press (compact press) for direct extrusion

causes problems with the geometry and the guiding system for the die carrier. There is limited space around the housings with larger columns, resulting in an increase in the press cross section and thus the size of the extrusion press.

A bed plate is needed for the guideways of the die carrier. The total extrusion load is produced by the main cylinder and, when fitted, by the two advance cylinders. The forces needed for the auxiliary operations, including billet loading, ram return, container sealing, and stripping, and the resultant cycle times must be taken into account in the design of the cylinders.

The container sealing forces and the stripping forces depend on the design of the tooling and the extrusion technology as well as the discard thickness. The container stripping force for aluminum extrusion is determined as follows:

$$F_{R-St} = D_0 \cdot \pi(l_F + l_R) \cdot \tau_S \quad \text{(Eq. 6.1)}$$

where F_{R-St} is the container stripping force, D_0 is the container diameter, l_R is the discard thickness, l_F is the dummy block land length, and τ_S is the shear stress of the billet material (see Section 3.1.1.4 in Chapter 3).

The auxiliary loads of the extrusion press are determined by the relevant functions. The ability to remove a billet stuck in the container from the press (sticking billet) is one factor that must be taken into account.

The tool carriers for the stem and container can be moved and are fitted with double-acting cylinders. The space-saving oil hydraulic double-acting cylinder offers advantages for both access and press maintenance.

Usually, the die carrier and the tools for die changing are fitted with rapid-locking systems. Bayonet fittings, which enable the tool to be locked or released by a simple partial rotation, have proved successful.

The discard separators do not belong directly to the extrusion press. Discard shears and/or discard saws are configured in the design of the extrusion press to ensure the optimal operation.

The competition among press manufacturers during the 1950s and 1960s resulted in extrusion presses that were simple to build, cost-effective, and that met the demands of the aluminum industry. This resulted in machines that had and still have identical main subassemblies throughout the world.

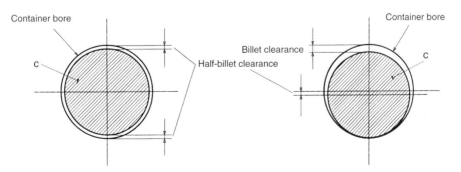

Different upsetting processes

Upsetting of billet clamped on press centerline

Upsetting of billet resting in container

View in cross section

a = Die; b = Container; c = Billet; d = Stem for loose dummy block; ds = Loose dummy block

Fig. 6.5 Upsetting of a billet clamped on the press centerline (good), and upsetting of a billet resting in the container (poor)

For reasons of quality and economy, modern extrusion press manufacture requires a machine design based on function specific subassemblies.

Extrusion presses of modular design can have common functional components and still be tailored to specific applications, depending on the product and the process. The press types described can be configured for a specific application in an extrusion plant by the addition or removal of components, for example, a discard saw instead of a discard shear. This also applies to the power system (water or oil hydraulic). Some of the most important presses for direct extrusion are:

- Extrusion presses for aluminum extrusion for the production of bar, section, and hollow sections

- Extrusion presses for copper alloys for the production of wire and/or bar and section

Indirect extrusion presses and tube presses, which are similar to direct-extrusion presses in the main components, are discussed in more detail in sections 6.1.2 and 6.2.2.

The components of the extrusion press must form a structural unit that ensures a systematic functionality and combination (Fig. 6.7). It must be possible to combine the modular units so that depending on the application of the press, the desired production can be guaranteed. Table 6.2 gives a general overview to assist in the understanding of a rational modular system and encompasses the modern extrusion press and its products, including wire, rod, section, hollow sections, and flat sections.

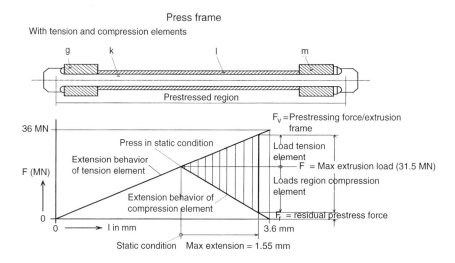

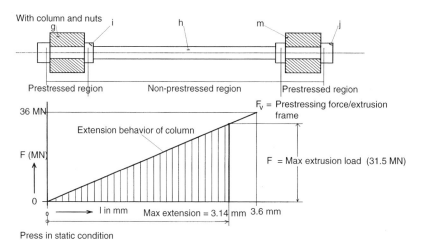

Fig. 6.6 Load diagram of a prestressed and non-prestressed press frame at a load of 31.5 MN. *g*, platen; *h*, column; *i*, inboard nut; *j*, outboard nut; *k*, tension element; *l*, compression element; *m*, cyclindar housing

The examples shown can differ from each other in the arrangement of the subassemblies. Combined direct- and indirect-extrusion presses are known that have, for example, one shear for direct extrusion and one for indirect extrusion.

Table 6.3 gives the steps in press power of modern extrusion presses. This range corresponds (in bold type) to the standard range R10 (from the tool standard DIN 25540). The intermediate sizes (standard type) occur more frequently in the United States than in Europe.

The design of the press frame (Fig. 6.8) must take into account the extrusion load, container and tool changing, and freedom for manipula-tion, including billet loading. The extrusion load is used as a defining parameter for all components. The press stroke determines the column length according to the design of the press and not the cross section. A bed plate is not required with a prestressed design. This design enables X-guiding to be readily realized. Flat guiding can also be provided by the inclusion of suitable structural elements that have to be independent of the elastic behavior of the press frame. The symmetry of the press frame is very important for the elastic behavior of the press under the extrusion load. A square column arrangement is preferred, because it simplifies the components and results in uniform stresses.

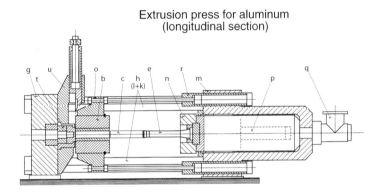

Extrusion press for aluminum
(longitudinal section)

g, platen; u, shear; o, container holder; e, extrusion stem with fixed pad; r, container-moving cylinder; q, prefill valve; t, die cassette; b, container; c, billet; h, columns; m, cylinder housing; p, advance-return cylinder; n, moving crosshead; l + k, compressive elements + tension elements

Fig. 6.7 Direct extrusion press for aluminum showing the components

Table 6.2 Components of direct-extrusion presses

| Structural element | | Direct-extrusion presses(a) | | | |
| | | Light metal | | Heavy metal | |
Main subassembly	Subassembly	Standard press	Special press	Standard press	Special press
Press frame	Cylinder housing	I, II, III, IV	. . .	I, II	. . .
	Platen	I, II, III, IV	. . .	I, II	. . .
	Columns	I, II, III, IV	. . .	I, II	. . .
	Bed plate	. . .	I, II, III, IV	. . .	I, II
Moving crosshead	Moving crosshead	I, II, III, IV	. . .	I, II	. . .
	Advance-return cylinder	I, II, III, IV	. . .	I, II	. . .
Container holder	Container holder	I, II, III, IV	. . .	I, II	. . .
	Moving cylinder	I, II, III, IV	. . .	I, II	. . .
Die carrier	Die cassettes	I, II, III, IV	. . .	I, II	. . .
	Die slide	. . .	I, II, III, IV	. . .	I, II
	Die rotating arm	. . .	I	. . .	I, II
	Stationary die holder(b)	. . .	I, II, III, IV	. . .	I, II
Extrusion separator	Shear	I, II, III, IV	. . .	. . .	I, II
	Saw	. . .	. . .	I, II	. . .

(a) Product: wire, bar = I; section = II; hollow section = III; flat section = IV(c). (b) Only on small presses. (c) From rectangular containers

Table 6.3   Standard force ratings of commercial presses

Extrusion load	
MN	kip(a)
5	1100
6.3	1400
8	1800
10	2250
12.5	2810
16	3600
18	4000
20	4500
22	5000
25	5600
28	6300
31.5	7080
35.5	8000
40	9000
50	11,200
63	14,000
71	16,000
80	18,000
100	22,500
125	28,100

Bold type are standard range (RIO from DIN 25540). Standard type are intermediate sizes more common in the United States. (a) Kip, 1000 lb force is derived from MN, meganewton.

The tool carrier moving crosshead (Fig. 6.9) provides the advance, extrusion, and return strokes. It is moved by the two double-acting cylinders and the main cylinder and transfers the load to the extrusion stem. Quick release systems are used to locate the extrusion stem. The moving crosshead is guided by adjustable guide shoes on the press frame guides. Upper locating guide shoes are used to provide better alignment accuracy during the movement of the extrusion stem (X-guiding).

The tool carrier container housing (Fig. 6.10) can be moved by two double-acting cylinders. To ensure that the working area is as open as possible, the container-moving cylinders are located in the main cylinder housing.

Adjustable guide shoes are used to guide the container housing. The guide-ways are primarily determined by the container housing because it houses the container, which is the largest tooling item. The container working temperature depends on the production. To achieve a positive location in the container housing independent of the temperature, the container is located in the container housing by four keys. It is located virtually without any play in both the cold and the hot condition.

In horizontal extrusion, the maximum temperature occurs in the region of the container housing at approximately 20% of the external container diameter above the press centerline. This is because the container housing, which is also hot on the outside, induces an air current. This cools the bottom half more severely, whereas the upper part of the container housing falls in the wind shadow of the chimney effect and increases in temperature. Locating the thermal center of the container housing requires the center of the container to be measured in both the cold and the hot condition. The difference can exceed 5 mm on large extrusion presses.

The guide-ways for the container housing are arranged as a prism (half X-guiding) to maintain the central location of the container within the tightest limits possible at different operating temperatures. In order to achieve better and reproducible guiding, an upper guide is used that often extends the guiding to X-guiding. The location of the guide-ways with X-guiding should take into account the thermal center point to ensure that the container housing is free from play

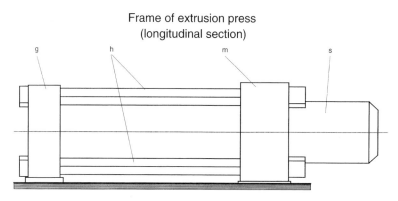

Frame of extrusion press
(longitudinal section)

g = platen; h = columns; m = cylinder housing; s = main cylinder housing

Fig. 6.8 Press frame

as far as possible and is accurately located within the extrusion press, even with temperature variations.

Flat guiding is also encountered, and this is simpler to adjust but assumes constant thermal conditions in the container holder under produc-

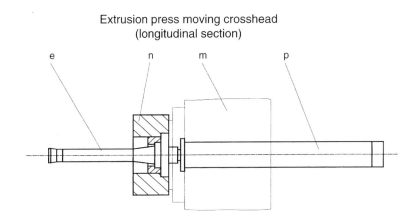

e = extrusion press with fixed pad; *n* = moving crosshead; *m* = cylinder housing; *p* = advance-return cylinder

Fig. 6.9 Moving crosshead for direct extrusion

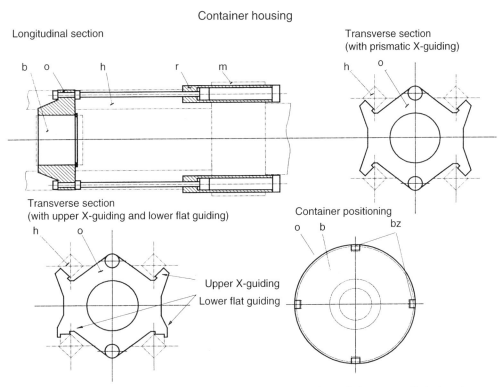

b = container; *o* = container holder; *h* = columns; *r* = container-moving cylinders; *m* = cylinder housing; *bz* = container keys

Fig. 6.10 Container housing

tion conditions. If the production conditions do not require different working temperatures, then flat guiding is used. The geometry of the flat guiding requires a central guide at the bottom as well as the supporting guides.

Top guides to improve the running and guiding reliability are used in a wide range of configurations.

The container heating has a significant influence on the container housing. Induction and resistance heating affect the design of the container housing in different ways. In each case, the internal space must be thermally insulated to ensure that the container loses as little heat as possible and to protect the housing from overheating. Resistance heating can be used instead of induction heating, and this requires insulation from the body of the housing. It heats the container from the outside. In this case, it is difficult to bring the temperature above 400 °C.

Various designs are used for the tool carrier for the dies. Four different designs are usually used (Fig. 6.11).

Die shuffles are used almost exclusively today for aluminum alloy extrusion presses. Two die carriers are used with a changing table outside the press (Fig. 6.12). The die shuffle can be used, if necessary, as an auxiliary shear to cut the sections behind the die by using a larger shear cylinder. The operating position must be adjustable. The design height of the die stack must be held to tight tolerances to guarantee the exact shear position for correct separation of the discard from the section.

It is important to always locate the die stack in the same shear position; otherwise, material can build up in the area of the die front face, which results in problems.

Die slides are used for copper alloy extrusion presses. They have a die and an ejection position for the discard, dummy block, shell,

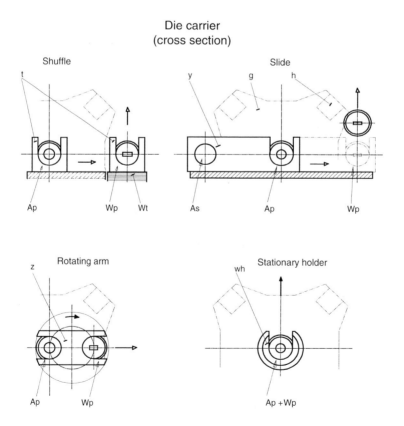

Die carrier
(cross section)

t = die shuffle; y = die slide; g = platen; h = columns; z = rotating arm; wh = stationary die holder, Ap = working position; Wp = changing position; Wt = changing table; As = sticking billet position

Fig. 6.11 Die carrier

Fig. 6.12 Die changing by exchanging tool carriers on the shuffle table outside the press

and cleaning block. The die position can also be a carrier that can be connected and disconnected.

Die rotate systems with two positions are used for loading the die sets. Die rotate systems are more commonly seen on copper alloy extrusion presses. Depending on the operational sequence, a faster die change is required for short cycle times. A special discard remover is needed for the discard, dummy block, shell, and cleaning block.

Stationary die carriers are mainly used for small extrusion presses up to 8 MN because of the good accessibility. They guarantee accurate and reliable location and therefore are also

sometimes found on large presses and for indirect-extrusion presses.

Discard separators separate the discard from the section. With aluminum alloys, the separation is carried out directly at the front face of the die or the feeder chamber by a shear. A saw is used for copper alloys, and this cuts the extrusion between the container and the die. The discard in this case is still in the container bore. A shear is often used for separation in the extrusion of brass wire. Shears and saws are always part of the extrusion press and are usually mounted on the top of the platen.

6.1.1.3 Auxiliary Equipment for Direct Extrusion

The auxiliary equipment is integrated with the press and enables the automation of the operating cycle (Fig. 6.13, 6.14). The integration of loading, removal, and additional equipment enables the manipulation of billet discards and shells, dummy blocks, and cleaning disc, dies and tool sets as well as their cleaning and lubrication to be incorporated in an automatic extrusion operation (Table 6.4).

The auxiliary equipment needed is determined by whether extrusion is carried out with or without a shell or with a fixed or loose dummy block, and whether it is direct or indirect extrusion. The auxiliary equipment for the most common presses can be divided into two main groups.

Auxiliary Equipment for Direct Extrusion with Fixed Dummy Block and without a

Fig. 6.13 16 MN aluminum alloy press with auxiliary equipment. (Factory assembly Danieli Breda)

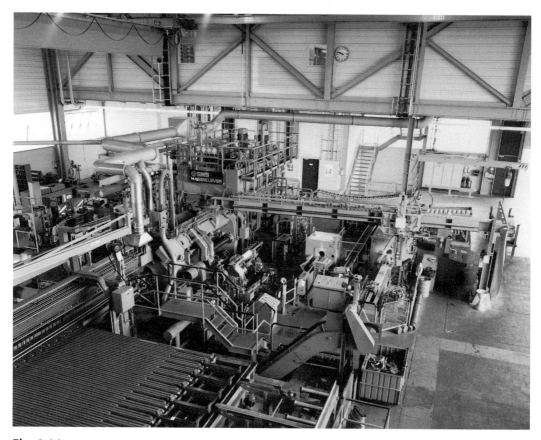

Fig. 6.14 22 MN copper alloy press. (Wieland-Werke)

Table 6.4 Auxiliary equipment for direct extrusion

Auxiliary equipment for direct extrusion	For manipulation of:	Extrusion press(a)			
		Light metal		Heavy metal	
		Standard Press	Special press	Standard press	Special press
Loader	Billet	I, III	II, III, IV	. . .	I, II
	Billet, dummy block	. . .	II, III, IV	. . .	I, II
	Billet, dummy block, cleaning block	. . .	. . .	I, II	. . .
Removal tool	Discard, dummy block	. . .	II, III, IV	. . .	I, II
	Discard, dummy block, shell, cleaning block	. . .	. . .	I, II	. . .
Separator	Discard, dummy block	. . .	II, III, IV	. . .	I, II
	Discard, dummy block, shell	. . .	. . .	I, II	. . .
Circulation	Dummy block	. . .	II, III, IV	. . .	I, II
	Dummy block, cleaning block	. . .	. . .	I, II	. . .
	Die	. . .	. . .	. . .	I, II
Die changer	Die	II, III	. . .	I, II	. . .
	Die set	II, III	. . .	I, II	. . .
Cooling system	Die	. . .	. . .	I, II	. . .
	Container	. . .	. . .	I, II	. . .
	Dummy block	. . .	. . .	I, II	. . .
Lubrication system	Dummy block	. . .	. . .	I, II	. . .
	Billet	II, III	. . .	. . .	I, II
	Container, die	. . .	. . .	I, II	. . .
Removal transport	Discard	II, III	II, III, IV	I, II	. . .
	Shell	. . .	. . .	I, II	. . .

(a) Product: wire(b); bar = I; section = II; hollow section = III; flat section = IV (c) (b) Billet-on-billet extrusion with aluminum alloys. (c) From rectangular container

Shell. If no shell that must be removed is formed in the liner, extrusion is carried out with a fixed dummy block. Multipart fixed dummy blocks are used for aluminum extrusion. The billets are lubricated for the extrusion of the difficult copper and brass alloys and steel. A shell does not then form. Extrusion is then carried out using the lubricated-without-a-shell process. In this case, a single-piece fixed dummy block is used for expedience.

A swinging or a linear billet loader is used. The lubrication of the billets before loading is carried out with special systems. The handling of the sawn or punched discard is carried out by means of a chute or a conveyor. The tooling requires special care, including cooling, cleaning, and lubrication, and special devices (including die rotation systems with corresponding service locations) are used.

The auxiliary equipment is therefore restricted to billet loader, discard removal, and, rarely, dummy block lubrication (in case no billet end face lubrication is provided) and a die change system.

Auxiliary Equipment for Direct Aluminum Extrusion (Extrusion without a Shell and with a Fixed Dummy Block). The development of the expanding fixed dummy block eliminated the need for the previously necessary circulation of several dummy blocks. Two-piece billet loaders are used to load a standard-stroke press with a billet (Fig. 6.15). This enables reliable and fast

loading of the billet into the container bore. This is particularly important if a two-piece billet is produced by the log shear. The billet is held by jaws without clamping. The dimensions and shape depend on the diameter of the billet or whether a rectangular billet is used.

To ensure reliable automatic operation of the extrusion plant, the front face of the fixed dummy block or the billet on the end facing the dummy block must be lubricated. The sheared discard is removed in a controlled manner by a chute and a conveyor after every extrusion cycle. If the discard sticks to the shear blade or the die, it is removed by a knocker that is operated after shearing.

Auxiliary Equipment for Direct Extrusion with a Shell and with a Separate Dummy Block and Cleaning Block. This is always necessary when a shell is formed in the container bore for quality reasons. If short billets are used or if a good billet surface enables extrusion to be carried out with a thin shell, then a separate combination dummy block and cleaning block is both possible and economic. A separate dummy block must be used for difficult-to-extrude aluminum alloys. The cleaning block is used at alloy changes and with high-value materials.

The extrusion press for copper alloys is fitted with a separate dummy block and a separate cleaning block and leaves a shell in the container bore after each extrusion. The auxiliary equip-

(a) (b)

Fig. 6.15 (a) Two-part billet loader in the start position outside the press (billet-receiving position). (b) Two-part billet loader in the center of the press during the loading of the container

ment needed include a billet and dummy block loader (which also loads the cleaning block), removal system for the discard, dummy and cleaning blocks as well as the shell, discard and shell separator with a recycling system for the dummy and cleaning block, die change system, and system for cleaning the tooling.

Auxiliary Equipment for Direct Copper Alloy Extrusion with a Shell. A two-piece billet loader is used here in the same way as with aluminum alloy extrusion. The operating sequence differs from that for aluminum alloy extrusion in that it is necessary to operate with dummy blocks, and cleaning blocks, because a shell is formed in the container bore.

One of the loader arms of the billet loader is needed to load the cleaning block. A removal tool is used to remove the discard, dummy block, shell, and cleaning block as a complete package, which is transferred to a separator. First, the free-standing cleaning block is transferred to a block recycling system with magazine and, if necessary, a cooling station. Monitoring of the dummy block separation operation by the operating personnel is necessary. Although intervention is not always required, problems can occur with uneven or torn shells. The shell is removed simultaneously with the separation of the discard from the dummy block, which moves into the block recycling system. The discard and shell finish up in the scrap container via a chute and a conveyor. Because several dummy and cleaning blocks are used, these are held in a magazine, ready for use. A distributor supplies the dummy block on demand, and it is always loaded together with a heated billet into a transfer system. At the end of extrusion, the cleaning block is also loaded into the transfer system. One of the billet loader arms moves the cleaning block into the center of the press in order to clean the shell from the container bore.

6.1.1.4 Hydraulic Drive and Control Systems for Direct Extrusion

When hydraulic presses were first built, the operating medium was exclusively water. Over a period of time, emulsifying agents were added to the water to protect the machine components against corrosion. Oil hydraulic presses did not become popular until approximately 1950. Today, water hydraulic extrusion presses are rarely seen in new plants. Although the reduced environmental impact, the absence of fire risk, and the possibility of short-term high-energy avail-

ability are advantageous, these are offset by the investment costs and the wear in the valves as well as the corrosion of the machine components and the high maintenance and repair costs.

Water hydraulic drive is only used today when short-term, very large press powers are required for the deformation process. This is the case for steel extrusion presses in which, for example, a 1000 mm long billet must be extruded within 3 seconds.

Figure 6.16 shows the schematic diagram of a water hydraulic accumulator drive system for a direct-extrusion press.

Figure 6.17 shows an example of a pressure-demand diagram for the water hydraulic accumulator drive system, shown schematically in Fig. 6.16.

At an operating pressure of 315 bar (4.57 ksi), approximately 22,600 L/min (5970 gal/min) are needed for a 35 MN press, that is, a drive power of approximately 14,500 KW. A direct pumping drive would be both economically and technically unviable for such a high power. Because, for example, the steel 35 MN extrusion press requires an extrusion time of 3 seconds, which is approximately 10% of the total operating cycle, a drive of approximately 1800 KW would be sufficient. The lower pump power can be advantageously utilized with an accumulator.

Even during the dead cycle, the pumps supply pressurized water to the accumulator, where the required water volume is stored. These accumulator systems were used previously as central power supplies for several presses. They are now occasionally found in large extrusion plants operating a large number of presses for aluminum and copper alloys.

The water hydraulic drive pumps for operating the presses are high-pressure pumps with three or four pistons (Fig. 6.18). They have a constant delivery and operate at working pressures between 200 and 315 bar (2.90 to 4.57 ksi). They are fitted with return and safety valves. Reduction gears are necessary between the pumps and the electric motors to ensure a technically acceptable rotation speed, which should be less than 300 rpm. The low rotation speed of the crankshaft is essential for the function and service life of the piston seals. If the piston speed is too fast, the seals and pistons can overheat, reducing the functionality.

The overhead reservoir tank serves as a container for the entire working medium (emulsified water). The unpressurized water is fed back here by the control valves and from the prefill tank.

The high-pressure pumps and the filling pumps suck the emulsified water from the overhead reservoir tank.

The accumulator consists of a series of high-pressure containers (high-pressure bottles) that are supplied with the emulsified water and the compressed air. The high-pressure pumps are switched on and off by the water level measured in the bottles by ultrasonic probes. To avoid an unacceptably high pressure drop during the removal of the pressurized water, the ratio of the compressed air volume to the pressurized water volume should be greater than 10 to 1. The pressure

drop that can be allowed in an application must be verified. The accumulator station includes high-pressure compressors for the air bottles, hydraulic controls that can be operated by hand or electrically, safety and shut-off valves for water and air, and optical as well as acoustic safety devices.

The prefill tank, which is also referred to as an air reservoir, is a low-pressure container. It is used to move the ram during billet loading (standard-stroke press) and to move the mandrel forward on tube presses into pre-pierced or bored billets. This saves pressurized water. Prefill valves are needed with a

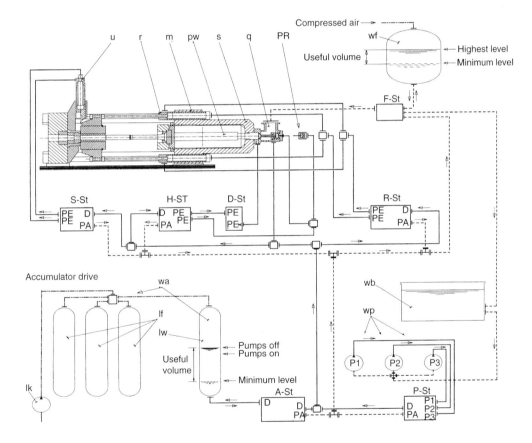

u = shear; r = container movement; m = cylinder housing; pw = return cylinder; s = main press cylinder; q = prefill valve; wf = prefill tank; wb = high-level container; wp = high-pressure pumps; wa = accumulator; lf = air bottles; lw = water bottles; lk = compressor

Controls: F-St = prefill; S-St = shear; H-St = press; D-St = valve to control the extrusion speed; R-St = container movement; P-St = pumps; A-St = accumulator

D = high pressure connection; PE = high-pressure water inlet to the cylinders; PA = exhaust from cylinders; PEx = throttled high-pressure water; PR = high-pressure water to the return cylinder

Fig. 6.16 Schematic arrangement of a water hydraulic accumulator drive system for an extrusion press

prefill tank. The working pressure of the prefill tank is between 8 and 16 bar. Decompression shocks are largely avoided by taking the exhaust water from the hydraulic controls.

The hydraulic controls consist of manifolds with valves and connections for pressurized water and exhaust water pipes. Depending on the function, they are used as speed controls for different speeds, as the main control for the press, or as control for the container movement, piercing system, and shear. They are seated valves and operate as pressure water inlet or outlet valves, as nonreturn valves, decompression valves, and as safety valves. They are fitted with throttle valve plugs or throttle valve cages and can have a stacked multistage design to ensure a smooth connection and disconnection from cylinders during the press cycle. The valves are either operated by oil hydraulic pilot valves or motor-driven cams or by a lever system moved by hand or servo-cylinders.

Oil Hydraulic. Water hydraulic systems have been displaced in press manufacture by oil hydraulics (Fig. 6.19). Today, accumulator systems are also common in oil hydraulic systems. In contrast to water, oil can be used as the operating medium without packings and thus without expensive seals, because of its viscosity and its lubrication effect, for the pump pistons of the high-pressure pumps and for the directional valves. Axial piston high-pressure pumps are relatively simple to adjust, so that variable deliveries are possible.

Proportional and servo-valves can be used for controlled operations or control loops. The components in oil hydraulic systems are significantly cheaper than those used in water hydraulic systems. Mass production provides both a lower cost and a high-quality standard. The drive pumps are axial piston pumps with constant and/or variable deliveries. Submerged pumps are placed directly in the oil tank. The working pressure ranges from 200 to 315 bar. For economic reasons, a working pressure of 250 bar (3.62 ksi) is preferred for extrusion presses. The power supply speed of rotation is 1000 rpm for submerged pumps and 1500 rpm for prefilled pumps.

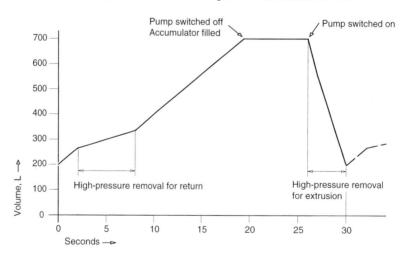

High-preassure utilization diagram for an accumulator drive

Data for high-preasure water consumption diagram:

Accumulator	700 L useful volume
Pump power	1920 L/mm
Operating cycle of the period	30 s
Extrusion time	4 s
Return time	6 s

Fig. 6.17 Pressurized water-demand diagram

Some examples for the required operating power for different extrusion presses are:

- 12.5 MN extrusion press for aluminum alloys; 3×90 KW = 270 KW
- 35 MN rod-and-tube press for copper alloys; 5×320 KW = 1600 KW
- 35 MN indirect rod-and-tube press for aluminum alloys; 5×200 KW + 1×75 KW = 1075 KW

These examples show that the power of the pumps relative to the extrusion press powers increases in larger steps. This results in maximum extrusion speeds that often exceed the required values for the different press sizes.

The oil tank is often located over the main cylinder housing. It can hold the entire oil volume for the plant. It is connected as a nonpressurized container directly to the main cylinder through a prefill valve. On the oil tank are the controls and, in the case of submerged pumps, the high-pressure pumps, the low-pressure pumps with low-pressure accumulators, the auxiliary pumps for the cooling and filter circuits, the pilot pressure pumps, and, in the case of

Fig. 6.18 Water hydraulic pump system

separate high pressure pumps, the filter, the cooler, and the valves (Fig. 6.20, 6.21).

To reduce the noise level, the high-pressure pumps are preferably installed as floor mounted pumps in a cellar or a special pump room. The spatial needs for the hydraulic system are advantageous with submerged pumps, because shorter pipe lengths can be used.

The controls in oil hydraulic systems can be divided into high-pressure and low-pressure controls. The high-pressure controls are arranged in function-specific manifold blocks similar to water hydraulic systems. The various directional valves are attached to the manifold blocks. Access must be taken into account. The exhaust oil goes directly from the manifold block back into the tank. The directional valves are controlled indirectly by electrically controlled pilot valves (solenoid valves) that operate the large directional valves. Mechanical control systems are not used, unlike water hydraulic systems.

Cartridge (seated) valves are being used more and more instead of directional valves (slide valves). As with water hydraulic systems, they are installed in manifold blocks. The cartridges are hydraulically controlled by pilot valves.

The low-pressure control with an operating pressure up to 100 bar (1.45 ksi) is arranged in stacked elements, either as a central control system in an easily maintained location or in the immediate vicinity of the cylinders, high-pressure variable delivery pumps, or high pressure controls. The low-pressure control consists of directional valves, and proportional and/or servo valves, depending on the application.

The low-pressure control is used for:

- Hydraulic pilot control of the high-pressure directional valves
- Control of the auxiliary systems (billet loading, discard removal, tool recycling)
- Control of additional systems (saw, lubrication, cooling, etc.)
- Control of pumps and cylinders
- Control of the press-handling system

6.1.1.5 Electrical Drive, Control, and Regulation for Direct Extrusion

Electricity was initially used in hydraulic press construction only for the drive system and later for the container heating. Electricity was used less for the control side and more for the power side of the extrusion plant. The demand for automation has increased with increasing mechanization of the operations in the extrusion plant. A plant is only economic to-day if it has a data processing system as well as automatic control.

The electrical drive system belongs to the power part of the electrical control system. The oil hydraulic high-pressure pumps are usually driven by three-phase motors (up to approximately 300 KW). For example, a 50 MN extrusion press for copper alloys requires six motors, each of 320 KW, or eight motors of 250 KW. Approximately 85% of an installed total power of 2300 KW is needed for the high-pressure pumps. Apart from the low-pressure pumps and those for the auxiliary, there are no larger electrical drive systems around the extrusion plant.

Additional electrical drives are needed for the handling system.

Direct current or frequency-controlled three-phase motors are used for coilers and for extrusion puller systems. The power requirements of these machines fall between 20 and 80 KW. The cut-off saws in the run-out system require between 5 and 40 KW, depending on the material and the cross section.

Electric heating is needed in hot working for the extrusion press container. Independent of the material being extruded, controllable resistance and/or induction heating is used. Induction heating of the container is often seen today. Resistance heating is now preferred for new plants. In

Extrusion press controls

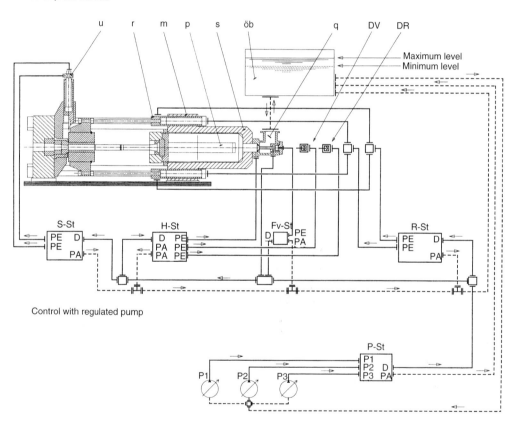

Control with regulated pump

u = shear; r = container movement; m = cylinder movement; p = advance-return cylinder; s = main press cylinder; q = prefill valve; $öb$ = oil tank

Controls: S-St = shear; H-St = press; Fv-St = prefill valve; R-St = container movement; P-St = pumps

D = High-pressure connections; PE = pressurized oil inlet to the cylinders; PA = exhaust oil from the cylinders; DV = pressure/exaust oil to advance connections; DR = pressure/exhaust oil to the return connections

Fig. 6.19 Schematic arrangement of an oil hydraulic drive system for an extrusion press

contrast to induction heating, it can be designed so that it is possible to adjust the container temperature over the length of the container. The heating power depends initially on the required operating temperature in the container (500 °C for aluminum alloys and approximately 400 °C for copper alloys) as well as on the container surface and the insulation of the container. The required heating power ranges from 30 to 200 KW, depending on the press size and type of construction.

The electrical control system is a programmable logic control (PLC) system. It can be readily programmed and thus includes many

Fig. 6.20 Oil hydraulic drive system with controls, tank, filters, coolers, and valves

Fig. 6.21 Control desk

possibilities for the optimization of the operating sequences [Iwa 84]. It is therefore possible at any time to monitor the operational conditions and possible faults as well as to transfer protocols and data via a centralized computer. An operating control system for the extrusion process can also be included. Orders can be controlled, processed, and monitored [Bug 88].

Different manufacturers of the PLC can be used for the control units that are arranged in independent blocks for the furnace line, the extrusion plant, and the handling system. In many cases, they are specified by the plant for internal reasons (experience, existing systems). Special systems have been developed for the extrusion process, including:

- Process monitoring with fault diagnostics and visible production sequence on a computer screen
- Storage of production and operational data and material flow in the manufacturing process
- Control of container temperature over the container length
- Billet temperature over the billet length and ram speed over the ram displacement, with the aim of a constant exit temperature over the ram stroke or over the length of the extrusion

6.1.1.6 Typical Operating Sequence for Direct Extrusion

Four main operations characterize the procedures in extrusion:

1. *Loading:* The hot billet must be brought into the press. This is carried out by a billet loader. The design depends on the construction of the press. For example:
   a. Standard stroke, corresponding to the overview of types of long-stroke extrusion press (Fig. 6.2). Stem in the starting position, container in the extrusion position, billet loading between the stem and the container, the billet is pushed by the stem into the container bore, and the stem moves in the working direction.
   b. Short stroke, corresponding to the overview of types of short-stroke extrusion press (Fig. 6.2). Stem on the press centerline in the starting position, container over the stem, billet loading between the stem/container and the die. The billet is clamped between the stem and the die,

and the stem and container move in the working direction. Or stem outside the press centerline (Fig. 6.2) container in the extrusion position, billet loading between the container and the moving crosshead, the billet is pushed with a special device into the container bore, stem on the moving crosshead from the side position to the extrusion position. Or container rotating on an extrusion press column or cross slide, stem in starting position, billet loading in the container outside the press with a special device, container from the side position into the extrusion position.

2. *Extrusion:* The main operation after the billet is in the extrusion position consists of upset, initiation of the extrusion process, and when the preset discard length has reached decompression.
3. *Clearing:* The tooling is opened, the extruded section is separated from the discard and transported away, the discard and, if present, the shell are removed, and the tooling is moved to the starting position.
4. *Tool preparation:* Depending on the material being deformed, the tooling is cooled, cleaned, lubricated, and changed if required.

Operating Sequence Direct Extrusion. The times in the operating sequence described as follows apply to a medium-sized extrusion press (20 to 35 MN). They take into account the most important operating sequences, sometimes in a summarized format.

The sequential times have not been adjusted for maximum speed but more to operational and economically viable values that can be achieved during the operation of an extrusion press without risks of breakdown.

Tool change times, program changes, breakdowns, and continuous maintenance can significantly reduce the productivity during an extended production period. The annual throughput can be reduced to approximately 70%.

Table 6.5 shows the working cycle for an aluminum alloy press for easy and moderately difficult-to-extrude alloys with a standard stroke and fixed dummy block. The operating steps are shown in Fig. 6.22. The working cycle and the operating steps for a short-stroke press are shown in Table 6.6 and Fig. 6.23.

6.1.2 Machines for Indirect Extrusion

In the past, extrusion presses for indirect extrusion were installed in only a few locations.

They were used for the production of brass wire. Production plants for indirect extrusion are now seen more frequently. The high demands on quality and productivity have resulted in the development of indirect-extrusion plants [Yok 77]. New indirect-extrusion press plants for the production of brass wire and rod operate with high economic success. The moderately difficult and the difficult-to-extrude aluminum alloys are not processed to any significant degree on indirect-extrusion presses. In contrast, indirect tube extrusion for aluminum alloys is used to a significant extent.

The design of an indirect-extrusion press is determined by the following factors:

- Product
  a. Difficult-to-extrude aluminum and aluminum alloys, rod, and section
  b. Brass—easy to extrude and/or difficult to extrude (wire, rod, and section). Steel and copper are not extruded by the indirect process.
- Process technology
  a. Indirect extrusion without lubrication and without a shell
  b. Indirect extrusion without lubrication and with a shell

6.1.2.1 Press Design

Today, there are a large number of different designs for indirect-extrusion presses that oper-ate with varying degrees of success (Fig. 6.24). A tendency for high-throughput machines can be seen in brass wire and rod indirect-extrusion presses. High-value products can be produced in difficult-to-extrude aluminum alloys on indirect-extrusion presses. The extrusion presses described as follows only cover designs with significant output. These are classified as standard in Table 6.7.

The points made in the section about machines for direct extrusion must be covered in the design of indirect-extrusion presses.

The characteristic feature of indirect-extrusion presses (including indirect rod-and-tube presses even though these have only been produced to a limited extent) is the container linked to the moving crosshead during extrusion. With copper alloys, the moving crosshead usually has a sealing tool, and the press has a standard stroke.

With aluminum alloys, the short-stroke press (Fig. 6.25) is preferred [Asa 84]. A sealing stem is used. The advantage of this sealing stem is:

- Reliable billet loading of all billet lengths without the billet jamming
- Possible for a sticking billet to be pushed out with the press power into a discard carrier

In all indirect-extrusion presses, the stationary die is located at the front face of the extrusion

Table 6.5 Operating sequence of an extrusion press for easy and moderately difficult-to-extrude aluminum alloys with standard stroke and fixed dummy block

	Operating stage	Time sequence in seconds: 5 / 10 / 15 / 20	Comments
1	Billet loader in		Billet loading
2	Extrusion stem advance		Billet pushed against die
3	Billet loader out		Loading position / starting position
4	Extrusion stem advance and return		Upsetting, decompression / air removal
5	Extrusion stem extrusion		Upsetting, extrusion
6	Decompression		Press under no pressure
7	Container strip		Discard clear, shear position
8	Extrusion stem return		Starting position
9	Discard shear		Discard removal monitoring
10	Container moves to die		Press in starting position

stem located on the platen. The die block located in front of the hollow stem enters the container bore during extrusion. The billet is then extruded to the discard length without any relative movement between the billet and the liner (i.e., without friction), in contrast to direct extrusion.

The tooling is similar in design and structural details to direct extrusion and is based on DIN 24540. The tool set of the die block is relatively small and multipiece for copper alloys and both multipiece and single piece for aluminum alloys. The external diameter is limited by the container bore. The maximum cross-sectional area of the extruded profile is determined by the largest possible stem bore and is significantly limited, in contrast to sections produced by direct extru-

sions. Apart from this, the tooling differs only in its application for a specific production, as discussed previously for direct extrusion. The design for the indirect-extrusion press must allow for the container movement over the press stroke plus clearance for other operations; also, the press stem is located on the platen, with the discard being removed between the moving crosshead and the container. If a sealing tool is used and the billet is loaded between the container and the extrusion stem, the press must be designed as a standard-stroke press. The short-stroke press is used:

- When the billet is loaded between the sealing tool and the container, and the billet is clamped

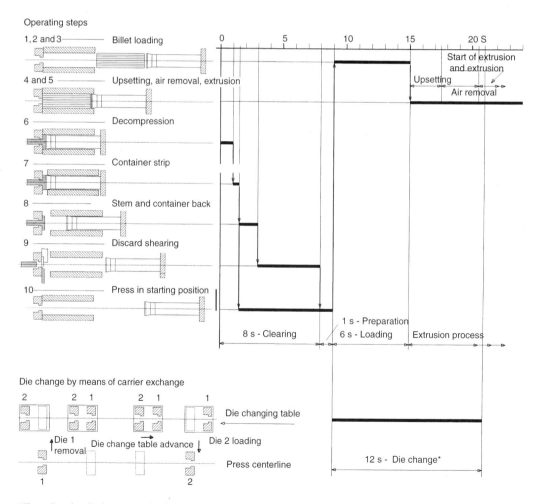

Fig. 6.22 Operating steps in extrusion, time dependent

- When a press with a sealing stem is used, and billet loading takes place between the container and the sealing stem

6.1.2.2 Main Structural Components of Indirect-Extrusion Presses

As in section 6.1.1.2, a typical design is described here (Fig. 6.26, Table 6.8). Note: The examples given may differ in the arrangement of the main subassemblies. Combination direct- and indirect-extrusion presses are known that have, for example, a shear for direct extrusion and a shear for indirect extrusion. The main subassemblies are almost identical for direct and indirect extrusion. The modular units already described enable all current press designs to be produced.

6.1.2.3 Auxiliary Equipment for Indirect Extrusion

Similar to that of direct-extrusion presses, the auxiliary equipment associated with indirect-extrusion presses is necessary for a more or less automatic press operation. The development of the auxiliary equipment for automatically operating extrusion plants has not reached the desired level in all areas. The shell frequently prevents full automatic operation of an extrusion plant. A relatively thin shell is produced in indirect extrusion.

The transfer of the extruded section to the runout system occurs after separation from the discard, similar to direct extrusion. The auxiliary equipment required for indirect extrusion depends to a large extent on whether copper alloys or aluminum alloys are being extruded and whether a fixed or a loose die block is used.

The auxiliary equipment systems used in the most common indirect-extrusion plants are described in the following sections.

Auxiliary Equipment for the Indirect Extrusion of Aluminum Alloys. The short-stroke press with two stems (extrusion stem and sealing stem) is the most common for indirect aluminum alloy extrusion. The auxiliary equipment is designed accordingly. Because in indirect extrusion the container moves over the billet during billet loading, the pivoting billet loader is movable in the direction of extrusion. Without opening the billet clamps, it withdraws over the sealing stem as the container moves over the billet. This loading process ensures reliable and efficient billet loading between the sealing stem and

Table 6.6 Operating sequence of an extrusion press for easy and moderately difficult-to-extrude alloys with a short stroke and a fixed pad

Half-seconds have been rounded up to the next highest value.

	Operating stage	Time sequence in seconds:				Comments
		5	10	15	20	
1	Billet loader in					Billet loading
2	Extrusion stem advance					Billet clamping
3	Billet loader out					Loading position / starting position
4	Container advance					Extrusion position
5	Extrusion stem advance and return					Upsetting, decompression / ni removal
6	Extrusion stem extrusion					Pressure buildup, extrusion
7	Decompression					Press under no pressure
8	Container strip					Discard clear, shear position
9	Extrusion stem return					Starting position
10	Discard shear					Discard removal monitoring
11	Container over extrusion stem					Press in starting position

the container. In order to produce high-value extruded products, a loose die block is used, which cuts a thin shell in the container bore during extrusion (Fig. 6.27). The die block is fitted with recesses to receive the shell. The die block is loaded with a special loader that loads it between the extrusion stem and the container. At the end of the extrusion process, the discard and the die block with the shell are pushed into a removal tool. The discard is then sheared and the removal tool swung from the press center into the transfer position. The sheared discard is transferred to a scrap container via a chute and a conveyor.

The die block with the shell is transferred from the removal tool into a transporter that first moves to a shell separator to remove the shell and to lubricate the shell recess. The die block is then moved to the pivoting loader. A changing and maintenance station is used, depending on the program, and, if required, a heated holding station.

Auxiliary Equipment for Indirect Extrusion of Copper Alloys (Standard-Stroke Press with

Sealing Tool). On a standard-stroke press with a sealing tool, the pivoting billet loader that moves in the extrusion direction is functionally the same as the billet loader described for indirect aluminum alloy extrusion (Fig. 6.28). It withdraws over the shaft of the extrusion stem without the billet clamp opening as the container moves over the billet. Although extrusion is carried out without lubrication, as is the case in direct extrusion with a shell, there are differences in the operating sequences for the auxiliary equipment. The discard is sheared in front of the die in the same manner as in indirect and direct extrusion of aluminum. After the shearing process and the subsequent stripping from the container bore, a removal tool collects the packet consisting of the die block, shell, and cleaning block and transfers it to a working table adjacent to the press. An operator then must transfer by hand the cleaning block to the block recycling system and the die block first to the shell separator and then to the recycling system.

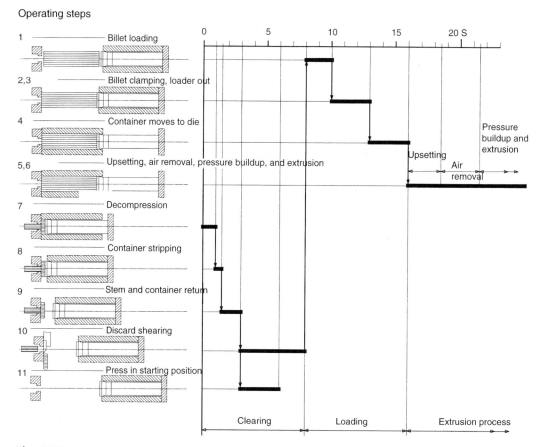

Fig. 6.23 Operating steps in aluminum extrusion with a short stroke, time dependent

The shell must be removed in the same way as the discard, via a chute and a conveyor. The die block and the cleaning block are loaded with a pivoting loader.

The development of automatic auxiliary systems for copper alloy extrusion has not been realized in the area of separation devices because of the shell formed from the use of dummy blocks or die blocks as well as cleaning blocks. Manual operations are still necessary, even if only sporadically. The auxiliary equipment described as follows depicts an in-

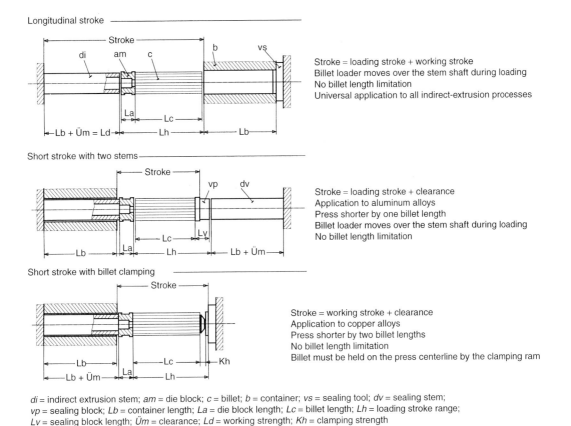

Longitudinal stroke

Stroke = loading stroke + working stroke
Billet loader moves over the stem shaft during loading
No billet length limitation
Universal application to all indirect-extrusion processes

Short stroke with two stems

Stroke = loading stroke + clearance
Application to aluminum alloys
Press shorter by one billet length
Billet loader moves over the stem shaft during loading
No billet length limitation

Short stroke with billet clamping

Stroke = working stroke + clearance
Application to copper alloys
Press shorter by two billet lengths
No billet length limitation
Billet must be held on the press centerline by the clamping ram

di = indirect extrusion stem; am = die block; c = billet; b = container; vs = sealing tool; dv = sealing stem; vp = sealing block; Lb = container length; La = die block length; Lc = billet length; Lh = loading stroke range; Lv = sealing block length; $Üm$ = clearance; Ld = working strength; Kh = clamping strength

Fig. 6.24 Arrangements for indirect-extrusion presses

Table 6.7 Equipment for indirect extrusion with equipment for the different operations

| | Indirect extrusion(a) | | |
| | Light metal | | Heavy Metal |
Equipment	Special Case	Standard	Special case
Press			
Discard shear	I, II	I	I, II
Saw	. . .	. . .	I, II
Press drive			
Oil hydraulic drive to 25 mm/s	I, II	. . .	. . .
Oil hydraulic drive to 60 mm/s	. . .	I	I, II
Manipulation systems			
For fixed-die block	I, II	. . .	. . .
For loose die and loose cleaning block	. . .	I	I, II
For loose combination die and cleaning block	I, II	. . .	I, II

(a) Product: wire, bar = I; section = II

teresting approach to solving the shell problem.

Auxiliary Equipment for the Indirect Extrusion of Copper Alloys with an Extrusion and a Cleaning Stem. The short-stroke press is equipped with a tool slide that carries the extrusion stem and the cleaning stem. The sealing tool contains a ram to clamp the billet loaded into the press center so that a single-piece billet loader with a swinging loading head (in contrast to the two-part pivoting billet loader) can be used. This method of billet loading requires accurate central location of the clamped billet. The container is positioned over the cleaning stem with a fixed cleaning block. While the billet is clamped between the ram and the cleaning block, the con-

SMS
HASENCLEVER

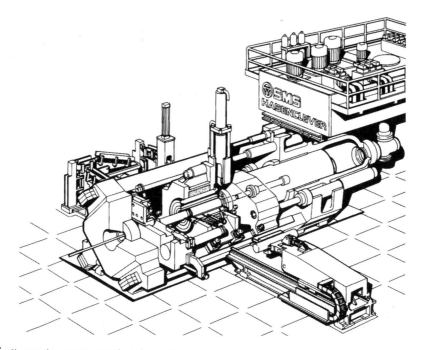

Fig. 6.25 Short-stroke extrusion press for indirect extrusion

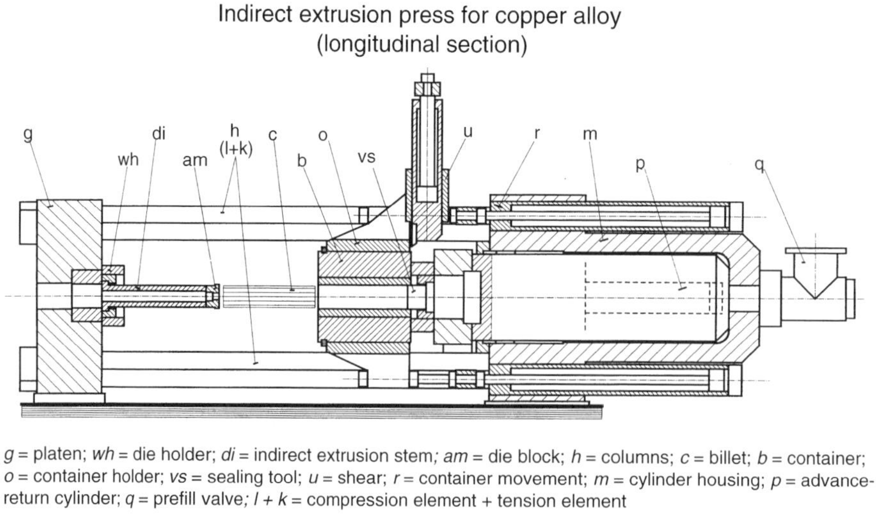

Indirect extrusion press for copper alloy
(longitudinal section)
g
wh
di
am
h
(l+k)
c
b
o
vs
u
r
m
p
q
g = platen; *wh* = die holder; *di* = indirect extrusion stem; *am* = die block; *h* = columns; *c* = billet; *b* = container; *o* = container holder; *vs* = sealing tool; *u* = shear; *r* = container movement; *m* = cylinder housing; *p* = advance-return cylinder; *q* = prefill valve; *l* + *k* = compression element + tension element

Fig. 6.26 Components of an indirect-extrusion press with tooling

tainer moves over the billet to clear the space for the extrusion stem with the die block.

After extrusion and the shearing of the discard in front of the container bore, the die block is pushed into a removal tool. The shell remaining in the container bore is cleared by the cleaning stem and finishes in a scrap bin, along with the discard, via a chute and a conveyor. The removal tool passes the die block into a recycling system where, if necessary, die changing, cooling, cleaning, and lubrication are possible. A loader transfers the prepared die block for a new extru-

Table 6.8   Presses for indirect extrusion of aluminum (light metal) and copper alloys (heavy metal)

Structural components		Indirect-extrusion presses(a)			
		Light metal		Heavy metal	
Main subassemblies	Subassemblies	Standard press	Special press	Standard press	Special press
Press frame	Cylinder housing	I, II	. . .	I, II	. . .
	Platen	I, II	. . .	I, II	. . .
	Columns	I, II	. . .	I, II	. . .
	Bed plate	. . .	I, II	. . .	I, II
Moving crosshead	Moving crosshead	I, II	. . .	I, II	. . .
	Advance-return cylinder	I, II	. . .	I, II	. . .
Container holder with shear	Container holder	I, II	. . .	I, II	. . .
	Moving cylinder	I, II	. . .	I, II	. . .
	Shear	I, II	. . .	. . .	. . .
Die carrier	Die slide	. . .	I, II	I, II	. . .
	Die shuffle	. . .	I, II	. . .	I, II
	Die rotating arm	. . .	. . .	. . .	. . .
	Stationary die holder	I, II	. . .	. . .	I, II
Extruded product separator	Shear	I, II	. . .	I, II	. . .
	Saw	. . .	. . .	. . .	. . .

(a) Product: wire, bar = I; section = II

(a)   (b)   (c)

(d)   (e)

Fig. 6.27   Auxiliary equipment for the loose die block of an indirect aluminium alloy extrusion. (a) Discard shearing in collector. (b) Die block, loader, and transporter. (c) Shell separation in operation; transporter with die block. (d) Die block changer in operation. (e) Change and maintenance station, heat retention station, and transporter

Fig. 6.28 Auxiliary equipment for the indirect extrusion of copper alloys. (a) Billet loading. (b) Discard shearing and removal. (c) Collector for discard, cleaning block, and shell

sion cycle to the extrusion stem located outside the press while the cleaning stem is in the center of the press.

6.1.2.4 Hydraulic Drive Systems and Control for Indirect Extrusion

Because in principle, direct extrusion with the associated auxiliary equipment and the necessary handling system differs from indirect-operating plants only in design details, tooling, and operating sequence, the oil hydraulic system is practically identical in design and component details.

There is no requirement for water hydraulic systems in indirect-extrusion plants, although there is no reason why they could not be used.

Differences in the hydraulic system are attributable to process technological-related items, including the higher demands on the quantity and quality of the extruded products.

The hydraulic drive must be able to accurately control the extrusion speed. The tolerances for extrusion speeds below 5 mm/s are particularly demanding. The drive pumps must be capable of being reliably and accurately controlled at different working pressures. The advantage of the higher extrusion speeds usually associated with indirect extrusion can only be fully utilized if the pumps are suitable.

The important specific features of indirect extrusion that must be taken into account in the design of the press are:

- The extrusion cycle is longer because of the significantly longer billet, and hence, oil cooling and oil filtration is very important.
- Exact control of the extrusion speed places corresponding demands on the high-pressure pumps, the oil cooling, and the oil filtration.
- The die block requires additional auxiliary equipment for the maintenance and manipulation of the die in automatic operation. This requires expensive controls.

6.1.2.5 Electric Drive and Control for Indirect Extrusion

In the case of aluminum extrusion, it should be pointed out that extremely precise temperature control of the billet container is required.

Reliable maintenance of the preset extrusion speed is definitely necessary in order to utilize the advantages of indirect extrusion of good quality and throughput.

6.1.2.6 Typical Operating Sequence in Indirect Extrusion

The points raised in section 6.1.1.6 also apply here. Four main operations can be identified for the operational sequence of the extrusion press, taking into account the special features of indirect extrusion:

1. *Loading:* The hot billet must be loaded into the press by a billet loader. The design of a billet loader depends on the type of press.
   a. *Standard stroke:* The stem is stationary on the platen, and the container is in the loading position on the sealing tool, which is attached to the moving crosshead. Billet loading is between the stem and the container. In this case, the billet loader withdraws over the stem shaft while the container is pushed over the billet.
   b. *Short stroke:* The stem is stationary on the platen, and the container is over the stem. Billet loading is between the stem, with the die/container on one side and the sealing tool on the other side. In this case, the billet is clamped between the stem with the die and the sealing tool. The container is pushed over the clamped billet.
2. *Extrusion:* The billet is upset after it has reached the extrusion position. Extrusion is then carried out until decompression, when the discard thickness is reached.
3. *Clearing:* The tools are opened, and the extruded section is removed from the discard and taken away. The discard and, if necessary, the shell are removed, and the tooling is moved to the starting position.
4. *Tool preparation:* Depending on the material being extruded, the tooling is cooled, cleaned, lubricated, and changed if necessary.

The example of an operating sequence shown in Table 6.9 is for a middle-sized extrusion press (25 MN) and covers the most important operating steps, in some cases in a summarized format (Fig. 6.29). The chronological sequence is trimmed to a realistic operating speed and thus to operationally and economically viable values. It should be possible to reliably attain these values. Unplanned interruptions must be taken into account, and these will reduce the production in practice. From experience, the annual average plant availability is approximately 70% for continuous production.

6.2 Presses and Plant for Tube Extrusion

The presses and associated plant for tube extrusion are more flexible than for rod extrusion. They are suitable not only for tube extrusion but also for the extrusion of wire, rod, and section. Presses and plant for tube extrusion are installed when other processes for tube extrusion are uneconomical.

Extrusion plants that only produce tube are well known in the case of copper alloys (Fig. 6.30). There are also presses for the production of tubes in iron and nickel alloys. In contrast, plants that exclusively produce tube in aluminum alloys are only encountered in special cases. Because tube presses can be used to produce both seamless tubes and rod, it is usual to refer to tube presses as rod-and-tube extrusion presses.

The difference between the tube extrusion press and the rod press is the mandrel, which determines the internal contour of the tube or the hollow section. It must be possible to move the mandrel in tube extrusion independent of the extrusion stem. The extrusion stem and the dummy block must have a bore corresponding to the mandrel diameter. Whereas in rod extrusion a solid billet is deformed, in the tube extrusion press the billet must be pierced before tube extrusion. This assumes there is a piercing system built into the press. Often, prebored or externally pierced billets are used so that the internal press piercing system is not required [Ste 91].

Direct and indirect tube extrusion includes combinations of the two processes, which depend on the geometry and the extrusion program. Basically, there are the following four extrusion programs:

- Direct tube extrusion over a stationary mandrel. Friction at the container liner wall and friction on the mandrel surface
- Direct tube extrusion over a moving mandrel. Friction at the container liner wall, no friction on the mandrel surface outside the deformation zone
- Indirect tube extrusion over a stationary mandrel. No friction at the container liner wall, friction at the mandrel surface
- Indirect tube extrusion over a moving mandrel. No friction at the container liner wall and no friction at the mandrel surface outside the deformation zone

Table 6.9   Operating sequence of an indirect-extrusion press for brass with an extrusion stem and a cleaning stem

Times have been rounded to 1.5.

	Operating step	Time in seconds													Comments
		3	6	9	12	15	18	21	24	27	30	33	36	39	
1	Billet loading in									▓	▓				Billet + die block loading
2	Container advance											▓			Billet into container up to sealing tool
3	Billet loader out													▓	Loading position/ initial position
4	Container and moving crosshead advance													█	Upsetting extrusion
5	Decompres-sion	▓													Press under no load
6	Moving crosshead return	▓													Clearance for shearing
7	Container stripping	▓													Discard clear
8	Discard shear		▓												Extrusion cut from discard and cleared
9	Container back			▓											Loading position for cleaning block
10	Loader in				▓										Cleaning block loaded
11	Shell removal					▓									Moving crosshead advance, shell compacted
12	Moving crosshead return						▓								Clearance for removal tool
13	Removal tool in							▓							Removal of block and shell
14	Container and removal tool advance							▓							Removal via extrusion stem
15	Removal tool out									▓					To transfer position to auxiliary equipment
16	Container + moving crosshead return									▓					Press in loading position

6.2.1 Direct Tube Extrusion

Tube presses are extrusion presses with an internal piercing system or a mandrel-moving system. The construction and function of tube extrusion presses corresponds to the machines used for direct extrusion, but they are also fitted with a piercing or a mandrel-moving system.

6.2.1.1 Machine Construction Details of Tube Extrusion Presses

The main subassemblies—moving crosshead for tube extrusion presses, piercing system, and mandrel-moving system—are largely standardized. The design of a direct tube extrusion press is mainly determined by the following factors (Table 6.10):

- *Product:* Tube, hollow section
  a. Aluminum, aluminum alloys, easy to work and/or difficult to work
  b. Copper, copper alloys including brass, easy to work and/or difficult to deform
  c. Steel, high-strength steel alloys, easy to deform and/or difficult to deform
- *Process technology:* Extrusion program
  a. Tube extrusion over a stationary mandrel without lubrication
  b. Tube extrusion over a stationary mandrel with lubrication
  c. Tube extrusion over a moving mandrel without lubrication
  d. Tube extrusion over a moving mandrel with lubrication
  e. Tube extrusion over a stationary mandrel without lubrication and with a shell

Operation

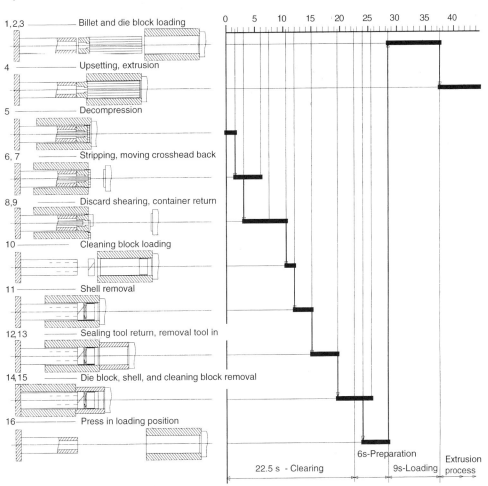

Fig. 6.29 Operating steps in the indirect extrusion of brass. See Table 6.9.

f. Tube extrusion over a moving mandrel without lubrication and with a shell

- *Tooling:* Container, stem, mandrel, dummy block, and die

The products described apply to presses that extrude only seamless tubes and sometimes seamless hollow sections that cannot be produced with a welding chamber die. Products produced by rod extrusion presses can also be produced with tube extrusion presses. However, in this case, the machines must be matched and specified to the required production range.

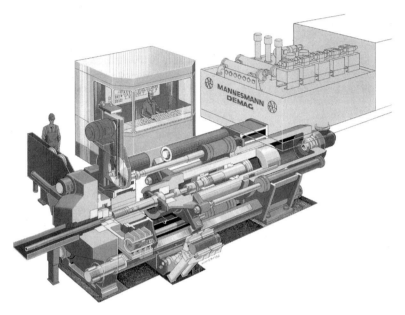

Fig. 6.30 Direct copper tube press. Source: Mannesmann Demag

Table 6.10 Presses for the direct tube extrusion of aluminum (light metal,), copper (heavy metal), and steel

| | Direct tube extrusion press(a) | | | | | |
| | Light metal | | Heavy metal | | Steel | |
Equipment	Standard press	Special press	Standard press	Special press	Standard press	Special press
Press						
Discard shear	I, II	. . .	. . .	. . .	. . .	. . .
Separating saw	. . .	I, II	I, II	. . .	I, II	. . .
Container length, standard	I, II	. . .	I, II	. . .	I, II	. . .
Container length, short	. . .	. . .	I	. . .	I	. . .
Piercing system(b)	I, II	. . .	I, II	. . .	I, II	. . .
Mandrel movement(c)	. . .	. . .	. . .	. . .	I, II	. . .
Mandrel internal cooling	. . .	. . .	I, II	. . .	. . .	. . .
Press device						
Oil hydraulic drive up to 25 mm/s(d)	I, II	. . .	. . .	. . .	. . .	. . .
Oil hydraulic drive up to 60 mm/s(d)	. . .	. . .	I, II	. . .	. . .	. . .
Water hydraulic drive up to 150 mm/s(e)	. . .	. . .	. . .	I	I, II	. . .
Water hydraulic drive up to 300 mm/s(e)	. . .	. . .	. . .	. . .	I	. . .
Manipulation systems						
For fixed dummy block	. . .	I	. . .	. . .	I, II	. . .
For loose dummy block without cleaning block	I, II	. . .	. . .	. . .	. . .	I, II
For loose dummy block and cleaning block	. . .	. . .	I, II	. . .	. . .	. . .
For loose combination dummy and cleaning block	. . .	. . .	. . .	I	. . .	. . .

(a) Product: tube = I; hollow section = II. (b) With mandrel stroke limitation and mandrel rotate. (c) With hollow billets. (d) Direct pump drive. (e) Accumulator necessary

Because tubes are produced from shorter billets, tube extrusion presses can be designed with a reduced container length and a relatively short working stroke. In this case, a container length of approximately two-thirds of the standard length according to DIN 24540 has proved successful. These tube extrusion presses are used mainly with copper alloys for the production of tubes. Solid billets are used that are pierced in the press. In order to obtain concentric tubes within the required tolerances, the piercing ratio mandrel diameter/billet length should not be greater than 1 to 7, which limits the billet length.

6.2.1.2 Main Subassemblies and Modules of Direct Tube Extrusion Presses

In tube extrusion, a die is used to form the external shape of the tube, and a mandrel is used for the internal contour. Depending on the program, the mandrel can be provided with a mandrel tip that usually can be changed. This can only be used in tube extrusion over a stationary mandrel. The tool set shown in Fig. 6.31 is used for the production of copper alloy tubes. It includes:

- Die holder with a taper seal
- Container with induction heating
- Mandrel (only partly visible)

- Hollow stem
- Dummy block (not visible)

The stem and the container are fitted with a bayonet lock for rapid tool changing. The container can be turned through 180° so that the stem and the die faces can be exchanged. The extrusion of tubes over a mandrel requires a piercing system and a mandrel holder, or a mandrel-moving system with a mandrel holder. The piercing system can be located in the press in the moving crosshead or behind the main cylinder housing.

The press frame of the tube extrusion press consists of the following main subassemblies:

- Moving crosshead (Fig. 6.32) as stem carrier with internal piercing or mandrel-moving system
- Tool carrier, moving crosshead for rod and tube extrusion with press return and advance cylinders with oil hydraulic or, in the case of water hydraulic drive, with return cylinder and with integrated piercing or mandrel-moving system
- Piercer system as a mandrel carrier consisting of the important components
- Piercer crosshead
- Piercer cylinder with piercer return
- Piercer stroke limiter

Fig. 6.31 Direct tube extrusion tooling. Source: Schmidt & Clemans

Longitudinal section

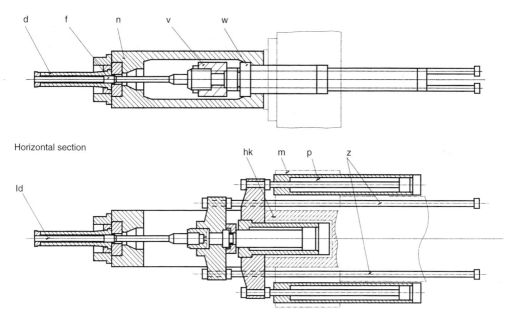

Horizontal section

d = stem with dummy block; f = mandrel holder; m = cyilinder housing; n = moving crosshead; p = advance-return cylinder; v = piercing crosshead; w = piercing cylinder; z = mandrel stroke limitation; hk = main ram; ld = piercing mandrel

Fig. 6.32 Moving crosshead of a direct tube press

Table 6.11 Main subassemblies of a direct tube extrusion press

| Main subassemblies | Subassemblies | Direct tube extrusion press(a) | | | | | |
| | | Light metal | | Heavy metal | | Steel | |
		Standard	Alternative	Standard	Alternative	Standard	Alternative
Press frame	Cylinder frame	I, II	. . .	I, II	. . .	I, II	. . .
	Platen	I, II	. . .	I, II	. . .	I, II	. . .
	Columns	I, II	. . .	I, II	. . .	I, II	. . .
	Bed plate	. . .	I, II	. . .	I, II	. . .	I, II
Moving crosshead	Moving crosshead for piercing system	I, II	. . .	I, II	. . .	I, II	. . .
	Moving crosshead for mandrel movement	. . .	. . .	. . .	. . .	. . .	I
	Advance-return cylinder	I, II	. . .	I, II	. . .	I, II	. . .
Piercing system	Piercing moving crosshead	I, II	. . .	I, II	. . .	I, II	. . .
	Piercing cylinder and return cylinder	I, II	. . .	I, II	. . .	I, II	. . .
	Piercing cylinder(b)	. . .	. . .	. . .	I, II	. . .	. . .
	Mandrel stroke limitation	I, II	. . .	I, II	. . .	I, II	. . .
	Mandrel rotate system	I, II	. . .	I, II	. . .	I, II	. . .
	Mandrel internal cooling	. . .	. . .	I, II	. . .	. . .	. . .
Mandrel stroke movement	Moving crosshead	. . .	. . .	. . .	. . .	. . .	I
	Moving cylinder(b)	. . .	. . .	. . .	. . .	. . .	I
Container holder	Container holder	I, II	. . .	I, II	. . .	I, II	. . .
	Moving cylinder	I, II	. . .	I, II	. . .	I, II	. . .
Die carrier	Die shuffle	I, II	. . .	I, II	. . .	. . .	. . .
	Die slide	. . .	. . .	. . .	I, II	. . .	. . .
	Die rotating arm	. . .	I	I	. . .	I, II	. . .
	Stationary die holder(c)	. . .	I, II	. . .	I, II	. . .	. . .
Extrusion separator	Shear	I, II	. . .	. . .	. . .	. . .	. . .
	Saw	. . .	. . .	I, II	. . .	I, II	. . .

(a) Product: seamless tube = I; seamless hollow section = II. (b) As differential cylinder. (c) Only with small extrusion presses

Table 6.12   Operating sequence of a direct copper alloy tube press for easy and moderately difficult-to-extrude copper-base alloys with standard stroke and loose dummy block

Times have been rounded to 2 s.

	Operational stage	Time in seconds:	Comments
1	Billet loaders 1 + 2 in		Billet and dummy block loading
2	Extrusion stem advance		Billet pushed to die
3	Billet loaders 1 + 2 out		Loading position / starting position
4	Extrusion stem advance		Upset
5	Extrusion stem back		Air removal, clearance for piercing
6	Piercing		Until just before the die
7	Extrusion stem extrusion		Start of extrusion, extrusion
8	Decompression		Press depressurised
9	Piercing mandrel return		To starting position
10	Extrusion stem return		To cleaning block loading position
11	Billet loader 1 in		Loading cleaning block
12	Container decompress and return		To saw position, tube exposed
13	Tube sawn in front of die		Tube separated from discard and pulled clear
14	Container back		To loading position of the cleaning block
15	Extrusion stem advance		Cleaning block pushed into the container
16	Billet loader 1 out		Loading position / starting position
17	Removal tool in		Between die and container
18	Container and extrusion stem to removal tool		Pushing out of discard, shell and block
19	Removal tool out		To transfer system to auxiliary system
20	Extrusion stem back		To starting position
21	Container back		Intermediate position
22	Die change		Rotating arm through 180¡
23	Container to die		Press in loading position
24	Mandrel lubrication		Mandrel advance and back

Time in seconds scale: 10   20   30   40

- Mandrel-moving system as mandrel carrier consisting of:
  a. Mover crosshead
  b. Mover cylinder with return
  c. Container holder (main structural group extrusion press)
  d. Tool slide or carrier or rotating arm or stationary (main subassembly extrusion press)

e. Discard shear and/or cut-off saw (main structural component extrusion press).

Basically, the designs of tube extrusion presses can be classified into:

- Tube extrusion presses for aluminum alloys for the production of tubes and hollow sections

Operating steps in tube extrusion, time dependent

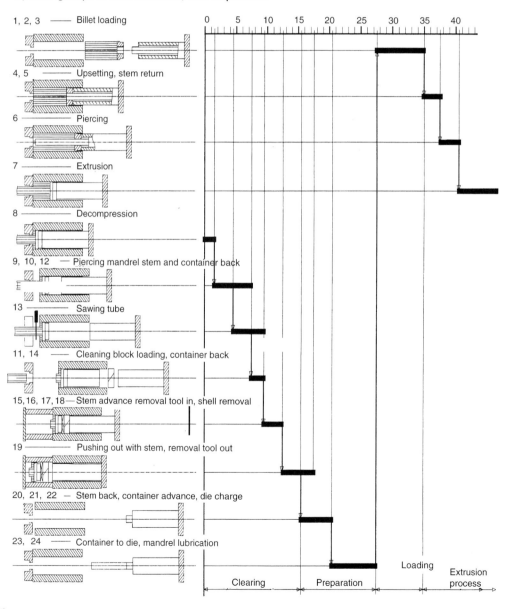

Fig. 6.33 Operating sequence of a direct tube extrusion press, time related. See Table 6.12 (in the table, times have been rounded to 2 s).

- Tube extrusion presses for copper alloys for the extrusion of tubes and hollow sections
- Tube extrusion presses for steel for the production of tubes and hollow sections

Depending on the application of the tube extrusion press, the modules must be capable of being assembled in such a way that the desired production is guaranteed. Table 6.11 shows an overview to help clarify a rational modular system. It does not contain all possible combinations but does take into account current tube extrusion presses for aluminum alloys, copper alloys, and steel alloys (including nickel alloys).

The examples mentioned can differ from each other in the arrangement of the subassemblies. Direct-extrusion presses are known that process copper alloys, iron alloys, and nickel alloys.

The piercing and the piercer return cylinder loads must be sufficient for piercing, mandrel return, and overcoming the billet friction on the mandrel during extrusion and during the auxiliary movements (container and moving crosshead).

The frictional forces on the mandrel depend on the material being extruded and the process technology, that is, whether a stationary or a moving mandrel is used. The forces on the mandrel can be very high with aluminum alloys. The maximum tensile force on the mandrel during extrusion can be calculated from:

$$F_D = D_D \cdot \pi \cdot l_0 \cdot \tau_S \qquad \text{(Eq. 6.2)}$$

where F_D is the tensile load on the mandrel, D_D is the mandrel diameter, l_0 is the upset billet length, and τ_S is the critical shear stress of the material being extruded.

To protect the mandrel from overloading, a safety system must be provided to control the resultant tensile forces. The container must remain in its sealing position during piercing. The friction between the billet and the container should not displace the container as the billet expands. The mandrel return force must be set to enable the mandrel to be withdrawn from a pierced or sticking billet.

The moving crosshead for tube extrusion presses is designed to accommodate the piercing system in a frame construction. The piercing system consists of a piercing cylinder and two return cylinders. A differential cylinder that acts as the piercing cylinder is an alternative, provided that the required mandrel return force allows this system to be used. In addition, a

piercer crosshead with a mandrel-holder carrier for the mandrel holder must be present. If required, internal cooling and/or mechanical or hydraulic mandrel stroke limitation that is used for the extrusion of tubes over a stationary mandrel or over the mandrel tip can be installed. The different functions of the piercing system for tube extrusion depend on the material and the process.

The following factors influence the design of the press:

- The piercing load and mandrel return load—different for aluminum and copper alloy extrusion
- Mandrel internal cooling—necessary for copper alloys to improve the mandrel life
- Mandrel stroke limitation for tube extrusion over a stationary mandrel or over a mandrel tip (positioned mechanically or hydraulically)—necessary for aluminum and copper alloys
- Mandrel rotate system—required for rapid mandrel changing and for positioning of a profiled mandrel for hollow sections
- Relative stroke of the mandrel during extrusion—useful to improve the service life of the mandrel in the extrusion of copper alloy tubes

6.2.1.3 Auxiliary Equipment for Direct Extrusion

The auxiliary equipment for direct tube extrusion is similar to that used for direct rod extrusion. Mandrel lubrication is the only addition that may be necessary.

6.2.1.4 Hydraulic Control Systems

The hydraulic drive, control, and additional equipment for direct tube extrusion correspond to that for direct rod extrusion. An additional hydraulic control is needed for the piercer system. If the mandrel stroke limitation is hydraulic, an accurately operating control must be included for precise location of the mandrel in the die. It must provide a stable location of the mandrel during extrusion.

6.2.1.5 Electrical Drive, Controls, and Additional Equipment for Direct Tube Extrusion

No additional equipment is required in the areas of drive and heating electrical systems for

Table 6.13 Equipment for indirect tube extrusion plants

	Indirect tube press(a)	
	Light metal	
Equipment	Standard press	Special press
Press		
Discard shear	I, II	. . .
Saw	. . .	I, II
Piercing system(b)	I, II	. . .
Press drive		
Direct oil hydraulic drive up to 25 mm/s	I, II	. . .
Manipulation systems		
For fixed-die block	. . .	I, II
For loose, combination die and cleaning block	I, II	. . .

(a) Product: Seamless tube = I; seamless hollow section = II. (b) With mandrel stroke limitation and mandrel rotation

the electrical drive and controls. The hydraulic and the electrical control systems must be expanded to meet the requirements of the additional components needed for the tube extrusion press.

6.2.1.6 Typical Operating Sequence for Direct Tube Extrusion

Five main operations characterize the tube extrusion operation:

1. Loading
2. Piercing with a mandrel. The piercing system is used. The loaded billet is first upset in the container to center it. The stem with the dummy block is withdrawn to leave an empty

space for the billet as it increases in length during piercing.
3. Tube extrusion
4. Clearing
5. Tooling preparation

The operating sequence described in Table 6.12 and Fig. 6.33 applies for the times required for a medium-sized extrusion press (20 to 35 MN). It takes into account the most important operating sequences, to some extent, in a summarized format.

6.2.2 Indirect Tube Extrusion

6.2.2.1 Machine Design Details

The indirect tube extrusion press contains a piercing system or a mandrel-moving system similar in design and function to that in direct extrusion [Zil 84]. Until now, only a few indirect tube extrusion presses have been built for difficult-to-extrude aluminum alloys. Although combined direct and indirect rod-and-tube extrusion presses have been built for copper-base alloys, there is no significant tube extrusion of copper alloys by the indirect tube extrusion process. The design of indirect tube extrusion presses is based on:

- Product:
  a. Tube and hollow sections in difficult-to-deform aluminum alloys
- Process technology:
  b. Tube extrusion over a stationary mandrel without lubrication with a shell

Table 6.14 Main subassemblies of indirect tube extrusion presses

	Indirect tube press(a)		
	Components	Light metal	
Main subassemblies	Subassemblies	Standard press	Special press
Press frame	Cylinder housing	I, II	. . .
	Platen	I, II	. . .
	Columns	I, II	. . .
	Bed plate	. . .	I, II
Moving crosshead	Moving crosshead for piercing system	I, II	. . .
	Advance-return cycle	I, II	. . .
Piercing system	Piercing crosshead	I, II	. . .
	Advance cylinder and return cylinder	I, II	. . .
	Piercing cylinder(b)	. . .	I, II
	Mandrel stroke limitation	I, II	. . .
	Mandrel rotation system	I, II	. . .
Container housing	Container holder	I, II	. . .
	Moving cylinder	I, II	. . .
Die carrier	Die shuffle	. . .	I, II
	Stationary die holder	I, II	. . .
Discard separator	Shear	I, II	. . .
	Saw	. . .	I, II

(a) Product: Seamless tube = I; seamless hollow section = II. (b) As differential cylinder

Table 6.15 Operating sequence of an indirect aluminum alloy tube extrusion press with two stems for difficult-to-extrude aluminum alloys

	Operational stage	Time in seconds												Comments
		4	8	12	16	20	24	28	32	36	40	44	48	
1	Billet loader in						▓							Billet + sealing block loading
2	Container back							▓						Billet + sealing block in container
3	Billet loader out								▓					Loading position / starting position
4	Die loader in									▓				Die block loading
5	Moving crosshead advance										▓			Die block in container
6	Container advance										▓			Die loader moves away
7	Die loader out										▓			Loading position / starting position
8	Mandrel advance											▓		Up to die position (extrusion position)
9	Container + moving crosshead advance											█		Upsetting, pressure build up + extrusion
10	Decompression	▓												Press decompressed
11	Mandrel back		▓											To starting position
12	Moving crosshead back			▓										Clearance for removal tool
13	Removal tool in				▓									Removal of discard + sealing tool
14	Moving crosshead + container advance					▓								Pushing out with stem
15	Discard shearing						▓							Separation of discard from tube and removal
16	Moving crosshead back						▓							Clearance for removal tool
17	Removal tool out						▓							In transfer position to auxiliary system

c. Tube extrusion with a moving mandrel without lubrication with a shell
- Tooling:
  a. Container, stem, mandrel, combination die block (Table 6.13)

Only seamless tubes and seamless hollow sections are extruded. The products that are produced on the indirect-extrusion press can also be produced on an indirect tube extrusion press. However, the machine must be fitted with the tooling for the range of products required.

6.2.2.2 Main Subassemblies of Indirect Tube Extrusion Presses

The indirect tube extrusion press contains, independent of the design, the same subassemblies as the direct tube extrusion press. The few indirect tube extrusion presses built so far are restricted to aluminum alloys, as can be seen from the following overview (Tables 6.14, 6.15, Fig. 6.34).

Operation

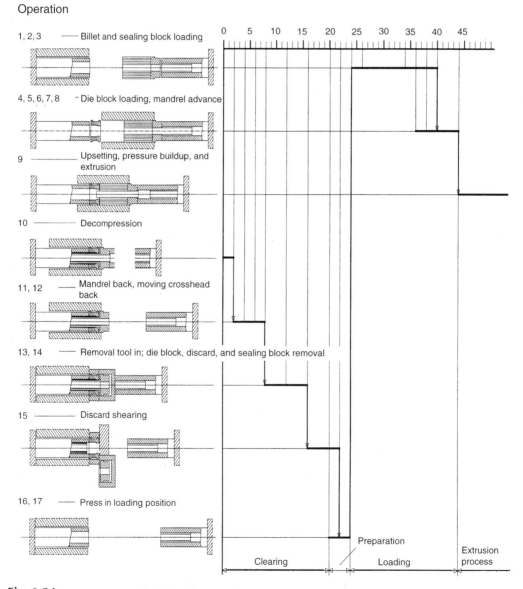

Operation		
1, 2, 3	Billet and sealing block loading	
4, 5, 6, 7, 8	Die block loading, mandrel advance	
9	Upsetting, pressure buildup, and extrusion	
10	Decompression	
11, 12	Mandrel back, moving crosshead back	
13, 14	Removal tool in; die block, discard, and sealing block removal	
15	Discard shearing	
16, 17	Press in loading position	

Fig. 6.34 Operating sequence for indirect aluminum tube extrusion, time dependent. See Table 6.15

6.2.2.3 Typical Operating Sequence for Indirect Tube Extrusion

The operating sequence shown here has proved suitable in many applications. However, for quality reasons, prebored fully machined billets are used. They are not pierced in the press!

Billet Heating Systems

Josef Putz*

Today, billets are usually heated to the desired operating temperature in main frequency induction or rapid-heating gas-fired furnaces. These two furnace types are used because they are best suited to meet the requirements of temperature control, flexibility, floor space, and so on of a billet-heating furnace in a modern extrusion plant. However, specific requirements often cannot be fulfilled by the standard designs of these furnaces, for example, extremely high throughputs, axial temperature distribution, and so on. Changes in the plant must be carried out or additional equipment provided.

6.3 Induction Furnaces

6.3.1 General

In the induction furnace, the heat is produced uniformly within the billet in a layer over the full circumference, referred to as the penetration depth, δ (Fig. 6.35). This defines the thickness of the peripheral layer in which approximately 87% of the energy transferred to the billet is converted to heat. The thickness of this peripheral layer, which depends on the electrical and magnetic material properties of the billet as well as the frequency of the power supply, is approximately 70 mm for steel, 20 mm for copper, 30 mm for brass, and 25 mm for aluminum at their extrusion temperature.

The heat transfers by conduction into the core region from the peripheral layer in the billet, where the induced current flow causes heating. There is thus a temperature difference between the billet periphery and the billet core that develops from zero to a specific value and remains practically constant up to the end of the heating of the peripheral layer (Fig. 6.36). The magnitude of this temperature difference depends on the thermal conductivity of the material and on the diameter of the billet as well as the specific energy input. Because the peripheral layer is uniformly heated around the periphery, the heat flow to the core is uniform in all directions, and the isotherms can be represented as concentric circles.

This radial temperature difference in the billet at the end of the heating process is too large in many cases to enable the billet to be immediately extruded, and therefore, it must be equalized to a value suitable for extrusion. Naturally, the time needed depends on the material and diameter of the billet as well as on the energy input, because this parameter significantly affects the developed temperature difference. In order to retain the peripheral layer at the final tem-

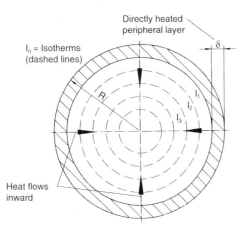

I_n = Isotherms (dashed lines)

Directly heated peripheral layer

Heat flows inward

Fig. 6.35 Development of heat in a billet by induction

*Billet Heating Systems, Josef Putz

perature, the heat flow to the core in the temperature equalization is continuously replaced by the input of a corresponding energy amount.

The electromagnetic field lines run parallel to the billet axis in the middle of the billet (relative to the length) within the directly heated peripheral layer of thickness, δ. At the end of the billet, the field lines can be subjected to a change in direction toward the billet edge or the billet core, depending on the size of the extension of the coil over the end of the billet (Fig. 6.37). Only a specific extension length of the coil guarantees a homogeneous field and temperature profile over the billet length. This optimal coil extension varies with the billet material and the billet diameter as well as the energy input.

If the coil extension is below the optimum, the field is weakened, resulting in a lower temperature at the end of the billet. The reverse effect occurs if the optimal coil extension is exceeded. This produces a field concentration and thus overheating at the billet end relative to the billet central region.

6.3.1.1 Single-Billet Furnace

The basic form of the induction furnace is the single-billet furnace, which, as the name suggests, is designed to heat a single billet. The simplest furnace design is when only a single billet length is processed, because the coil length can then be exactly matched to the billet length, tak-

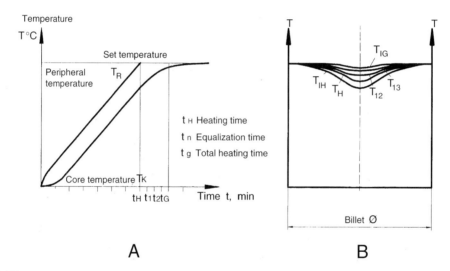

Fig. 6.36 Temperature variation in heating and equalization

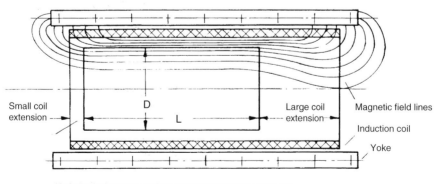

Variation in the magnetic field lines with large and small coil extension at the end faces

Fig. 6.37 Distribution in the electromagnetic field line in the induction coil

ing into account the optimal conditions. If the billet length changes, additional equipment is needed to obtain uniform heating over the billet length. The uniform heating is achieved at the billet end when the location of the billet in the coil is designed to always produce the optimal coil extension. The necessary additional equipment is only provided at the one coil end, and this is, for expediency, selected to be the billet charging end.

These additional systems serve to match the coil length to the billet length. This is carried out as shown in Fig. 6.38, with the aid of tappings on the coil. However, the only billet lengths that can be covered, taking into account the optimal projection, are those that can be correlated by a tapping to a defined partial coil length. These tappings only provide an approximate matching for continually varying billet lengths.

The fine matching takes place by influencing the electromagnetic field configuration, using a so-called field extender. This field extender works by homogeneously extending the electromagnetic field from the billet so that a uniform temperature profile up to the end of the billet is ensured. The single-billet furnace with these additional systems enables the optimal axial temperature uniformity to be achieved. The heating temperature can also be rapidly changed in any desired sequence. The single-billet furnace also has great operational flexibility, because there is no requirement for a startup or billet-removal procedure at the start of production or program change, and changing to different billet lengths is also quick.

The single-billet induction furnace would definitely be the ideal heating system to meet the high specifications of an extrusion plant for the billet heater if it did not have the disadvantage of a low throughput. Only a relatively low throughput can be achieved with a single-billet furnace, even with the maximum billet length. In addition, the throughput drops even further if the billet length is reduced. The furnace can only heat the same number of billets in a given time, regardless whether the billets are long or short. In almost all cases, several single-billet furnaces must be installed to achieve the desired throughput.

6.3.1.2 Multibillet Furnaces

The multibillet induction furnace is the most widely used design and can, without doubt, be considered as the standard configuration for induction billet furnaces. As the name suggests, these furnaces contain several billets (Fig. 6.39) that are pushed, one by one, in billet-length steps through the furnace. In other words, when one billet is pushed into the furnace, one billet must be removed from the exit. If the billet length is changed, then, by necessity, the coil extension,

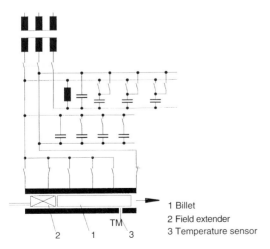

1 Billet
2 Field extender
3 Temperature sensor

Fig. 6.38 Single-billet induction coil with field extension and tappings

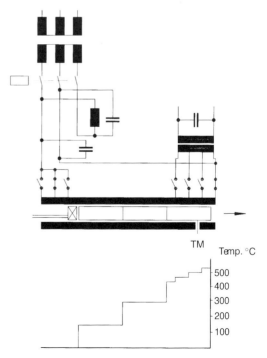

Fig. 6.39 Multibillet induction coil with integrated shock heating coil. TM, temperature sensor

which is always constant at the exit end, varies at the input end.

The control system is designed so that the transport mechanism always keeps the furnace correctly filled; that is, the furnace charge at the entry side is always within the minimum and the maximum limits. In a multibillet furnace for n billets, the maximum furnace load is n times the next smaller billet length that $(n + 1)$ times just exceeds the maximum furnace charge.

In practical press operation, the coil extensions at the entry end are usually larger than desired, and, as described, the billet ends will overheat. The excess temperature in this case will naturally not be as high as with single-billet furnaces, because the billet is not heated over the full temperature range but only over a fraction, the magnitude of which depends on the number of billets in the coil. Accordingly, the excess temperature at the end of the billet is naturally only a fraction of the excess temperature with single-billet furnaces.

These excess temperatures practically even themselves out, particularly with billet materials with a good thermal conductivity. In cases in which a suitable temperature accuracy is not achieved, this can be remedied, as described for single-billet furnaces, by matching the coil length to the billet column length, using tappings on the coil. If this is still insufficient, then a field extension must be used.

Multibillet furnaces can be classified into two designs according to the electrical connection. The first has a single-phase connection to the coil, and the second a three-phase connection (Fig. 6.40). With the single-phase coil connec-tion to the mains, the furnace is usually balanced to give three-phase connection of a single control zone at the end of the furnace.

Depending on the final temperature and the coil length, there is a more or less steep temperature gradient in the furnace that is linear but not continuous. The number of steps corresponds to the number of billets in the furnace (Fig. 6.39). This temperature profile in the furnace requires a special start up operation where two-thirds of the furnace charge must be removed, because the first billets do not have the desired temperature.

Prolonged holding periods create problems, because the temperature profile in the billet column in the furnace can vary significantly, so restarting the production requires the linear temperature gradient to be repeatedly redeveloped, which usually requires the removal of billets due to incorrect temperatures. Maintaining the approximately linear temperature gradient is, however, important for the production, because variations in the temperature steps from one billet to another result in changes in the billet-removal frequency. The production sequence then falls out of synchronization.

The problems associated with the startup and shutdown operation are significantly less with a three-phase furnace connection, because in this case, there are three separately controllable part coils. This simplifies the attainment and maintenance of the linear temperature gradient in the furnace. However, there is the problem that at the boundary between the coils, the phase shift results in field weakening and thus temperature reductions. These temperature shadows often

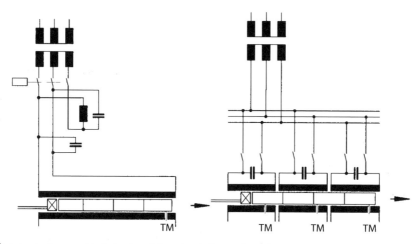

Fig. 6.40 Induction furnace with single-phase (left) and multiphase (right) coil connection. TM, temperature sensor

cannot be fully eliminated, particularly with low–thermal-conductivity materials.

Compared to single-billet furnaces, much higher throughputs can be achieved with multibillet furnaces. The throughput of a multibillet furnace with n billets in the furnace corresponds to the throughput of n single-billet furnaces with the same specific energy input. In contrast to the single-billet furnaces, there is only a slight throughput reduction with shorter billets in the multibillet furnace, and this is associated with the possible reduced furnace load and the higher number of dead cycle times when the billets are removed.

6.3.1.3 Induction Furnace with a Heated Holding Chamber

Even the multibillet furnace has limitations similar to the single-billet furnace in terms of throughput. In many cases, the required throughput is so high that it cannot be achieved even in a multibillet furnace, and two possibly slightly smaller furnaces must be provided. The operation of two or more furnaces that must feed the heated billets, in turn, is naturally associated with problems, particularly on startup after production interruptions and breakdowns, as well as with production changes—all things that frequently happen in normal extrusion plants. The combination of an induction furnace with a heated holding chamber was developed to overcome these problems, with the heated holding chamber located immediately after the induction furnace so that the heated billets pass directly from the induction coil into the heated holding chamber (Fig. 6.41).

The holding chamber has electric heating elements. The brickwork used has a low thermal capacity in order to be able to change the temperature of the hot holding chamber as quickly as possible. The length of the heated holding chamber is 2.5 to 4 times the maximum billet length.

The heated holding chamber fulfills two tasks:

- Equalization of axial and radial temperature differences that occur during heating in the induction furnace
- Storage of heated billets to cover press interruptions

This combination enables the induction furnace to be fitted with more economic three-phase coils, because possible temperature differences at coil junctions can be rectified.

The advance of the billets in the combination does not occur in increments of billet length, as in a standard furnace, but in small steps of approximately 120 to 150 mm. In order to be able to operate as a billet buffer, the removal system is designed so that billets can be removed from different positions within the heated holding chamber. In standard operation, the billet removal from the heated holding chamber takes place when the front edge of the billet is approximately in the center of the heated holding chamber. If the billet cannot be removed at this point, the induction furnace is switched to a low load; that is, it operates at approximately 20% power and 20% of the speed until the billet has reached the position at the exit of the heated holding chamber. This enables an interruption of 15 to 20 min to be bridged. If the stoppage is longer, the billet advance is stopped, and the in-

Fig. 6.41   Induction furnace with integrated heat holding chamber for heating of copper and brass billets

duction furnace is switched to heat-holding operation. In other words, the temperature gradient in the induction furnace is maintained in the individual coil segments by energy input corresponding to the heat losses.

In contrast to the standard design, in which the furnace must be switched off during billet removal to avoid ejection of the billets from the furnace, with the combination of the heated holding chamber it is not necessary to switch off the heating when a billet is removed. There is, therefore, no interruption to the heating process during billet removal and, in addition, the dead cycle times for radial and axial temperature equalization are not required, because this takes place in the hot holding chamber. The combination enables the same throughput as a standard furnace but with a significantly lower connected load. The elimination of the dead time on one hand and the continuous full loading of the coil on the other also ensure that the throughput is the same at all conceivable billet lengths. In addition, optimal temperature uniformity within the billets as well as between billets is guaranteed on removal from the furnace.

In most cases, two conventional multibillet furnaces are replaced by a single unit—one combination induction furnace/heated holding chamber. This considerably simplifies the operations. In particular, startup, alloy change, as well as dry-cycling operations can be carried out semiautomatically, which is not possible with a double plant.

The previously mentioned technical advantages of the combination induction furnace/heated holding chamber over the standard furnace reduce the plant costs, even if concrete numbers cannot be given. The main saving is in the investment costs, with the lower equipment cost of a single plant compared to the double plant and the smaller footprint as well as the significantly reduced connected electrical power.

If the required throughput is in a range that would not cause problems with a standard multibillet furnace, the combination of the connected heated holding chamber and the more complex transport mechanism is more expensive to purchase. There are still the operational advantages and the resultant cost savings, but these are too small to be able to compensate for the higher investment costs of the combination over an acceptable time. The use of the combination is concentrated on the range of higher throughputs in which at least two conventional multi-

billet furnaces are necessary. The combination is also used for copper alloys and steel.

6.3.1.4 Boost Heating

The extrusion process frequently requires a temperature gradient over the billet length. The requirement for aluminum alloys, in particular, is for an axial billet temperature profile (see the section "Process Control in Direct and Indirect Hot Extrusion of Aluminum Alloys without Lubrication" in this chapter).

The heat developed by friction during extrusion is compensated by a temperature decrease toward the end of the billet. With suitable selection of the temperature gradient from the front of the billet to the back, the billet cross-sectional discs always enter the deformation zone with the same temperature.

With continuous billet-on-billet extrusion, the air in the container must be completely removed during upsetting. The billet should bond with the previous billet. The front of the billet should have a higher temperature. Only a relatively low temperature gradient is needed for air removal. The temperature gradient, therefore, has a maximum value at the front of the billet and then drops rapidly and continues almost flat to the back of the billet.

In indirect extrusion, as with direct billet-on-billet extrusion, the removal of the air from the container is an important requirement. The billets must also be heated in the furnace with a temperature that decreases toward the back.

The axial temperature gradients fall in a range up to 100 °C. The magnitude selected depends on several factors, including the extrusion process, billet material (alloy), and billet dimension.

In contrast to aluminum alloys, the temperature gradient used with copper alloys has the maximum temperature at the back of the billet, to compensate for the heat that flows into the colder container.

Only the induction furnace is suitable for such a preheating process. Two different designs of boost heating systems are used to develop a temperature gradient over the billet length: the single-coil boost heater, which is the simplest design, and the somewhat more expensive but more universally applicable segmented-coil boost heater.

The single-coil boost heater consists of a continuous coil fitted with several connections. These connections enable the coil to be heated in several partial lengths that are successively shortened (Fig. 6.42).

The distance between the individual connections is 150 to 300 mm. The number of connections, and thus heating steps, is determined by the maximum billet length.

After the billet has been heated uniformly to the base temperature over the entire billet length, which is the requirement for single-coil boost heating, the entire coil is connected to connection 1. Finally, the subsequent partial lengths are connected through connections 2, 3, and 4. This produces an almost linear temperature gradient over the billet length if the temperature is increased by the same amount in the individual heating stages. The waves that form in the temperature gradient as a result of the reduced heating lengths disappear, in practice, almost completely within a short time, and the extrusion process is not impaired. Any desired temperature profile decrease toward the end of the billet can be produced by suitable selection of the temperature jumps and connection times in the individual heating stages.

In the segmented-coil boost heater, the coil consists, as the name implies, of several coil segments, the lengths of which act in the same manner as the distances between the individual connections in single-coil boost heater. Each of these coil segments is fitted with its own temperature measurement and control system and can be individually switched. This enables any desired temperature gradient to be developed, even where the billet was not supplied with a uniform base temperature.

The two types of boost heater design are used in various versions. The simplest is the boost heater built into the coils of the preheat furnace (Fig. 6.39).

Here, similar to the single-coil boost heater in Fig. 6.42(a), the coil of the preheat furnace is fitted with several connections at the exit side, so that the coil end can be separately heated in several length segments to develop the desired temperature gradient. The standard heating and the boost heating cannot, however, be simultaneously switched on, which naturally results in a throughput reduction for the preheat furnace.

Another possible arrangement for the boost heater is to integrate it into the preheat furnace. As shown schematically in the segmented-coil heating system in Fig. 6.43, the boost heating coils are located directly after the coil of the preheat furnace. Because the coils of the standard heater and the boost heater are electrically separated from each other, they can operate simultaneously, so that in this version there is no reduction in the throughput of the preheat furnace from the boost heater.

A further possibility is to locate a separate boost heater in the transport of the billet between the preheat furnace and the press loader. In this case, it is worthwhile to have greater flexibility by designing the boost heater as a combination single-billet preheat and boost heater in order to be able to raise the temperature of maximum-length billets, which is often necessary when developing the desired temperature profile after

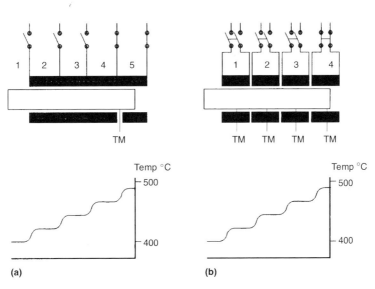

Fig. 6.42 (a) Single-coil heating. (b) Partial-coil boost heating. TM, temperature sensor

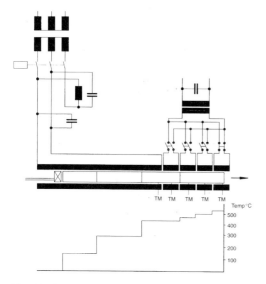

Fig. 6.43 Induction heating furnace with integrated partial-coil boost heating. TM, temperature sensor

long press interruptions. Unlike the single-billet furnace (Fig. 6.38), the coil tappings in this case are not used to approximately match the coil length to the billet length but only for the boost heating. Overheating at the billet end from an excessive coil extension with shorter billets is prevented by the field extender.

In indirect extrusion, the boost heater furnace is needed, because the billet must have a decreasing temperature from the front to the back over the entire length to avoid air entrapment during upsetting in the container. Only the boost heater separate from the preheat furnace is used, because of the high throughput from these presses.

6.3.1.5 Induction Furnaces with Hot Log Shear

In aluminum alloy extrusion plants, sawn billets often are no longer used, for economic reasons. Instead, after preheating, they are sheared to the desired length in a hot log shear (Fig. 6.44). The temperature gradient that automatically forms (Fig. 6.45) during preheating of a log in the induction furnace because of the short furnace length depends on the coil length, the billet length to be sheared, as well as the billet end temperature. It is therefore constant for a specific combination of variables, provided there are no production interruptions. Because these cannot be avoided, it is not possible to always supply billets with the same temperature gradient. Therefore, the temperature gradient produced during the preheating process must be flattened or raised. This can only be achieved by a boost heater. Because the cast log does not have a uniform base temperature in the shearing region and, depending on the production sequence, also has a varying temperature profile, the significantly more flexible segmented coil is the preferred option. The guidelines given previously about the location of the boost heater also apply here.

6.3.2 Gas-Fired Billet Preheat Furnace

6.3.2.1 General

The rapid-heating gas-fired preheat furnace is the alternative to induction heating. The fact that in many plants significantly cheaper gas energy is available compared to electricity resulted in the development of these furnaces to save energy costs and to produce a combustion-based furnace equivalent to the induction furnace. This

Fig. 6.44 Induction furnace combined with a hot log shear for heating aluminum logs

resulted in a furnace that satisfactorily met the many requirements of a modern extrusion plant. The rapid-heating gas-fired preheat furnace is therefore now extensively used in extrusion plants.

In rapid-heating gas-fired preheat furnaces, the furnace chamber (Fig. 6.46) is a tunnel, similar to induction furnaces. However, in contrast to the induction furnace where a coil is needed for each billet diameter, only one furnace tunnel, matched to the maximum billet diameter, is used for all billet diameters.

Heating is by a number of burners uniformly distributed on either side of the furnace tunnel over the full tunnel length. For rotational symmetrical heating of the billets, it is necessary to arrange the burners in several rows, one above the other, depending on the billet diameter. The exhaust gases are transferred via an exhaust duct to the entry side and then fed into a flue.

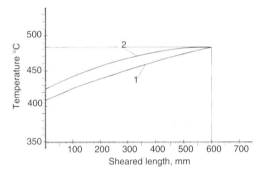

Fig. 6.45 Temperature variation (1, theoretical; 2, practical) over the length of the billet in the cast logs in an induction furnace

Fig. 6.46 Furnace tunnel of a rapid-heating gas-fired furnace for heating copper alloy billets

In this heating method, the entire heat input must be through the billet surface. Therefore, the energy input cannot be as high as with the induction furnace, and rapid-heating gas-fired preheat furnaces require a correspondingly longer time for heating than induction furnaces. The long furnace length requires the rapid-heating gas-fired preheat furnace to be divided into several zones, for good temperature control.

6.3.2.2 Rapid-Heating Gas-Fired Preheat Furnace with Billet Preheating

The exhaust gases are very hot and contain significant heat energy and therefore, provided sufficient space is available, are used to preheat the billets. A zone is added to the heated section of the furnace on the entry side, within which preheating is carried out with the exhaust gases. The length of this preheat zone should, for maximum effectiveness, approximately correspond to the heated length of the furnace. There are two types of preheat zones. In the simpler but also less effective design, the gases flow in a tunnel built onto the heated zone past the billets to the entry side. Adequate turbulence of the exhaust gas flow is needed for good heat transfer.

The second method of preheating is to have the returning hot exhaust gases blown through nozzles at a high velocity onto the billet (Fig. 6.47). However, the recycling of the exhaust gases only functions over a limited length, so that the preheat section must be divided into several recycling zones or fan fields. These preheat zones have a significantly higher utilization of the exhaust gas heat than the simpler design described previously.

Part of the increased saving of thermal energy is countered by the electrical current consumed for the recycling fans in this version. The effectiveness of this preheating is, by necessity, the greatest at the maximum throughput and reduces as the throughput falls, because the power needed for the fans is independent of the throughput.

6.3.2.3 Combination Induction Furnace and Rapid-Heating Gas-Fired Furnace

In spite of the degree of development, the rapid-heating gas-fired furnace is not the equal of the induction furnace. It requires significantly more space and is less flexible because of the longer furnace length. In addition, at higher tem-

Fig. 6.47 Furnace tunnel of a rapid-heating gas-fired furnace with nozzle boxes and nozzles for preheating the billets by exhaust gas circulation

peratures, the advantages of the rapid-heating gas-fired furnace over the induction furnace no longer dominate. The induction furnace is often better.

When the advantages and disadvantages of both furnace types are compared, a combination of the two furnaces is preferred in many applications. The billets are preheated in the rapid-heating gas-fired furnace using the cheaper gas

energy, and only the final heating in the higher temperature range takes place in the induction furnace. This combination is an optimization of the advantages of both furnaces. Both furnace types are used in the temperature range in which they offer the best advantage. There are numerous cases where such a combination represents the best solution, always when, for example, a second furnace must be installed alongside an existing gas or induction furnace to increase throughput capacity. The arrangement of a combination rapid-heating gas-fired furnace/induction furnace is shown schematically in Fig. 6.48.

The installation of this combination is only sensible and viable from an investment-cost point of view in a new installation if the required throughput is so high that it cannot be achieved from a single furnace, and a double installation is required in any case. The installation of such a combination in cases of lower throughput where one preheat furnace alone would suffice is not recommended, except with very frequent billet temperature changes.

6.3.2.4 Rapid-Heating Gas-Fired Furnace with Boost Heater

As mentioned previously, in many cases in aluminum alloy extrusion plants, the billets must have an axial temperature profile. It is not possible to develop a reproducible arbitrarily preselectable axial temperature profile in the rapid-heating gas-fired furnace, as is the case with the induction furnace.

Where this requirement exists and the billets are heated in a rapid-heating gas-fired furnace, an induction boost heater, as described previously, must be fitted to the preheat furnace. Obviously, only a boost heater separate from the

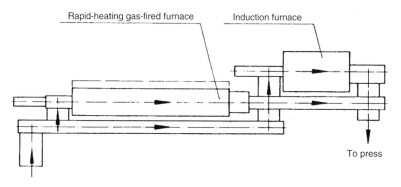

Rapid-heating gas-fired furnace   Induction furnace

To press

Fig. 6.48 Combination rapid-heating gas-fired furnace/induction furnace

preheat furnace can be used for this application. A typical installation is shown in Fig. 6.49.

6.3.2.5 Rapid-Heating Gas-Fired Furnace with Hot Log Shear

The rapid-heating gas-fired furnace is frequently used in combination with a hot log shear to shear the extrusion billets from the heated aluminum log. The furnace only supplies billets with an axially uniformly heated billet. If an axial temperature gradient is required, an induction boost heater, as described in section 6.3.1.5, must be installed between the hot log shear and the press (Fig. 6.49).

6.3.3 Temperature Measurement and Control

The temperature measurement and control is by direct measurement of the billet temperature in both induction and rapid-heating gas-fired furnaces. The measurement points are always at the exit of the individual zones. The energy input is always controlled as a function of the billet temperature. Thermocouples are used for temperature measurement with aluminum alloys, and optical systems for copper alloys. Care is needed in the use of optical instruments in rapid-heating gas-fired furnaces to ensure that the temperature measurement is not affected by the gas flames.

6.3.4 Economics

With induction furnaces, the specific energy consumption is practically independent of the throughput, provided a coil is available for each billet diameter. In other words, if several billet diameters are being used, then a separate coil is needed for each billet diameter.

The efficiency of the induction furnace is between 48 and 53% with conventional coils, and 58 to 67% for furnaces with low-loss coils.

The efficiency of a rapid-heating gas-fired furnace without billet preheating is between 30 to 35%. This efficiency decreases when the throughput is reduced and also if billets with smaller diameters than the maximum are heated. Efficiencies of 50 to 55% are obtained with a preheat zone of the simplest design described previously, and 60 to 65% with a preheat zone with air circulation. The efficiencies given refer to pure heat energy and the drive energies are not considered.

6.3.5 Extrusion Billet Transport Mechanisms

No specific transport mechanism is needed in the furnace section of an induction furnace, because of the short furnace length. The billets are pushed through the furnace on a slide plate. In contrast, with the rapid-heating gas-fired furnace, a transport system must be included in the furnace, because of the long length. Various systems are used for the billet transport through the furnace, including chain, rollers, slide bars, and walking beams.

The walking beam (Fig. 6.50a), which is by far the most suitable version of all the systems mentioned, consists of two longitudinal supports on which billet carriers in high-hot-strength ma-

Fig. 6.49 Rapid-heating gas-fired double plant for heating copper and brass billets

terial are located. The spaces between the billet carriers are filled with heat-resistant ceramic. These billet supports taper upward and are located in the lower position of the walking beam in specific slits in the furnace floor slightly below the billet column.

The billet column rests on heat-resistant steel supports in the hearth bottom and thus seals the furnace floor at the bottom apart from the short operational time of the walking beam.

However, the walking beam can only be used if sawn billets are being heated. It cannot be used with a rapid-heating gas-fired furnace/hot log shear combination. In this application, nondriven rolls fitted in the furnace floor have proved successful (Fig. 6.50b–6.53).

The transport mechanism outside the furnace is practically identical for the induction furnace and the rapid-heating gas-fired furnace. The billets from the billet store, which, in the simplest case, consists of a sloping storage table, are transferred on demand onto a feed chute from where they are pushed by a billet pusher into the coil of the induction furnace. At the same time, a billet at the extrusion temperature is removed on the exit side. In the rapid-heating gas-fired furnace, the billet on the feed chute is only pushed up to the billet column, and further transport through the furnace is taken over by the walking beam or the transport chain. If the furnace has slide-ways or rolls, the billet pusher naturally pushes the billet through the furnace in a manner similar to the induction furnace.

With both furnace types, the removal system consists of a clamp that pulls the billet from the furnace. The next billet in the furnace is then transported to the removal position. The billets removed from the furnace are transported by a specific transport mechanism to the press billet loader.

If the furnace is combined with a hot log shear, the log is pushed out of the furnace into the hot log shear by the billet-pusher system. After shearing the billet, the remaining log is pushed by a billet pusher from the shear and back into the induction or rapid-heating gas-fired furnace.

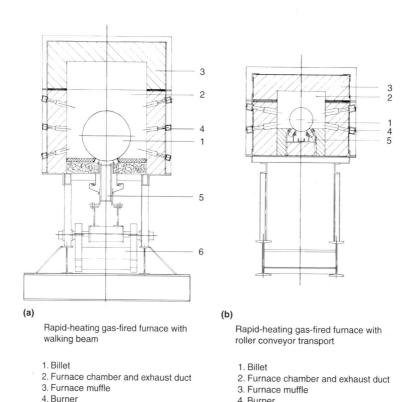

(a)

Rapid-heating gas-fired furnace with walking beam

1. Billet
2. Furnace chamber and exhaust duct
3. Furnace muffle
4. Burner
5. Walking beam
6. Walking beam transport

(b)

Rapid-heating gas-fired furnace with roller conveyor transport

1. Billet
2. Furnace chamber and exhaust duct
3. Furnace muffle
4. Burner
5. Roller conveyor transport system

Fig. 6.50 Cross section of a rapid-heating gas-fired furnace with (a) walking beam transport system and (b) roller conveyor transport system

The subsequent transport of the sheared billet to the press takes place in the normal way, either directly or via a boost heater.

Handling System

Horst H. Groos*

The finishing system, consisting of the downstream system for extrusion presses, is referred to in the industry as the handling system. The downstream system and the finishing machines for the handling and preparation of the extruded products vary considerably.

The downstream equipment for the production of wire is largely independent of the material and is simple in principle. The method of cooling the wire is important. With water cooling, the space required is small. If air cooling is necessary, the space needed is significantly larger. Downstream equipment for the production of wire is not nearly as complex as for rod, section, hollow section, and tube. With extrusion

Fig. 6.51 Rapid-heating gas-fired furnace for aluminum bars in combination with a hot billet shear and shock heating furnace

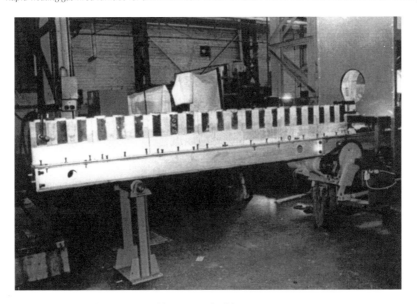

Fig. 6.52 Assembly of a walking beam for a rapid-heating gas-fired furnace

*Handling system, Horst H. Groos

Fig. 6.53 Rapid-heating gas-fired furnace with transport rolls

plants that are only designed for the extrusion of tubes, the downstream equipment is relatively simple, depending on the method of cooling.

When the extruded products leave the press, they are at approximately the temperature of extrusion. In many cases, they are bent and twisted, and in addition, they also have, to some extent, unusable front and back sections. They are too long for further processing if they cannot be coiled. The handling system corresponding to the operational conditions must guide, cool, straighten, and section the extruded product as well as handle the end discards and scrap.

The handling system also must prepare the extruded product so that it is ready for sale or optimally prepared for further processing. The aim is always to produce products that are as close to being finished as possible. Aluminum alloy sections are an example that are cut in the extrusion plant to the length needed by the end user, for example, for window manufacture. Whether direct or indirect extrusion is used is of secondary importance for the handling system.

The many different handling systems cannot be fully described in the context of this discussion. Therefore, only the most common handling systems are described in detail, along with the relevant correction machines.

Handling systems for aluminum alloys have undergone a development in recent years that has resulted in a certain standard.

A wide range of downstream equipment is used for:

- High-throughput plants in terms of quantity and quality. They are used for easy and moderately difficult-to-extrude aluminum alloys for rod, section, hollow sections, and tubes.
- Multipurpose extrusion plants produce wire, rod, section, hollow sections, and tubes from easy, moderately difficult, and difficult-to-extrude copper alloys. With brass, no water cooling is used, whereas with copper, water cooling is necessary.

Table 6.16 gives an overview of the complexity of practical extrusion plants.

6.4 Handling Gear for Aluminum Alloy Products

Originally, a stationary table was located after the platen as the run-out table. The extruded sections were guided by hand by the operators with tongs. Later, as more and more easily extruded aluminum alloys (e.g., AlMgSi0.5) were processed to architectural sections, handling gear was installed that made it possible to economically extrude large lots. The slat conveyor was widely used as the press run-out table, running approximately 3% faster than the exit speed. The cooling took place immediately behind the platen with air or, when necessary, on the walking beam transverse conveyor forming the cooling table, leading to the stretcher, storage table, and saw line with roller conveyor, cut-to-length saw and saw gage, as well as the necessary transfer systems. This system is still used in many extrusion plants.

The handling system described here is always suitable when from the point of view quantity and quality, the operating procedures guarantee an economic extrusion. The operating procedure is simple and easy to follow under normal production conditions.

During extrusion, the section or sections are guided by the slat conveyor. After extrusion, the section is separated from the discard at the die. The slat conveyor then increases speed and moves so that the section or sections are in the

Table 6.16 Downstream equipment for different products in aluminum (light metal), copper, and steel

Downstream equipment	Extruded product and material										
	Wire			Bar / section				Tube			
	Light metal	Brass	Cu	Light metal	Brass	Cu	Steel	Light metal	Brass	Cu	Steel
Run-out table											
Longitudinal transport:											
Dry table				■				■			
Table with water bath	■					■				■	
Roller conveyor					■		■		■		■
Plate conveyor				▒							
Slat conveyer											
Machines:											
Puller				■	▒						
Shear and/or saw				■							
Coiler, dry		■									
Coiler, wet			■								
Coiler with baskets		■									
Winder with auxiliary equipment	■									▒	
Cooling table											
Transverse conveyor											
Transverse belts				■				■			
Transverse chain				▒		■		■			■
Walking beam				▒	■	■		▒	■	■	
Machines											
Stretcher without detwist				■							
Stretcher with detwist				▒		■					
Collection table											
Transverse conveyor											
Transverse belt				■	■			■	■		
Saw line											
Longitudinal transporter											
Roller conveyor				■	■	■	■	■	■	■	■
Transport belts				▒							
Machines											
Cut to length saw				■	■	■	■	■	■	■	■
Section stop				■	■	■	■	■	■	■	■
Removal transport											
Transverse conveyor system				■	▒						
Longitudinal transport system		■	■								

(continued)

Dark shading, standard equipment; light gray, alternative equipment; open spaces, special.

Table 6.16   Continued

Downstream equipment	Extruded product and material										
	Wire			Bar / section				Tube			
	Light metal	Brass	Cu	Light metal	Brass	Cu	Steel	Light metal	Brass	Cu	Steel
Machines											
Stacker				▓				░			
Collection system		▓	▓								
Capstan		▓	▓								
Auxiliary systems											
Racks				▓	░			▓	░		
Collection trough					▓	▓			▓	▓	▓
Scrap handling				▓	▓	▓			▓	▓	▓
Cooling system											
Air cooling				░					░		
Air water cooling				░				▓			
Nozzle jet tube	▓		▓							▓	
Water wave											
Water trough	▓		▓			▓				▓	

Dark shading, standard equipment; light gray, alternative equipment; open spaces, special.

position of the walking beam cross-transfer system. Lift-off arms are then moved between the static arms of the walking beam cross transfer. These lift the section, move it out, and place it on the walking beam table. After the transport time, which is also the cooling time, the sections are transferred from the walking beam cross-transfer conveyor to the stretcher for correction. After the stretcher, the sections arrive at the storage table, where batches of several sections are collected. These are then transferred to the saw line. The longitudinal conveyor of the saw line consists of a roller conveyor or a belt conveyor. In the saw line, the sections are cut and divided into commercial lengths. Two stops that can be adjusted and swung out of the way are used. The scrap ends and the excess lengths of scrap are removed in front of and behind the cut-to-length saw by tilting table segments. After the cut-to-length saw, the sections cut to commercial lengths are transported to the manual-removal section, where they are placed in racks. The subsequent treatment of the extruded sections, including age hardening, anodizing, painting, packing, and so on, are carried out according to requirements. [Ell 88]

The development of the automatic aluminum alloy handling system commenced in the European extrusion plants (Fig. 6.54). The intention was to obtain a cost advantage in the face of hard competition by saving personnel. This led to favorable lot sizes as well as profile cross sections and lengths that were easily transported. The most important requirement is to be able to extrude continuous sections, for example, billet-on-billet extrusion.

In the deformation zone in front of the die, there is always sufficient material being deformed so that welding of the material with the new billet is ensured [Thu 84].

The press run-out table consists of an intermediate table between the platen of the extrusion press and the cooling table, followed by a slat conveyor that can be lowered. This is fitted with a **puller** and guide rail with a movable shear and/or saw for cutting the extruded sections.

The intermediate table is a movable slat conveyor. The length depends on the maximum commercial lengths. A shear or saw (or both in combination) for cutting the hot continuous extrusions is linked to the movable slat conveyor and can be positioned according to the commercial length. The slats in the run-out table consist of supports with graphite inserts.

The shear or saw is positioned to produce the desired commercial lengths without unnecessary scrap. After cutting the extruded product, the shear or the saw withdraws in the opposite direction to the extrusion to obtain receive a free-standing section. The puller picks up the still-

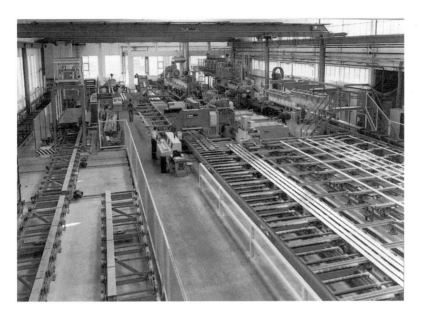

Fig. 6.54 Aluminum alloy extrusion plant

stationary section (it could also be several sections) in the area of the intermediate table.

At the start of extrusion, the puller starts to move synchronously with the section exit speed and guides the extruded product under controlled tension. After the billet, the length of which has been determined from the number of possible commercial lengths and the expected scrap, has been extruded to the discard length, the puller stops. The extruded product is cut in the region of the intermediate table, and the puller pulls it to the transfer position to the cooling table. As the slat conveyor lowers to enable the section or sections to be moved to the transfer table, the puller returns at high speed to the collection position for the next extrusion. The transfer belts of the cooling table that extend into the slat table are below the run-out table during extrusion.

All the transfer conveyors, including the cooling table, the stretcher transfer, the stretcher clearance, as well as the collection table, consist of fixed transport belts that can be moved longitudinally for transfer. Graphite-lined chain conveyors are used for extremely demanding operating conditions. Transfer belts are more flexible and better suited for manipulation than walking beams. The fans for cooling the sections before stretching are located under the cooling table as well as the run-out table (Fig. 6.55).

The stretcher is designed for automatic operation. If necessary, it can be used for one- or two-

man operation. Automatic operation of the handling gear is only possible if several sections from one billet are always manipulated as a batch into the stretcher and stretched.

The sections or batches are gathered on the collection belts of the collection table. These batches should also consist of the same products. The width of the saw line is determined by the economic production of the extrusion press and the shortest still-practical commercial length. Even if the cut-to-length saw has a fast cycle time, it can be a bottleneck if short commercial lengths are required and/or the saw line is not wide enough. The extrusion press then stops because of the delay in the sawing area.

The saw line consists of the roller conveyor before the cut-to-length saw and the cut-to-length saw with double-cut end clearance and swarf extraction. The roller conveyor behind the cut-to-length saw is fitted with scrap and section gage stops that can be adjusted to different commercial lengths. Both roller conveyors in front of and behind the cut-to-length saws can be lowered for feed and removal of the extruded sections. The cut-end removal is carried out on both sides of the saw blade by tilting conveyor units. The scrap is transferred by chutes and conveyor belts to a container or collection area (Fig. 6.55).

The extruded sections cut to commercial lengths are transported by belt conveyors to a stacking machine. Here, the sections are stacked on transport racks with spacers located between the individual layers so that the aging oven can be supplied with a sufficient quantity of extruded sections. After age hardening, the transport racks reach the destacking machine. Here, the sections are placed on the belt conveyor of the packing line. The empty transport racks and the

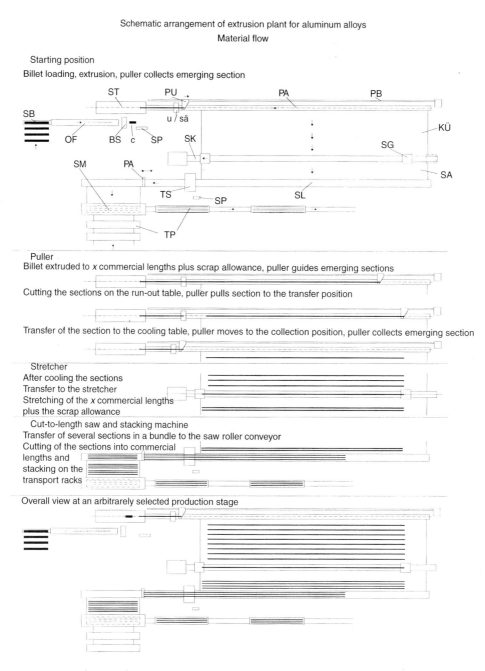

Schematic arrangement of extrusion plant for aluminum alloys
Material flow

Starting position
Billet loading, extrusion, puller collects emerging section

Puller
Billet extruded to *x* commercial lengths plus scrap allowance, puller guides emerging sections
Cutting the sections on the run-out table, puller pulls section to the transfer position
Transfer of the section to the cooling table, puller moves to the collection position, puller collects emerging section

Stretcher
After cooling the sections
Transfer to the stretcher
Stretching of the *x* commercial lengths
plus the scrap allowance

Cut-to-length saw and stacking machine
Transfer of several sections in a bundle to the saw roller conveyor
Cutting of the sections into commercial lengths and stacking on the transport racks

Overall view at an arbitrarely selected production stage

ST, extrusion press; PU, puller; PA, run-out table; PB, puller track; SB, cast logs; OF, furnace; BS, billet shear; c, billet ; SP, control desk; u, shear; sä, saw; SK, stretcher; SG, stretcher tail stock; KÜ, cooling table; SA, collection table; SM, stacker; PA, saw gage stop; TS, cut-to-length saw; SL, saw roller conveyor; TP, transport racks

Fig. 6.55 Schematic drawing for the operational steps in an aluminum alloy extrusion plant

spacer are returned again to the stacking machine [Höl 88].

6.5 Handling System for Copper Alloy Products

The handling system for copper alloys is, to a large degree, determined by the extruded product. (Fig. 6.56). It is necessary to differentiate between handling systems for copper and copper alloys and brass as well as handling systems for mixed programs. There are additional differences between wire, strip, section, and/or tube production. Frequently, mixed programs are necessary, which result in multifunctional and thus expensive handling equipment. Copper is preferably extruded directly into water to avoid undesired oxidation of the surfaces. Brass, however, cannot be extruded directly from the extrusion temperature into water. Water cooling is first used when the temperature of the extruded section is less than 350 °C. In contrast to aluminum alloys, there has not been any development toward a standard handling system with copper alloys.

6.5.1 Wire Lines: Brass Wire Transport with Protective Baskets

Two down coilers with coiler crowns to receive protective baskets that can be raised and lowered are preferably located after the press platen. Between the press and the coilers are wire guide channels. The channels are preferably fitted with replaceable graphite strips to protect the wire surface. The coilers usually have direct current drive and are synchronized with the press via the extrusion ratio. Because the exit speed cannot be held constant, due to production tolerances and wear of the die as well as other operational conditions, and cannot be directly determined from the emerging wire, the irregularities must be manually controlled.

The wire coil is layered during the coiling by a wobble control to produce coils for the further processing of the wire. The protective baskets filled with the coils are transferred on a longitudinal conveyor designed as a cooling section. In the last part of the cooling section, the coils are also cooled with water. After this, the coils (wire and bar) are transferred by a coil handler to a capstan or directly to a hook conveyor. The empty protective pans are transferred from the position of the coil handler to a parallel second conveyor that returns them to the coiler. The coils are transferred from the capstan or the hook conveyor for further processing.

6.5.2 Wire Line: Brass Wire Transport without Protective Baskets

Two down coilers with integrated coil pans and elevating pan bases are preferably located after the press platen. The wire guide channels, coiler drive, and coiler control are identical to those already described. Because the pan base must be raised to transport the coil, additional mechanical and hydraulic systems are needed. The larger masses require a more powerful drive. After the transfer of the loose hot coils, they are transferred by a plate conveyor forming the longitudinal conveyor. The plate conveyor is

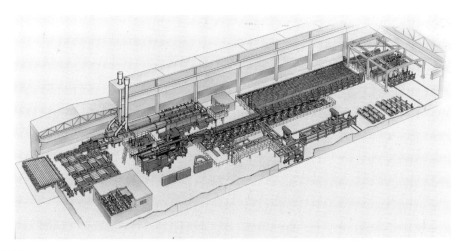

Fig. 6.56 Copper alloy extrusion plant

designed as the cooling stage for the wire coils and must be of sufficient length to correspond with the press cycle time and the maximum wire volume. To avoid surface defects, the transfer and transport must be carefully carried out. Pushing and sliding of the wire coils can result in transverse grooves on the wire surface. At the end of the plate conveyor, there is an immersion bath for cooling, coil binding machines to bind the open wire coils, and a coil handler to transfer the wire coil to a capstan or a hook conveyor. The coils are then moved on for further processing.

6.5.3 Wire Line: Copper Wire Transport without Protective Baskets, Cooling under Water

One or two down coilers with solid coiler bodies and elevating pan bases are located after the press platen. The coiler bodies are in the water container. The coiler drive located outside the water basin and the coiler control have already been described. The wire guide channels are designed without graphite blocks. They are flooded with treated water during wire production up to the die to attempt to prevent possible oxidation of the wire surface. A special jet tube between the extrusion tooling and the channel within the press platen keeps the water from the die when extrusion is stopped. The channel can be closed with sluices in front of the coiler inlet so that the water cannot run out after coiling. The operating sequence after coiling is coil elevation, push off, and transport away via a short plate conveyor, as well as coil binding, coil collection, and transfer to a capstan or hook conveyor.

6.5.4 Straight Line: Brass Transport for Rod, Tube, and Section

Handling systems for brass products are used to handle extremely sensitive extruded products. The surfaces in the hot phase, in particular, can be easily damaged immediately after extrusion. The problem is that these defects are often only detected much later during further processing. Therefore, procedures must be put in place to produce qualitatively defect-free products.

Behind the press, the run-out table is connected to the platen by a short intermediate table that is as close as possible to the die and is matched to the height of the extrusion cross section. This enables the extruded products to be guided safely and carefully. The run-out table itself must have a smooth, nonabrasive table surface. Roller conveyors have proved successful. These have smooth surfaces apart from a relatively narrow region in which the rolls stand out only a few millimeters. The roller conveyor operates all the time during extrusion. The roller conveyor speed is synchronized with the extrusion speed, as described for coiler systems. To ensure that the emerging extrusion is guided safely and straight, the roller conveyor must be approximately 3% faster than the extrusion speed. The rolls stop with the extrusion and are lowered. The section is then resting on an almost closed table with only slots at the location of the rolls. The slots do not have any negative effect on the already partly cooled extrusion. After separation of the section from the discard, the extruded product is transported by rolls into the area of the walking beam cross-transfer conveyor. A sweep push-off arm pushes the section onto the walking beam cross-transfer conveyor, which acts as a cooling table. The static and movable walking beams must be as close to each other as possible. The section pushed off by the sweep-off arm is straightened over its length and rests on the walking beam cross-transfer conveyor at a suitable distance from the previous section. This produces the optimal conditions for cooling and subsequent transfer to the saw roller conveyor. A test roller conveyor with a fracture test machine is located in the area of the walking beam cross-transfer conveyor and is used for material control of the extruded product. The cooled sections are transferred as a batch to the saw line, where they are sectioned to commercial lengths or to lengths for subsequent processing and finally transferred to a collection trough.

Alternatives to the systems described are:

- Instead of the run-out roller conveyor, a closed run-out table with single or multiple pullers. One or more sections are individually guided and pulled. The sections are then guided in the same manner as aluminum alloys but with significantly more care with tension control during the extrusion.
- Instead off the sweep-off arm, longitudinally moveable solid arms extend from the walking beam cross-transfer conveyor, which rest in the run-out table during extrusion. After the section is in the position of the walking beam cross-transfer conveyor, the run-out table is lowered, and the movable solid beams

carry the section into the cooling bed area. This ensures careful handling of the sections. Transverse scoring on the surface of the sections does not occur.

6.5.5 Straight-Line: Copper Tube and Section

As with the production of copper wire, the other extruded products, including tube, section, strip, and hollow section in copper and corresponding alloys, are extruded directly into water. The total run-out table during the extrusion process is flooded with treated water up to the die to largely suppress oxidation of the surfaces of the extruded products. A special jet tube within the press platen between the extrusion tooling and the extrusion run-out table keeps the water from the tooling when extrusion is not being carried out and prevents the escape of treated water. The run-out table consists of a flat elevating table, the surface of which must be resistant to abrasion. The puller running under water operates under controlled tension during the extrusion of the section. The extruded product is pulled into the area of the transverse conveyor for the removal. When the run-out table is lifted from the water bath, the puller returns in an elevated position over the water level at high speed back to the section collection position. A sweep-off arm pushes the section lifted from the water onto a small cross-transfer conveyor. It is then transferred to a saw line, where the ends of the extruded section are removed, and then cut to commercial lengths or lengths suitable for fur-

ther processing and finally transferred to a collection trough (Fig. 6.57).

6.6 Extrusion Cooling Systems

The extruded products have a relatively high exit temperature in extrusion. The cooling of the various products is carried out by different cooling processes after the press exit. The quality of the section, rod, tube, and wire is influenced by the cooling used. It can be improved in a controlled manner [Hue 92, Str 96].

The cooling can take place in the die, directly behind it or behind the extrusion press platen, at the run-out table, and on the cooling bed that is adjacent to the run-out table. Coolants used include liquid nitrogen, water, and air as well as air-water mixtures. The coolant is applied directly to the surface of the extruded product. Liquid nitrogen is also used to cool the die in the extrusion of aluminum alloys.

The extrusion cooling system has an influence on the run-out system. Air cooling with the associated equipment is relatively simple to integrate into a handling system. With water, cooling systems are needed that, depending on the material being extruded, consist of a water standing wave or a cooling tunnel or cooling tube (jet tube) with a water bath as well as the associated water circulating system. If different copper-base alloys are extruded, then handling systems that operate both wet (water) and dry (air) are recommended. This type of plant for

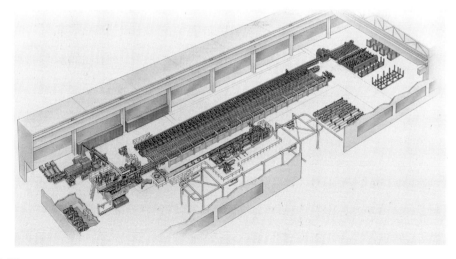

Fig. 6.57 Copper alloy extrusion plant (wire, bar, and section)

the extrusion of brass and copper is expensive and therefore rarely seen.

The extrusion cooling system is designed for the specific function, depending on whether aluminum alloys, copper alloys, or austenitic steels are being extruded. Air cooling is used for aluminum sections that are easy to extrude and do not have a large cross section and for brass alloys that must not be cooled with water. The intensity of the air cooling is relatively low. Increasing the cooling is possible if water is added in the form of a spray mist, provided that the water addition does not result in a fog that would be detrimental to personnel and equipment.

Water cooling is used for moderately difficult and difficult-to-extrude aluminum sections with large cross sections as well as for copper and copper alloys and austenitic steels, which can be water quenched. The water cooling has a high cooling effect. Although direct contact between the water and the surface of the extrusion is not possible at high temperatures for physical reasons, the cooling effect of water is approximately 100 times that of air.

Cooling results in:

- Restriction of grain growth
- Attainment of the solution heat treated quenched condition for age-hardening alloys
- Improvement of the quality of the surface
- Prevention of oxidation
- Development of nonsensitive surfaces
- Protection of the handling system from direct overheating and abrasion
- Possibility of sawing the section at room temperature
- Increase in the exit speed of the extrusion and the ram speed (compare the section "Process Control in Direct and Indirect Hot Extrusion of Aluminum Alloys without Lubrication" with Section 6.6.1).

The disadvantages are

- Distortion of the section
- Increased expenditure to prevent mechanical and electrical water damage
- Press operators subjected to noise and water vapor

6.6.1 Nitrogen Cooling

Nitrogen is used to cool the extruded section and to cool specially designed dies in the extrusion of aluminum alloys. The extrusion press must be designed for the feed of liquid nitrogen through a suitable tube system in the platen area

up to the die holder. The feed to the tool set, which can be changed, must be reliable and capable of being disconnected. When integrating such a cooling system with liquid nitrogen, the low temperatures that occur must be taken into account. Care must be taken to ensure that undercooling of the tool zones and involved press components does not result in failure from thermally related stress concentrations.

The advantage of this method of cooling is the good transfer of the deformation heat from the die region and an improved section surface finish. In addition, the nitrogen also acts as an oxidation barrier. The production output is increased by the faster exit speeds, and the quality of the products is improved [Mar 88].

The cost of nitrogen cooling in the area of the tooling is significant. In the case of die cooling, the complex special design of the die increases the cost. Nitrogen cooling is used for special applications in the extrusion of aluminum alloys.

6.6.2 Water Cooling

Cooling extruded sections of aluminum alloys with water was used at a relatively early stage. Systems were developed for specific applications.

A very effective water spray system was successfully developed for aluminum cable sheathing that acted immediately behind the die. The cable insulation, which is extremely temperature-sensitive, must be protected from damage or even combustion. Although the dead cycle periods when the billets are loaded are particularly critical, the extremely effective cooling is sufficient.

In the extrusion of sections of higher-alloyed aluminum materials, a high material strength must be achieved. Immersion cooling in the form of a standing wave located after the press platen can be fitted in the run-out table for this purpose. It consists of a flat water chamber that is open along the press axis. The water wave is formed by two flat nozzles angled toward each other to produce a standing wave. The extruded sections then undergo a type of immersion cooling as they are extruded. The section is intensively cooled in a minimum of time. The disadvantage is that the upper section side is cooled less than the lower section side. The high cooling rate is associated with distortion of the section with unequal cross sections, and this hinders further transport. The resultant downstream correction results in considerable additional costs for the extrusion plant.

More recently, water section cooling systems have been built with spray cooling, which represents a technically acceptable solution for efficient and economical operating handling gear. With an acceptable effect on the surrounding area, defects including distortion of sections, inadequate operational safety, noise levels, and water mist for the operating personnel can be avoided. The intensity of the water quenching can be varied by the use of different nozzles and adjustable water pressure. The spatially controlled cooling produces a symmetrical cooling effect on sections with unequal cross sections and/or unequal wall thickness [Edw 92]. The water section cooling system behind the press platen is part of the run-out table. It consists of a lower and an elevating upper section to give access to the extrusion run-out table if water cooling is not used. If required for production, it can be brought into operation from a control desk.

The cooling of copper alloy extrusions with water is only used for copper and specific alloys. Brass, which may not be direct water cooled for metallurgical reasons, cannot be immediately quenched in water from the extrusion temperature.

The recrystallization of copper takes place in a very short time interval during extrusion at temperatures of approximately 900 °C. The coarse grain that would form without water cooling is undesirable for further processing of the extruded section. Oxidation in this high-temperature region also commences immediately after the die. Coarse grain formation is prevented, and oxidation is largely avoided by using cooling tubes that extend into the tooling. The cooling tube carries the cooling water up to the die during extrusion. Outside the extrusion time, it acts as a jet tube and prevents the water flowing from the water bath into the extrusion run-out region. The intensive cooling effect of the water ensures that the extruded section is thoroughly cooled during an extrusion cycle and can be taken in a bright condition from the water bath.

6.6.3 Air Cooling

Handling systems were and still are, to a large extent, fitted with a cooling table. The size is determined by the cooling effect of the air cooling. To keep the size of the cooling table within limits, the cooling air must be circulated.

With aluminum alloys, the section cooling commences immediately after the platen.

With aluminum sections that are easy to extrude and do not have a massive cross section, sufficient cooling can normally be achieved with overhead fans (Fig. 6.58) (axial fans with sheet metal deflectors) and with undertable fans (simple axial fans) arranged under the press run-out table as well as additional undertable fans standing in rows under the cooling table. The sections should only be hot enough to hold during stretching, never exceeding 60 °C (140 °F). In addition, with age-hardening alloys, specific cooling rates must be maintained.

The method of working with air can only be used to a limited extent, for economic reasons and the effect on the surroundings (including noise level). The maximum air velocity is 15 m/s (50 ft/s).

A significant improvement in the air-cooling intensity is obtained with high-speed air-cooling systems operating as a closed system. The cooling intensity of the system is optimized by matching the cooling intensity of the system with the geometry of the section being cooled. The use of these high-speed air-cooling systems has already proved successful in well-known extrusion plants. They consist of an upper and a lower slit-shaped nozzle system transverse to the extrusion direction, an extrusion run-out section as a roller conveyor, the radial fans, and the housing. The length of the high-speed air-cooling system can extend to 5 m (16 ft). This cooling enables the cooling effect to be matched to different sections by control of the nozzle exit velocity over the section width and by the height adjustment of the upper slit nozzles.

Fig. 6.58 Overhead fans for aluminum alloys

Fig. 6.59 Axial fans for wire coils in baskets

For brass wire, air cooling is used for the wire coils on the plate conveyor acting as the longitudinal conveyor. In the case of wire coils in baskets, the cooling of the wire is also carried out by air in the area of the longitudinal conveyor. However, the cooling section must have sufficient length. In the last part of the cooling section, the wire coils are also cooled with water. Axial fans along the side of the cooling section are arranged as overhead fans for the air cooling (Fig. 6.59).

With rod, section, and tubes in brass alloys, cooling from the extrusion temperature is carried out on the cooling table without forced cooling. The cooling rate of the extruded sections determines the width of the cooling table.

Age-Hardening Ovens for Aluminum Alloys

Willi Johnen*

The age hardening of aluminum sections is usually carried out as a batch process; that is, the extruded aluminum sections stacked in racks are collected into a batch and heat treated in a chamber oven.

6.7 Heat Transfer by Convection

The heat is transferred to the heat treated component via the circulating hot air, that is, by pure convection. A large circulation volume is needed to achieve the desired uniform tempera-

---

*Age-Hardening Ovens for Aluminum Alloys, Willie Johnen

ture tolerance of approximately $\pm 2.5\ ^\circ$C (± 4.5 °F). Particular attention is required on the side of the furnace by the manufacturer to ensure that the connected heating load (wattage) is compatible with the circulating air volume; otherwise:

- If the connected load is too low, the air takes too long to return to the desired temperature after loading a batch.
- If the connected load is too high, the circulating air volume is insufficient to transfer the heat available to the charge being heat treated.

Excessive connected load is not worthwhile, because the reduction in the heating time is relatively small compared to the total time due to the long holding time during age hardening.

Figure 6.60 shows the temperature curves in an age-hardening oven where the heating time is approximately 1.5 h and the subsequent equalization time is approximately 1 h. The heating in the outer regions of the section stack is faster than in the core. Sections with a high weight per linear meter density heat up more slowly than small sections.

6.7.1 Methods of Air Circulation

The air circulation within the oven is usually longitudinal, that is, parallel to the section (Fig. 6.61).

Uniform stacking of the sections being heat treated in the oven as well as a uniformly distributed air input into the furnace working space are particularly important for efficient air distribution.

The air flow can be further divided in the longitudinal direction, as shown in Fig. 6.62. The

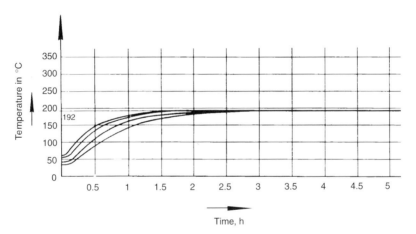

Fig. 6.60 Material temperature curves for an age-hardening furnace

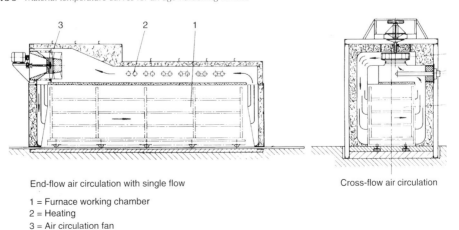

End-flow air circulation with single flow

Cross-flow air circulation

1 = Furnace working chamber
2 = Heating
3 = Air circulation fan
⟶ = Air flow direction

Fig. 6.61 End-flow air circulation/cross-flow air circulation

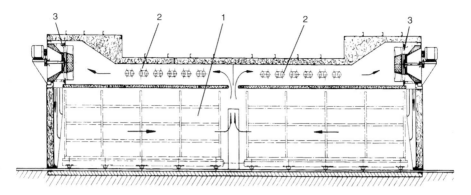

1 = Furnace working chamber
2 = Heating
3 = Air circulation fan
➡ = Air flow direction

Fig. 6.62 Double-end flow circulation

oven operates with two air currents, each with a separate heating and control.

6.7.2 Fans

The circulation of the hot air is carried out by axial or radial fans. Axial fans have the advantage that the air current can be reversed by reversing the fan motor. They have the disadvantage that the air volume and air pressure are restricted; that is, axial fans cannot be used for larger air velocities and larger furnaces and the associated larger pressure losses. In addition, the axial fans only achieve 60 to 70% of the maximum air throughput when reversed.

With radial fans, there is practically no restriction in the pressure and air capacities. The dis-advantage of these fans is that reversible air flow can only be achieved by additional dampers.

6.8 Design of the Chamber Furnace

Age-hardening ovens consist basically of a steel sheet external and internal housing (Fig. 6.63, 6.64). The insulation in the form of mats or loose insulation material is located between these housings. It is possible to also have the oven without an inner housing. The heating duct within which the heating is installed is located above and separate from the oven working space.

Fig. 6.63 Age-hardening furnace with bogie transport

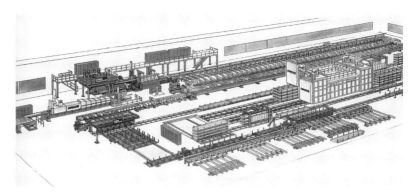

Fig. 6.64 Extrusion plant including semiautomatic age hardening

The oven doors through which the charges are loaded into the oven are located at one or both ends. There are basically two types of doors:

- Hinged doors that are operated by hand or pneumatically
- Electromotor-operated elevating doors

6.9 Heating

The age-hardening oven can be heated by gas (directly or indirectly) or electrically. The choice of heating the oven by gas or by electricity depends mainly on the available energy and the cost. The gas-heated ovens are usually heated indirectly through gas-heated steel tubes.

6.10 Transport Mechanisms

There are basically two methods for loading and unloading the oven with the furnace charge:

- *Bogies:* These are flat-bed wagons that are moved by fork lift trucks or chain transport systems located on one or both sides of the furnace ends.
- *Roller transport:* Here, roller conveyors are located in the oven, and in front of and behind the oven, on which up to four charge racks stacked above each other can be transported. The roller transport has the advantage over bogies in that less dead weight is heated and that continuous material flow through the oven is possible.

Equipment for the Production of Extrusion Billets

Wolfgang Schneider*

The structure of the extrusion billets has a significant influence on the extrudability and the quality of the extruded sections. It is developed by the melting and casting processes and also—particularly with aluminum alloys—by the subsequent high-temperature heat treatment (homogenization).

The melting and casting systems that have developed from the requirements for the best possible uniform, fine, segregation-free, low-precipitation, and crack-free structure are described in this chapter. The restriction to aluminum and copper alloys corresponds to the importance of these two material groups.

Homogenization systems are also described for aluminum alloys.

6.11 Equipment for the Production of Aluminum Billets

6.11.1 Design and Configuration of Modern Continuous Casting Plants

The production of extrusion billets in aluminum alloys can be divided into three production steps:

1. Production of the melt in the melting or casting furnace

---

*Systems for the Production of Extrusion Billets, Wolfgang Schneider

2. Transfer of the melt from the casting furnace to the casting system
3. Casting the melt

A typical continuous casting plant can have two melting or casting furnaces that are charged with solid metal (scrap, billet off-cuts, ingots) or with liquid metal, either from a remelting plant (aluminum alloys) or from an electrolytic cell in a smelter (pure aluminum). The casting furnace can also be connected to separate melting-furnaces and melt-treatment furnaces. Melt-cleaning operations, including settling, salt, and scavenging gas treatment, are carried out in the furnace to remove nonmetallic impurities. In modern continuous casting plants, additional melt-cleaning systems for scavenging gas treatment and filtration are integrated into the casting launder between the furnace and the casting system. These are referred to as in-line melt-refining systems. In addition, the standard equipment includes a dosing unit for the continuous feed of AlTiB grain-refining alloy into the melt in the casting launder. The actual casting system casts multiple logs semicontinuously. The number of simultaneously cast logs depends on the diameter, the size of the casting plant, the casting length possible, and the furnace capacity. Extrusion billet diameters vary from 80 to 800 mm, with a casting or log length of up to 8 m. There are extrusion billet casting plants that can simultaneously cast 150 billets. The arrangement of the molds depends on the method of feeding metal into the molds. This is discussed later.

Continuous casting plants are being fitted with process control systems to an increasing extent, and the most sophisticated enable a fully automatic casting process from the tilting of the furnace, control of the metal head in the casting launder and molds, to setting and control of the casting parameters and the start of the dropping of the casting table. The most important aim of this full automation is to increase the operational reliability of the casting process and to improve reproducibility of the billet quality.

Before the billets are delivered to the extrusion plant, they are given a homogenization heat treatment and then sawn to the billet lengths required by the extrusion plant.

6.11.2 Melting and Casting Furnaces

The furnace used for melting aluminum include hearth furnaces, hearth furnaces with closed-front hearth, dry hearth melting furnaces with built-in holding chamber, shaft furnaces, channel induction furnaces, crucible induction furnaces, and resistance furnaces. Of these furnace types, the combustion-heated furnace is the most suited for melting, from a thermal technological point of view. The hearth melting furnace is of particular importance (Fig. 6.65) [Hen 83]. Figure 6.66 shows a hearth melting furnace plant.

These furnaces are usually heated with gaseous (e.g., natural gas) or liquid fuel (oil). The design of the furnace attempts to achieve an optimal balance between the shape of the furnace

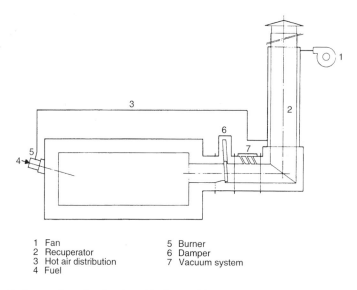

1	Fan	5	Burner
2	Recuperator	6	Damper
3	Hot air distribution	7	Vacuum system
4	Fuel		

Fig. 6.65 Schematic diagram of a modern hearth smelting furnace [Hen 83]

Fig. 6.66   Modern hearth melting furnace. Source: Gautschi, Tägerwillen, Switzerland

chamber, the type, number, and spatial arrangement of the burners, as well as the controlled flow of the hot gases in order to transfer a high fraction of the heat to the charge by convection. Hearth furnaces are built with rectangular or oval cross sections as well as circular furnaces, although the rectangular design is the most common furnace type [War 77]. A shallow bath depth and a relatively flat hearth space are characteristic of these furnaces [Hen 80]. The temperature difference in the melt is minimized by the shallow bath depth.

The heat energy is supplied by burners. The choice of the burner depends on the type of fuel and the furnace design. The burner capacity is limited by the available furnace space, the furnace lining, and the exhaust gas flue. To ensure the maximum convective transfer to the charge, the arrangement of the burner system in the furnace chamber is of particular importance. In practice, burner arrangements in which burners of different capacities and characteristics are angled relative to each other and inclined to the charge have proved successful [Pas 84]. Burners that transfer a large part of the heat by convection are usually high-velocity burners (convection burners) in which the combustion gases have a high-velocity (>100 m/s, or 300 ft/s). The burners are usually operated with a slight air excess resulting in a fast, complete combustion; afterburning in the furnace chamber is excluded. This results in economic fuel use.

An unavoidable standard component of a modern melting furnace is the furnace chamber pressure control. This ensures that in every operational condition neither cold air nor entrained air can be sucked in nor hot gases forced out of the furnace chamber. A slight positive furnace chamber pressure has proved successful in practice.

In modern melting plants, the thermal content of the hot gases is utilized as much as possible to reduce the energy consumption in melting. For example, this can be by preheating the combustion air. Heat-resistant steel or ceramic recuperators are used. The preheat temperatures developed are between 300 and 540 °C but can reach 800 °C with ceramic recuperators [Rei 80, War 85]. The preheating of the combustion air can be carried out with recuperative burners instead of separate recuperators [Rot 84]. Ceramic regenerative burners can also be used [Jas 86]. These enable significantly higher preheat temperatures to be used.

Air preheating by recuperative or regenerative systems, however, is associated with harmful emission problems, because high combustion temperatures, which inevitably occur with preheating of the combustion air, promote the formation of nitrogen oxides (NOX) [Jun 84]. Combustion must be carried out with a low air excess and the temperature in the combustion zone reduced to limit the NOX emissions.

Casting furnaces are usually hearth furnaces fitted with less powerful burners than the melting furnaces, because the melt only has to be held at temperature. Heat transfer by radiation is more suitable. Radiation burners are used, and these have a significantly lower combustion gas velocity (50 m/s, or 150 ft/s or less) [Wie 83]. However, because the main heat input into the melt is through the surface, there is a temperature gradient that depends on the bath depth, the furnace temperature, and the holding period. This can result in localized overheating in the surface regions of the melt. Therefore, modern furnaces are also fitted with a system for melt circulation. This is designed so that turbulent currents do not occur. The advantages of metal circulation are the reduction of the temperature differences in the melt bath, homogenizing of the melt, higher melting rates by more rapid dissolution of solid metal into the melt, lower energy costs, and lower melt losses. The metal circulation is carried out by metal pumps or electromagnetic stirring systems installed under the furnace base [Nef 93, Saa 93].

Finally, it should be mentioned that both stationary and tilting design are used for the hearth furnaces for melting and casting aluminum.

6.11.3 Processes for Melt Refining

The impurities in the aluminum melt can be divided into dissolved and undissolved impurities.

Hydrogen is the most important of the dissolved impurities. Hydrogen enters the melt mainly from reaction of water vapor, which can come from several sources, with the liquid aluminum. Excessive hydrogen can result in porosity in the extrusion billet and heat treatment blisters in further processing.

The undissolved nonmetallic impurities are far more important to the quality and further processing of an extrusion billet. The inclusions form either during the melting process, the melt treatment, or the casting process. The various types of inclusions must be differentiated. Oxides, nitrides, carbides, and borides are the most frequent inclusions. The oxides are mainly Al_2O_3, which can exist in amorphous form as a thin oxide skin and also as very fine polygonal crystals. In magnesium-containing aluminum melts, magnesium oxides (MgO) and/or AlMg mixed oxides (Al_2MgO_4) are frequently observed along with aluminum oxides. These oxide particles usually also have a polygonal for-

mat. The oxide inclusion forms described previously frequently occur as agglomerates and are then referred to as oxide flakes [Lec 79].

The impurity content of an aluminum melt is mainly influenced by the individual production steps in the production of extrusion billets. The various dissolved and undissolved nonmetallic impurities in the extrusion billets can result in different defects during further processing. The nature and extent of these defects depend on the shape of the impurities and also on the further processing, the treatment processes used, as well as the quality requirements. The occurrence of the impurities in aluminum melts requires a melt-refining process. The melt-refining processes used in continuous casting plants can be classified into the following cleaning methods:

- Settling treatment
- Vacuum treatment
- Salt treatment
- Scavenging gas treatment
- Filtration

The settling, vacuum, and salt treatments are usually carried out in the casting and/or melting furnaces, whereas filtration takes place in the casting launder between the furnace and the casting plant. A scavenging gas treatment can be carried out in the furnace in a separate chamber integrated into the casting launder system or in a combination of both. The methods listed above have different effects on the different types of impurities in aluminum melts. Whereas the primary purpose of vacuum and scavenging gas treatments is to remove hydrogen, the settling, salt treatments, and filtration processes only remove undissolved impurities.

In the settling treatment, the reduction of the content of undissolved impurities is by the deposition or the collection of the inclusions on the furnace floor or the bath surface. In the salt treatment, the inclusions are removed by the injection of salts into the melt in the furnace. The salts consist mainly of mixtures of chlorides and fluorides of sodium and potassium. Their effect is mainly attributable to a flotation effect.

The scavenging gas treatment is particularly effective in the removal of dissolved impurities, particularly of hydrogen. In this refining method, inert gases (argon and nitrogen) or reactive gases (chlorine) are passed through the melt. The hydrogen dissolved in the melt diffuses into the scavenging gas bubbles formed and is removed from the melt by the rising bubbles. A high rate of degassing requires a uniform

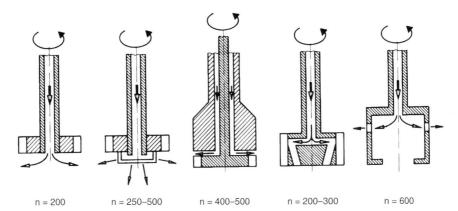

n = 200	n = 250–500	n = 400–500	n = 200–300	n = 600

Fig. 6.67 Schematic diagram of the rotors in scavenging gas treatment systems. *n*, rotational speed (rpm) [Ter 87]

distribution of the bubbles in the melt and a large total bubble surface. The latter requires a large number of small bubbles at a constant gas flow rate. Accordingly, the injection process must be designed so that small scavenging gas bubbles are produced.

In the furnace, the scavenging gas is injected by lances. In order to treat the entire melt, the lance must be moved through the melt bath.

In-line treatment has become very important for scavenging gas treatments. The treatment is carried out in a separate chamber between the casting furnace and the casting plant. In this process, rotors fitted with nozzles are used to inject the scavenging gas, and these produce a good distribution of the fine scavenging gas bubbles within the melt in the treatment chamber. The processes available at the moment operate using the same principle but differ in the design and the shape of the rotor. Figure 6.67 shows the design of some rotors [Ter 87]. These rotors are made from graphite and differ in the shape, the arrangement of the nozzles, as well as the rotation speeds. The nozzle shape and the rotation ensure that fine gas bubbles are produced with uniform distribution in the melt within the treatment chamber.

The principle of the design of an in-line scavenging process (SNIF) is shown in Fig. 6.68 [Sze 78].

The design consists of a twin-chamber system with two rotors. The melt passes through both treatment chambers and flows out into a forehearth, in which the melt turbulence is stabilized so that it flows smoothly from the treatment chamber in the direction of the casting plant. The chamber volume of the in-line process is determined by the necessary melt flow volume per unit time. This rate varies in practice because it depends both on casting speed as well as on the number and size of the extrusion billets that are simultaneously cast. For this reason, systems with different capacities are used that operate with one, two, or three rotors. The chambers are heated electrically, either with wall heating, tubular heaters immersed in the melt, or with inductors installed in a chamber. The chamber is clad with either graphite or suitable refractory ceramics. The system can be tilted to empty the chambers. The efficiency of the systems now in use enable hydrogen contents of <0.15 Ncm^3/100 g aluminum ($<0.15 \times 10^{-9}$ cm^3/100 g aluminum) to be achieved.

A scavenging gas treatment reduces the content of undissolved impurities as well as reducing the hydrogen content. The inclusions are removed by the flotation of the gas bubbles. This requires the presence of small gas bubbles and larger-diameter inclusions so that contact between the gas bubble and the inclusion can occur for flotation. In order to also remove fine inclu-

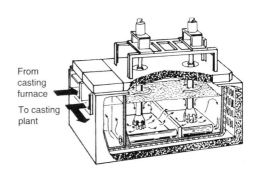

From casting furnace

To casting plant

Fig. 6.68 Schematic diagram of the in-line scavenging gas (SNIF) system [Sze 78]

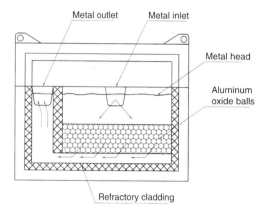

Fig. 6.69 Principal construction of a deep-bed filter

sions, which otherwise would be unsuitable for flotation, they must be agglomerated in the melt. This can be achieved and accelerated by the development of turbulence in the melt. Both requirements for the removal of inclusions by scavenging gas treatment—fine gas bubbles and sufficient melt turbulence for inclusion agglomeration—are fulfilled by the in-line process.

Filtration is the best option for the removal of undissolved nonmetallic particles. Deep-bed filters and porous ceramics have also proved very effective for the removal of very fine inclusions. The deep bed filter is usually filled with various Al_2O_3 particle shapes, whereas the porous ceramics are in the form of sintered or foamed ceramic with defined pore sizes. In these filter systems, the inclusions are removed by their deposition on the surface of the filter medium. This process is referred to as deep-bed filtration [Ape 80]. The filtration of inclusions can be divided into two stages. There is the transport of the inclusion to the surface of the filter medium and the subsequent adhesion to the filter medium

[Ape 80]. The main transport mechanism is sedimentation, whereas pressure forces are mainly responsible for the particle adhesion [Eng 91]. The effectiveness of deep-bed filtration is largely determined by the speed of the melt through the filter, the filter height, the filter pore size, and the specific weight of the inclusions being removed [Des 89]. The filter effectiveness increases the lower the melt flow rate, the higher the filter and the greater the difference between the specific weight of the inclusion and that of the melt.

As mentioned earlier, deep-bed filters and porous ceramics are used for filtration in continuous casting plants. Two types of these filters are described as examples. A typical deep-bed filter is shown in Fig. 6.69. The filling consists of Al_2O_3 balls of a specific size. The filter chamber is electrically heated to maintain the melt that remains in the filter at temperature until the next cast. The chambers can also be emptied when required for alloy changes.

By far, the most common filtration technology is porous ceramics in the form of ceramic foam filter plates [Dor 90]. These plates consist of aluminum oxides and contain a labyrinth of pore ducts within which the metal streams are repeatably diverted before emerging from the bottom of the plate. The size of the pore ducts can be varied. The fineness degree is determined by the number of pores per inch (ppi). Filters with 30 ppi are usually used. The ceramic foam filters are located in a relatively small unheated chamber in the casting launder, as shown schematically in Fig. 6.70. Foam ceramic filters are usually one-way; that is, they should only be used for one cast.

As with the scavenging gas treatment, the size of the filtration systems used in continuous casting plants depends on the metal quantity to be

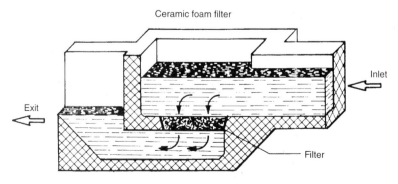

Fig. 6.70 Arrangement of a ceramic foam filter plate in a casting launder

processed per unit time. This again depends on the casting capacity, which is determined by the billet diameter and length, the number of billets, and the casting speed. For this reason, all systems are designed so that they can be offered in any sizes to be able to match the casting capacity available in the continuous casting plant.

6.11.4 Mold Casting Systems

The main task of the casting mold technology is the production of extrusion billets with a high-quality surface and peripheral structure. Therefore, the measures that must be fulfilled by the mold technology are well known. Of particular importance is the reduction of the heat extraction through the mold wall, because this influences the peripheral shell formation and depth. This can be achieved either by the use of a short effective mold wall or by a low metal head in the mold. In both cases, the method of metal feed into the mold and the control of the metal head are of great importance. The traditional continuous casting system, which is still used today for the casting of extrusion billets, is casting with a nozzle and a float, as shown schematically in Fig. 6.71.

In this system, a cast iron or refractory material nozzle feeds the metal from the launder into the mold. The float, also made from refractory material, controls the metal head in the mold. The limitation of this system of a short

mold wall and a low metal head in the mold is the ability to reliably control the metal head in all molds in a multimold plant and to accurately control the casting process. The cleaning costs and the demands placed on the casting personnel with these mold casting plants are considerable. These difficulties resulted in the development of mold casting systems that enabled the use of efficient short mold walls without the problems of controlling the metal head. These mold casting systems for the production of extrusion billets are described in this chapter, with reference to some examples. The development of the hot-top technology was a decisive step in improving the casting technology for the casting of aluminum extrusion billets [Ber]. The design concept of this mold system is shown by the example of a hot-top mold type in Fig. 6.72 [Los 76].

In this mold system, the metal feed and the metal head control in the form of an insulating attachment made from a refractory material, known as the hot top, is placed over the mold. The effective mold wall is determined by the design and is not influenced by the metal feed. Therefore, uniformly short mold walls can be realized for all molds in a multiple system. Hot-top systems are distinguished by the shape of the hot top used and the method of metal feed as well as in the design of the cooling water system. Figure 6.73 shows two different hot-top shapes and metal feed systems [Sch 89].

The metal feed in the hot top is either from the side at a constant level or centrally into the hot top through a bore from the casting launder.

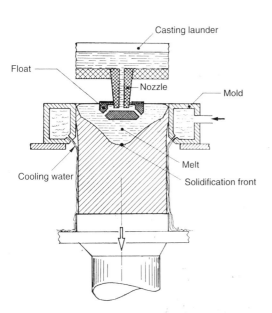

Fig. 6.71 Schematic arrangement of the continuous casting of aluminum alloys with a nozzle and a float

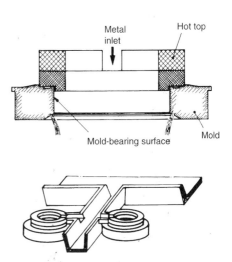

Fig. 6.72 Schematic arrangement of a hot-top casting mold for casting aluminum extrusion billets [Los 76]

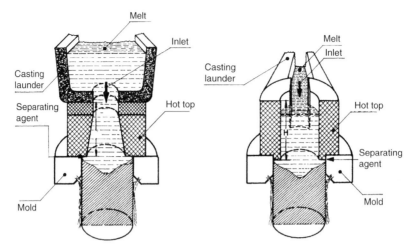

Fig. 6.73 Schematic arrangement of different hot-top molds and metal launders [Sch 88]

Figure 6.74 shows a modern mold casting plant with constant-level metal feed from the casting launder.

The separating agent necessary to minimize the friction forces between the billet surface and the mold wall needed for a defect-free casting process is usually fed into the mold wall under pressure between the mold and the hot top.

A new generation of hot-top molds are the mold systems, that work with gas. In these systems, the mold wall is continually fed with a gas as well as the separating agent, with the aim of further reducing the heat extraction through the mold wall. Mold systems that operate using this principle include the Airslip and the Airsol-veil processes [Fan 84, Sch 88]. Whereas the Airsol-veil process uses metal mold walls, the Airslip system uses mainly a porous graphite ring located between the hot top and the metallic mold wall parts, as can be seen in Fig. 6.75.

The mold wall separating agent and a mixture of argon and oxygen are fed through this porous graphite ring. The supply and distribution of gas and separating agent is different in the Airsol-veil process. This is shown in Fig. 6.76.

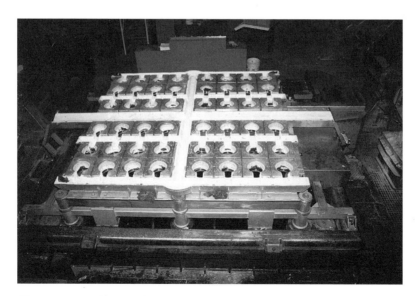

Fig. 6.74 Mold casting system with constant-level metal feed from the casting launder. Source: VAW-Elbewerk, Stade

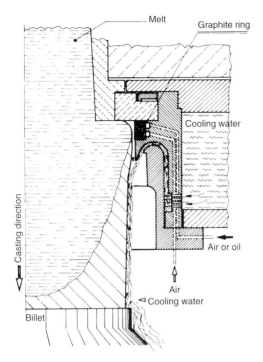

Fig. 6.75 Schematic arrangement of the air-slip mold

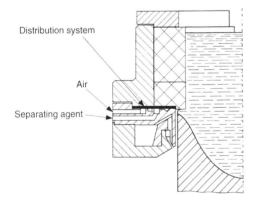

Fig. 6.76 Schematic arrangement of the Airsol-veil mold [Fau 84]

In this case, the separating agent and air reach the mold wall through a specially designed distribution system between the hot top and the mold wall. The simultaneous supply of gas and separating agent results in a significant reduction in the heat extraction through the mold wall in both mold casting systems compared to the conventional hot-top system. Extrusion billets cast with these molds are characterized by the absence of a definite peripheral shell, the occurrence of only minimum peripheral segregation,

and the formation of a smooth surface. Accordingly, no coarse cell structure is observed in the billet peripheral region. To ensure that the required billet quality is achieved, the molds must be supplied with defined gas and separating agent quantities, depending on the mold diameter. A specific control system is needed for the gas and separating agent supply. The mold system, therefore, must be equipped with suitable measurement and control devices [Sch 94]. In addition, the casting parameters are important for achieving the most suitable billet quality. These include, in particular, the casting speed, the quantity of cooling water, and the height of the hot top. This also applies to the operation of the conventional hot-top systems.

6.11.5 Casting Plants

Aluminum extrusion billets are produced on vertical and horizontal casting plants. The following discussion concentrates on the vertical casting plant because this is the most common. The requirements of the vertical casting plants and machinery have increased along with the ongoing development of the mold casting system. These include, in particular, accurate and smooth descent, automation of the casting parameters, and visualization of operating processes with fault detection and recording. The important components of a typical casting plant are the casting frame, the tilting frame, casting table with cylinder and table guiding, cooling water level control in the casting pit, and the plant control system, for example, descent rate of the casting table (casting speed), cooling water feed rate, metal head control in the mold and casting launder, as well as tilting of the casting furnace.

The casting frame, mainly fabricated from hollow sections, supports the molds, the casting launder system, and the mold cooling water supply. It is connected to a tilting frame. When the format is changed, the complete casting frame with the associated molds is lifted from the tilting frame. There are two types of tilting frame. In one version, the tilting frame is swung high over the casting pit. This ensures easy and safe access to the bottom of the molds, for example, for cleaning the molds. In the lowered position, the tilting frame rests on the frame of the casting pit. Another version is the movable tilting frame. In this case, the tilting frame can be moved away from the casting pit. This version has the advantage that inspection and maintenance as well as mold changing are simplified. The disadvantage is the space required.

The arrangement and guiding of the casting table plays a decisive role in the straightness of the extrusion billet, in particular, for casting lengths up to 8 m (26 ft). For guiding, the choice is between rails and cylinder guiding. The internally guided nonrotating cylinder is being used to an increasing extent because of its relatively simple installation. The necessary resistance to twisting is achieved by a relatively large cylinder diameter. The casting table is mounted directly onto the cylinder ram. In rail guiding, the guide rails are vertically located in the casting pit. The machining and materials selection of the rails is critical. The so-called guide shoes are located on the side of the casting table. The earlier roller guide has been replaced by the guide shoe with synthetic fluorine-containing resin-coated guides. The rail guide requires accurate installation and flat parallel machining of the distortion-free guide rails.

Horizontal casting plants, developed originally for the casting of bus bars for electrolysis, are used today for casting extrusion billets in simple alloys for casting up to diameters of approximately 200 mm. The casting plants available can cast several logs but nowhere near as many as can be simultaneously cast with vertical casting plants (Fig. 6.77). A restriction on billet quality must also be taken into account.

Modern continuous casting plants are equipped with computer-based plant control systems in which keyboards and computer screen displays are used to select and monitor the process parameters. In a further advance, a fully automatic casting process including metal head control in the mold and casting launder using capacitor or laser beam measurement systems is possible. This includes fully automatic furnace tilting to control the desired constant metal head in the casting system. These plant control systems enable the process parameters to be held within narrow limits, producing a uniform and reproducible billet quality.

6.11.6 Homogenization Plants

Section 4.2 in Chapter 4 describes how homogenization treatment is very important for the subsequent processing of the extrusion billets and the quality of the extruded sections produced from them. This requires accurate maintenance of the temperature and the processing time. Accordingly, the furnace for the homogenization treatment must be designed to provide controlled heating and cooling of the billets.

Chamber furnaces or continuous homogenization plants are used for the homogenization of aluminum extrusion billets. Stacks of billets are used with the chamber furnaces, and these are moved into the oven and then cooled in a separate cooling chamber. The billets must be stacked to give almost uniform heating and cooling of all billets. Often, specific billets are fitted with thermocouples to monitor the actual temperature cycle. Chamber homogenization plants consist of chamber furnaces, storage areas, and a transverse movable charging machine for the transport of the billet stacks. Figure 6.78 shows the schematic arrangement of a chamber homogenizing plant. The chamber furnaces are heated either electrically, indirectly with gas, or by direct heating with hot gases. The cooling in the cooling chamber is usually carried out with forced air.

In a continuous homogenization plant, the billets initially move one behind the other, following a preset cycle into a heating zone [Her 90] where they are raised to the heat treatment temperature. They then pass through a holding zone before entering the cooling zone. Figure 6.79 shows a continuous homogenization plant. These plants offer advantages in the wide flexibility of billet cooling as well as a better consistency of the heat treatment and cooling parameters. Large plants with production throughputs greater than 15,000 metric tons per year are linked to casting plants so that the extrusion billets can be taken directly from the casting pit to the homogenization plant via, for example, the intermediate stages of feed loading table and inspection conveyor. Continuous homogenization plants are heated electrically, and cooling is by forced air.

Equipment for the Production of Copper Billets

Adolf Frei*

Trials and discussions on the continuous casting of metals were carried out approximately

---

*Systems for the Production of Copper Billets, Adolf Frei

Fig. 6.77 Horizontal casting plant for casting aluminum extrusion billets. Source: Hertwich, Braunau, Austria

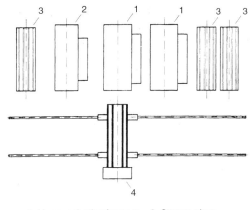

1 Homogenization furnaces   3 Storage place
2 Cooling chamber   4 Charging machine

Fig. 6.78 Schematic design of a chamber homogenization plant [Her 90]

Fig. 6.79 Continuous homogenization plant for aluminum extrusion billets. Source: VAW-Elbeweke, Stade

150 years ago. However, the development of an industrially usable process was unsuccessful for a long time.

After initial work in the Vöhringen plant of Wieland-Werke AG, Ulm, Sigfried Junghaus is believed to have installed a plant in 1934 that was capable of withstanding the hard conditions associated with casting in a semifinished product plant. Although initially developed for brass, the process was quickly extended to a wide range of copper alloys of various formats and to aluminum alloys.

The new process brought so many advantages in terms of economy and quality that within two decades the customary processes of casting in sand or static molds used by semifinished product plants had largely been superseded.

A general overview of the development of the continuous casting process can be found in the literature [Swa 57, Hem 58, Hem 80, Kre 60].

6.12 Plants with Furnace-Independent Molds

The important features of the process developed by Junghans are summarized in a 1933 patent [Jug 33]. This adopted the simple metal feed from a forehearth connected to the casting furnace into the free-standing and thus furnace-independent mold. The metal flow to the mold, which was originally controlled by a nozzle in the feed tube, is today controlled by a plug.

The principle of continuous casting is described in the metallurgical principles section, "Casting and Cast Structure of Copper Alloys," in Chapter 4.

Figures 6.80 and 6.81 show the schematic arrangements of a fully continuous and a semicontinuous casting plant, respectively. Fully continuous plants are preferred for casting billets of all dimensions. Semicontinuous plants are more for plates and large slab formats.

6.12.1 Melting and Casting Furnaces

Induction-heated channel or crucible furnaces are mainly used for melting of copper alloys. They have qualitative advantages, for example, degassing the melt, and are very economic (Fig. 6.82).

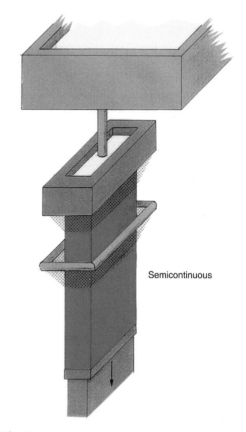

Fig. 6.81 Semicontinuous (slab) casting plant (vertical plant)

For plants that are exclusively used for casting pure copper (mainly in smelters), oil- and gas-fired shaft systems from Asarco (American Smelting and Refining Company, Perth Amboy, United States) [Bis 80] have proved to be the most economic melting systems. The in-line casting furnace can be an induction furnace with a connected forehearth or a rotary furnace with induction or gas heating. In the latter case, an intermediate tundish is needed between the casting furnace and the mold.

6.12.2 Melt Feed to the Mold

The ceramic feed tubes successfully used for aluminum alloys, for example, in Marinate, are not suitable for copper alloys because of the temperature. Tubes of high-chromium alloy steels must be used. At casting temperatures over 1000 °C, additional ceramic internal cladding is required. Tubes in electrographite are also used.

In order to obtain a suitably shaped solidification front in the mold, the feeder tube for cop-

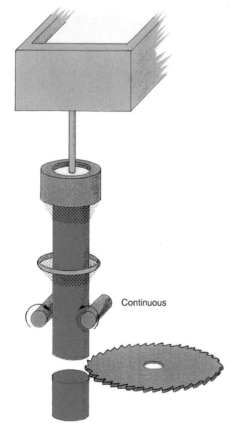

Fig. 6.80 Fully continuous (billet) casting plant

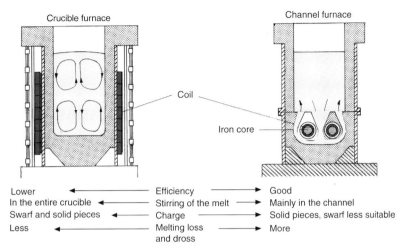

Fig. 6.82 Design of copper alloy melting furnaces

per alloys must be closed at the end with a distributor.

Typical shapes for casting billets and slabs are shown in Fig. 6.83 and 6.84, respectively.

Chromium steel or electrographite are used as the material for the distributor. In almost all cases, the metal feed system must be preheated before starting the casting of copper alloys.

6.12.3 Molds

The mold in the casting of aluminum alloys and copper alloys has basically the same task: to act as the form-producing shape in the transition from the molten to the solid state. The basic arrangement is therefore the same for both alloy groups: indirect heat extraction through the mold wall within the water-cooled mold, followed by a more or less severe direct cooling of the log with sprayed water or by feeding the log into a water-filled pit.

The different properties of both alloy groups require different mold formats. Whereas extremely short molds with lengths of 100 to 120 mm are used for aluminum alloys, molds between 250 and 400 mm are mainly used for the casting of copper alloys. Sigfried Junghans originally used 900 mm long molds. Today, these "long molds" are only used for casting copper alloys that are very prone to stress cracking and are unable to withstand direct water cooling.

Copper or CuCrZr is used as the mold material, and sometimes, the mold surface on the log side is hard chrome plated to reduce wear.

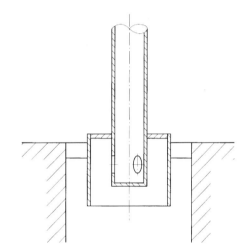

Fig. 6.83 Casting distributor for billets

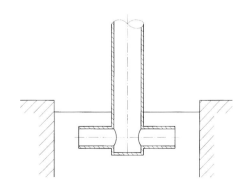

Fig. 6.84 Casting distributor for slabs

6.12.3.1 Special Mold Designs

Hot-top molds similar to those used for aluminum alloys are occasionally used for casting copper alloys.

The Wieland-Werke AG has developed a graphite cladding for the internal mold surface specifically for the casting of copper [Wil 51]. The graphite lining has self-lubricating properties, and the reduced heat transfer contributes to an improved billet surface. This design can be classified somewhere between copper molds and hot-top molds.

Asarco uses a mold machined from a large graphite block with internal cooling channels for casting copper billets and plates. This, in combination with extreme direct cooling within the mold, enables very high casting rates of up to 30 metric ton/h per log.

Attempts to use electromagnetic molds for casting copper alloys have not progressed from the experimental stage, as far as is known.

6.12.4 Protective Cover

Covering agents—oil (+ protective gas), carbon black, fine-grained graphite, or special salts—must be applied to the casting head for copper casting. They act not only as a separating and lubricating medium between the mold wall and the melt but also protect the liquid metal surface from oxidation in the mold.

The extensive replacement of carbon black and graphite by a salt covering since approximately 1980 has contributed to an improvement in the operational hygiene and cleanliness in the plant.

An oscillating displacement of the mold during casting is necessary; it ensures that there is always sufficient separating agent between the mold wall and the melt. The usual amplitude is a few millimeters, with frequencies of a few cycles per minute to well over 100 cycles per minute.

6.12.5 Cooling and Control

The type of direct cooling below the mold depends to a large extent on the properties of the metal being cast. The range extends from no direct cooling with very stress-sensitive materials, through mild cooling with only a water air mist, to intensive cooling of the log with a large water volume immediately on the exit from the mold. The mold water can be fed directly from an annular slot in the mold base directly onto the log, which is guided through a water-filled tank or by a lowering system into a water-filled pit.

In fully continuous plants, the preference is for spray bands or spray rings, chambers, or tubes bent to a ring, from the internal side of which water emerges onto the log through holes or nozzles. The optimal cooling for the special properties of each individual material can be obtained by arranging these elements in different planes.

The success of the casting also depends to a great deal on the practical skills of the operator. A constant metal head in the mold is very important for a good log surface. Today, the control of the metal feed to the molds is carried out using inductive or capacitive transducers that monitor the metal head in the mold and send the necessary commands to control the metal feed via a computer to a servo-motor.

Modern electronics and transducer technology now enable the casting process to be automated, including process control of all important casting parameters by computer programs for the different alloys and formats. A particular advantage is that the complete casting process can be recorded for quality control, and all deviations from the preset values can be retained. The activity of the operator can be limited to the preparation of the plant, some adjustments during the operation and at the end of casting, as well as monitoring during the casting.

The temperature-related difficulties and the problem of controlling the metal flow into the mold are the reasons why full and semicontinuous plants for copper alloys are usually only designed for casting three and, exceptionally, four and five logs.

6.13 Plants with Furnace-Dependent Molds

6.13.1 Stimulus for the Development

Casting to almost-finished dimensions is only possible to a limited extent with furnace-independent molds. As the dimensions of the log are reduced, the metal feed system becomes thermally unstable, the casting production reduces to unacceptably low values, and the control of the casting level to a constant value in the mold becomes more difficult.

The lower limit of the log diameter is approximately 40 to 60 mm. There are plants casting copper billets with a diameter of 76 mm. These

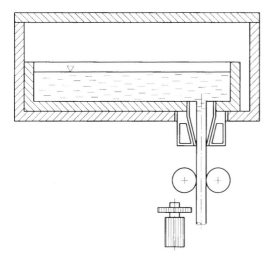

Fig. 6.85 Design of an Asarco plant

problems can be surmounted by combining the casting furnace and the mold.

A metal column extends over the mold up to the bath surface in the casting furnace. Control of the feed during the casting is therefore not required. If necessary, a simple on/off control is needed. The material for the melt container and the mold in these plants is nearly always graphite.

6.13.2 Asarco System

After numerous trials (e.g., Eldred, USP 1868 099, 1930/32 [Bai 58]) without any real success, Asarco developed the plant shown in Fig. 6.85 [Bet 39] in 1935. The dimensional range of these vertical casting plants extends from 10 to 240 mm diameter for solid bar and 20 to 240 mm diameter for tubes with a wall thickness >4 mm.

Starting material for extrusion is only produced on these plants in special cases because

of the high costs. The main application is the casting of bronze with up to 14% Sn or 22% Pb, gun metal, and other copper alloys to the finished dimensions.

6.13.3 Horizontal Casting Plants

Horizontal casting plants (Fig. 6.86) have increased in popularity since the mid-1960s. (Wertli, Metatherm, Krupp-Technics, etc.) [Kra 83].

Compared to vertical plants with building heights that can exceed 8 m (26 ft), these plants do require more floor space but significantly lower investment costs overall. However, there are some downsides in terms of quality that must be taken into account, but this is not important for many applications.

A wide range of copper cast and wrought products can be processed. The casting of strip, wire, or thin bar represents a large step toward close-to-final-dimension casting of feed stock for the production of semifinished products.

Billets for extrusion are also extensively cast horizontally. Initially, there were problems in the extrusion of these billets, because the solidification center did not coincide with the log axis as a consequence of the severe cooling of the bottom of the log. Today, advances in design enable better adjustment of the plant so that the solidification center is close to the log axis corresponding to vertical casting.

6.13.4 Continuous Casting of Steel and Other Materials

Today, not only are formats continuously cast in all important nonferrous metals but also in special metals.

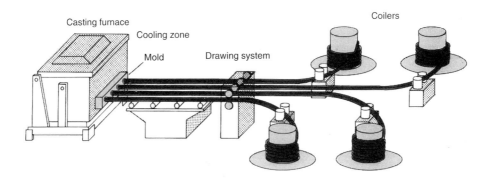

Fig. 6.86 Design of a horizontal casting plant (illustrating wire as an example)

In 1936, S. Junghans investigated the continuous casting of various aluminum alloys and then steel. After a delay due to the war, he also developed a convincing solution for steel continuous casting that resulted in the installation of the first systems in metal working plants after 1950 [Spe 56].

Today, the classic monoblock casting in static molds only has a minor role, even with steels.

Compared to copper alloys, the casting speeds for steel are faster by a factor of 5 to 10. Only in this way can the large quantities that must be cast be produced. The molds are 1 to 1.5 m long, and the casting pipe extends over a meter down from the mold. The properties of steel enable the still-red-hot log to be bent from the vertical to the horizontal and thus significantly saving on the plant building height. This is favored by casting in a curved mold from which the logs emerge at a downward angle.

Process Control in Direct and Indirect Hot Extrusion of Aluminum Alloys without Lubrication

Klaus Siegert*

Process control in direct and indirect hot extrusion of aluminum alloys plays an important role in obtaining the maximum productivity and a predetermined reproducible product quality. The following discussion concentrates first on direct hot extrusion and then on indirect hot extrusion of aluminum.

6.14 Process Control in Direct Hot Extrusion of Aluminum Alloys without Lubrication

As already covered in Chapter 3, the friction between the billet and the container plays an important role in the thermal behavior in direct hot

*Process Control in Direct and Indirect Hot Extrusion of Aluminum Alloys without Lubrication, Klaus Siegert

extrusion of aluminum alloys without lubrication. This friction is characterized by shearing of the billet from the material adhering to the container wall. With increasing friction displacement or shear displacement, with increasing ram displacement, the temperature with which the billet material enters the deformation zone, ϑ_E, increases if the initial billet temperature is approximately equal to the container temperature and the ram speed is constant.

In the deformation zone that forms in front of the die during the nonsteady processes at the start of extrusion, the material being deformed undergoes a temperature increase, $\Delta\vartheta_U$, corresponding to the transformed work of deformation. This results in the temperature with which the material being deformed enters the die aperture, ϑ_{MK}, as the sum of the entry temperature, ϑ_E, and the temperature increase in the deformation zone, $\Delta\vartheta_U$:

$$\vartheta_{MK} = \vartheta_E + \vartheta_U \qquad \text{(Eq. 6.3)}$$

It should be noted that even in the die aperture, friction occurs between the material being deformed and the die bearing surface. This can also be described as the shearing of the material being deformed from that adhering to the die bearing surface. This results in a temperature increase, $\Delta\vartheta_{MK}$, in the outer zone of the extruded section. The temperature of the outer zone of the extruded section is then given by:

$$\vartheta_{SA} = \vartheta_{;E} + \vartheta_U + \Delta\vartheta_{MK} \qquad \text{(Eq. 6.4)}$$

Temperature equalization across the cross section of the extruded product results in an exit temperature, $\Delta\vartheta_U$. The influence of the friction between the material being deformed and the die bearing can, to a first approximation, be neglected, and so:

$$\vartheta_S \cong \vartheta_E + \Delta\vartheta_U \qquad \text{(Eq. 6.5)}$$

The parameters that influence the temperature with which the billet material enters the die aperture, ϑ_{MK}, are discussed later. The temperature changes in the die area and the measurement of the temperature of the extruded product are then covered.

6.14.1 Influence of the Friction between the Billet and the Container as well as the Deformation in the Deformation Zone on the Temperature of the Extruded Material as It Enters the Die Aperture

As already covered in Chapter 3, the container temperature is by no means constant over the container length (see Fig. 3.19 in Chapter 3) and changes in line with the intensity of the press production [Ake 71] (see Fig. 3.20 in Chapter 3).

If the initial billet temperature, ϑ_B, is equal to the container temperature, ϑ_R, and is constant over the billet volume, and if the stem speed is constant over the stem displacement, then there is an increase in the temperature with which the material being extruded enters the deformation zone, ϑ_E, over the stem displacement, due to the friction between the billet and the container wall. The temperature ϑ_E increases with increasing stem displacement, that is, with increasing friction path covered.

As the material being extruded crosses the deformation zone, it undergoes a temperature increase, ϑ_E, corresponding to the conversion of the deformation work into heat. This falls slightly with increasing stem displacement because of the decrease in the flow stress in the deformation zone resulting from the higher temperature of the billet volume entering the deformation zone.

However, the influence of the friction between the billet and the container dominates so that the temperature ϑ_{MK} of the material being deformed increases as it enters the die aperture (see Fig. 3.22 in Chapter 3).

6.14.2 Heat Transfer in the Die Area

As the material being extruded passes through the die aperture, the external zones of the extruded section increase in temperature as a result of the friction with the die bearings. Tensile stresses in the external zones also form when there are compressive stresses in the interior of the extrusion. The heating of the external zones of the extrusion reduces the flow stress.

Taking into account the tensile stresses and the flow stresses in the external zones of the extruded product as well as the compressive stresses and higher flow stresses inside the extrusion, the temperature in the external zones should not be allowed to exceed a critical limiting value where transverse cracks can form on the extrusion.

Depending on the magnitude of the temperatures, the tensile stresses, and the flow stresses in the external zones of the material being extruded, transverse cracks can form on the extrusion, and this should be avoided.

Die cooling can be used to avoid transverse cracks on the extruded section so that heat from the extruded material preferentially flows from the external zones of the extruded product into the colder die.

This effect is more pronounced the slower the extrusion flows through the die aperture; for example, the slower the extrusion speed, the greater the heat that can flow from the extrusion into the colder die. Die cooling should be considered, in particular, for the alloy types Al-ZnMgCu, AlCuMg, and AlMg (see Fig. 5.21 in Chapter 5).

Liquid nitrogen has proved successful in practice as the cooling medium. This is supplied behind the die so that it provides both die cooling and cooling of the section as it leaves the die into a protective gaseous atmosphere.

Depending on the alloy, this allows recrystallization to be retarded in the external zone of the extruded section as it leaves the die. Cooling of the die and the extruded section gives higher extrusion speeds and better surface quality and therefore higher productivity with a better product quality (see also the section "Heat Removal" in Chapter 5).

6.14.3 Measurement of the Extrusion Temperatures

The determination of the temperatures of the material being extruded as it enters and leaves the die aperture and as it enters the downstream cooling system plays an important role in the reproducible trouble-free and economic extrusion of a defect-free product.

As shown in Fig. 3.23 in Chapter 3, it is possible with microsheathed thermocouples to measure the temperature at the leading edge of the die aperture. This process is very reliable and accurate. It is useful for calibrating radiation pyrometers, for the measurement of the temperatures at which transverse cracking on the extruded product occurs, and for verifying theoretical models on the thermal changes in the process. It is, however, too complex for production. Between 1980 and 2000, radiation pyrometers were developed, but there are problems associated with the accuracy of the measured temperature because of the low emissivity of aluminum alloys. A combination of a ratio pyrometer with a fixed-wavelength pyrometer [Yao 91] [Rep 94] as well as a full-spectrum pyrometer are known [Pan 95]. It is also possible to measure the radiation intensity in several spectral regions [Yao 91] [Pan 95] [Sch 94].

It is particularly difficult to accurately determine the temperature of the surface of the extrusion. It is possible to directly measure the temperature of the surface using thermocouples and to use this to calibrate the radiation pyrometer. In this way, it is possible, as described in Schiewe [1994], to collect emissivity data for the application of a four-channel pyrometer by measuring the surface temperature of the extruded product with a surface thermocouple probe.

6.14.4 Methods of Achieving Constant Exit Temperatures over the Length of the Extrusion or Ram Displacement in the Direct Hot Extrusion of Aluminum Alloys

As already discussed in Chapter 3, the following possible methods can be used to achieve as near as possible a constant exit temperature over the extruded length. They are not usually used alone but in combination:

- Optimization of the difference between the initial billet temperature and the container temperature

- Axial initial billet temperature profile, with a decreasing temperature from the front to the back of the billet
- Ram speed as a function of the ram displacement, for example, the ram speed decreases with increasing ram displacement
- Zone heating and zone cooling of the container, with the aim of maintaining the temperature fields of the container constant, independent of the intensity of the press operation

The results of these measures must be that the temperature ϑ_E of the billet material is constant over the ram displacement as it enters the deformation zone; for example, the heating of the billet from the friction with the container must be compensated. Therefore, the temperature field of the container should not change as a function of the intensity of the press operation during extrusion. Zone heating and zone cooling are now standard technology.

However, if the temperature field of the container does change, then the ram speed over the ram displacement and the axial temperature profile of the billet can be adjusted accordingly.

The intention should be to ensure that the material being extruded always enters the deformation zone with a constant temperature ϑ_E. If one or a combination of the measures described previously are used to successfully keep ϑ_E constant over the ram displacement, then the exit temperature, ϑ_S, will be higher than the entry temperature by $\Delta\vartheta_U$, which is the heat generated in the deformation zone, but constant over the ram displacement or the length of the extrusion (Fig. 6.87).

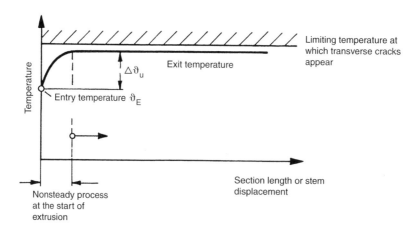

Fig. 6.87 Desired exit temperature variation over the length of the extrusion or the stem displacement in the direct hot extrusion without lubrication of aluminium alloys

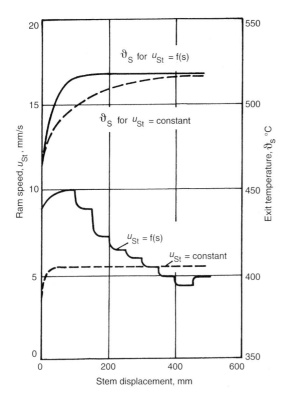

Fig. 6.88 Extrusion with and without a speed profile for the same maximum exit temperature in the direct hot extrusion without lubrication of AlMgSi0.5 [Rup 77]

Figure 6.88 compares two extrusions with and without speed control for the same maximum exit temperature for direct extrusion without lubrication of AlMgSi0.5. It can be seen that there is an almost constant exit temperature, ϑ_S, over the ram displacement or from $u_S = V \cdot lu_{St}$ over the length of the extrusion, where u_S is the ram speed, V is the extrusion ratio, and u_{St} is the exit speed. It can then be ensured that the maximum possible exit temperature without the occurrence of transverse cracks is not exceeded.

Figure 6.89 shows the variation of the exit temperature over the ram displacement for an approximately constant initial billet temperature (Fig. 6.89a) and for an optimized temperature profile over the billet length (Fig. 6.89b). It can be seen that it is also possible in this case to obtain an almost constant exit temperature over the ram displacement or extrusion length after the nonsteady start of the extrusion process.

6.15 Process Control in Indirect Hot Extrusion of Aluminum Alloys without Lubrication

As already discussed in Chapter 3, there is no friction between the billet and the container in

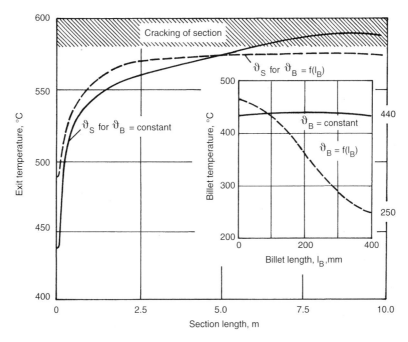

Fig. 6.89 Variation in the exit temperature over the stem displacement [Rup 75]

indirect extrusion. With a constant ram speed over the ram displacement the material being deformed enters the deformation zone that forms during the unsteady start of the extrusion process, always with the same temperature, ϑ_E, if the initial billet temperature, ϑ_B, is the same as the container temperature, ϑ_R.

In the deformation zone, the material being extruded undergoes a temperature increase, $\Delta\vartheta_U$, which is constant over the ram displacement after the unsteady start of the extrusion process, corresponding to the deformation work required. Then, according to Eq. 6.6, the exit temperature, ϑ_S, must be constant over the length of the extrusion or the ram displacement. For the quasi-stationary deformation process (see Fig. 3.50 in Chapter 3):

$$\vartheta_S = \vartheta_E + \Delta\vartheta_U = \text{constant} \qquad \text{(Eq 6.6)}$$

where

$$\vartheta_B = \vartheta_R = \vartheta_E \text{ and } u_{St} = \text{constant} \qquad \text{(Eq 6.7)}$$

The profile shown in Fig. 6.87 for the set temperature over the length of the extrusion or the ram displacement can thus be achieved without any special measures, for example, special ram speed profile over the ram displacement and/or special initial billet temperature variation over the billet length.

In indirect hot extrusion, the billet length is only limited by the buckling length of the hollow stem. Initial billet lengths of five to eight times the billet diameter are possible in indirect hot extrusion. With these initial billet lengths, air removal during upsetting of the billet in the container can be a problem. It is therefore advisable to have a temperature profile in the billet so that the front of the billet is the hottest and the temperature decreases toward the back end of extrusion. The upsetting process then takes place from the front to the back, enabling the trapped air to be released without any problem.

As described in sections 6.3.1.4 and 6.3.1.5, a billet axial temperature profile is possible with induction billet heating.

The container can give additional problems. If the container is only fitted with induction heating, then there are axial temperature profiles along the container wall, with a maximum value in the middle of the container and minimum at the container ends because of the cooling of the end faces (see Fig. 3.19 in Chapter 3). Combinations of induction heating combined with re-

sistance heating and, when needed, zone cooling have proved successful in practice. A constant container temperature over the container length would be ideal.

Process Control Concepts for Extrusion Plants

Armit Biswas*

The productivity of a modern extrusion plant is influenced by a wide range of different factors. The process control has the task of reconciling the individual production stages with each other. This should produce a product that meets the requirements of the customer. The priorities can vary considerably. The quality requirements in terms of surface finish, mechanical properties, and dimensions of the section can be rigorous or not, depending on the specific customer requirements. The process optimization must deal with the changing requirements to achieve the maximum throughput while maintaining the quality specified.

6.16   Electrical-Electronic Control

Control and data collection on extrusion presses plays a special role in the overall plant system. They form the basis for optimization for product quality, quality control, as well as the optimal utilization of the extrusion plant. This section describes the current state of the technology.

The extrusion process determines the type of press. The press movements are coordinated by the electrical control system, which uses sensors and hydraulic and electrical components as the operating elements.

The plant operator has the task of monitoring the extrusion process. He should always be able to access the current production process and, if necessary, change the press parameters. This requires a suitable visualization system that is also realized by the electronic control.

*Process Control Concepts for Extrusion Plants, Armist Biswas

A data collection system collects all the relevant process data and evaluates them. It should cover not only the actual data from the press but also from the auxiliary equipment (e.g., furnaces, run-out, stretcher saw). The data collection system can also store optimized process parameters for specific orders and make them available for future orders as well as passing them on to affiliated systems (Fig. 6.90).

The role of the maintenance personnel is to optimize the plant availability. They require a meaningful fault detection system to be able to select the suitable corrective measures to be taken.

Control technology, visualization, process control technology, process planning, and maintenance support are central components of the process control system and contribute to ensuring the product quality and to the increase in productivity of the complete plant.

An example of a hierarchical control system could be structured as:

- Programmable logic control (PLC) system on the lowest level that controls the machine
- Then an interface that collects the relevant data, visualizes process relationships, and optimizes
- Followed by process technical software in which the extrusion process is optimized both qualitatively and quantitatively

- A production planning system on the top level that is specifically configured for the requirements in the extrusion plant

The PLC system coordinates the sequential movement of the plant components. The data input for the entire process is enabled by this system. Software routines for fault diagnostics and defect evaluation are also included. It is linked to the higher-level processing system. The extrusion speed and the extrusion pressure are digitally controlled by the system. With copper alloy presses, the PLC system also controls the coiler.

The interface for the visualization and the optimization is a man-machine interface supplying information to the operator and the maintenance personnel. It is also linked to the central data processing system. This system enables the control of the furnace and the press as well as all the downstream equipment. All relevant data are displayed on screens and control desks. Changes in the default data can be entered by a keyboard.

Software for the optimization of the actual extrusion process can be linked to the control system. The production planning system contains die-specific optimal process data. It enables the production of a press order with order-related data (e.g., type of section, length, quantity). The production of reports with statistical data (e.g.,

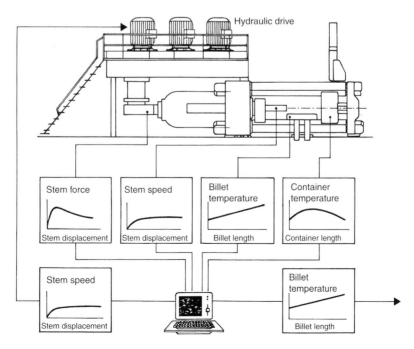

Hydraulic drive

Stem force / Stem displacement

Stem speed / Stem displacement

Billet temperature / Billet length

Container temperature / Container length

Stem speed / Stem displacement

Billet temperature / Billet length

Fig. 6.90 Schematic arrangement of a data collection system for an extrusion press

shift, daily, monthly, annual reports) is also possible.

The advantages of such a system are obvious [Schü 96].The most important advantages are:

- System enables fast and direct information flow, and a central point can control all process procedures.
- Automatic control of all processes gives quality control as well as continuous quality and production monitoring.
- All areas involved in the production process can exchange information with each other.
- Historic information can be extracted from the data bank at any time.

6.16.1 Factors that Influence the Productivity and Quality of the Products in the Extrusion Process

The following factors influence the productivity and quality of the products in the extrusion process:

- Initial billet temperature and the radial and axial temperature profiles
- Time for the transport of the billet from the furnace to the loader
- Dwell time in the billet loader
- Mean container temperature and temperature distribution
- Thermal capacity of the container (mass of the container) compared to the thermal capacity of the billet
- Number and location of the heating elements in the container, and the ability to switch individual heaters on and off

- Possibility of container cooling, and the location of the cooling zones
- Location and number of thermocouples in the container to control the heating and cooling zones
- Possibility of fine continuous adjustment of the extrusion speed
- Die design
- Die temperature
- Dummy block temperature
- Sealing tool or sealing stem temperature in indirect extrusion
- Quality of the data-monitoring system

6.16.2 Improvement in the Productivity and Product Quality by the Optimization of the Extrusion Process

Influencing the extrusion process by on-line control of the container temperature can be excluded, because the temperature of the container cannot be changed quickly enough. However, the axial temperature distribution in the container can be held to a more or less uniform level by suitable heating and cooling systems, which ensures that this state remains thermally stable. The practical variables for the optimization of the extrusion process are the initial billet temperature and the extrusion speed. Some improvement can naturally be achieved by a trial-and-error method.

However, greatly simplified finite element process simulation programs offer the possibility of determining the initial billet temperature profile and/or the ram speed profile for a given

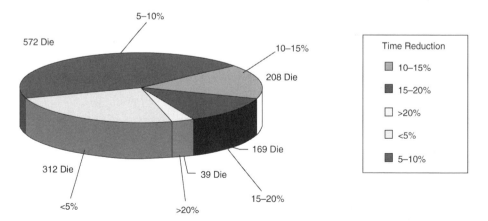

Fig. 6.91 Press cycle time reduction with a computer-based control system. Statistic evaluation of the results of 1300 dies in 10 different extrusion plants

container temperature field, so that a predetermined exit temperature is obtained after the unsteady initial extrusion process.

A statistical study of the extrusion time reductions that can be obtained from a simulation process is shown in Fig. 6.91 [Rep 96a]. The evaluation is based on the results of approximately 1300 dies in 10 different extrusion plants. Comparable evaluations for iterative learning programs that operate with the exit temperature measurement are not yet available.

REFERENCES

[Ake 68]: R. Akeret, Untersuchengen über das Strangpressen unter besonderer Berücksichtigung der thermischen (Investigations into Extrusion with Specific Reference to the Thermal Processes), Vorgänge 5, Int. Leichtmetalltagung (Int. Light Alloy Conference), Leoben-Wien, 1968, p 304–307

[Ake 71]: R. Akeret, Die Produktivität beim Strangpressen von Aluminumwerkstoffen—Einfluß von Werkstoff und Verfahren (The Productivity in the Extrusion of Aluminum Alloys—Influence of Material and Process), Z. Metallkd., Vol 62 (No. 6), 1971, p 451–456

[Ake 80]: R. Akeret, Das Verhalten der Strangpresse als Regelstrecke (The Extrusion Press as a Controlled System), Z. Metallkd, Vol 34 (No. 8), 1980, p 737–740

[Ant 77]: E.J. Anthofer, "Press Alignment," Second International Aluminum Extrusion Technology Seminar, 1977

[Ape 80]: D. Apelian and R. Mutharasan, J. Met., Vol 32 (No. 9), 1980, p 14–19

[Ape 85]: D. Apelian, C.E. Eckert, R. Mutharasan, and R.E. Miller, Proc. Refining and Alloying of Liquid Aluminum and Ferro Alloys, The Norwegian Institute of Technology, Trondheim, Aluminum Verlag, Düsseldorf, 1985, p 123–143

[Asa 84]: A. Asari, T. Noyori, and M. Ueda, Recent Technology of Indirect Extrusion, Third International Aluminum Extrusion Technology Seminar (Atlanta, GA), 1984

[Bai 58]: R. Baier (Asarco), Pouring Technique for Continuous Casting, U.S. patent 3,066,364, 1958–1962

[Bam 90]: J. Baumgarten, EDV-gestützte Instandhaltung und Schwachstellenanalyse (Computer Based Maintenance and Weakpoint Analysis), G. Jung, Ed., Strangpressen, DGM-Informationsgesellschaft m.b.H., 1990, p 99

[Ber]: W.I. Bergmann, U.S. patent 298,3972

[Bet 39]: I.O. Betterton and F.F. Poland, Vorrichtung zum kontinuierlichen (System for Continuous Casting of Metals), U.S. patent 2264,488, Gießen von Metallen, 1939–1951

[Bis 66]: A. Biswas and A. Steinmetz, Rechnerische Simulation des Strangpreßvorganges (Computer Simulation of the Extrusion Process), Aluminum, 1966

[Bis 80]: A.K. Biswas and W.G. Davenport, Extractive Metallurgy of Copper, 2nd ed., Pergamon Press, Oxford, 1980, p 339–343

[Bis 89]: A. Biswas and A. Steinmetz, "Rechnerische Simulation des Strangpreßvorganges," Vortrag auf dem Symposium Strangpressen der DGM ("Computer Simulation of the Extrusion Process," Papers at the Symposium on Extrusion of the DGM), 1989

[Bis 92]: A. Biswas, B. Repgen, and A. Steinmetz, Computer Simulation of Extrusion Press Operation, Experience with CADEX, a New Computer Aided Process Optimizing System, Proceedings, Fifth International Aluminum Extrusion Technology Seminar, Vol II, 1992, p 149–155

[Bri 96]: R. Brioschi, "New Technology in Extrusion Presses Design," International Aluminum Extrusion Technology Seminar (Chicago, IL), 1996

[Bro 80]: J. Broichhausen and F.U. Heute, Gekühltes Strangpressen von Schwermetallen (Coded Extrusion of Copper Alloys), Z. Metallkd., Vol 34 (No. 1), 1980, p 40–44

[Buc]: Iterativ lernende Regelung für zyklische Systeme (Iterative Learning Control and Cyclic Systems), VDI-Verlag, Düsseldorf

[Bug 88]: J.C. Bugai, "CIEM: Computer Integrated Extrusion Manufacturing," Fourth International Aluminum Extrusion Technology Seminar (Chicago, IL), 1988

[Des 89]: T. Desmoulins, H. d'Hondt, J.M. Hicter, and P. Netter, Light Met., 1989, p 757–767

[Dor 90]: J.E. Dore, Light Met., 1990, p 791–796

[Edw 92]: J.A. Edwards, "Automatic Handling Systems and New Equipment for Heavy-Duty Extruding," Fifth International Aluminum Extrusion Technology Seminar (Chicago, IL), 1992

[Ell 88]: L.D. Elliot, "Optimation—Not Necessarily Automation," Fourth International Aluminum Extrusion Technology Seminar (Chicago, IL), 1988

[Eng 91]: T. Engh, F. Frisvold, and S.T. Johansen, Continuous Casting DGM—Information Society, Oberursel, 1991

[Fau 84]: J.P. Faunce, F.E. Wagstaff, and H. Shaw, *Light Met.*, 1984, p 1145–1158

[Fis 97]: G. Fischer, *Von der Qualitätssicherung zu Business Excellence* (*From Quality Control to Business Excellence*), K. Schimmelpfennig, Ed., Strangpressen, DGM-Informationsgesellschaft, Verlag, 1997, p 179

[Gär 80]: H. Gärtner, *Temperaturmodell einer Strangpresse* (*Temperature Model of an Extrusion Press*), Technischer Bericht, Schloemann-Siemag AG, 1980

[Ger 96]: H. Gers, Theoretical and Practical Consideration for the Application of "Fuzzy Logic" in the Aluminum Extrusion Industry, *Proceedings Sixth Int. Aluminum Extrusion Technology Seminar*, Vol 1 (Chicago IL), 1996, p 51–55

[Hem 58]: E. Herrmann, *Handbuch des Stranggießens* (*Continuous Casting Handbook*), Düsseldorf, Aluminum Verlag GmbH, 1958

[Hem 80]: E. Herrmann, *Handbook on Continuous Casting*, Düsseldorf, Aluminum Verlag GmbH, 1980

[Hen 80]: A.J. Hengemolen, "Aluminum Industry Energy Conservation Workshop V Papers" (Washington D.C), Sept 1980, p 93–104

[Hen 83]: A.J. Hengemolen and R. Moser, *Aluminum*, Vol 59, 1983, p 516–521, 602–605

[Her 90]: G. Hertwich, Strangpressen (Extrusion), DGM—Information Society, Oberursel, 1990

[Höl 88]: H. Höller, "Experience with the Automated Press Line of Hydro Aluminium Nenzing," Fourth International Aluminum Extrusion Technology Seminar (Chicago, IL), 1988

[Hue 92]: P. Van Hue, "Heat Transfer Model for Temperature Profile of Extruded Sections at the Extrusion Press Exit," Fifth International Aluminum Extrusion Technology Seminar (Chicago, IL), 1992

[Iwa 84]: M. Iwata, "Extrusion Press Control by Microcomputer Assistance and Automatic Billet Handling System," Third Aluminum Extrusion Technology Seminar (Atlanta, GA), 1984

[Jas 86]: H. Jasper, *Gas-Wärme-Int.*, Vol 35, 1986, p 136–140

[Jug 33]: S. Junghans, Verfahren und Vorrichtung zum Gießen von Metallsträngen (Process and Equipment for Casting Metal Logs), DRP 750, 301, 1933–1945

[Jun 84]: K. Junge and R. Jeschar, *Gas-Wärme-Int.*, Vol 33, 1984, p 371–380

[Kra 83]: H.A. Krall, *Metall*, Vol 37, 1983, p 466–471

[Kre 60]: H. Kreil, H. Vosskühler, and K. Walter, The Continuous Casting of Copper and Its Alloys, *Metall. Rev.*, Vol 5, 1960, p 413–446

[Lec 79]: G.B. Leconte and K. Buxmann, *Aluminum*, Vol 55 (No. 6), 1979, p 387–390

[Loh 89]: T. Lohikoski and M. Lohikoski, *Metall*, Vol 43, 1989, p 531–533

[Los 76]: E. Lossack, *Light Met.*, 1976, p 413–424

[Mar 88]: M.A. Marchese and J.J. Coston, "Efficient Use of Liquid Nitrogen for Aluminum Extrusion Die Cooling and Inerting," Fourth Inernational Aluminum Extrusion Technology Seminar (Chicago, IL), 1988

[Mül 59]: E. Müller, *Hydraulische Pressen und Druckflüssigkeitsanlagen* (*Hydraulic Presses and Accumulation Systems*), 3rd ed., Springer-Verlag, 1959

[Nef 93]: D.V. Neff, *Light Met.*, 1993, p 805–812

[Neu 97]: R. Neugebauer, "Steuerung und Datenerfassung an LM-Strangpressen," Vortrag anläßlich der SMS-Pressentagung ("Control and Data Collection on Aluminum Extrusion Press," Paper at the SMS Press Conference), Leverkusen, 1997

[Out 85]: Prospekt "Upcast," Outokumpu Industrial Equipment Division, 1985

[Pan 95]: M. Panduit and K. Buchheit, Isothermes Strangpressen von Aluminum (Isothermal Extrusion of Aluminum), *Z. Alum.*, Vol 71, 1995, p 483–487, 614–619

[Pan 96]: M. Pandit and K. Buchheit, A New Measurement and Control System for Isothermal Extrusion, *Proceedings: Sixth International Aluminum Extrusion Technology Seminar*, Vol 1, 1996, p 79–86

[Pas 84]: J.A. Passeri, *Proc. of Third International Aluminum Extrusion Technology Seminar*, Vol 1 (Atlanta, GA), April 1984, p 149–151

[Put 71]: J. Putz, Moderne Blockanwärmanlagen (Modern Billet Heating Plants), *Z. Metallkd.*, Vol 62, 1971, p 21–26

[Put 83]: J. Putz, Gasschnellanwärmofen für Preßbolzen mit Hubbalkentransport (High Speed Gas Fired Billet Furnaces with Walking Beam Transport), *Metall*, Vol 37, 1983, p 451–454

[Put 87]: J. Putz, Preßbolzenanwarmöfen (Billet Heating Furnaces), *Metall*, Vol 41, 1987, p 371–381

[Rei 80]: W. Reinke and K. Alker, *Aluminium*, Vol 55, 1980, p 383–387

[Rep 89]: B. Repgen, "Untersuchung zur Produktionsoptimierung beim Isothermen Strangpressen" ("Investigation into Production Optimization in Isothermal Extrusion"), Diplomarbeit, Inst. für bildsame Formgebung, R.W.T.H., Aachen, 1989

[Rep 94]: B. Repgen, "Möglichkeiten der Prozeßoptimierung beim direkten Strangpressen von Aluminiumlegierungen," Seminar Grundlagen des Strangpressens ("Potential for Process Optimization in the Direct Extrusion of Aluminum," Basics of Extrusion Seminar), T.A. Eßlingen, 1994

[Rep 96a]: B. Repgen and V. Rothweiler, Erfahrung mit dem Einsatz einer Prozeßoptimierung für das Strangpressen (Experience with the Application of Process Optimization for Extrusion), *Aluminum*, Vol 72, 1996, p 868–870

[Rep 96b]: B. Repgen and A. Biswas, Isothermal and Isopressure Extrusion—Results of Process Optimization in Various Extrusion Plants, *Proceedings Sixth International Aluminum Extrusion Technology Seminar,* Vol I (Chicago, IL), 1996, p 37–43

[Rog 96]: A.P. Roger, "How to Operate Extrusion Presses Well . . . ," International Aluminum Extrusion Technology Seminar (Chicago, IL), 1996

[Rot 84]: W. Roth, *Aluminum*, Vol 60, 1984, p 249–250

[Rup 75]: D. Ruppin and W. Strehmel, Axiale Temperaturprofile in Strangpressbolzen aus Aluminumwerkstoffen (Axial Temperature Profiles in Extrusion Billets in Aluminum Alloys), *Aluminum* Sonderdruck aus dem, Vol 51 (No. 9), 1975, p 585–588

[Rup 77]: D. Ruppin and W. Strehmel, Direktes Strangpressen mit konstanter Austrittstemperatur-Einsatz variabler Pressgeschwindigkeit (Mitteilungen der Forschungsgruppe Strangpressen an der Technischen Universität Berlin) (Direct Extrusion with Constant Exit Temperature-Application of Variable Extrusion Speed), *Aluminum*, Vol 53, 1977, p 233–239, 543–548, 674–678, 773–776

[Rup 81]: D. Ruppin and K. Müller, Temperaturverhaltnisse beim direkten Strangpressen von Rohren aus Aluminum-Legierungen über stehenden und mitlaufenden Dorn (Temperature Variation in Direct Extrusion of Aluminum Alloy Tubes over Fixed and Moving Mandrels), Tagungsbericht der 7, Int. Leicht-metalltagung (Int. Light Alloy Conference), Leoben-Wien, 1981, p 294–295

[Rup 95]: D. Ruppin, Temperaturführung beim direkten Strangpressen von Aluminumlegierungen, *Grundlagen des Strangpressens* (Temperature Control in the Direct Extrusion of Aluminum Alloys, *Principles of Extrusion*), K. Herausgegeben von Müller, Ed., Kontakt & Studium, Bd. 286, Expert Verlag, 1995

[Saa 93]: A. Saavedra, *Light Met.*, 1993, p 739–743

[Sch 89]: W. Schneider and E. Lossack, *Proc. New Developments in Metallurgical Processing*, Vol 2, Verein Deutscher Eisenhüttenleute, Düsseldorf, 1989

[Sch 88]: W. Schneider and E. Lossack, *Metall*, Vol 42 (No. 2), 1988, p 124–128

[Sch 94]: W. Schneider, *Light Met.*, 1994, p 985–989

[Sch 94]: C. Schiewe, Pyrometrische Temperaturmessung beim Aluminum-Strangpressen (Temperature Measurements with Pyrometrics in Aluminum Extrusion), *Metall,* Vol 48, 1994, p 628–632

[Schl 89]: D. Schluckebier, Induktive Blockerwärmung (Induction Billet Heating—Extrusion Billets), Extrusion Symposium DGM, 1989, p 87–98

[Scho 76]: H.E. Scholz, "Werkstoffkundliche, experimentelle und theorethische Untersuchungen zur Optimierung des Strangpressens metallischer Werkstoffe" ("Material Scientific Experimental and Theoretical Investigation into the Optimization of the Extrusion of Metallic Materials"), Dissertation, R.W.T.H., Aachen, 1976

[Schü 96]: K.H. Schütte, Neue Modernisierungskonzepte für Strangpreßanlagen (New Modernization Concept for Extrusion Plants), *Aluminum*, Vol 72, 1996, p 468–474

[SMS]: Das CADEX Software Programm (The CADEX Software Program), SMS-Hasenclever-Schrift, p 2–314

[Spe 56]: K. Speith and A. Bungeroth, *Stahl Eisen*, Vol 76, 1956, p 437–442

[Ste 91]: A. Steinmetz and W. Staschul, Strang- und Rohrpressen von Kupfer und Messing (Rod and Tube Extrusion of Copper and Brass), *Metall*, Vol 45 (No. 11), Nov 1991

[Str 96]: W. Strehmel, M. Plata, and B. Bourqui, "New Technologies for Cooling and Quenching of Medium-to-Large-Sized Aluminum Extrusions," International Aluminum Extrusion Technology Seminar (Chicago, IL), 1996

[Stre 82]: W. Strehmel, "Untersuchungen zum rechnergestützten direkten Strangpressen von Aluminum-Legierungen," Fortschrittsberichte VDI-Z, Reihe 2 ("Investigations into Computer Controlled Direct Extrusion of Aluminum Alloys," Progress Report, VDI-Z, Series 2), No. 51, VDI-Verlag GmbH, Düsseldorf, 1982

[Stt 96]: B. Steinert, Einflußmöglichkeiten zur optimalen Werkzeugabstützungn in Leichtmetall-Strangpressen (Possible Methods for Achieving Optimum Tool Support in Aluminum Extrusion), Sonderdruck aus *Aluminum,* Vol 72, (No. 5), 1996

[Swa 57]: W. Schwarzmeier, *Stranggießen (Continuous Casting),* Stuttgart, Berliner Union GmbH, 1957

[Sze 78]: A.G. Szekely, *Erzmetall,* Vol 31 (No. 3), 1978, p 110–117

[Ter 87]: S. Terai and M. Yoshida, *Proc.* Eight Int. Light Alloy Conference, Leoben-Wien, 1987, p 236–243

[Thu 84]: F. Thurnheer, "Automated Extrusion Plants Come of Age in Europe," Third International Aluminum Extrusion Technology Seminar (Atlanta, GA), 1984

[War 77]: O.H. Warwick, *Proc. of Second International Aluminum Extrusion Technology Seminar,* Vol 1 (Atlanta, GA), Nov 1977, p 81–86

[War 85]: M.E. Ward, *Adv. Ceram. (Ceram. Heat. Exch.,)* Vol 14, 1985, p 71–77

[Wie 83]: J.J. Wiesner, *Aluminum,* Vol 59, 1983, p 493–496

[Wil 51]: H. Wieland, Verfahren zum Stranggießen metallischer Werkstoffe (Process for Continuous Casting of Metallic Materials), DBP 892, 230, 1951–1953

[Yao 91]: Ch. Yao, "Isothermes direktes Strangpressen von Aluminumlegierungen" ("Isothermal Direct Extrusion of Aluminum Alloys"), Dissertation, Berlin, 1971

[Yok 77]: H. Yokobayashi, T. Chiba, and J. Morooka, "Study of the Indirect Extrusion Process of Aluminum Alloy," Second International Aluminum Extrusion Technology Seminar, 1977

[Zie 73]: W. Ziegler and K. Siegert, Indirektes Strangpressen von Leichtmetal (Indirect Extrusion of Aluminum), *Z. Metallkd.* Vol 64 (No. 4), 1973, p 224–229

[Zil 84]: F.-J. Zilges, Aufbau und Arbeitsweise einer neuen Indirekt-Strang-und Rohrpreßlinie für Aluminum (Design and Operation of a New Indirect Rod and Tube Extrusion Line), Sonderdruck aus *Aluminum,* Vol 60 (No. 6), 1984

CHAPTER 7

Extrusion Tooling

Günther Sauer and Adolf Ames*

QUALITATIVELY HIGH-VALUE SEMI-FINISHED PRODUCTS require uniform quality throughout the production run, with high retention of shape and dimensions as well as good mechanical properties.

7.1 Requirements of Tooling and Tooling Material

Extrusion tooling can be broadly classified into tooling that is directly involved in the shape forming of the material being extruded, tooling that is not directly involved, and tooling that fulfills auxiliary and support functions. The first group includes extrusion dies, porthole and bridge dies, as well as mandrels. These extrusion tools come into direct contact with the billet material heated to the deformation temperature. The second group includes extrusion tooling that does not have any shape-producing function but, at the same time, is indirectly involved in the shape-changing process. This includes container liners, extrusion stems, dummy blocks, and mandrel holders as well as die-carrying stems, container-sealing plates, and container-sealing stems with sealing discs in indirect extrusion. The third group is represented by the auxiliary tooling, including die holders, tool holders, pressure plate holders, as well as support tooling including the container mantle, liner holder, and subbolsters and bolsters in the direct-extrusion tool stack.

7.1.1 Requirements of the Extrusion Tooling

High demands are placed on the design of the extrusion tooling, the hot working materials used, and the manufacturing process so that the following requirements can be met in production.

Extrusion tooling for direct external and internal shape forming must:

- Be produced from a hot working material with adequate temperature resistance
- Require only minimum correction and be ready for production after as few trials as possible
- Permit the optimal exit speeds
- Ensure uniform material flow across the section as well as defect-free extrusion welds in the extruded section with hollow sections and tubes
- Enable high throughputs with simultaneous optimal quality of the produced extrusion for dimensional stability, shape accuracy, and surface quality
- Have low maintenance costs
- Offer a favorable price/throughput ratio
- Ensure that repeat tooling in comparison to the first tooling not only produces the same quality but also is ready for production without trial extrusions, as far as possible

Extrusion tooling for indirect shape forming must:

---

*Tools for the Extrusion of Materials with Deformation Temperature of 600 to 1300 °C, Martin Bauser
Recent Developments in Resistance Heating of Containers, Wolfgang Eckenbach
Static- and Elastic-Based Analysis and Dimensioning of Containers Loaded in Three Dimensions, Günther Sauer
Hot Working Materials for the Manufacture of Extrusion Tooling, Günther Sauer

- Be produced from hot working material with adequate temperature resistance
- Exhibit a high functional efficiency
- Offer a favorable price/throughput ratio

Auxiliary tooling and support tooling must:

- Be dimensioned so that the shape-producing regions of the extrusion tooling undergo only insignificant elastic deformation under the extrusion loads, ensuring that material flow and shape are not negatively influenced

7.1.2 Requirements of the Tooling Materials

Depending on the billet material, the materials for extrusion tooling are more or less highly stressed, both thermally and mechanically. With fast extrusion cycles, the associated high thermomechanical stressing can be considered as continuous loading, and with slow extrusion cycles, as interrupted creep loading, as discussed in more detail in section "Hot Working Materials for the Manufacture of Extrusion Tooling" in this chapter. The highest thermomechanical stressing is found in the tooling areas that come into direct contact with the billet material heated to the deformation temperature. Friction and shear stresses occur in the thermomechanically stressed contact areas of the tooling as well as the deformation forces. Friction and shearing in the container and on the working surfaces of the shape-producing tools can have a significant effect on the total extrusion load, depending on the material being extruded. In direct extrusion without lubrication, the friction and shear forces can be up to 60% of the total extrusion load. Wear and adhesion at the tool working surfaces render the tooling unusable in the medium and long term.

Friction and wear at the working faces of the extrusion tooling and the desire to minimize them enable the sliding partners of the billet material/tooling to be considered as a tribosystem. There are hardly any selection options because of the deformation function of the extrusion process, but process-specific dry friction with unlubricated direct extrusion, boundary, and mixed friction in extrusion with lubrication as well as liquid friction in hydrostatic and lubricated extrusion can occur.

Sliding wear occurs on the tool working surfaces and mainly consists of abrasive and adhesive wear. For example, whereas the adhesive wear in the shape-forming aperture of an extrusion die has an unfavorable effect on the quality of the surface of the extrusion, the abrasive wear leads to shape and dimensional inaccuracies of the cross section of the extrusion. In the advanced stage, both types of wear can seriously impair the extrusion of sections to final sizes or even make it impossible. This gives rise to the need to reduce the adhesion and abrasion as far as possible, for example, by lubrication, or by a thermochemical surface treatment such as peripheral layer formation by nitriding, or by the deposition of wear-resistant surface coatings by the chemical vapor deposition process. Die and mandrel inserts in hot working materials that can withstand higher thermal stresses can also be used.

Depending on the deformation temperature, significant operating temperatures can develop on the working surfaces of the extrusion tooling. Suitable hot working materials and application-specific heat treatments are needed to ensure long tooling service life. The property requirements for a material suitable for the manufacture of extrusion tooling are:

- Temperature resistance combined with optimal values for creep and fatigue strength in the operating temperature range
- Hot toughness
- Hot wear resistance to abrasion and adhesion
- Resistance to temperature fluctuations
- Thermal conductivity
- Resistance to chemical reaction with the extruded material

In the stress collective of a tribosystem, a reactive body always moves against a reaction body [Gah 90, Bun 81, Hab 80, Bre 79]. The tribological system between the working surfaces of the extrusion tooling and the billet material has the tooling as the reaction body and continuously changing extruded material resulting from the deformation-related material flow as the reactive body.

The extrusion tooling is deformed elastically during the extrusion process, and the extruded material plastically. During the deformation by extrusion, the following tribological conditions between the extrusion tooling as the reaction body and the billet material as the reactive body must be taken into account:

- At the working surfaces, an effective normal force as the contact force

- Temperatures developed at the working surfaces
- Flow rate of the extruded material at the working surfaces and, if necessary, the occurrence of deformation-related relative movement or relative speeds
- Changes in the extruded material associated with the deformation process
- Stress duration

These result in:

- Decrease in strength up to softening of the tool working surfaces and, as a result, creep and flow processes under thermomechanical loading with temperatures in or above the tempering region of the tooling material
- Melting in the surface region of the extruded material in extreme cases, due to thermomechanical stresses
- Adhesive wear with metallic contact between the two sliding partners without lubrication as an intermediate material; the metallic contact results in the transfer of the softer extruded material to the working surface of the extrusion tooling.
- Abrasive wear of both sliding partners in spite of lubricated working surfaces

7.2 Design of Tool Sets for Direct and Indirect Extrusion

In direct extrusion, the tool set for the production of section, rod, and round and shaped tubes is located in a tool holder. This is a cassette in Fig. 7.1. Previously, tool heads, tool slides, or rotating arms were used.

In contrast, in indirect extrusion, the tool set must be located on a tool carrier stem or by a tool holder in the tool carrier stem, as shown in Fig. 7.2.

7.2.1 Design of the Tool Set for Direct Extrusion

Figures 7.3 to 7.5 depict the tool set necessary for direct extrusion. This consists of the tooling for the external and internal shape-forming, including the die, the mandrel or the hollow section die, as well as the support tooling. In extrusion, the container is pushed against the die or the die holder by its hydraulic drive. The entire tool set is then clamped between the container and the pressure ring in the press front platen with a load up to 16% of the installed press power. Simultaneously, the container is sealed

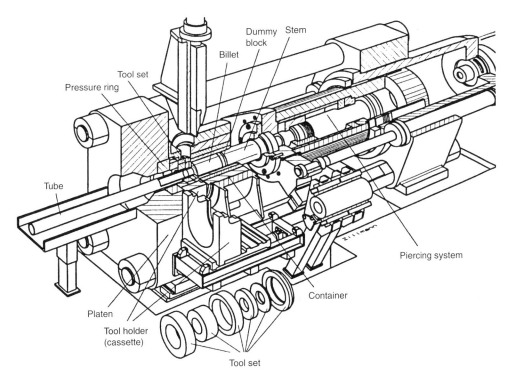

Fig. 7.1 Assembly of the tool set in a direct tube extrusion press. Source: Ames

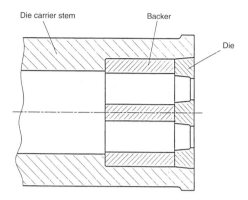

Fig. 7.2 Indirect extrusion with the die holder machined into the die carrier stem. Source: Ames

against the die as described in section 7.2.3. This container load is superimposed cumulatively onto the shear and friction loads developed in the container during the deformation.

There are three types of extrusion tooling, depending on the cross-sectional geometry of the extrusion:

- Flat dies with and without a feeder chamber for the production of rods and solid sections. Figure 7.3 shows the tool set required. These extrusion tools can be used for all extrudable metallic materials.

- Tube tools for the production of round and shaped tubes as well as hollow sections, as shown in Fig. 7.4. These extrusion tools can also be used for the working of all extrudable metallic materials.

- Porthole and bridge dies for the production of hollow sections and thin-wall tubes in long lengths. A tool stack of this type is shown in Fig. 7.5.

The latter cannot, in general, be subjected to very high thermomechanical stresses, especially at high temperatures. They can therefore basically be used only for the extrusion of lead, tin, magnesium, and aluminum alloys. Nevertheless, these tools are used to a limited extent for the extrusion of copper alloys, including pure copper and copper-zinc alloys. In these cases, the extrusion tooling is subjected to very high thermomechanical stresses.

The extrusion die is always located in a die holder. There is a specific holder for each die diameter. The height of the holder is usually constant for a press type and depends on the press power, the container internal diameter, and the circumscribing circle of the cross section of the extruded section. It is designed so that a full-height hollow die can be fitted, as shown in Fig. 7.6. For the production of solid sections, there

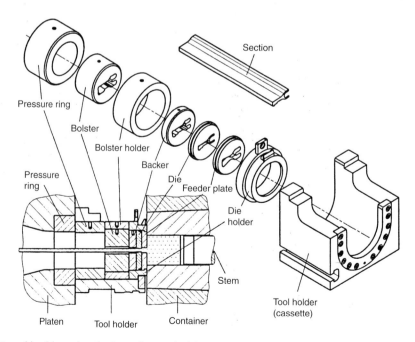

Fig. 7.3 Assembly of the tool set for the production of solid sections with a flat die. Source: Ames

is a backer as a support tool directly behind the die, as shown in the top part of Fig. 7.6.

The total height of the die and backer is then equal to the height of the die holder. The die holder must be designed so that a rapid change of the die is possible at any time.

For direct rod and tube extrusion of aluminum as well as copper alloys, the press size and the dimensions of the tooling involved directly and indirectly in the shape production, as well as the auxiliary and support tooling, are specified in DIN 24540, published in 1986 [Ame 71]. The

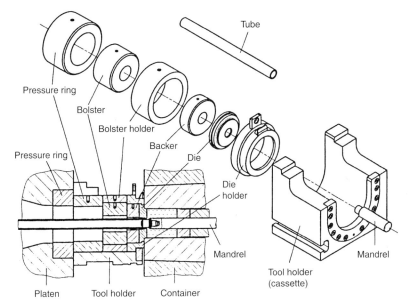

Fig. 7.4 Assembly of the tool set for the production of round and shaped tubes and hollow sections using tube or section dies together with a stepped mandrel. Source: Ames

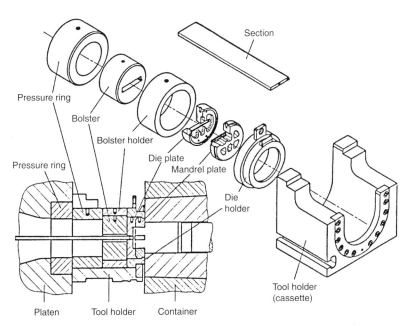

Fig. 7.5 Assembly of the tool set for the production of hollow sections in aluminum alloys using a porthole die. Source: Ames

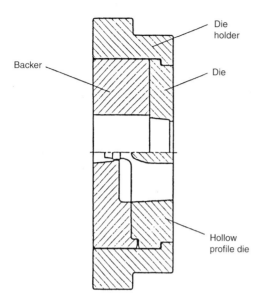

Fig. 7.6 Die holder with a die and backer above and a port-hole die below the centerline for aluminum alloys.
Source: Ames

part of the standard "General, Aluminum and Copper Alloys" gives the principal dimensions of the tooling as a function of the press size.

The dimensions of the tool stack have a decisive role in the dimensional and shape quality of the extruded semifinished product. These must be such that the shape-forming tools practically undergo no or only insignificant elastic deformation under the extrusion loads. This applies in particular to the production of sections

to the finished dimensions. Therefore, the dimensioning has particular importance in this context. It should also be taken into account that the temperature of the shape-forming extrusion tooling is dependent on the material being extruded and can be well over 1000 °C. The specific mechanical stresses from the extrusion load can be more than 1100 N/mm².

A finite element method study was carried out by SMS-Eumuco GmbH [Ste 96]. This study considered the bending of the tool stack at the intersection points of the pressure ring/tool stack and the pressure ring/press front platen under different parameters and gave the following results:

- The decisive factor for tool bending is the ratio of the tool diameter, d, to the diameter of the pressure ring in the front platen of the extrusion press, D, as a function of increasing pressure ring radius, as shown in Fig. 7.7. If the diameter ratio is 0.9 to 1.0, then, according to Fig. 7.7, the bending of the pressure ring in the front platen and thus of the tool stack can be close to zero.
- A further reduction of the tool bending is achieved by increasing the height of the pressure ring or the pressure ring thickness in the front platen.
- The thickness of the press front platen itself has no influence on the bending of the tool set. Therefore, the height of the press front platen depends only on the dimensions required for the dynamic loading that occurs during deformation.

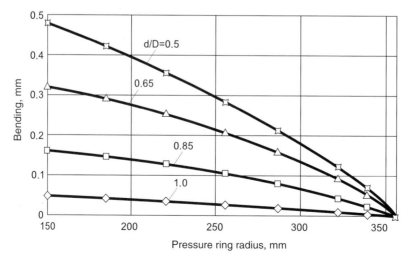

Fig. 7.7 Influence of the ratio tool set diameter, d, to the diameter of the pressure ring in the press front platen, D, on bending as a function of the increasing pressure ring radius. Source: SMS-Emoco

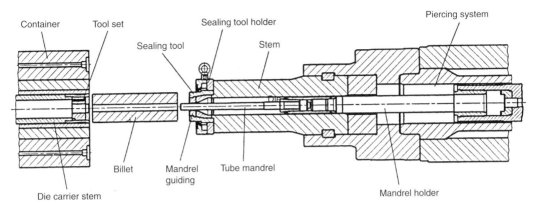

Fig. 7.8 Assembly of the tool set in an indirect tube extrusion press. Source: Ames

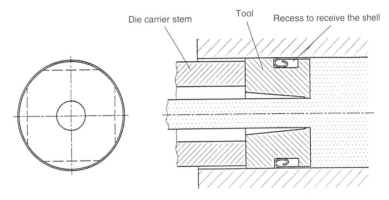

Fig. 7.9 Indirect extrusion of aluminum alloys with a loose die holder on the tool carrier stem with the functions: extrusion die, backer, die holder, dummy block, and cleaning block. Source: Ames

7.2.2 Design of the Tool Set for Indirect Extrusion

In comparison to direct extrusion, the tool set of an indirect-extrusion press consists of the stem tool carrier and the die holder with the die and the backer, as shown in Fig. 7.2 and 7.8 to 7.10. There are two options for locating the die on the head of the stem tool carrier in indirect extrusion. In one system, the die holder is simply placed on the stem tool carrier during every extrusion cycle, using a manipulator, as shown in Fig. 7.9 and 7.10. The other system operates with a die holder machined into the stem tool carrier, as shown in Fig. 7.2. The loose die holder is easy to handle and is therefore preferred. It is used for the extrusion of aluminum alloys as well as copper alloys. This extrusion tool has several functions and, in the working of copper, is both the die holder and the dummy block. In the working of aluminum alloys, the tool shown in Fig. 7.9 is the extrusion die, die

holder, and scalping block all in one. There are always two tool sets in operation to ensure continuous production. While one is being used for extrusion, the other, in the case of aluminum alloy extrusion, is having the shell removed and being cleaned or, after copper alloy extrusion, being cleaned together with the die ready for reuse. Nevertheless, in some applications, the shell in the container in aluminum extrusion is

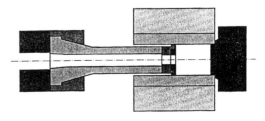

Fig. 7.10 Indirect extrusion of copper alloys with a loose die holder and built-in extrusion die in front of the die carrier stem. Source: Wieland-Werke AG

also removed in a separate operation. In this case, the die holder shown in Fig. 7.2 is used. One disadvantage of working with loose die holders is the cooling during the cleaning operation.

When dimensioning a tool set for indirect extrusion, it must be remembered that the stem die carrier undertakes the same function as the support tooling of the direct-extrusion tool set, with the exception of the backer. The bore should of course have the optimal dimensions for the removal of extrusions, with the maximum possible cross-sectional area. At the same time, particular attention also must be given to the load-carrying capacity in its support role to avoid unacceptable elastic deformations in the shape-producing areas of the extrusion tooling. Both the deformation loads as well as the deformation temperatures are the determining factors in the dimensioning and the materials selection.

7.2.3 Sealing of the Shape-Producing Tooling with the Container

In direct extrusion, the shape-producing tools of the die or hollow die or their holder must be sealed against the container with sufficient compressive force so that extruded material cannot be forced out between the container and the tooling during extrusion. Sealing surfaces are therefore machined onto both the container and the

dies or their holder, as shown in Fig. 7.11 and 7.12.

These sealing surfaces must be subjected to a specific load of at least 70 to 90 N/mm^2 to fulfill the sealing role. The maximum is 350 N/mm^2 to avoid plastic deformation of the sealing surfaces. In direct extrusion, these loads are applied by the container hydraulic sealing load. The loading on the sealing surfaces is at the maximum at the start of extrusion, due to the friction or shear forces acting on the container liner wall during extrusion.

To ensure adequate sealing at the end of extrusion, the container hydraulic system is designed to give a sealing force of a maximum of 16% of the press power. In the sealing process, the tool stack with the die in the press must be clamped between the pressure ring in the front platen of the press and the container, so that the centerline of the tool stack coincides with the centerline of the extrusion press.

Figures 7.11 and 7.12 describe the three sealing designs used today, and these are conical, cylindrical, and flat sealing. Originally, the sealing between the container and the die stack was basically designed as a conical sealing system. Conical sealing has proved successful over many years, because it not only seals well but also provides alignment of the die with the press and container centerlines. Conical seals are also used for the extrusion of materials with high

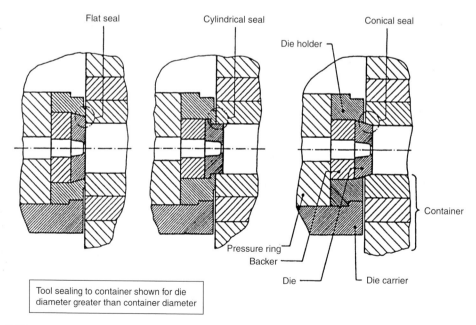

Tool sealing to container shown for die diameter greater than container diameter

Fig. 7.11 Schematic arrangement of the three methods of sealing the container against the die. Source: Sauer

working temperatures, for example, copper, iron, and nickel alloys. DIN 24540 part 1 gives a conical angle of 10° and a conical length of 30 mm.

At the same time, conical sealing has a clear disadvantage. Under the effect of the sealing load, A, the force component, R, develops in the cone and radially stresses the container in the conical area (Fig. 7.13). The reaction force also stresses the die tooling. From Fig. 7.13, the radial force is not only dependent on the sealing load A but also on the cosine of the cone angle, α. From this dependence, the radial force decreases with increasing cone angle, α. For this reason, for years the press manufacturers have increased the cone angle of $\alpha = 10°$, according to DIN 24540, to $\alpha = 35°$ to reduce the radial force, after trials with an angle of 45° resulted in a negative effect on the alignment of the tool set with the press centerline. Cone angles of 40° are common in copper alloy extrusion plants.

Figure 7.14 describes conical seals for the extrusion of copper alloys. If the circumscribing circle of the cross section of the extruded product is small, then a seal between the die holder and the container, according to Fig. 7.14(a), is preferred. With larger-diameter circumscribing circles, sealing must be between the extrusion die and the container, as shown in Fig. 7.14(b). With high sealing loads, there is the risk of die deformation. For this reason, the sealing be-

tween the extrusion die and the container should only be used in exceptional cases. A conical entry on the die holder and on the die (Fig. 7.14) can prevent shell defects, particularly with large rod and tube dimensions in difficult-to-extrude copper alloys and lubricated containers. In this case, there is the risk with flat die holders and flat dies of the shell flowing in over the dead metal zone.

Under the action of the radial force, R, the container opens up elastically in the sealing area, but in contrast, the shape-producing aperture of a die is elastically compressed. This can distort the material flow in the shape-producing tool area. This has a negative effect on the accuracy of the shape and the dimensions of the extruded product, in particular on filigree cross sections in the easy-to-extrude aluminum alloys. It does happen that the cross-sectional dimensions of the extruded section vary from extrusion to extrusion due to variations in the friction conditions in the sealing conical faces. The majority of aluminum extrusion plants have therefore moved from the conical seal to the flat and cylindrical sealing in which there are no radial forces from the sealing force A. Figures 7.11 and 7.12 as well as 7.15 and 7.16 describe these sealing designs.

The extrusion of round and shaped tubes over an extrusion mandrel requires accurate alignment of the extrusion die to the centerline of the

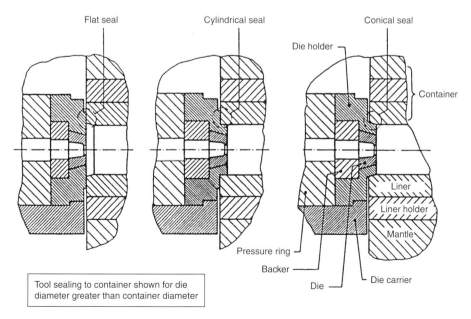

Flat seal   Cylindrical seal   Conical seal

Die holder

Container

Liner

Liner holder

Mantle

Pressure ring

Backer

Die carrier

Die

Tool sealing to container shown for die diameter greater than container diameter

Fig. 7.12 Schematic arrangement of the three methods of sealing the container against the die holder. Source: Sauer

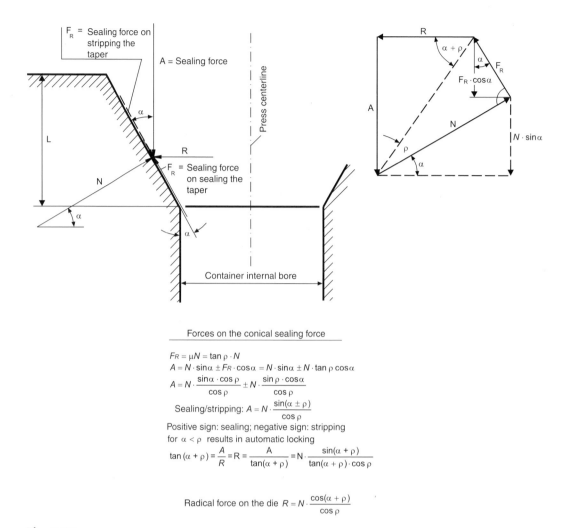

Fig. 7.13 Forces in the conical surface of the container under the effect of the container sealing force. Source: Sauer

Forces on the conical sealing force

$F_R = \mu N = \tan \rho \cdot N$

$A = N \cdot \sin\alpha \pm F_R \cdot \cos\alpha = N \cdot \sin\alpha \pm N \cdot \tan\rho\,\cos\alpha$

$A = N \cdot \dfrac{\sin\alpha \cdot \cos\rho}{\cos\rho} \pm N \cdot \dfrac{\sin\rho \cdot \cos\alpha}{\cos\rho}$

Sealing/stripping: $A = N \cdot \dfrac{\sin(\alpha \pm \rho)}{\cos\rho}$

Positive sign: sealing; negative sign: stripping
for $\alpha < \rho$ results in automatic locking

$\tan(\alpha + \rho) = \dfrac{A}{R} = R = \dfrac{A}{\tan(\alpha + \rho)} = N \cdot \dfrac{\sin(\alpha + \rho)}{\tan(\alpha + \rho) \cdot \cos\rho}$

Radical force on the die $R = N \cdot \dfrac{\cos(\alpha + \rho)}{\cos\rho}$

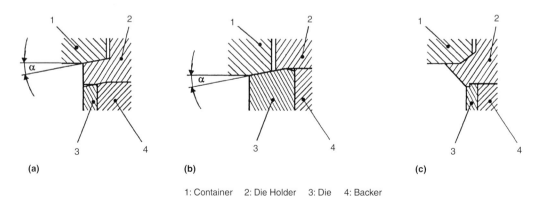

1: Container   2: Die Holder   3: Die   4: Backer

Fig. 7.14 Taper sealing faces for sealing between the die set and the container. (a) Taper seal between the die holder and the container, to DIN 24540. (b) Taper seal between the die and the container, to DIN 24540. (c) Additional internal taper on the die holder and the die, not included in DIN 24540. Source: Wieland-Werke AG

container and the extrusion press. This cannot be accomplished with a flat seal, as shown in Fig. 7.15, and is only possible with a cylindrical seal, as shown in Fig. 7.16. The protruding cylinder on the die centers this in the container, similar to the conical seal. However, with this design, there are no undesired radial forces from the sealing load that could influence the shape-forming area of the die.

With all sealing designs, partial plastic deformation of the sealing faces cannot be avoided during production after many extrusions, and re-machining may be required to ensure perfect sealing. It is a good idea to extend the flat sealing

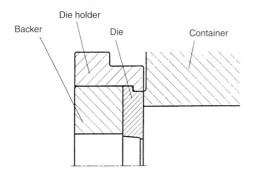

Fig. 7.15 Flat seal between the container and a flat die. Source: Ames

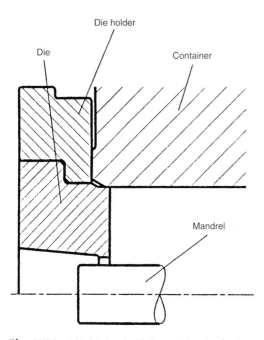

Fig. 7.16 Cylindrical seal with the container for aluminum tube extrusion. Source: Ames

surface as well as the conical sealing surface by 8 to 10 mm on the container face facing the tool set, to allow for regrinding, as seen in Fig. 7.15 and 7.16.

7.3 Extrusion Tooling for Direct External and Internal Shape Production

As shown in Fig. 7.3, 7.4, 7.17, and 7.18, the extrusion die is used for direct external shape formation in extrusion. The direct formation of the internal shape is produced by a mandrel, as depicted in Fig. 7.4, 7.19, and 7.20. Extrusion dies and extrusion mandrels are practically the standard tools for extrusions. They can be used for the working of all extrudable materials. In addition to these standard tools, there are special tools, including porthole and bridge dies, as shown in Fig. 7.21 to 7.23. These combine the direct external and internal shape formation into a single tool.

Extrusion dies can be divided into flat entry and conical entry. Extrusion dies with flat entries are used for extrusion with or without a shell and without lubrication. Extrusion dies with conical entries (Fig. 7.17) or angled entries (Fig. 7.24) are used for lubricated extrusion. The die can also have one or more shape-forming cavities. Figure 7.18 shows a three-cavity extrusion die and a flat material entry for the production of hinges in an aluminum alloy. Extrusion dies for the production of solid sections can have up to eight shape-forming cavities and even more in special cases.

The full container bore cannot be used to determine the cross-sectional geometry of the extruded section, defined by the circumscribing circle of the cross section. The circumscribing circle of the sections usually must be restricted to 80% of the container internal diameter to avoid the inflow of unclean billet peripheral regions into the deformation zone. However, this value can be increased to 90% of the internal container diameter, for example, with aluminum billets cast in a magnetic field and turned.

When the section leaves the shape-forming aperture, it has its final shape. To ensure trouble-free exit, the extrusion die is opened up after the shape-producing aperture, as shown in Fig. 7.17. The subsequent support tools increase in size from one to another in the direction of extrusion

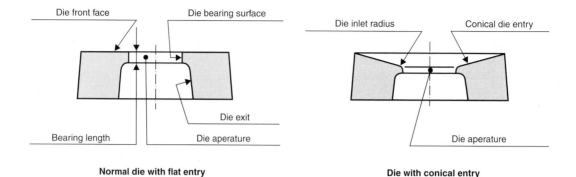

Fig. 7.17 Schematic arrangement of extrusion die variations. Source: Sauer

to avoid touching of the extrusion and sometimes plugging of the support tooling.

The shape-producing apertures in the extrusion die are more or less subjected to high thermomechanical stresses, depending on the deformation temperature. This can result in deformation of the die close to the shape-producing apertures after only a few extrusions, for example, in the case of copper alloy extrusion. This risk is countered by the use of shrunk-in die inserts in higher hot strength hot working steels, including austenitic steels as well as cobalt and nickel alloys.

Only a few extruded materials can be used with porthole and bridge dies to produce tubes

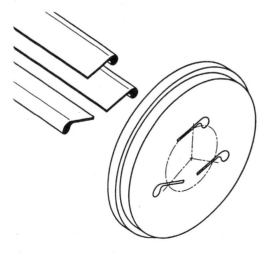

Fig. 7.18 Extrusion die with three shape-forming apertures (three-cavity die) for the production of aluminum alloy hinge sections. Source: Ames

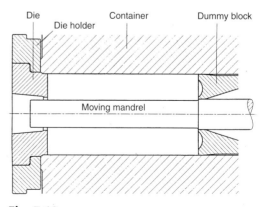

Fig. 7.19 Extrusion over a moving mandrel. Source: Ames

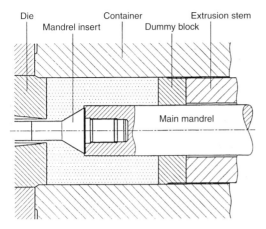

Fig. 7.20 Extrusion over a mandrel tip. Source: Ames

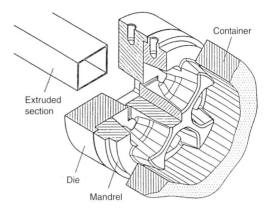

Fig. 7.23 Section through a two-part bridge die, with the bridge extending into the container, for the production of a rectangular section. Source: Ames

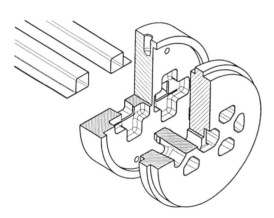

Fig. 7.21 Two-part porthole die with two shape-forming cavities for the production of quadratic case sections in AlMgSi0.5. Source: Ames

Fig. 7.24 Extrusion die with different-length tapered inlets to the die aperture for the production of a steel section. Source: Krupp-Hoesch

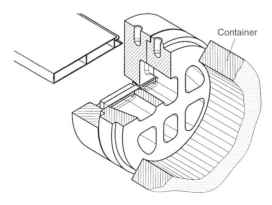

Fig. 7.22 Single-cavity two-part porthole die with six ports to produce the AlMgSi0.5 hollow section shown at the die exit. Source: Ames

and hollow sections. Either the extruded material has insufficient welding properties or the special die cannot withstand the thermomechanical stresses. In these cases, tubes and hollow sections are produced using a mandrel for the internal shape and a die for the external, as depicted in Fig. 7.19 and 7.20. The extrusion over a mandrel is mainly used for direct extrusion; however, the process is also used for indirect extrusion. In all cases, the mandrel is connected to a hydraulic piercing system that also controls it. Figures 7.1 and 7.2 show the location of the piercing system in a direct- and indirect-extrusion press, respectively.

During extrusion, the extrusion mandrel (Fig. 7.19) can, with its hydraulically controlled speed, move faster than the extrusion stem over an adjustable stroke (relative movement). This movement can also be at the stem speed. The extruded material slides in the deformation zone region and leaves the die with a relative speed to the mandrel, so that in the shape-producing region of the die new mandrel surfaces are being continuously thermomechanically stressed, in contrast to a fixed mandrel. This improves the service life of the mandrel. In addition, the forward movement reduces the tensile forces resulting from the friction between the extruded material and the mandrel surface. To ease the flow process and also to provide trouble-free withdrawal of the mandrel from the extruded tube or hollow section at the end of the extrusion process, the mandrel is slightly tapered. The use of conical mandrels results in a conicity of the bore of the tubes or hollow sections. The use of stepped-fixed mandrels (Fig. 7.20, 7.25) overcomes this problem. Cylindrical mandrels also eliminate this problem, but their use is generally limited to short aluminum and copper alloy billets.

The mandrel tip can be turned onto the mandrel shaft but also may be designed to be replaceable, as seen in Fig. 7.20 and 7.25. A threaded exchangeable mandrel tip not only allows a rapid change when subjected to high thermomechanical stresses, for example, in copper alloy extrusion, but because it sits in the main wear region, it can also be made from a hot working material with a better hot strength.

Figures 7.19, 7.20, and 7.25 show the most important types of mandrel. Using the hydraulic piercer on a tube press, solid billets can be pierced with all mandrel types. The mandrel is subjected to buckling during the piercing process and must be dimensioned accordingly.

The mandrel is connected by a mandrel holder to the mandrel bar, as seen in Fig. 7.25. This then connects it with the hydraulic piercing system of the press. In addition, the dummy block has a hole through it for the mandrel to move through. The conical part of the mandrel is frequently stepped down from the remainder of the shaft, that is, slightly smaller in diameter, as seen in Fig. 7.19. This ensures that the shape-producing outer surface of the mandrel cannot be damaged in the bore of the dummy block.

The mandrel is the most highly thermomechanically stressed of all the extrusion tools because of the deformation temperature of the extruded material. The mandrel is completely surrounded by the extruded material during the deformation process, so that the temperature of

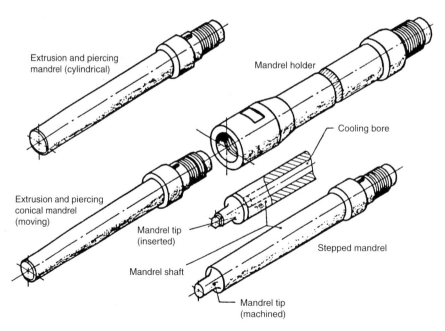

Fig. 7.25 Schematic arrangement of the most common types of mandrels for forming the internal profile of tubes and hollow sections. Source: Sauer

the extruded material is entirely directed to the mandrel surface. Heat can only be extracted internally through the mandrel cross section during the extrusion process. Only after completion of the deformation of the extruded material in the extrusion cycle can heat be removed from the mandrel surface. With high deformation temperatures, this can sometimes result in high temperature fluctuations in the mandrel surface region, so that the material resistance to sudden temperature changes is exceeded. This can result in a fine network of cracks in the area of the mandrel surface. In the limiting case, there is the risk of the mandrel necking and failing during extrusion under the tensile load even in the extrusion of aluminum alloys. Therefore, highly thermomechanically stressed mandrels are internally cooled. The cooling fluid flows through a ceramic tube with holes in the mantle surface up to the mandrel tip and then returns back around the ceramic tube. This internal mandrel cooling is shown schematically in Fig. 7.25. Mandrels used for deformation temperatures up to 600 °C are not usually cooled internally.

Porthole dies and bridge dies (Fig. 7.5, 7.21, and 7.22) are mainly used to produce thin-walled tubes and hollow sections from materials, the deformation conditions of which can be thermomechanically tolerated by the extrusion tool and their hot working material. The billet material divides into several metal streams under the influence of the extrusion load on the billet side of the die, according to the number of feeds, and then recombines in the shape-forming region of the die. The material being extruded must have adequate welding properties at the working temperature. These are mainly tin, lead, magnesium, and aluminum alloys. To a limited extent, copper alloys can be extruded to thin-wall tubes and hollow sections by using hot working materials for the die material. Figure 7.24 shows such a bridge die in an old design for the production of thin-wall brass and special brass tubes.

Porthole and bridge dies usually consist of two pieces: an upper part and a lower part, as seen in Fig. 7.21. The die upper part with the mandrel forms the internal shape of the extruded section, and the lower part the external shape. The upper part also contains the material feeds on the side facing the billet. These are usually arranged so that the material streams follow the shortest route through to the shape-forming region.

The hollow dies described can also be multi-cavity; that is, they have several shape-forming

apertures. In general, up to 12 cavities are possible for the production of small and stable hollow sections in the alloy AlMgSi0.5. In special cases, even more cavities can be included, as seen in the die in Fig. 7.27, used for the production of window spacer sections.

The thermal and mechanical stresses in a porthole or bridge die depend mainly on the deformation temperatures and the extrusion loads. Tensile, compressive, and bending stresses fluctuate during the extrusion cycle. The mandrel support in particular is subjected to fluctuating tensile and bending stresses. These stresses are superimposed on the local thermal stresses resulting from, for example, local heat buildup due to inadequate heat extraction with large extrusion dies and stress concentrations resulting from notch effects. The thermomechanical stressing of these tools is accordingly very complex. Heat buildup can result in plastic deformation in the shape-forming areas of large hot working steel porthole dies, and stress concentrations can result in cracks in fracture-sensitive areas, for example, at the roots of the mandrel. The die designer therefore attempts to make these areas that are at risk from fracture interchangeable. In addition, he also must ensure the optimal support for the die in the tool set. Insufficient heat extraction in large porthole dies

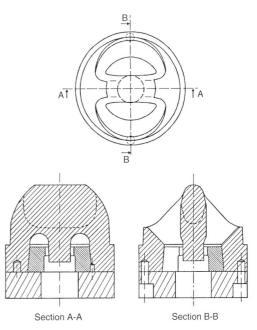

Section A-A   Section B-B

Fig. 7.26 Bridge die for the extrusion of a tube in special brass with interchangeable nickel alloy die

Fig. 7.27 Fourteen-cavity porthole die for the production of double-glazing spacers in the alloy AlMgSiO.5. Left, die plate with the fourteen-die apertures. Right, mandrel from the billet side. Source: Erbslöh Aluminium

also reduces the extrusion speed in aluminum alloy extrusion.

7.3.1 Control of Material Flow in the Shape-Forming Region of Extrusion Tooling

Asymmetrical extruded profile cross sections with nonuniform wall thicknesses and localized areas of thicker material require a mechanism for controlling the material flow in the shape-forming areas of the extrusion tooling. There is also the tendency for the material on the center-line of the die to flow faster. The aim is to control the material flow so that the extruded material flows out of the die with the same speed as far as possible over the full cross section.

Figure 7.17 shows that with all types of die, the shape-forming aperture has a die bearing surface in the direction of the material flow. Adjusting the bearing length to the cross section of the extruded profile and the location of the die cavity in the die produces die working surfaces that retard the extruded material to differing degrees by friction and shear stresses. This involves friction- and shear-related flow resistances, which are used to influence the material flow through the die. Figure 7.28 illustrates this with a die for the production of an aluminum alloy section.

Higher flow resistance values also occur in die cavities that are tapered in the extrusion direction, with the normally parallel bearings being given a very slight inclination. Figure 7.29(a) and (b) show these possible methods for additional material flow control.

The wide range of production-related small differences in the geometric design of the shape-forming tool areas can result in unstable material flow conditions. Inaccuracies in the production or correction of a die aperture and, in particular, the elastic deformations from the effect of the extrusion load can have a more or less severe influence on the flow resistance [Ake 85]. This explains the importance for a uniform flow of having, on one hand, an accurate flat parallel realization of the bearing surfaces in the die aperture and, on the other, the prevention of unacceptable elastic deformation of these tool areas. Nevertheless, with an estimated bending of the die under the effect of the extrusion load, the bearing surfaces of the die aperture can be given a slight angle in the extrusion direction so that this is reduced in size by the same magnitude that it opens under the bending. The bending-

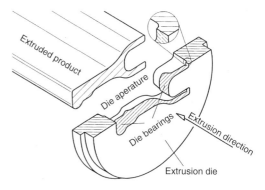

Fig. 7.28 Control of material flow using different bearing lengths in the die aperture of an aluminum alloy section die

related inclination of the bearing surfaces is then approximately compensated.

In addition, poor heat extraction from the shape-forming areas of the extrusion tooling can result in the temperature exceeding the tempering temperature of the tool material used, and plastic deformation occurring after a few extrusions.

The control of the material flow with the aid of varying flow resistances from longer or shorter bearing or shear surfaces in the shape-forming tool areas cannot be used for all extrusion processes. It is restricted to extrusion without lubrication. The friction in the shape-forming areas of the tooling in glass-lubricated extrusion, for example, of steel, and in lubricated extrusion, for example, of copper alloys, has little influence. Instead, the lubricant or the effective medium used as an intermediate layer separates the material being extruded from the working surfaces of the tooling in the shape-forming areas, so that mixed or even liquid friction occurs. Consequently, in these extrusion processes, an effective control of the material flow is far more difficult. In addition, there are differences in the specific slip behavior of the extruded materials at deformation temperature. Materials with good slip properties are, for example, lead and tin alloys. Over time, these properties of the materials being extruded have resulted in the development of material-specific tool designs for the shape-producing areas of the

tooling that take into account the flow behavior. Figure 7.30 describes extrusion dies for the production of round bars with material-specific die aperture designs [Lau 76]. The entry geometry to the die apertures of simple extrusion dies shown in Fig. 7.30 also show the variations in the radii of the leading edges and the conical entries. The use of larger inlet radii as well as differences in the lengths of the material flow paths by, for example, angled entry surfaces, as shown on a die for the production of steel sections by glass-lubricated extrusion in Fig. 7.24, can result in a retarding effect at the entry of the material flow within the geometry of the extruded section.

The desire for the extruded material to flow faster along the centerline of the container naturally influences the location of the cavities in multicavity extrusion dies. For this reason, the cavities must be located as far as possible from the centerpoint of the die, taking into account the container internal diameter. Areas of the profile cross section where the section is thicker should, in principle, be located on the outside. From experience, the cavities are usually arranged symmetrically on a circle that passes through the center of gravity of the relevant profile cross section. The axis of symmetry that passes through the center of gravity of the profile cross section should meet at the die center (Fig. 7.31). It must also be possible to remove the sections without any problems after they have

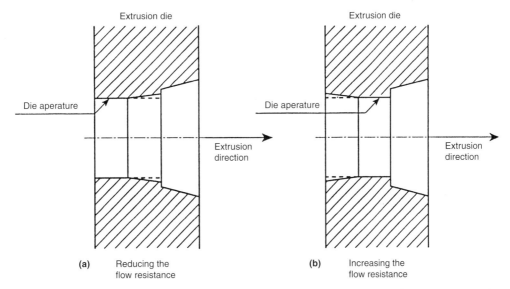

Fig. 7.29 Methods of controlling material flow using the friction between the extruded material and/or shearing. (a) Reduction of the bearing length to reduce the flow resistance. (b) Tapered feed to the die aperture to increase the flow resistance by reducing the material flow cross section and increasing the bearing length. Source: Sauer

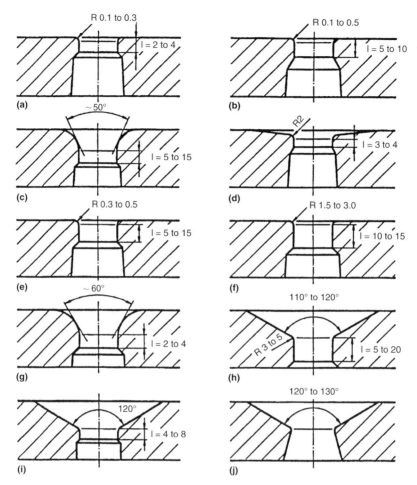

Fig. 7.30 General extruded material-specific design of the shape-forming aperture and entry form of extrusion dies. The designs apply to (a) pure and low-alloyed aluminum alloys, (b) higher-alloyed aluminum alloys, (c) magnesium alloys, (d) lead alloys, (e) copper-zinc alloys, (f) copper and low-alloyed copper alloys, (g) zinc alloys, (h) iron alloys, (i) titanium alloys, and (k) heat-resistant alloys, including nickel alloys. Dimensions in mm [Lau 76]

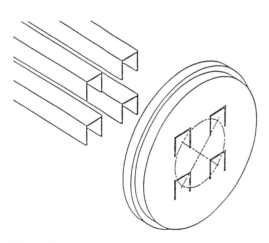

Fig. 7.31 Symmetrical arrangement of a multicavity extrusion die designed for correct material flow for the production of a U-section in an aluminum alloy

left the die, without them contacting or damaging each other. This can also influence the location of the cavities in the die. In practice, these requirements result in the cavity arrangements for multicavity dies shown in Fig. 7.32 [Lau 76].

Hollow sections of most copper alloys as well as the difficult-to-extrude aluminum alloys cannot be extruded with porthole or bridge dies. They must be produced using the classical tube extrusion and a mandrel. However, the classical tube extrusion of hollow sections with asymmetrical cross-sectional geometry in copper alloys and the more highly alloyed aluminum alloys using profiled fixed or moving mandrels is frequently marred by the material flow-related transverse forces developed in the shape-producing die areas pushing the mandrel away from the press axis. These transverse forces also occur

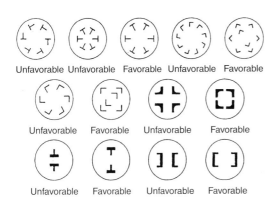

Unfavorable Unfavorable Favorable Unfavorable Favorable

Unfavorable Favorable Unfavorable Favorable

Unfavorable Favorable Unfavorable Favorable

Fig. 7.32 Example of unfavorable and favorable layouts of die apertures in multicavity extrusion dies [Lau 76]

in hollow section dies, including porthole and bridge dies. These have a mandrel solidly machined into the upper section of the die and can, to a certain extent, withstand transverse forces without any movement. In contrast, in such cases, the flowing extruded material in classical tube extrusion tries to move the mandrel to a position in which uniform material flow can form in the shape-forming region formed by the die and the normally fixed-stepped mandrel. For example, as a result of this mandrel displacement, the hollow in the terminal section on the left side of Fig. 7.33 in lead-containing brass moves down along the vertical axis in the direction of the thick hollow wall, which is reduced in thickness. The thin hollow wall at the top increases accordingly. Similar unacceptable wall thickness variations occur from transverse force-related mandrel movement in the military bridge ramp section produced in a moderately difficult-

to-extrude aluminum alloy on the right side of Fig. 7.33. The material flow can be equalized to overcome the transverse forces by using a relieving extrusion, also referred to as a follower. This relieving extrusion is usually a round bar, as shown in Fig. 7.33. An additional insert die can be machined into the die body of large extrusion tools, for example, the ramp section shown in Fig. 7.33, to produce the relieving section. The diameter of the follower bar can then be carefully determined to balance the material flow.

7.3.1.1 Control of Material Flow in the Shape-Producing Regions in the Extrusion of Materials with Working Temperatures from 0 to 300 °C

Lead alloys are extruded without lubrication, and the shape-producing areas of the nitrided extrusion tools are not lubricated. Only statistically selected billets are given a measured brush stroke of a lubricant onto the surface. This production process ensures a good product surface and no lubricant in the transverse and longitudinal welds in the extruded section, for example, when using hollow dies as well as the production of cored solders. The extrusion without lubrication is helped by the good slip properties of the base metal, which is the reason why it is also the base metal for bearing alloys. The good slip properties of lead results in dry lubrication in the shape-forming regions of the tool. The formation of layers on the working surfaces as a result of adhesion does not occur, unlike aluminum

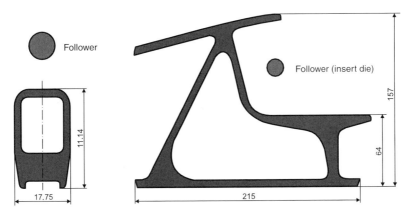

Fig. 7.33 Principle of the follower for the classic extrusion of asymmetrical hollow profile cross section over a mandrel. Left, terminal section in CuZn39; right, hollow section in AlZn 4.5Mg1 for military bridges. Source: Sauer

and copper alloys. The material flow control in the production of sections occurs in the die apertures by the use of different bearing lengths, as described in section 7.3.1.

Tin Alloys. Similar to lead, tin is a metal with good slip properties and is therefore also a base metal for bearing materials. Tin alloys are extruded without lubrication, similar to lead alloys. Lubrication of the nitrided die aperture is not used. As with lead extrusion, statistically selected billets are given a very controlled brush stroke of lubrication on the surface before loading into the container. Dry friction occurs between the working surfaces and the extruded material. There is no layer formation on the die bearing surfaces as a consequence of adhesion. Material flow control in the die aperture region can be achieved by using different bearing lengths.

7.3.1.2 Control of Material Flow in the Shape-Producing Regions in the Extrusion of Materials with Working Temperatures from 300 to 600 °C

Magnesium Alloys. Magnesium-base alloys form intermediate layers of the extruded material on the nitrided bearing surfaces in the shape-forming region of the tool under the effect of the adhesion forces, the deformation temperature, the specific extrusion load, and the extrusion speed. After a certain number of extrusions, the extruded material slides to an increasing extent over the intermediate layers that form by overcoming the permanent shear processes. The equalization of the material flow necessary for the production of sections is obtained in the same way as with aluminum alloys: by different lengths of the working and shear surfaces in the shape-producing tool area. Practically the same rules apply as with aluminum extruded alloys.

Aluminum Alloys. The hot extrusion of aluminum alloys is by far the most important application of extrusion. Therefore, there has been considerable research into the flow in the shape-forming regions of aluminum extrusion tooling [The 93, Ake 85, Lan 84, Ake 83, Lan 81].

Aluminum-base alloys are extruded without lubrication; that is, the shape-forming region of the die and the container are not lubricated. An effective control of the material flow in the tooling shape-forming areas can be achieved relatively easily by changing the flow resistance by increasing or shortening the bearing lengths. The

careful control of the material flow over the profile cross section is an important requirement in the production of aluminum sections to the finished dimensions to maintain the permitted shape and dimensional tolerances.

Aluminum has a high affinity for iron and thus also for hot working tool steels. The associated adhesive tendency to hot working steels results in the formation of an intermediate layer of the extruded material several micrometers thick on the bearings of the die aperture after a certain number of extrusions. The deformation temperature, the deformation forces, and the extrusion speed also have an influence on the layer formation [The 93, Ake 83]. The formation of this layer commences at the exit edge of the die and then develops back against the extrusion direction. The extruded material now slides more over the intermediate layer and no longer on the die bearing surface. The flow resistance in the shape-forming areas of the die changes as the intermediate layer is formed. Sliding friction occurs between the extruded material and the die bearing before the layer is formed, and shearing occurs after the formation of the intermediate layer. This leads to permanent shear forces between the flowing extruded material and the intermediate layer during the extrusion, as is also the case at the liner wall in aluminum alloy extrusion.

Nitriding can reduce the adhesion of the extruded material to the die bearings, but it is not eliminated. However, nitriding does hinder the layer formation; a compact intermediate layer forms slowly on the die working surfaces. Better results are currently obtained with dies with chemical vapor deposition (CVD)-coated die apertures. The formation of a layer of pure aluminum and low-alloy aluminum alloys such as AlMgSi0.5 on the bearings can be retarded more effectively with a 5 to 7 μm thick titanium carbide or titanium nitride layer than with nitriding, but the formation cannot be totally prevented. The vapor-deposited CVD layers are extremely resistant to wear and achieve a very high die life.

The closed intermediate layer that forms against the material flow after a certain number of extrusions and which subsequently increases to 4 to 6 μm or more thick determines the surface roughness of the extruded section. The homogeneous formation of the thin intermediate layer is consequently a determining factor for the surface roughness of the extruded product, although investigations have revealed a higher surface roughness of the intermediate layer compared to the surface of the section [The 93]. Finally, thinner layers are always more stable than thicker layers because of the better support from the layer carrier. This also results with increasing thickness in unstable conditions in the intermediate layer adhering to the die bearings. The shear forces between the intermediate layer and the flowing material can then partly tear pieces from the intermediate layer, which attach themselves to the surface of the section. If the shear forces in the adhesive zone of the intermediate layer with the die bearing exceed the effective adhesive forces, entire pieces of the intermediate layer can break away.

In addition, according to experience in aluminum extrusion plants, after a large number of extrusions, a rather deep score forms from wear in the die bearing at a distance approximately one-third of the bearing length from the material entry side. If this reaches a specific value, the scoring of the section surface increases. Extrusion plants prevent this by limiting the number of extrusions after nitriding the dies. The relevant limiting number of extrusions is known from trials; that is, the dies are consequentially used after surface treating by nitriding only up to the point where there is definitely no severe wear of the die bearings. For example, this can be up to 70 extrusions for porthole dies for working easily extruded alloys and even more for dies for solid sections. The number of extrusions can be increased after the second nitriding, because the bearing wear resistance is increased by the additional nitriding. The die can also give a higher throughput after the second and third nitriding.

The minimum length of the die bearing surfaces for hot working aluminum alloys depends on the alloy. If the bearing lengths reach the minimum length as a result of correction to balance the material flow, then further correction is no longer possible. In this case, an angled shape to the die aperture with otherwise parallel bearings in the areas that are still flowing too quickly can give an effective flow restriction (Fig. 7.24).

In addition, the material flow in the shape-forming aperture of a die can be influenced by the geometric location of a milled shaped feeder chamber in front of the die cavity. Figure 7.34 shows an example of a feeder chamber. The entry edges of the shape-forming die aperture in the heavy regions of the profile cross section must be in the zone of influence of the dead metal zone that forms at the external periphery of the feeder chamber, as seen in Fig. 7.34 and

in more detail in Fig. 7.35 and 7.36.

With extrusion tooling for the production of hollow sections, the material flow can be influenced by the geometry of the material entry ports to increase or decrease the flow resistance.

The bearing or shear area lengths in the shape-forming regions of the die depend on:

- The location of the section in the die relative to the center of the container
- Cross-sectional variations in the section geometry

The bearing lengths of the section depend on its location relative to the container center and must take into account that the billet material flows more quickly in the center of the container than close to the periphery of the container bore. Consequently, to ensure a straight extrusion with the correct cross-sectional geometry from the die aperture, the bearing lengths at the container periphery must be shorter and correspondingly longer toward the die center. This is shown by the bearing lengths of the section in Fig. 7.37 and 7.38, together with their location relative to the center of the container. They show typical values used in practice for round and flat containers.

The bearing length differences needed to control the material flow of an extrusion die moving out radially from the container center depend on the following rules:

- For round containers, the bearing lengths must be reduced by 1 mm for each 25 mm moved from the container center (Fig. 7.37).

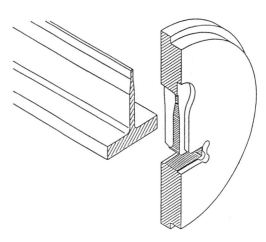

Fig. 7.34 Feeder chamber to control material flow. Source: Ames

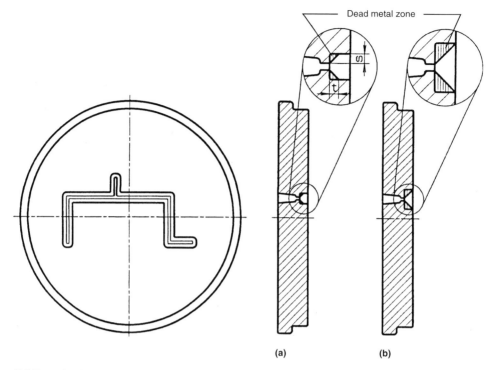

Fig. 7.35 Feeder chamber geometry for material flow control. (a) Shows correct feeder chamber size for material flow control (b) Has no effect on the material flow. Distance s ≤ t provides correct feeder chamber geometry for material flow control. Source: Ames

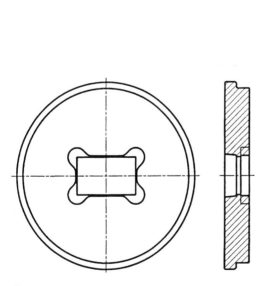

Fig. 7.36 Shaped feeder chamber for the extrusion of thick-wall profile cross section. Source: Ames

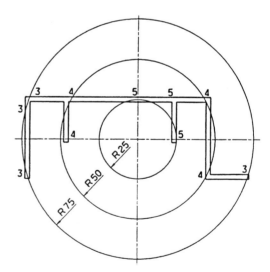

Fig. 7.37 The bearing lengths in the die aperture needed to achieve a uniform flow across the profile cross section according to the location of the section relative to the centerline of a round container. Source: Ames

• For containers with an oval cross section, the die bearings must also be reduced by 1 mm according to the radial distances given in

Fig. 7.38 and the section circumscribing diameter.

For material flow control with cross-sectional

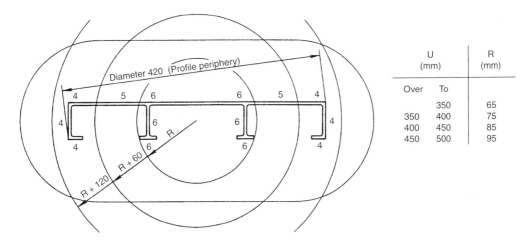

U (mm)		R (mm)
Over	To	
	350	65
350	400	75
400	450	85
450	500	95

Fig. 7.38 Bearing lengths needed in the die aperture to achieve a uniform flow across the profile cross section according to the location of the section relative to the center line of an oval container. Source: Ames

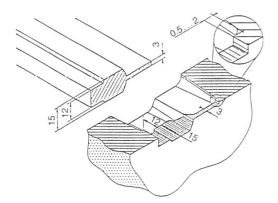

Fig. 7.39 Bearing lengths as a function of the variations in the profile cross-sectional geometry

variations within the profile geometry, the following rules apply:

- With wall thickness differences less than 5 to 1, the length of the bearings increases in proportion to the wall thickness, as shown in Fig. 7.39.
- With wall thickness differences greater than 5 to 1, the material flow must be further reduced with the feeder chamber (Fig. 7.34) or slowed at selected feeds on hollow dies.

In practice, the length of the bearing or shear surfaces is mainly determined by a combination of the rules according to:

- The location of the section in the die relative to the center of the container
- The cross-sectional variations in the profile cross-sectional geometry

The starting point is always the shortest sensible bearing length. A length of 2 to 2.5 mm has proved successful with thin-wall sections and sections with small circumscribing diame-

Table 7.1 Minimum bearing lengths for easy-to-extrude aluminum alloys as a function of the wall thickness and circumscribing circle of the cross section of the semifinished product

	Minimum bearing length, mm								
	Diameter of the circumscribing circle, mm								
Wall thickness, mm	30	60	100	150	200	250	300	400	500
To 1.5	2	3	3.8	3.8	4.5	4.5	. . .	. . .	. . .
2	3	3	3.8	4.5	4.5	5	5	. . .	. . .
3	3	3.8	4.5	4.5	5	6	6	6.8	. . .
4	4.5	4.5	4.5	5	6	6	7.5	9	9
5	4.5	6	6	6	7.5	7.5	9	9	10.5
6	6	7.5	7.5	7.5	9	9	10.5	10.5	12
8	7.5	7.5	7.5	9	9	10.5	10.5	12	12
10	9	9	9	10.5	10.5	10.5	12	12	12
13	9	10.5	10.5	12	12	12	12	12	13.5
16	10.5	10.5	12	12	12	13.5	13.5	13.5	15
Over 16	10.5	12	12	13.5	13.5	13.5	15	15	18

Source: Ames

ters in easy-to-extrude aluminum alloys. Table 7.1 gives an overview of the minimum bearing lengths for the easy-to-extrude aluminum alloys.

Dies for moderately difficult and difficult-to-work alloys require longer minimum lengths. For the moderately difficult-to-extrude aluminum alloys, the minimum lengths given in Table 7.1 must be increased by 15% and by 30% for the difficult-to-extrude alloys. These extruded alloys are listed in Table 7.2.

Section surface areas with grooves or protrusions (Fig. 7.40) require a 30 to 50% reduction of the bearing lengths given in Table 7.1.

The bearing lengths in the shape-forming regions of round bar and round tube dies are a function of the bar or tube diameter. The extrudability of the relevant aluminum alloy must be taken into account. Figure 7.41 gives more information.

Taken altogether, the guidelines mentioned enable, for example, the production of an extrusion die with a bearing geometry of the shape-producing aperture suitable for the manufacture of extruded sections with the cross section shown in Fig. 7.39.

After leaving the die bearing in the shape-producing region, the section is fully formed. To enable it to emerge from the die without any contact problems, the bearing surface is relieved by 0.5 to 3 mm, depending on the bearing length (Fig. 7.17), and the die exit is relieved by an angle of 1 to 5°. There are also section areas, for example, legs, where the exits from the bearings must be relieved cylindrically for reasons of die stability, as seen in an enlarged section in Fig. 7.39. The relief of the die bearings is selected so that deformation of the bearing by the forces developed during extrusion cannot occur.

The bearings of a mandrel in a hollow section die are mirror images of the bearings of the die aperture. For example, the bearings in the die plate of a porthole die to produce thin-wall tubes have an annular shape, and the bearings on the mandrel with which the die forms the shape-forming region also have an annular profile. Because of possible deflection of the mandrel by transverse forces, for example, from wall thickness variations in the profile cross section, the bearings at the entry to the shape-forming region are extended by 1.0 to 2.5 mm to prevent defective material flow.

Table 7.2   Bearing length addition as a function of the extrudability of specific aluminum alloys

| Extrudability | Alloys | | |
	Easy	Moderate	Difficult
Addition, %	None	15	30
Material	1350	5049	2014A
	6060	5051A	2017A
	6082	5251	2024
		7020	5083
		7022	
		7075	

Source: Ames

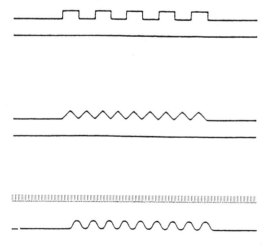

Fig. 7.40 Grooves and protrusions or the surface of the section. Source: Ames

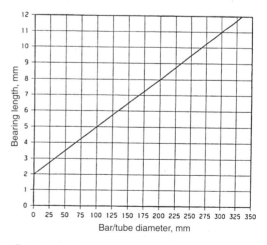

Fig. 7.41 Die aperture bearing lengths for the production of round bar and tubes as a function of the diameter of the semifinished product. Source: Ames

7.3.1.3 Control of Material Flow in the Shape-Producing Regions in the Extrusion of Materials with Working Temperatures from 600 to 1300 °C

Copper Alloys. Up to the shape-forming tooling, the extrusion of copper alloys is carried out without lubrication and with a shell. In contrast, the shape-forming area is carefully lubricated to avoid layers of the extruded material forming on the die bearings at the high deformation temperature. Copper and copper alloys with a zinc content up to 20% become coated with copper oxide during heating to the extrusion temperature, and this acts as a lubricant. Occasionally, in special cases, copper alloys are also hot extruded with a lubricant. In this process, the lubricant moves with metal flow into the die area. Overall, the lubrication in the shape-producing tooling produces friction conditions in the mixed-friction range.

Different bearing lengths are also used with copper alloys for necessary flow control for producing sections, as shown in Fig. 7.42 and 7.43. However, compared to aluminum dies, these must be longer because of the fundamental lubrication of the shape-forming area and the significantly higher thermomechanical stresses. The lubricant reduces the abrasive wear of the bearings as far as possible and practically eliminates the adhesive wear. If necessary, localized material flow variations that are not too severe in dies in production can be compensated by controlled lubrication of the die aperture. The material flow of profile cross-sectional areas flowing too slowly can be improved by increasing the localized lubrication. If necessary, parts of the cross section that are flowing too quickly can be retarded by tapering the die inlet, as shown in Fig. 7.29(b). Whereas extruded profiles in copper or copper alloys that can be readily cold worked can, in principle, be brought to the specified dimensions by drawing, sections in the high-zinc-containing α-β brasses must be extruded close to the finished size or, as with β brass, to the finished size. A balanced material flow control is therefore essential for the production of a quality product. However, in contrast to copper, these materials require considerably lower working temperatures. Consequently, the die bearings are subjected to significantly lower temperatures. This enables effective flow control to be achieved with varying bearing lengths, as shown on the right side of Fig. 7.42.

Extrusion dies and inserts for the production of brass bar and wire usually have bearing lengths of 5 to 10 mm in the die aperture and an entry radius of 0.5 to 1 mm. Extrusion dies for copper-zinc alloy sections normally have bearing lengths of 5 to 15 mm and, in individual cases, even 25 mm. However, there is no fixed rule for the final bearing length dimensions in a die. Designers and die manufacturers must cooperate to find the optimal solution based on experience. The different bearing lengths are produced either by back milling the previously eroded die aperture or by eroding the die exit before wire eroding the die aperture. The exit from the die is usually undercut by 1 to 3 mm and then tapered to avoid contact with the extruded section, similar to aluminum alloys. The leading edges of the die are usually broken with a radius of 0.3 to 0.5 mm, in other words, almost a sharp edge. In addition, the same basic rules as those for aluminum sections apply to the material flow in the die apertures of dies for the production of brass sections.

Titanium, Iron, and Nickel Alloys. Materials extruded at temperatures above 1000 °C are extruded at high speeds with glass lubrication to avoid thermal overstressing of the extrusion tooling. A disc of compacted glass granules between the end of the billet and the die separates the front of the extrusion from contact with the die bearings at the start of extrusion. Fluid pressure forms in the glass film through a lubricant wedge between the extruded material and the die on the feed surfaces to the die aperture as a result of the high extrusion speed. Liquid friction then occurs on the shape-producing areas of the tooling. A balanced material flow over the profile cross section is therefore not possible. Nevertheless, some material flow control can be achieved by using angled feed paths of different lengths and variations in the entry radii, as shown in Fig. 7.24. This enables simple cross-sectional geometries without excessive wall thickness variations and large masses to be produced as solid sections and hollow sections over a mandrel.

7.3.2 Dimensions of the Die Apertures in Relation to the Specified Section Dimensions at Room Temperature

In hot working processes, the material has a larger volume during the deformation than at room temperature, depending on the specific material and temperature. The material volume

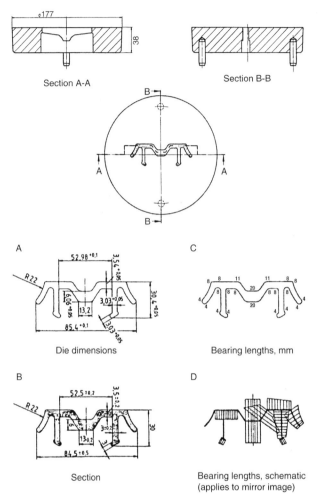

Fig. 7.42 Extrusion dies for the production of CuZn39Pb3 sections. Source: Sauer

correspondingly decreases on cooling. The extent of the volume change (shrinkage) varies with the material. This also applies to the hot working material used for the die. Because most extruded materials in nonferrous metals have coefficients of expansion significantly higher than the hot working materials, this means that the extruded section has cross-sectional dimensions smaller than the corresponding dimensions in the die cooled to room temperature. The difference is referred to as the shrinkage. This must be taken into account by adding a factor when determining the tool dimensions in the die apertures. However, these shrinkage allowances are only one of the measures that must be taken to determine the necessary dimension of the shape-forming part of the die to achieve the correct specified dimensions in the profile cross section. Additional additive dimensional differences from other causes also must be taken into account.

Additions to the specified dimensions of the profile cross sections arise from the following:

- Specific coefficients of expansion of the extruded material heated to the deformation temperature
- Specific coefficient of expansion of the hot working material used for the manufacture of the tooling heated to the working temperature
- Tolerance fields of the profile cross-sectional geometry
- Tendency of the extruded material to flow more quickly in the center of the container
- Tendency of the extruded material to flow more slowly in thin-wall areas of otherwise

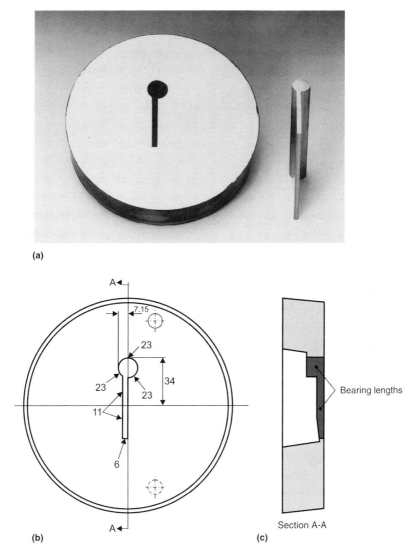

Fig. 7.43 Extrusion die for the production of a furniture hinge section in brass. (a) Die and profile cross section. (b) Die aperture bearing lengths. (c) Section through die aperture. Source: Wieland-Werke AG

massive cross sections, particularly in the outer regions. Particularly high dimensional additions are needed in this case.

- Elastic deformation of the shape-producing tool areas under the effect of the extrusion load, which cannot be completely avoided in spite of good support
- Additions to allow for the stretching of the extruded section

The dimensions for the die aperture are determined for the example of the aluminum section in AlMgSi0.5 shown in Fig. 7.44, taking the aforementioned parameters into account. This is divided into three stages for clarification.

The first stage is to determine the additions to the specified dimensions to compensate for the pure thermal volume change (shrinkage). The percent material-dependent dimensional additions are taken from Table 7.3. This is 1.2% for the alloy AlMgSi0.5, corresponding to the alloy number 6060. The resultant die aperture dimensions are given in Fig. 7.44(a) in parentheses.

In the second stage, the die aperture dimensions given in parentheses in Fig. 7.44(a) for the pure thermal volume change are placed in the relevant tolerance field, taking into account the tolerances of the specified section dimension and the die wear. The permitted deviations from the nominal dimensions are shown in Fig.

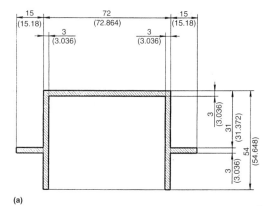

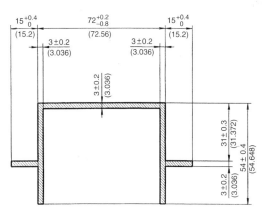

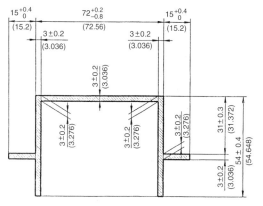

Fig. 7.44 (a) An AlMgSi0.5 section with the desired room-temperature dimensions and the resultant die aperture dimensions (in parentheses) from the relative additions in Table 7.3 required to compensate for the volume change (shrinkage) of the extruded material on cooling from the deformation temperature to room temperature. (b) Same as (a) but with the die apertures matched to the tolerance bards (in parentheses). (c) Final die aperture dimensions (in parentheses). Source: Ames

Table 7.3 **Percent dimensional increase according to the extruded aluminum alloy to compensate for the volume change (shrinkage) on cooling from the deformation temperature to room temperature**

Extrudability	Easy and moderate	Heavy		
Addition, %	1.2	1.3	1.5	1.8
Material	1350	7003	2014A	5083
	5051A	7020	2017A	7022
	6005A	. . .	2024	7075
	6060	. . .	. . .	. . .
	6061	. . .	. . .	. . .
	6082	. . .	. . .	. . .
	6101B	. . .	. . .	. . .
	6106	. . .	. . .	. . .

Source: Ames

count the effect of the elastic deformation of the die, in particular, the bending of the die aperture region. In addition, the reduction in the profile cross section from the stretching, with approximately 1 to 1.5% residual elongation, must be compensated for by an additional dimensional compensation. The final die aperture dimensions are given in parentheses in Fig. 7.44(c).

The accuracy of the production of the section is obtained by measuring a sample after manufacturing the die, giving the actual measured values of the extruded section cooled to room temperature. When determining the increase in the die dimensions, it is also possible to have to reduce the dimensions at certain areas of the profile cross section below the corresponding specified dimensions.

As shown in Fig. 7.45, similar concepts are used for the design of the die apertures for the production of copper-zinc alloy sections, where higher deformation temperatures must be considered in comparison to aluminum alloys. Depending on the deformation temperature, the increase in dimensions for the shape-producing aperture of the die is 1 to 1.5% of the specified dimensions of the cross section of the finished profile. However, the influence of the deformation temperature, the extrusion load, and the contact time during the extrusion process is so high that in certain areas of the die aperture, the dimensional increase must be higher as a result of elastic as well as some plastic deformation. It can be as high as 5% in some localized areas in the die aperture. A tongue in the die can easily be pushed in under the influence of the thermomechanical loading and therefore reduce the die aperture. The die aperture of dies for the production of rod and wire in copper-zinc

7.44(b). This gives the die aperture dimensions shown in parentheses in Fig. 7.44(b).

Finally, in a third step, the die aperture dimensions must be determined, taking into ac-

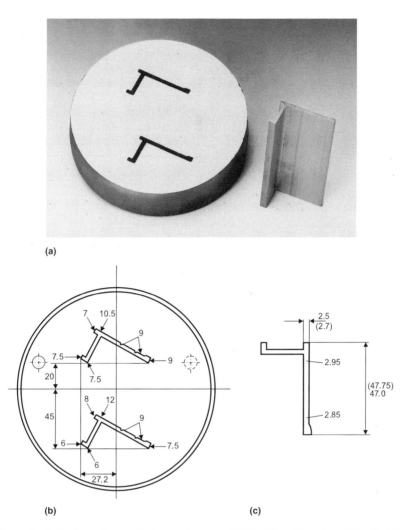

Fig. 7.45 Two-cavity die for the production of a brass angle section. (a) Die with profile section. (b) Specified dimensions of the section and increased dimensions in the die aperture. (c) Die aperture bearing lengths. Source: Wieland-Werke AG

alloys requires an increase in dimensions of 1 to 2%.

Moreover, the production of the same section in copper alloys on different extrusion presses with different die stack arrangements or maximum extrusion loads requires different die aperture dimensions. The radial force R shown in Fig. 7.13 from the conical sealing of the tooling can also play a role. Naturally, whether the aperture of the die backer is optimally matched to the cross-sectional geometry of the die aperture also plays a role. Identifying the correct increase in the dimensions for the die aperture of a die for the deformation of copper alloys does require considerable experience and cannot be covered by a specific formula, although the collection of statistical data is informative.

In the production of steel sections, the die apertures are generally produced with the cross-sectional dimensions of the section being increased by 2%, whereby the final dimensional increase must be left to the experience of the designer. In comparison to dies for the extrusion of copper alloys, even stricter relationships apply because of the particularly high thermomechanical stresses in the die aperture region and the rapidly occurring plastic deformation.

7.3.3 Tooling for the Extrusion of Materials with Deformation Temperatures in the Range of 0 to 300 °C

Tooling for the extrusion of tin and lead alloys follows a similar but simpler design to alumi-

Fig. 7.46 Four-cavity extrusion die for the production of pencil sharpener sections in magnesium alloy. Source: Housel AG

num tooling. Porthole dies and occasionally bridge dies are used in addition to the standard single-cavity or multicavity dies. Feeder chambers are used for billet-on-billet extrusion. Extrusion tooling for the production of cored solders can be found in Chapter 5 and Fig. 5.8 and 5.9.

7.3.4 Tooling for the Extrusion of Materials with Deformation Temperatures in the Range of 300 to 600 °C

7.3.4.1 Tooling for the Extrusion of Magnesium Alloys

Tools for the extrusion of magnesium alloys correspond in principle to those for aluminum

alloys. However, because of the inferior workability of these alloys, they have a different die aperture geometry, as shown by the examples in Fig. 7.30(c) for the extruded alloys MgAl2 and MgAl6Zn compared to those in Fig. 7.30(a) and (b) for extruded aluminum alloys and the die inlets in Fig. 7.46. The extruded alloys cannot withstand any sharp flow deviations, and therefore, large radii must be used. In addition, the die bearing surfaces in the die aperture generally must be longer than those used in dies for aluminum alloy extrusion. In particular, porthole dies for magnesium alloys have round inlets in contrast to porthole dies for aluminum alloys (Fig. 7.47). Circular inlets demand less effort from the extruded material and have lower flow resistance compared to other inlet geometries. Inlet geometries that deviate from circular cross sections require large fillets.

7.3.4.2 Tooling for the Extrusion of Aluminum Alloys

The hot working extrusion process has continued to increase in importance because of its continually improving tool technology. This applies in particular to the extrusion of aluminum alloys. Moderate working temperatures and the relatively good hot workability of these materials result in good control of the thermomechanical stresses that occur in extrusion in the tooling. The die designer is able to fulfill realistic and, at the same time, increasingly demanding customer requirements for ever more complicated section geometries. Figures 7.27 and 7.48 to 7.52 show the results of this long-term de-

Fig. 7.47 Split two-part porthole die for the production of an automobile roof section in magnesium alloy. Source: Honsel AG

Fig. 7.48 Flat die for the production of the solid AlMgSi0.5 section shown in front of the die. Source: Alusuisse

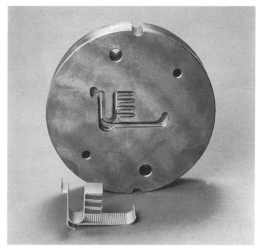

Fig. 7.49 Flat die with integrated feeder chamber for the production of the solid AlMgSi0.5 heat exchanger section in front of the die. Source: Alusuisse

velopment of die making, with examples of proven extrusion dies for aluminum alloy.

The experience of extrusion plants in the production of extruded aluminum products has resulted in the following basic rules for the design and manufacture of extrusion dies for aluminum:

- The material flow of the respective extruded material is the same for all types of dies and die sizes in the container in front of the shape-producing die.

- Geometrically defined material inlets bounded by so-called dead metal zones form in front of the shape-producing apertures of the die and in front of the die inlets in hollow dies as well as in the feeder chambers. The extruded material flows along the internal surfaces to the shape-forming die region. With round bar cross sections on the container centerline, the inflowing material describes a cone and the dead metal zone a funnel.

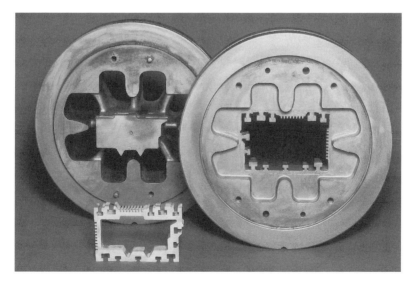

Fig. 7.50 Porthole die for the production of the AlMgSi0.5 flexible construction system section in front of the die. Left, upper part with ports and mandrel; right, die plate with welding chamber and die aperture. Source: Alusuisse

Fig. 7.51 Porthole die for the production of the AlMgSi0.5 hollow section shown in front of the die for a water-cooled exhaust duct from a marine diesel engine. Left, mandrel; right, die plate. Source: Alusuisse

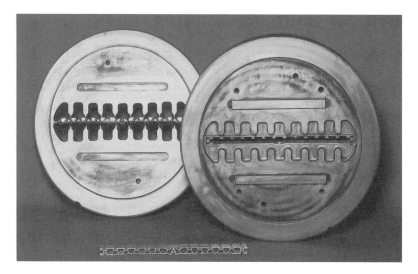

Fig. 7.52 Porthole die for the production of the AlMgSi0.5 section shown in Fig. 2.53 in Chapter 2 and in front of the die for pneumatic control elements. Left, mandrel; right, die plate. Source: Alusuisse

- The extruded material flows more quickly in the center of the container than in the peripheral zones.
- Large material masses in the section flow more quickly than thin-wall areas.
- The deformation loads acting on the die result in elastic shape changes in the die aperture.

The design- and production-related requirements of aluminum extrusion die manufacture increase with:

- Degree of difficulty of the profile cross-sectional geometry
- Size of the section circumscribing circle
- Flow stress of the material
- Weight per meter of the section

Aluminum Extrusion Dies. Figures 7.18, 7.28, 7.31, 7.34, and 7.39, as well as 7.48, 7.49, and 7.53 show single-cavity as well as multicavity extrusion dies, with and without a feeder chamber, used for the production of rod, tube, and solid sections. Feeder chambers were intro-

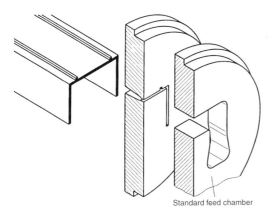

Fig. 7.53 Standard feeder chamber for billet-on-billet extrusion. Source: Ames

duced for extrusion dies to basically fulfill three roles:

- To allow continuous extrusion
- To preform as well as equalize the material flow in front of the die aperture
- To spread the material flow

Welding Chambers for Continuous Extrusion (Billet-on-Billet Extrusion). In the production of solid sections, the discard is sheared off at the end of every extrusion, and the end of the section is pulled out of the die with the puller or pushed out of the die aperture by the next billet. The disadvantage of this process is that with every subsequent billet, the section or sections must be guided through the tool stack and the press platen onto the run-out system. Kinks,

bends, and twists at the front of the extrusion cannot always be avoided.

This can be prevented by eliminating the front of the extrusion by continuous extrusion using a suitable feeder chamber in the die, as seen in Fig. 7.53. In this feeder chamber, the material from the new billet welds with the residue left in the feeder chamber after shearing the discard. The following extruded material enters as a tongue into the residual material and forms a transverse weld that extends to a specific length into the new section, depending on the extrusion ratio.

The standard feeder chamber used for endless extrusion has a large entry opening that opens still further by an angle of 15 to 30° toward the die in the extrusion direction, as shown in Fig. 7.53. Its radial extension should not exceed 80% of the container diameter. It contains a volume of the extrude material that allows defect-free welding with following billets. From experience, the feeder chamber must have a depth ≥10 mm. These standard feeder chambers are mainly used on extrusion presses up to 30,000 kN press power.

A good weld between the two billets is essential for straightening a section with a transverse weld on the stretcher. Otherwise, the transverse weld will fail, as seen in Fig. 7.54. Ultimately, the quality of the transverse weld depends on the tooling design and the extrusion procedures. The front surface of the following billet must be free of oxide. Particular care must be given to this requirement to achieve the necessary quality, because the transverse weld can remain in the delivered extruded section, provided the semi-finished product is not subjected to any high

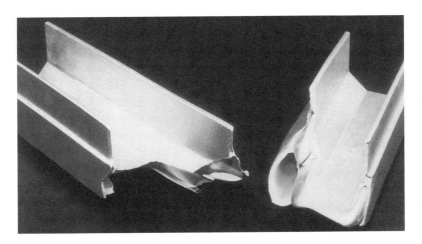

Fig. 7.54 Failed transverse weld in a solid section

mechanical stresses and the customer is in agreement. Finished products that are subjected to higher mechanical stresses must not contain any transverse weld.

Feeder Chambers. The material flow in the shape-forming die aperture in aluminum extrusion is controlled by increasing or decreasing the flow resistance by different bearing or shear surface lengths. This can be seen in Fig. 7.28 and 7.39. With complicated cross-sectional geometries with large variations in cross section (Fig. 7.34) and also in massive profile cross sections (Fig. 7.36), this technique of material flow control may not be sufficient in some applications. In these cases, a feeder chamber can help, as described elsewhere, because this enables an additional braking effect to be applied to the material flow.

The requirements to achieve this flow restriction in the feeder chamber are shown in Fig. 7.35. As shown in Fig. 7.34 to 7.36, the feeder chamber is milled into the front side of the die in such a way that the periphery is close to the entry of the die aperture area that must be slowed. This occurs, as depicted in Fig. 7.35(a), by dead metal zones forming in the areas of influence in the feeder chamber, which exert a braking effect.

Figure 7.36 shows this possibility of influencing the material flow in a profile with a massive rectangular cross section. The corner regions of the rectangular section naturally have more flow resistance to overcome as a consequence of friction and shear than the two side faces of the profile cross section. Consequently, the extruded metal flows more quickly in the free side areas of the cross section than in the corners. By locating the peripheral zones of the feeder chamber close to the die aperture at the leading edges of the free side surfaces of the extruded section, the dead metal zones that form here will influence the material flow in the same way as in Fig. 7.35(a). The material flow is retarded. The situation in the location of the section corners is different. Here, the peripheral areas of the feeder chamber have a definite distance from the die aperture. Consequently, there is no influence. Overall, this additional retarding of material flow using a feeder chamber can be used over the full periphery of the die aperture, as illustrated in Fig. 7.35, or locally, as in Fig. 7.36.

Spreader Chamber. From experience, the circumscribing circle of a profile cross section should not exceed 80% of the container diameter to prevent the inflow of the billet peripheral regions into the section. The maximum size of the cross section that can be produced is thus limited by the respective container and the press. In contrast, profile cross sections with a circumscribing diameter larger than the container diameter can be produced by using a spreader chamber, as shown in Fig. 7.55. This requires that sufficient material be fed to the shape-producing die aperture area through the spreader chamber during the extrusion.

Spreader chambers are increasing in importance. The development of spreader technology is used more and more to also produce flat and wide cross sections from round containers on small extrusion presses. In addition, the development has shown that it is possible to produce large flat and wide sections from round containers that previously could not be produced on large extrusion presses without using rectangular containers. To achieve strong transverse welds, adequate extrusion ratios as well as strict maintenance of the conditions described in the section about welding chambers for billet-on-billet extrusion must be fulfilled. It is particularly important that the front face of the following billet is largely free of oxide. It appears possible that in the future, flat containers, which are not particularly economic because of the low service life of the liner, will be largely replaced by round containers with spreader chambers.

Extrusion Mandrels. Difficult-to-extrude aluminum-base alloys, including the high-magnesium-containing alloy group AlMg from AlMg1.5 as well as the copper-containing alu-

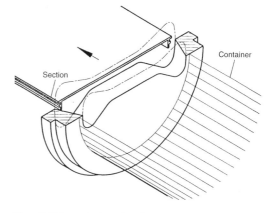

Fig. 7.55 Production of profile cross section with a circumscribing circle greater than the container bore using a spreader chamber. Source: Ames

minum alloys, cannot be extruded with porthole and bridge dies because of the high flow stress as well as the defective extruded weld strength. Tubes and hollow sections in these alloys must be produced on tube presses, as shown in Fig. 7.4, 7.19, and 7.20. This also applies to thick-wall tubes and hollow sections in the easy and moderately difficult-to-extrude aluminum alloys AlMgSi0.5 with wall thickness greater than 40 mm and AlMgSi1 with wall thickness over 30 mm, because of defective extrusion weld strengths. With large tubes, the maximum internal tube diameter is limited by the maximum possible stem bore and the related maximum possible mandrel diameter. The maximum tube external diameter is limited to 80% of the container liner diameter by the cylinder seal between the die and the container. Tapered moving mandrels as well as fixed mandrels with stepped mandrel tips are used, as shown in Fig. 7.19 and 7.20. Short billets can also be extruded to tubes, using cylindrical mandrels. In contrast to mandrels for copper production, mandrels for the production of aluminum tubes are not cooled externally or internally.

Moving tapered mandrels for the extrusion of aluminum alloys are usually given a taper of 0.08 to 0.09%. The taper ensures that the mandrel can be withdrawn without problems after extrusion, in spite of the shrinkage of the aluminum tube as a result of cooling. The axial movement ensures that the thermal stressing of the mandrel is minimized by ensuring that new mandrel surface areas in the die aperture continuously come into contact with the extruded material heated to the deformation temperature. In addition, billets can be pierced in the container with these mandrels immediately before extrusion, provided the piercer is powerful enough. Moving tapered mandrels also enable the maximum billet volume, which depends on the tube press, to be used. With a large 100 MN press power, this means, for example, mandrel lengths of 1200 mm with 1100 mm billet lengths.

Stepped mandrels cannot be used with these billet lengths, because the shaft lengths must be limited due to the higher mechanical stresses. Higher friction and shear forces between the extruded material and the axially located cylindrical mandrel shaft produce these stresses. Today, stepped mandrels are usually fitted with replaceable tips, as shown in Fig. 7.20 and 7.25, because fixed mandrel tips in the die aperture are subjected to the highest thermomechanical

stresses during the extrusion process and, consequently, severe wear. If necessary, the ability to change the mandrel tips enables them to be manufactured from hot working materials with a higher strength than that needed for the mandrel shaft. In addition, in specific cases, the mandrel tip can be increased to 200 mm to enable a small relative movement, giving a better control of the high thermomechanical stresses.

Porthole Dies. The most striking and most important tool for the production of sections in the low-to-moderately alloyed aluminum alloys is the porthole die. Figures 7.21 and 7.22 show schematically two typical porthole dies in two-cavity and single-cavity designs for the production of aluminum alloy hollow sections. With these dies, it is possible to produce very demanding extruded products in aluminum alloys with high dimensional and shape accuracy. Without these special tools, there would be no large-section technology with stress-specific profile cross-sectional geometry for demanding designs.

Porthole dies are usually two-piece (Fig. 7.50, 7.51). The internal shape formation takes place in the upper part, and the external in the lower section. The divided-material streams, corresponding to the number of ports formed in the upper part, are reunited in the welding chambers of the die lower section immediately in front of the die aperture. This produces longitudinal welds that should not be located in the decorative surface zones of the profile cross section. The design of the welding chambers can be seen in Fig. 7.50 to 7.52. The longitudinal welds themselves must be able to withstand adequate mechanical stresses. Therefore, the material properties in the region of the longitudinal weld should, in principle, be the same as in the core region.

Certain die-related rules must be taken into account to ensure defect-free longitudinal extruded welds:

- The material inlet ports must be large enough to develop a sufficiently high deformation pressure in the welding chambers.
- The material entry ports should not be too large, so that rapid emptying of the ports by the material from the next billet can occur, producing short transverse weld seams.
- The material entry ports should only be located in a circumscribing circle diameter up to approximately 90% of the container diameter. This prevents entry of material from

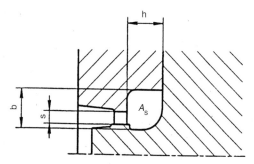

A_s = Welding chamber cross section
s = Section wall thickness, mm
h = Welding chamber height, mm
b = Welding chamber width, mm

Typical values for A_s : A_s = (s · (6 to 10)$)^2$, mm^2

Fig. 7.56 Welding chamber dimensions for porthole dies. Source: Ames

the periphery of the billet. If this percentage is exceeded, then the billets must be machined.

- To achieve a good decorative appearance, the extrusion welds must be located in the section corners or in areas where there are no decorative demands.
- The extrusion ratio should exceed 14 to 1 to obtain qualitatively good extrusion welds.
- Longitudinal welds with adequate mechanical properties require specific welding chamber dimensions. Guidelines are given in Fig. 7.56.

The size of the factors in the equation to estimate the welding chamber size, A_S, depends on the extrudability of the aluminum alloy used. Easily extruded alloys have a low factor, and moderately difficult ones a high factor. Defect-free welding of the material streams of the extruded material, and hence longitudinal welds with adequate strength, can be ensured by following this approach to estimate the size of the welding chamber. If dimensions below the guidelines are used, then this will impair the quality of the longitudinal welds. Exceeding the guidelines results in more severe bending of the mandrel area of the die upper section as a result of the associated increase in the height of the welding chamber. In addition, the quality of the longitudinal weld in single-cavity porthole dies can also be positively influenced by the location of the welding chamber relative to the cross-sectional geometry of the extruded section.

The material flow can be influenced by machining in a shaped feed chamber at the bottom of the welding chamber in front of the entry to the porthole die aperture, similar to that used for flat dies for aluminum, as shown in Fig. 7.57. This clearly shows that the shaped feeder chamber must be designed so that the distance

to the leading edges of the die aperture in the region of the mandrel circumference and the die aperture circumference is equal, to achieve a symmetrical dead metal zone.

The cross-sectional geometry and the location of the material inlet ports to the die axis on the billet-facing side of the porthole die have an important influence on the material flow and consequently on the deformation characteristics. Under normal extrusion conditions, the following design rules apply for this part of the die:

- The material entry ports in the porthole die should have a simple cross-sectional geometry and also have the same cross-sectional area for the same distance from the die axis. At the same central position of the port from the die axis, the extruded material will flow more quickly in a large port than in a small port.
- As a consequence of the faster material flow in the region of the die centerline compared to the material flow further away, the ports obviously must have different cross sections

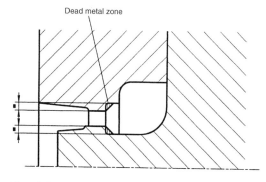

Dead metal zone

Fig. 7.57 Design of a shaped feed chamber in porthole dies. Source: Ames

to balance the different material flow rates (Fig. 7.58).

- The number of the material inlet ports depends on the profile cross-sectional geometry; that is, the more complicated the geometry, the greater the number of ports needed to ensure a uniform material flow.

Figure 7.59 shows the application of these rules.

The different location of the ports relative to the axis of the porthole die results in different port areas. This sensitive reaction of the material flow to the location and the cross-sectional area of the ports can be used with porthole dies in comparison to flat dies with feeder chambers for additional material flow control, which helps in the production of complicated profile cross-sectional geometries.

An economic production assumes the use of multicavity dies for large orders. This also applies to hollow dies. The die apertures must be arranged at specific distances from the die axis or the container centerline. To supply the die apertures with the extruded material, the ports are positioned at different distances from the center of the die, as seen in Fig. 7.21. This necessitates the application of the rules described for ports with different cross sections. The reduction in the material flow rate toward the container liner wall also must be compensated by increasing the size of the ports. This is explained in Fig. 7.60.

Guidelines for the specific increase in size of the port areas as a function of the distance from the die or container axis can be obtained using the relationships based on practical experience given as follows:

$$A_a = \left[1 + \frac{S_a - S_i}{100 \text{ mm}}\right] A_i \text{ (mm}^2)$$

where A_a is the area of the port located furthest from the die axis, A_i is the area of the port located next to the die axis, S_a is the distance of the center of the port furthest from the die axis, and S_i is the distance of the center of the port next to the die axis.

Applied to a port on the porthole die in Fig. 7.21, with $S_a = 62$ mm and $S_i = 12$ mm, gives:

$$A_a = [1 + 0.5]A_i = 1.5A_i (\text{mm}^2)$$

The legs supporting the mandrel in the upper section of the die also influence the material flow in the porthole die. Usually, for decorative reasons, the legs must be located in the corners of the profile cross section, as shown in Fig.

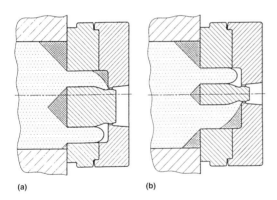

(a)   (b)

Fig. 7.58 Different material flow in a porthole die as a result of (a) unequal distance between the ports and the die centerline for the same port area, and (b) unequal port sizes with the same distance from the centerline. Source: Ames

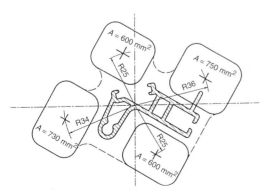

Fig. 7.59 Location and size of the ports. Source: Ames

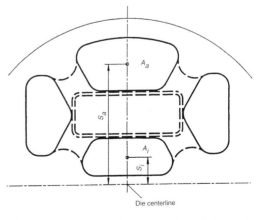

Fig. 7.60 Cross-sectional geometry of the ports for the die aperture of a two-cavity die. Source: Ames

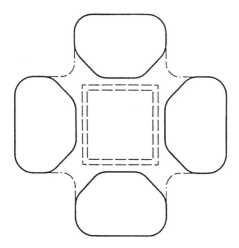

Fig. 7.61 Arrangement of the mandrel legs of a porthole die in the corners of a square hollow section. Source: Ames

7.61, or in cross-sectional areas where there are no decorative requirements.

Investigations into the optimal cross-sectional geometry of the mandrel legs for material flow have shown that circular-to-wedge-shaped leg cross sections on the exit side to the welding chamber favor the material flow. Figure 7.62 gives an overview of these results.

Naturally, these profiles for the mandrel legs result in a certain weakening in the mandrel support compared to leg profile 1. Die manufacturers prefer the leg cross-sectional shapes 3 and 4 over 5.

Bridge Dies. Compared to porthole dies, bridge dies have a lower flow resistance. With the bridge extending back into the container, the material flow can be guided to keep directional changes to a minimum. Changes in the material flow result in higher stem loads. This results in bridge dies being used in cases where the deformation of the extruded material in a porthole die requires more than the available maximum press power, or where the material being extruded has a flow resistance too high for a porthole die, making the bridge die the preferred option advantage from the beginning. It is also possible to produce sections without transverse welds using bridge dies, because the residual material in the feeds to the bridge die can be pulled out of the die at the end of extrusion by opening the container with the aid of the discard that is firmly located in it. This is referred to as stripping by extrusion press operators. To ensure that there is sufficient adhesion of the discard to the liner wall, stripping should not be performed too soon after the extrusion of the billet. After clearing the bridge die of the residual material, the discard, along with the attached content from the die, is pushed out of the container. The extruded material of the next billet finally pushes the end

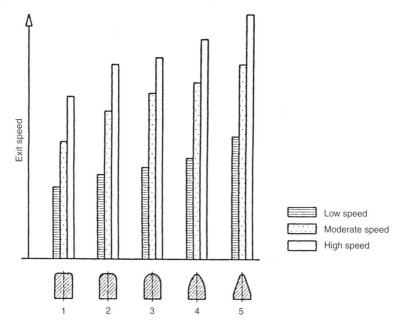

Fig. 7.62 Influence of the mandrel cross section on the section exit speed. Source: Ames

of the previously extruded bar out of the bridge die without welding to it.

The die design must take into account the stripping process. It can be seen in Fig. 7.23 that this type of die has die feeds of equal size, and the outer limit is determined by the liner wall. The legs and material feeds are designed so that they can be cleared without difficulty by pulling the material out. For this reason, the feeds open out toward the end facing the billet, and the bridge surface is conically tapered in the same direction. At the same time, this die design also ensures the feed of the metal streams into the interior of the die without any problems and with the exclusion of atmospheric oxygen, as with porthole dies, where they weld together. High-quality longitudinal welds are produced. This requires that only clean areas of the billet peripheral zone flow into the die; that is, the billets must be skimmed. The design ensures that bridge dies transfer their heat more easily than the closed porthole die. As a result, higher extrusion speeds are possible.

In addition to these advantages, bridge dies also have some disadvantages:

- Because billet-on-billet extrusion is not possible, the front end of every extrusion must be guided through the support tooling and the platen, producing a higher scrap rate.
- Water quenching of the extruded section with a standing wave is only possible to a limited extent.
- The maximum billet length is limited by the height of the bridge extending into the container.
- The thicker. discard needed for the stripping process reduces the useful length of the billet.

7.3.4.3 Manufacture and Operation of Aluminum Extrusion Tooling

Manufacture of the Extrusion Tooling. The introduction of efficient computer-aided design/computer-aided manufacturing (CAD/CAM) systems, combined with the application of numerically controlled machines, resulted in a permanent change in the design and manufacture of extrusion tooling [Kle 86]. The emphasis in aluminum tooling manufacture moved from the machining to the design. Previously, for example, the die aperture and exit of a simple die were marked out on an externally finish-machined tool steel blank, the exit clearance was milled out, and the die aperture sawn out

by machine. After the heat treatment of the blank, the die aperture was spark eroded to the finished size. With the introduction of CAD/CAM, the clearance can be finish spark eroded together with the production of the bearing lengths in the externally finish-machined and heat treated steel blank, and the die aperture cut out using a computer numerical controlled (CNC) wire erosion machine. Figure 7.63 gives an overview of the operations involved in the production of a section extrusion die. The production of a hollow die involves more milling, drilling, and grinding operations. However, the die undergoes the same operational steps as described in Fig. 7.63. The total production route for the manufacture of a two-piece porthole die is described in Fig. 7.64.

The CNC program is sent directly to the production machine from the CAD/CAM system. The storage of repetitive design operations is also a major advantage of a CAD/CAM system. For example, the following can be stored:

- Tool assembly in the extrusion press
- Tool set makeup
- Machine-dependent tool dimensions according to DIN 24540, including drill holes, keyways, and identification slots
- Dimensions of support tools
- Die holder design dimensions
- Pitch circle of the die cavities for a multicavity die
- Feeder chamber designs

For example, drawing elements and parts list can also be stored, readily called up, and included in the new design drawing. These aids have considerably reduced the design work by the die manufacturer as well as the possibility of manual errors. Naturally, the actual design is still dependent on the knowledge of the die designer and the way he uses the possibilities offered by CAD/CAM.

In addition, the application of CAD/CAM systems together with the use of CNC machines by the die manufacturer enable a previously unattainable and reproducible accuracy to be achieved. This has resulted in a reduction in die trials before the first production run of a die and, in particular, a high repeatability of the second and third die, which exactly match the original. In many cases, die trials are not needed for the second and third die.

Aluminum extrusion tooling undergoes high mechanical and moderate thermal stresses. At the stem head, specific pressures up to 1100 N/

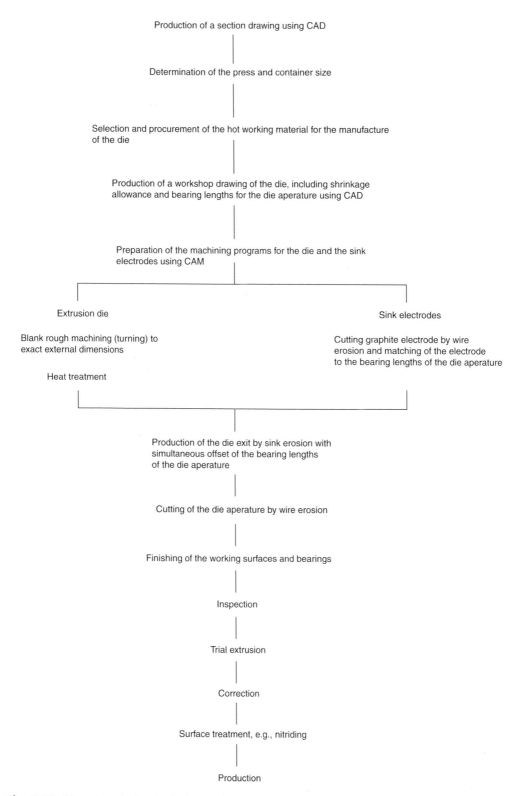

Fig. 7.63 Schematic production plan for the manufacture of a section extrusion die for the production of a flat aluminum alloy section. Source: Sauer

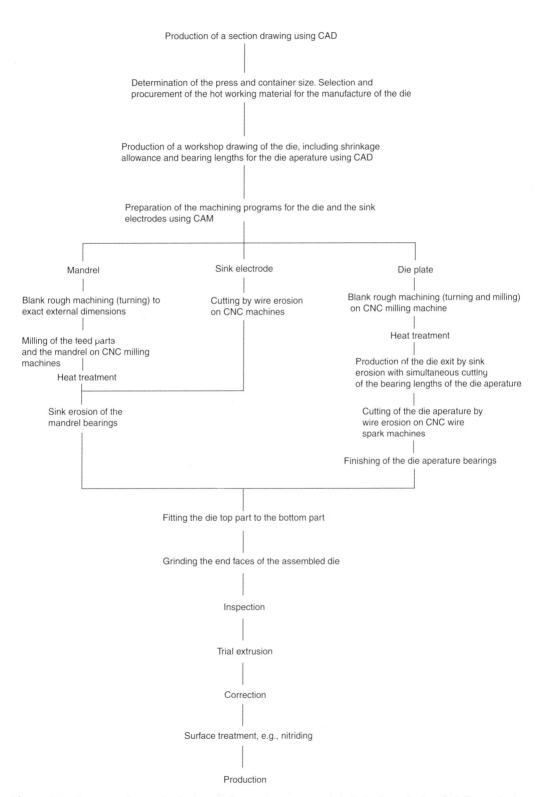

Fig. 7.64 Schematic production plan for the manufacture of a two-part porthole die for the production of a hollow section in a low-alloyed aluminum alloy. Source: Sauer

mm^2 can occur, and hollow dies must withstand temperatures up to 600 °C in the die apertures. Under these thermomechanical loads, the tool must produce an extruded geometry that is accurate in both dimensions and shape. The axial forces acting on the billet-facing surface cannot be withstood by the die alone. Optimal support from the support tooling must be provided as shown in section 7.2.1. The extrusion tooling must be capable of withstanding the deformation forces developed in the shape-producing areas. The tool designer, the extruder, and the customer must specify the final product cross-sectional geometry to be tool compatible by "simultaneous engineering." Figure 7.65 describes the path currently followed from order intake to the manufacture of the extrusion tool.

The deformation temperature of aluminum alloys is generally below the tempering temperature of the classic hot working tool steels. These steels are therefore used for the manufacture of aluminum extrusion tooling. In the die apertures of large-profile dies, operating temperatures up to 600 °C can develop from the heat produced during the extrusion, combined with the inadequate heat extraction through the tool surface. In these cases, hot working tool steels with a higher resistance to tempering must be used for the manufacture of these dies. The classic hot working tool steels are described in detail in the section "Hot Working Materials for the Manufacture of Extrusion Tooling" in this chapter.

Working with Extrusion Tooling. Die trials are carried out after the bearings have been polished and the hollow die assembled. Today, CAD/CAM manufactures second and third dies so closely to the first die that, to an increasing extent, die trials are not required for these tools.

Die trials are carried out under production conditions, that is:

- Extruded material and billet dimensions
- Billet and die temperature
- Extrusion speed

These correspond to the specified production data. During the die trial:

- Section or sections should run straight without twist.
- Section geometry should fulfill the quality requirements in terms of dimensions and geometry.
- Length differences between different extruded sections should be minimal.

Testing is carried out by taking samples along the length of the extrusion and measuring and recording.

The die is released for production or corrected, depending on the test results. Corrected dies must be retrialed. The most common corrections involve:

- Die dimensions to produce the specified finish dimensions in the cross section of the semifinished product at room temperature
- Unequal material flow across the section
- Feeder chamber geometry
- Port geometry with hollow dies
- Welding chamber dimensions with hollow dies

Aluminum extrusion die manufacturers are moving in the direction of higher die accuracy, with the intention of largely eliminating the expensive die trials.

If the die trial results are satisfactory, the tool is cleaned of aluminum in hot caustic soda, followed by wet or dry shot blasting with sand, glass, or steel balls. The die is finally nitrided. Coatings with titanium nitride or chromium carbide are also possible but require significant investment.

For production, the dies must be carefully and fully preheated. Support tooling should also be preheated to avoid heat loss from the die at the start of extrusion. Special die ovens located close to the extrusion press are used for die preheating. The furnace chamber must have precise temperature control. When a die is removed or a cold die loaded into the oven, the resultant temperature decrease must be taken into account by increasing the time. Strict maintenance of the specified billet temperature is also important for a long tool life.

The following rules apply in tool preheating:

- The toughness of the tool increases with through heating. Complete through heating of the hot working steel tool is therefore essential.
- A preheat temperature that is too low and a preheating time that is too short will give insufficient increase in toughness. The die can then fail in service.
- If the through-heating temperature is too high and the time in the preheat oven too long, tempering can occur. This is associated with a loss in strength and, in particular, with a diffusion of the nitrogen that ac-

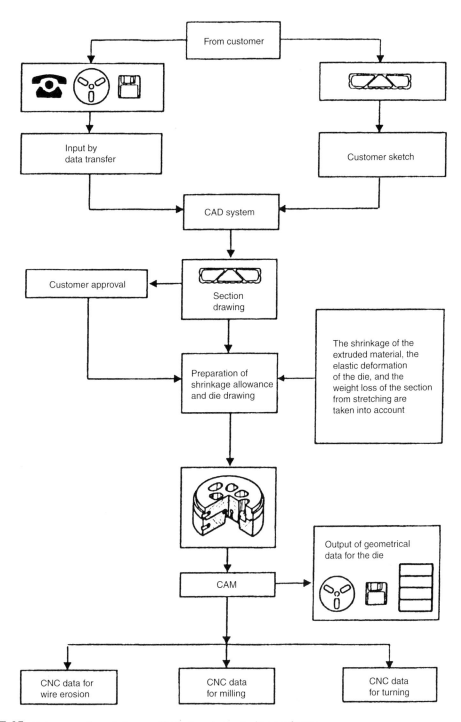

Fig. 7.65 Order processing path for a semifinished product up to die manufacture

cumulates in the surface of the die after nitriding into the interior of the die. The hardness of the bearings in the die aperture then decreases.

Table 7.4 gives the through-heating temperatures and times for the preheating of dies and support tools. Usually, the dies are heated with the holders. The die holder must be preheated.

Table 7.4 Preheat temperature and precheat times for aluminum extrusion tooling

Tool size diameter, mm		Solid section		Hollow section		Support tool	
		Extrusion die and backer with die holder		Porthole die Bridge die with die holder		Bolster Pressure ring	
From	To	Time, h	Temperature, °C	Time, h	Temperature, °C	Time, h	Temperature, °C
...	300	2.5–3	420–450	3–4	440–460	~3	350
300	500	3–4	420–450	4–5	440–460	~3	350
500	700	4–5	420–450	5–6	440–460	~3	350
Over	700	5–6	420–450	6–8	440–460	~3	350

Source: Ames

After preheating, the die must be transported into the press die holder (cassette) by the shortest and fastest route to avoid detrimental heat losses. After extrusion of the profile order, the die that has been removed must be slowly and uniformly cooled. This applies in particular to hollow dies. If the cooling is too fast and not uniform in the air outside, then thermal stresses can result in cracks. The cracking of a hollow die at critical areas can literally be heard.

Tools for the Extrusion of Materials with Deformation Temperatures of 600 to 1300 °C

Martin Bauser*

7.4 Tools for Copper Alloy Extrusion

In contrast to aluminum alloys, where the emphasis in semifinished product production is primarily on extruded profiles and where rods as well as tubes occupy only a small role, the most important products with copper alloys are extruded rod and wire, mainly in free-machining copper-zinc alloys. Tubes should also be included, mainly in oxygen-free copper. The extrusion parameters for copper alloys are discussed in the section "Extrusion of Semifinished Products in Copper Alloys" in Chapter 5.

The shape-producing tools are subjected to significantly higher thermomechanical stresses

compared to aluminum extrusion because of the higher working temperatures, which can vary from 600 to 1000 °C, depending on the alloy and the extrusion parameters. Consequently, higher hot strength and therefore more expensive hot working materials must be used for the manufacture of these tools. In spite of this, the tools deform and wear rapidly and are therefore frequently changed. Die inserts are used for the production of small semifinished product cross sections in which the shape-producing insert is fitted in a lower hot strength hot working material, usually a hot working steel.

The tolerance requirements for brass section extruded to finished sizes are not as tight as with aluminum sections; DIN 17674 applies. However, to meet customer requirements for tighter tolerances, the extruded sections frequently must be drawn on a draw bench. The extruded dimensions and their tolerances must be matched to the final dimensions of the section and the drawing tolerances so that the drawing process is successful, even with cross-sectional variations.

Drawing, straightening, and cutting to length as downstream operations are standard practice for rod with small dimensions in copper-zinc alloys where the feedstock is extruded as wire. These rods also represent the main product of extruded copper alloys. Extrusion presses and tooling are specially designed for their production. Indirect extrusion has proved the most successful process for the production of brass rod, but this does place particular requirements on the tooling.

Copper tube that can be cold worked without intermediate annealing is usually extruded as a thick-wall tube in a standard dimension and then drawn down to different finished sizes. Again, special designs for the extrusion press and the tools have developed over time. Basically, in the rod and tube extrusion of copper alloys, greater emphasis is placed on simple and

*Tools for the Extrusion of Materials with Deformation Temperature of 600 to 1300 °C, Martin Bauser

rapid die changing due to the high die wear. Because the shape-producing tools of the die and mandrel must be lubricated, good access to the press is also needed.

7.4.1 Construction of the Tool Set for Direct and Indirect Extrusion

DIN 24540 applies to the tool set in the same way as for aluminum (Ame 71). Part 3 of this standard summarizes the recommended tool dimensions for copper alloys. Before 1950, direct extrusion for hot working of copper alloys used a tool head as the tool holder, and this contained the entire tool set. Figure 7.66 shows an example. This tool head could be moved in both directions along the press axis by hydraulic power. To extrude, it was moved through the press platen against the container that had no axial movement, and then the transported tool set with its sealing faces pushed against the container sealing faces by a hydraulically operated wedge. It was then in the position shown in Fig. 7.66. From the point of view of a stable supporting tool set providing a solid support to the shape producing tools. This old tool holder design was relatively underdimensioned. This can be seen by comparing the tool set shown in Fig. 7.66 with the tool set in the slide in a modern standard press in Fig. 7.67. Extrusion presses built after 1950 were fitted with die slides or rotating arms as the tool holder, lo-

cated on the container side of the press front platen. Their arrangement only provides for movements of the tool holder transverse to the press centerline. The container can be moved axially and sealed with its hydraulic system through its sealing surfaces against the sealing surfaces of the tool set, with a facial pressure of at least 70 to 90 N/mm^2, as shown in section 7.2.3. Copper alloy extrusion presses usually operate with conical sealing surfaces, as depicted in Fig. 7.11, 7.12, and 7.14. Today, direct-extrusion presses for processing copper alloys up to temperatures of 800 °C are equipped with a cassette as the tool holder, and those for processing materials at temperatures over 800 °C are equipped with a rotating arm, as before. This contains two tool-holder positions so that it is possible to alternate between two dies.

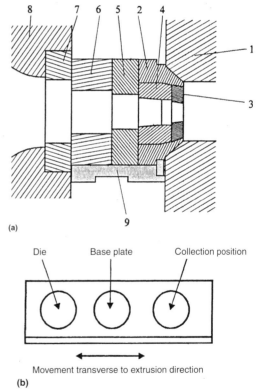

(a)

(b) Movement transverse to extrusion direction

Fig. 7.67 Toot set for the direct extrusion of copper alloys fitted in the tool holder of a die slide. (a) Axial section through the tool stock. 1, container; 2, die holder; 3, extrusion die; 4, backer; 5, bolster; 6, pressure ring; 7, pressure ring as support in the press platen 8, press platen; 9, die slide. (b) View of the three positions of the die slide. Between the die holder and the collection position for the discard and the shell there is a baseplate against which the billet can be pierced for the production of large-diameter tubes. Source: Wieland-Werke AG

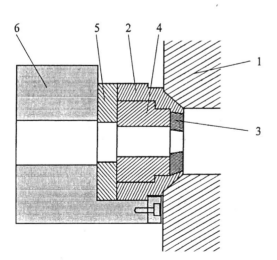

Fig. 7.66 Tool stack for the direct extrusion of copper alloys fitted in an axially moving die head acting as the die holder. 1, container; 2, die holder; 3, extrusion die; 4, backer; 5, bolster; 6, pressure bolster and die head. Source: Wieland-Werke AG

Easy access to the shape-forming tools that must be lubricated at every extrusion is an important requirement for all tool-holder designs for the extrusion of copper alloys.

The extrusion load and container-dependent dimensions of the tool set for direct-extrusion presses for processing copper alloys (Fig. 7.4, 7.67) are specified in DIN 24540 part 3. For the 200 mm container of a 20 MN extrusion press, as an example:

- Tool set external diameter is 425 mm
- Tool set length is 450 mm
- Subbolster thickness is 185 mm
- Bolster thickness is 130 mm
- Die holder thickness is 125 mm
- Backer dimension are 130 mm diameter by 95 mm thick
- Die dimensions are 130 mm diameter by 40 mm thick

For indirect extrusion, the tool or die holder is located at the head of the hollow tool carrier stem through which the section runs. As described in section 7.2, the tool set can be loose in front of the hollow stem, as shown in Fig. 7.10 and 7.68, or located in a tool holder machined into the tool carrier stem, as depicted in Fig. 7.2. Figure 7.10 gives an insight into the principal arrangement of the tool set of an indirect-extrusion press for copper alloys, and Fig. 7.68 shows the loose die holder with inserted flat as well as conical dies. The die holders in these tool sets usually have several functions, in this case, the function of a dummy block. The tool carrier stem itself replaces the support tools needed for direct extrusion.

The shape-producing tools for the different extruded products are described in this chapter. Reference should be made to "Copper Alloys" in section 7.3.1.3 for the material flow control and to section 7.3.2 for the dimensions of the die aperture for specific extrusion cross sections.

7.4.2 Extrusion Dies and Mandrels for the Production of Tubes

Extrusion dies for processing copper alloys usually have a conical outer surface face with a conical angle of 2 to 6°. These dies can be seen in the general view in Fig. 7.17 and in Fig. 7.69 and 7.70. A cylindrical die surface with a shoulder, as is common on aluminum extrusion dies (Fig. 7.15, 7.16), is associated with the risk of the extruded material penetrating between the die and the die holder in the extrusion of copper alloys. This makes it more difficult to separate the die from the die holder, but it is used in certain cases. Copper alloy extrusion

Fig. 7.69 Extrusion die for a handrail in CuZn44Pb2 extruded to the finished dimensions, and a profile cross section. Source: Wieland-Werke AG

Fig. 7.70 Two-cavity extrusion die for the extrusion to the finished dimensions of a small CuZn44Pb2 section, with a profile cross section. Source: Wieland-Werke AG

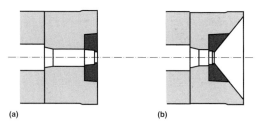

(a)   (b)

Fig. 7.68 Tool set of an indirect extrusion press for copper alloys with a loose die holder in front of the die carrier stem, as shown in Fig. 7.10, with (a) due holder with flat die, and (b) die holder and die with conical inlet. Source: Wieland-Werke AG

dies are often installed not from the exit side, as depicted in Fig. 7.3 and 7.4, but from the front, that is, from the billet side into the die holder. This applies in particular to the axially moveable die head, because it simplifies die changing. The die apertures for the production of tubes follow the designs shown in Fig. 7.71. However, the increase in the dimensions of the die aperture compared to the specified dimensions of the tube external diameter is less than for the die apertures for the production of rod. An extruded rod stresses the die radially more severely than a tube. The use of die inserts, similar to the extrusion of rod and sections, is recommended for the production of tubes with diameters that are not too large. Their geometric shape and dimensions are similar to that for dies for rods.

The extrusion of copper alloys does not use feeder chambers as with aluminum alloy extrusion. Billet-on-billet extrusion does not work with copper alloys, because at the end of the extrusion process, any material remaining in the feeder chamber cools so rapidly that it cannot weld with the subsequent billet.

The extrusion of tubes and hollow sections is usually carried out with a die and a mandrel. Mandrels for processing copper alloys follow the designs given in section 7.3 and, in particular, the designs in Fig. 7.25. The mandrels are usually internally cooled and have a slightly tapered shaft when extruding with a moving mandrel. However, cylindrical mandrels can also be used with short billets. With moving mandrels, the tip is usually flat with chamfered corners. Semicircular tips have proved more suitable for moving mandrels for working of difficult-to-extrude alloys such as the CuNi alloys. With flat tips, there is the risk that the edges will flow back because of the high thermal stressing of the mandrel surface. Hollow sections are rarely produced over profiled moving mandrels since the small mandrel cross sections prevent the use of internal cooling. Figure 7.72 shows one of the rare applications. Tubes with large dimensions are extruded over moving mandrels and those with small dimensions over the mandrel tip. In the production of tubes with small internal dimensions, an adequately stable location of the moving mandrel in the container axis cannot be guaranteed. In particular, movement of the mandrel from the container axis and thus an unacceptable wall thickness variation of the tube during the piercing of the billet cannot be avoided with any certainty. In these cases, extrusion must be carried out with a fixed mandrel over the stepped mandrel tip, as shown in Fig. 7.20 and 7.73. The stepped mandrel tip, which is often manufactured from high hot strength hot working material because of the high thermomechanical stressing and the absence of internal cooling, is screwed to the internally cooled carrier mandrel, as seen in Fig. 7.25 and 7.73. It is also possible to have the mandrel tip and the mandrel shaft as one piece for the extrusion of easily extruded copper alloys with low deformation temperatures, as seen in Fig. 7.25. Tubes with profiled internal contours are

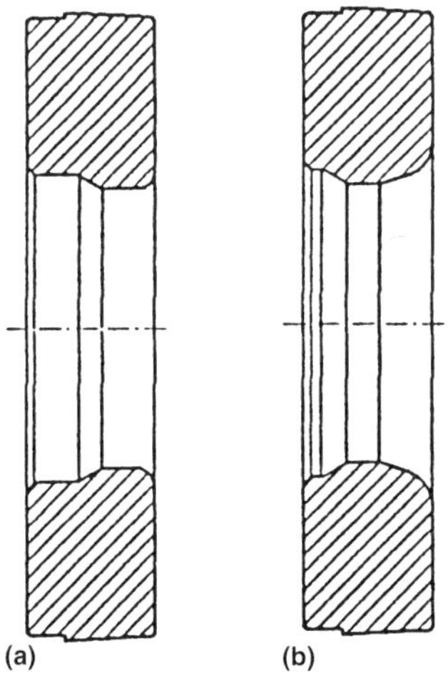

Fig. 7.71 Extrusion dies for the production of copper alloy rods for (a) easy-to-extrude alloys and (b) difficult-to-extrude alloys. Direction of extrusion: right to left. Source: Wieland-Werke AG

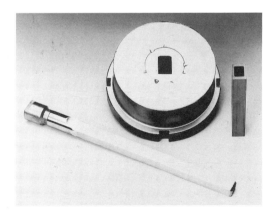

Fig. 7.72 Extrusion die with cobalt alloy insert shrunk and peened in, together with a moving mandrel, for the production of the terminal section shown at right. Source: Wieland-Werke AG

Fig. 7.73 Extrusion die and stepped mandrel for the production of the wristwatch housing section shown at right. Source: Wieland-Werke AG

usually extruded over the mandrel tip. A profiled tip is screwed onto the round mandrel shaft. A mandrel rotation system ensures the accurate positioning of the mandrel relative to the die aperture. The service life of the mandrel is determined by the frequency of lubrication, the correct dimensions of the cooling bore, and the cooling intensity. The contact time between the extruded material heated to the deformation temperature and the mandrel surface should be as short as possible.

7.4.2.1 Extrusion Dies for the Production of Solid Sections in Copper-Zinc Alloys

DIN 17674 covers the shape as well as the permitted deviations for sections extruded or drawn to finished dimensions in copper alloys. The copper alloy CuZn40Pb2 is usually used for the production of finish-extruded sections. The copper alloy CuZn39Pb3, with its limited cold workability, is used for sections produced to finished sizes with narrow tolerances by a calibration draw. Figure 7.69 shows a handrail extruded to the finished size in the alloy CuZn44Pb2, and Fig. 7.70 shows a smaller section extruded to the finished size in the same material, using a two-cavity die.

U-shaped sections, as shown in Fig. 7.74(a) as a finished product, require a die with a narrow tongue, which is at risk of failure under the effect of the extrusion load. To avoid failure in the area of the tongue root, the section is opened out for extrusion, which increases the critical bending cross section. Figure 7.74 shows a section opened out because of the narrow die tongue with the die that was brought to the finished shape in two draws.

For complicated sections, the die backer is matched to the die exit to obtain the maximum support of the die. However, the aperture of the backer is at least 5 mm larger on every edge than the associated die to avoid contact of the section with the backer during extrusion. Figure 7.74(b) shows this for the die and the backer. With simple geometric shapes for the section cross section, one backer can be used for different profile cross sections. Multicavity dies require multicavity backers.

In Fig. 7.66 and 7.67, the taper of the die holder butts against the internal taper of the container. For this arrangement, the following rules apply:

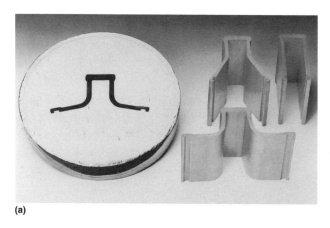

(a)

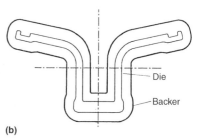

(b)

Fig. 7.74 Extrusion die and profile cross section for the extrusion of an opened-out U-section. (a) Extrusion die and profile cross section after extrusion and after the first and second draw. (b) Die aperture and the associated backer (support tool). Source: Wieland-Werke AG

- The die diameter (D_M) is 0.7 to 0.9 times the container internal diameter (D_R).
- To maintain die stability, the circumscribing circle (D_U) of the section should not exceed 0.7 times D_M. In DIN 24540 part 1, section 4.7.1, D_U is recommended as (0.6 to 0.8)D_M.
- The circumscribing circle of the section should be D_U = (0.5 to 0.6)D_R. This large distance between the container internal diameter and the billet surface to the section contour ensures a relatively uniform material flow.
- Larger circumscribing circles are possible if, as shown in Fig. 7.15, the tapered sealing face with the container is directly on the die and not on the die holder. It is then possible to achieve D_U = (0.7 to 0.8)D_R. The risk of damage to the extrusion die by plastic deformation from the thermomechanical stresses of the die material flowing in the direction of the die aperture is naturally greater with this design. With smaller-profile cross sections, die inserts are used, as seen in Fig. 7.72 and described in section 7.4.2.4.

7.4.2.2 Extrusion Dies for the Extrusion of Solid Sections in Copper and Low-Alloyed Copper Alloys

The criteria given in the first section for copper-zinc alloys also apply to the tooling for the extrusion of copper and low-alloyed copper alloys. Because, however, the extrusion temperatures of this material are approximately 200 °C higher, and the low-melting-point phases in the extruded material necessitate the use of slow extrusion speeds, the mechanical and thermal stresses as well as the stress duration are often several factors higher, which can result in plastic deformation of the die aperture. The tempering temperature of the hot working material can easily be exceeded by several 100 °C. Usually, compromises are found between the extrusion ratio, the billet length, and the contact time during the working of the material so that these tooling problems can be kept under control. New dies must therefore be conditioned, because plastic deformation will cause the die aperture to close in after only the first or second extrusion, and tool material will flow from the side facing the billet into the entry to the die aperture, as seen in Fig. 7.75. For this reason, new tools are removed after one or two extrusions and reworked by hand or by erosion. These dies exhibit a relatively stable behavior when used for the second time. However, particularly critical conditions occur if a heat treatment of the material being extruded must be superimposed for metallurgical reasons, for example, the working of CuZr alloys in the range of the solution heat treatment temperature. The thermal loading of the tooling is then even higher.

Groove formation on the surface of the extruded section of high-copper-containing materials is an additional problem. These materials often oxidize severely during preheating. In addition to descaling the heated billet, extrusion process techniques are also used to prevent the flow of oxides into the die aperture, which would result in surface defects. These include oxide traps (concentric grooves on the billet side of the dummy block and on the die holder).

Changes in the shape-forming tool areas under high thermomechanical stresses require larger tolerance bands on the extruded product. With extreme width-to-thickness ratios of the extruded semifinished product, as occurs with flat copper bar with dimensions of 200 by 12

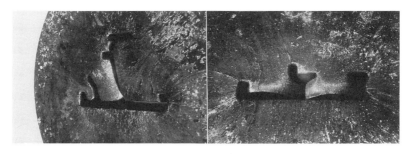

Fig. 7.75 Plastic deformation of the die aperture of copper section dies resulting from high thermomechanical stresses during extrusion. Source: Kabelmetall, Osnabrück

mm, the dimensions can vary by several millimeters between the front of the extrusion and
the end.

Copper sections are nearly always finished
by cold working, usually drawing, to meet the
tolerances and mechanical properties demanded
by the customer. Therefore, one of the most important aims in the extrusion of copper sections
is the production of a product that can be
drawn. Usually, no tolerance variations or
cross-sectional changes can occur on the section (even if permitted by DIN 17674, page 4)
if they can result in choking at the entry to the
drawing die or even overlaps. If the application
permits, these problems can be reduced by designing the corners with an undercut, as shown
in Fig. 7.76(a). These problems occur primarily
in sections with extremes in cross-sectional
variation. Progressive "trimming" of the extrusion die by reworking after each extrusion is
then essential and is frequently the only way to
solve the problem.

Today, profiles in copper and low-alloyed
copper alloys are mainly extruded on modern
presses into water. This is advantageous for
age-hardening alloys with working in the solution heat treatment range. Extruding into water also helps prevent oxidation of the section
as it leaves the die and, in particular, produces
a fine-grained structure. The disadvantage of
this process, however, is that the back face of
the die comes directly into contact with water.

7.4.2.3 Dies, Mandrels, and Bridge Dies for the Production of Hollow Sections

With aluminum alloys, the production of demanding hollow sections using porthole and
bridge dies is an important and essential process. In contrast, these methods can only be
used in a few cases for the extrusion of copper
alloys. Only bridge dies similar to Fig. 7.23 can
be used, in which the discard is completely
pulled from the die at the end of every extrusion cycle by opening the container so that no
extruded material remains in the bridge die.
This is important, because the die cools so severely between two extrusions at high extrusion
temperatures that any residual material cannot
be extruded with the next extrusion. If this does
not succeed, then the bridge die blocks and
must be removed. Clearing and cleaning a
bridge die for extruding copper alloys is extremely difficult. The more common porthole

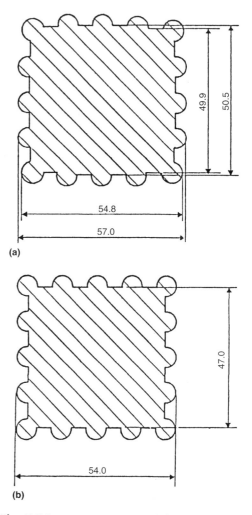

Fig. 7.76 Copper section. (a) Extruded with reduced corner
dimensions (undercut). (b) Extruded and drawn
with a single draw. Source: Kabelmetall, Osnabrück

die used with aluminum alloys is therefore
completely unsuitable for copper alloys, because they remain full of the extruded material
up to the next extrusion. Because the tooling
and billet in aluminum extrusion have approximately the same temperature, the press power
in this case is sufficient to clear the die by the
pressure from the next billet.

For the production of hollow sections in
copper alloys using a bridge die, the billet temperature must be even higher than for the production of solid sections with difficult cross-
sectional geometries, because of the long
friction faces in the die. This means that the
thermomechanical stresses and thus the risk of
plastic deformation in the die aperture region,

as well as the occasional risk of die failure, for example, in the region of the mandrel neck, are extremely high. For this reason, simple tool designs with replaceable mandrels and dies are used. The replaceable parts can be produced from higher hot-working-strength materials, for example, nickel alloys, as shown in the drawing of an old bridge die design in Fig. 7.26.

For this reason, if technically possible, hollow copper alloy sections should be produced with a die and a mandrel for process technological reasons and, above all, for economical reasons. If the internal contour is circular or the cross section at least large enough, then extrusion with a moving mandrel can be used, as shown in Fig. 7.19. Otherwise, extrusion over the mandrel tip as depicted in Fig. 7.20 is preferred. An example is the extrusion tools shown in Fig. 7.73 for the production of wristwatch housings.

Nevertheless, in special but rare cases, sections with a small cross-sectional profile with a profiled internal contour are extruded over a moving mandrel, for example, the terminal section in a copper-zinc alloy shown in Fig. 7.72.

Because it is not really possible to pierce a billet with a small cross-sectional mandrel, the billets for this process are prebored. In the production of hollow sections with opposing unequal wall thickness, as shown schematically by the terminal section in Fig. 7.33, the mandrel can deflect under the transverse forces away from the material flow during extrusion and toward the thicker wall. This phenomenon is avoided by including a follower adjacent to the thinner wall in the die, which equalizes the material flow. The necessary cross-sectional area of the follower must be determined by press trials.

Usually, hollow sections extruded from copper alloys are subsequently cold worked, for example, drawn, to be able to achieve the tight tolerances and surface quality required by the customer.

7.4.2.4 Extrusion Dies for the Production of Rod and Wire

The production of extruded rod and wire in free-machining copper-zinc alloys, usually CuZn39Pb3, is quantitatively the focal point for the extrusion of copper alloys. For the production of rod with diameters of 25 to 35 mm, solid dies are used, as shown schematically in Fig. 7.71. The die aperture has an entry radius of 3 to 5 mm and bearing lengths of approximately 10 mm. With the extrusion of difficult-to-extrude alloys, there is the risk of plastic compression of the die aperture from the prolonged stressing that results from the high extrusion temperatures and the slow extrusion speed. The extrusion die is therefore given a conical entrance, as shown in Fig. 7.71(b). To reduce the high extrusion loads and to ensure the ease of production of small rod dimensions, it is sometimes necessary to work with lubricated containers. In this case, the use of dies with a conical entry is necessary (Fig. 7.17), or a die holder and die similar to Fig. 7.68(b).

Copper alloy rod with small cross sections or diameters below 24 to 35 mm are produced from extruded wire on drawing, straightening, and cut-to-length automatic machines. This wire is usually extruded through die inserts in the same way as small cross-sectional profiles. The cylindrical inserts located in a hot working tool steel die body are made from high hot strength materials including cobalt alloys, metal-ceramic hot working materials, including the molybdenum-base cermotherm, and pure ceramic hot working materials such as zirconium oxide. These hot working materials usually have low toughness and therefore fracture quickly under the effect of tensile stresses, which can develop tangentially in the die from the extrusion load. The die inserts in these materials are shrunk into a hot working steel die body and thus subjected to compressive stresses. Under these conditions, die inserts in the hot working materials mentioned can withstand up to 100 extrusions without reworking and thus achieve many times the throughput of dies in high-quality hot working steels. Obviously, several inserts can be shrunk into a die body for multicavity extrusion. The production of solid dies in the materials mentioned is not possible because of the low toughness and also for economical reasons.

Figure 7.77 gives an overview of the different arrangements for extrusion dies with shrunk-in die inserts. Figure 7.78 illustrates the method of assembly. Die inserts are initially produced as cylindrical bodies. The external diameter is, as shown in Fig. 7.78, larger than the bore of the die holder by the absolute interference fit. The shrinkage allowance depends on the specific coefficient of expansion of the die insert and the die body material. For example, the frequently used austenitic hot working tool steel 1.2731 has a significantly higher thermal

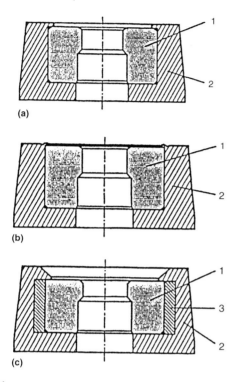

Fig. 7.77 Composite dies consisting of die body and die insert. (a) Manufactured using the production method in Fig. 7.78. Peered around the edge of the bore. (b) Manufactured using the production method in Fig. 7.78, with the die insert held in by individual center punch marks on the circumference of the bore, as shown in Fig. 7.72. (c) Copper intermediate ring. 1, die insert; 2, die body; 3, copper intermediate ring. Source: Wieland-Werke AG

expansion than classic hot working tool steel. This must be taken into account in determining the shrinkage allowance that has to be added to the die insert to ensure a shrinkage that still operates at the working temperature. Otherwise, the interference fit can be lost even during the preheating of the die. The following material-dependent interference fits have been established from many years' experience with die insert materials:

Die material	Relative interference, %
Cobalt alloys	1.0–1.5
Cermotherm	1.5–3.0
Zirconium oxide	1.5–5.0

Only cobalt alloys have thermal coefficients of expansion just above those of the classic hot working steels. The metal-ceramic-based and the pure ceramic-based hot working materials of interest are characterized by very low coefficients of thermal expansion. Consequently,

these die inserts can loosen under the high thermal stresses in spite of shrink-fitting with high shrinkage allowances. They will then fall out of the die body bore unless additional measures such as peening are used. However, loosening of the die insert can also occur by plastic deformation of the die body as a result of creep processes under high interference stresses. These are necessary for the die insert materials that have low coefficients of expansion to ensure adequate compressive stresses, even at the high temperatures used. The interference fit is produced by heating the die to a temperature high enough to enable the die insert to be dropped in.

When using die inserts for the production of sections with small cross-sectional areas, care should be taken to ensure that the die apertures do not have sharp corners. Even stellite can crack in these areas as a result of the stress concentration from the notch effect. The crack can leave a ridge on the extruded product if the extruded material penetrates into the crack. Pure ceramic inserts are only suitable for the extrusion of round bar, wire, and tubes because of the low toughness of the material.

The arrangement of the die insert in Fig. 7.77(a) corresponds to the description in Fig. 7.78. The production of the die in Fig. 7.77(b) follows, in principle, the production route shown in Fig. 7.78, with the exception of the peened edge of the die body bore for securing. Instead, this shrunk-in die insert is secured in the die body with center punch marks, as seen in Fig. 7.72. The two die assemblies seen in Fig. 7.77(a) and (b) are the most common, with the design in Fig. 7.77(a) for the extrusion of difficult-to-extrude copper alloys similar to CuZnNi or CuZr, and the design in Fig. 7.77(b) for the extrusion of CuZn.

7.4.3 Manufacture and Use of Copper Extrusion Dies

7.4.3.1 Manufacture of the Extrusion Dies

The design and manufacture of extrusion tooling for the extrusion of copper alloys is basically the same as that described for the production of aluminum extrusion tooling in section 7.3.4.3. The production route follows the manufacturing stages for dies and bridge dies shown in Fig. 7.63 and 7.64. The order and

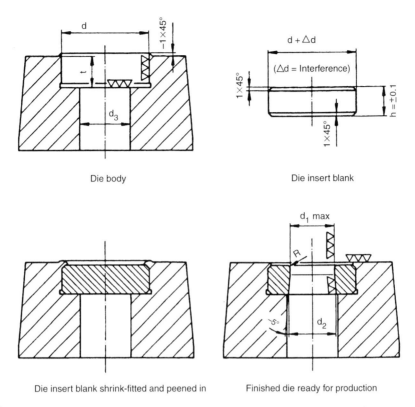

Die body   Die insert blank

Die insert blank shrink-fitted and peened in   Finished die ready for production

Fig. 7.78 Production route for the production of an extrusion die with shrunk-in die insert, according to Fig. 7.77(a). Source: Sauer

production route also fundamentally follows that given in Fig. 7.65.

However, tooling for the extrusion of copper alloys is subjected to significantly higher temperatures than aluminum tooling. The extrusion temperatures for copper alloys are well above the tempering temperatures of the classic hot working tool steels. Consequently, the classic hot working steels cannot be used for all applications. Instead, the manufacture of copper extrusion tooling requires the use of higher hot strength tool materials, including austenitic hot working steels, cobalt-base hot working materials, nickel-base hot working materials, molybdenum-base metal-ceramic materials, and pure ceramic hot working materials. These materials are discussed in the detail in the section "Hot Working Materials for the Manufacture of Extrusion Tooling" in this Chapter.

7.4.3.2 Use of the Extrusion Tools

Again, the handling criteria described in section 7.3.4.3 for aluminum extrusion tools apply. Extrusion dies for the production of brass sec-

tions to the finished size also must be trialled before they are first used, similar to aluminum extrusion dies. The die trials usually result in the correction of the die aperture until the desired profile dimensions are achieved. New dies for the extrusion of copper and low-alloyed copper alloy profiles also must be conditioned, as described in section 7.4.2.2.

Compared to aluminum extrusion tooling, higher thermomechanical stresses occur in the die aperture of copper extrusion dies, and this means that wear-resistant surface treatments are less effective. Surface treatments of hot working tool steel extrusion dies, for example, nitriding, can be excluded because of the temperature-related rapid diffusion of nitrogen into the interior of the die steel. Even chemical vapor deposition coatings do not offer any advantages. The coatings are destroyed by the frequent reworking of the die apertures.

Before use, the shape-producing tooling of the extrusion die and the mandrel are heated in a chamber furnace up to temperatures of 450 °C for 2 to 4 h holding time, depending on the size of the tooling. Complete through-heating over the cross section of the tool is necessary to avoid tool failure as a consequence of inadequate ductility in the heated tool. If the heating time is too short, then through-heating over the full cross section will not be achieved. If the heating temperature is too high, then oxidation of the tool surface will occur. Temperatures that reach the tempering range of the hot working material will result in a reduction in strength. To avoid unacceptable heat loss from the shape-producing tool to the support tooling, the latter should also be preheated. This applies in particular to backers that support the die under the extrusion load. The tooling should be loaded as quickly as possible in the die or tool holder after removal from the preheat furnace.

During the processing of an order on the extrusion press, the shape-producing tool is removed after a few extrusions and replaced with a tool held in the preheat furnace. Larger orders therefore require more tools in circulation. The removed tooling is cleaned and measured and the bearing quality checked. If necessary, the entire shape-producing area, which can exhibit plastic deformation resulting from the high thermomechanical loading, must be reworked.

The cooling of extrusion tooling after use requires special care because of the significant heating during the extrusion process. It should not be too rapid or asymmetrical, which can occur if the hot die is placed on the cold floor. Instead, careful, controlled cooling in sand or ash is advisable. Large mandrels can be cooled by standing on their end to avoid distortion.

After cooling, the tools are stored. They should first be cleaned and then shot blasted with sand or other materials, and the bearing surfaces should be honed to bring them back into a usable condition. If necessary, this also includes reworking of the die aperture. Even with severe plastic deformation in this region, a die can be brought back to a usable condition by a subsequent erosion operation.

7.4.4 Tooling for the Glass-Lubricated Extrusion of Titanium, Nickel, and Iron Alloys

Titanium-base extruded alloys with deformation temperatures of 900 to 1150 °C, nickel-base alloys with deformation temperatures of 900 to 1280 °C, and iron-base alloys with deformation temperatures of 1000 to 1300 °C can only be extruded with glass lubrication. The glass of a suitable composition, which is liquid at these temperatures, coats the billet and the container liner surface and thus separates the flowing extruded material from the surface of the shape-forming tooling during the extrusion process. Glass has poor thermal conductivity and therefore acts as an insulator. In addition, the use of glass lubrication allows high extrusion speeds to be used, which allows the effective exposure of the tooling to the temperature to be kept short. The extrusion of significantly shorter section lengths compared to aluminum and copper alloys helps in this context. In the deformation zone, quasi-adiabatic conditions exist, and as a result, temperatures up to 1300 °C can occur. The thermal stressing of the tooling, which only lasts for a few seconds, can be extremely high, even with the glass insulating layer and the high speeds. The extrusion die can only withstand a maximum of three extrusions before being reworked. This requires a large number of extrusion dies to be available, depending on the specific order size.

Direct contact of the extruded material with the tooling surface inevitably results in severe damage to the extrusion tooling and the extruded product. Laminar flow of the extruded material must be ensured to avoid a breakdown of the glass film surrounding the material flow. Sharp-edged transitions in the contact surfaces of the die in the entry and in the die aperture must be avoided at all costs. For rod, tube, and section dies, conical and angled as well as smooth transitions are necessary, as seen in Fig. 7.24 and 7.79. Fluid friction between the extruded material and the die bearing surfaces dominates and hardly allows any effective control of the material flow in the die apertures, in contrast to the extrusion of aluminum and zinc-containing copper alloys. This theme is discussed in section 7.3.1 and specifically for glass-lubricated extrusion in section 7.3.1.3.

Tubes and hollow sections are usually produced with moving mandrels and not over a mandrel tip. The mandrel shanks are slightly tapered, similar to the production of copper alloy tubes, and internally cooled, as depicted in Fig. 7.25. Because the outer surface is sprayed with a cooling medium to break off the glass layer at the end of every extrusion, mandrels are also externally cooled. For this reason, small extrusion mandrel cross sections and also massive mandrel shanks can be used without internal cooling.

Fig. 7.79 Section die for the production of the steel section at right. The die aperture has a heavily rounded entry. The mantle surface of the die is cylindrical, with a shoulder for location in the die holder. Source: Krupp/Hoesch, Schwerte

7.4.4.1 Design of the Tool Set for Direct Extrusion

The design of the tool set is similar to that used for the direct extrusion of copper alloys. This is shown in Fig. 7.67 for a tool head with a die slide as the die holder. It has the following features:

- The tool holder on current presses is a rotating arm, and on older presses a slide or a tool head.
- The seal between the container and the die holder is basically through conical surfaces. This classic sealing design is particularly relevant for the thermomechanical loading of the sealing region to ensure the accurate alignment of the tool set to the container for the production of extruded tubes with small variations in wall thickness.
- Rapid die changing is an important requirement for all die holder designs because of the high thermomechanical stressing of the tool and the resultant short extrusion times necessary.

7.4.4.2 Tooling for the Extrusion of Titanium Alloys

The high deformation temperature of titanium alloys requires high extrusion speeds to avoid detrimental cooling of the extruded material. For this reason and the increase in the flow stress with increasing rate of deformation, extrusion with glass lubrication is necessary [Lau 76]. Information on the extrusion parameters for titanium alloys can be found in Chapter 5.

Rod, tube, and section in low-alloyed titanium alloys, for which deformation temperatures of 900 °C or less are sufficient, are only required in small quantities. The main focus for extruded sections is the more highly alloyed titanium material similar to TiAl6V4. These require extrusion temperatures of 1000 to 1150 °C.

Extrusion tooling for glass-lubricated extrusion requires special design features that can be found in Fig. 7.24 and 7.79. Extrusion tooling in hot working tool steels is used for the production of tubes. Titanium sections with wall thickness >3 mm are produced using single-piece dies in high hot strength and wear-resistant materials. However, the extrusion of titanium sections with wall thickness <3 mm requires extrusion dies with ceramic coating, usually aluminum oxide or zirconium oxide. Ceramic coatings and glass lubrication enable thin-wall cross sections to be extruded in long lengths, particularly for the aircraft industry [Lau 76]. Information on the manufacture and use of these dies can be found in "Extrusion Tooling for the Production of Steel Sections" in section 7.4.4.4.

7.4.4.3 Tooling for the Extrusion of Nickel Alloys

Glass-lubricated extrusion is unavoidable when considering the high flow stresses of nickel alloys at deformation temperatures of 900 to 1280 °C. In spite of this, specific stem pressures up to 1350 N/mm^2 can occur for the extrusion of these materials. Because extrusion stems are stressed in buckling, short stems must be used, taking into account the high loads needed for the extrusion of nickel alloys. The extrusion stem material itself also must withstand this compressive load. Martensitic steels are used for the manufacture of the stems.

The process parameters for the extrusion of nickel alloys are discussed in Chapter 5. Materials with low-melting-point eutectics must be extruded relatively slowly to avoid hot transverse cracking in the extruded section. Contact times up to 20 s and occasionally up to 30 s can occur between the extruded material and the tooling. Extrusion dies in high hot strength hot working tool steels, which are used for the glass-lubricated extrusion of iron alloys, cannot withstand these contact times well. Throughputs approximately twice as high can be achieved with dies in Nimonic 90. Otherwise, the general considerations for tooling for glass-lubricated extrusion apply.

7.4.4.4 Tooling for Extrusion of Iron Alloys

Iron alloys require high deformation temperatures, and this necessitates rapid extrusion to avoid high heat losses. These extrusion conditions can only be realized by glass-lubricated extrusion. More detailed information can be found in the section "Extrusion of Iron Alloy Semifinished Products" in Chapter 5.

Tooling for the Extrusion of Alloy Steels. Alloy steel tubes are only produced with extrusion dies and mandrels. Porthole and bridge dies, which are used for the manufacture of tubes and hollow sections in aluminum alloys and occasionally also for copper alloys, are not suitable for the extrusion of iron alloys because of the high thermomechanical stresses. The extrusion dies used for the production of alloy steel tubes are usually made from hot working tool steels and have the usual conical entry for lubricated extrusion, with an opening angle of generally 120°. The dies are loaded either from the billet side or the exit side, depending on the design of the tool or die holder. They are located by a conical or a cylindrical surface with a shoulder. Figures 7.16, 7.17, and 7.79 show these methods of location. Fast and, if necessary, automated loading and unloading is important for tool changing because of the stress-related frequency. At the end of the extrusion process and removal of the section and discard, the tool holder, either a rotating arm or tool slide, is moved out of the press. After the die has been removed, it is cooled in water, inspected, and reused after preheating. Dies in the hotworking steel 1.2343 (H11 or T20811 similar U.S. grade) can be used up to 40 times in this way before they must be reworked, when they are usually opened out to a larger tube diameter. In this way, a single die can last for up to 400 extrusions with several rebores.

Numerous investigations have been carried out with other hot working materials, including those based on cobalt, nickel, and molybdenum, to reduce the number of dies in circulation by increasing the service life. These investigations did result in significantly higher outputs, particularly with molybdenum alloy dies, but no economic advantage over extrusion dies in hot working steel because of the higher material and production costs. Even coating the die surfaces has not proved successful. Frequently, the marked difference between the thermal expansion of the coating and the tool material under the high thermal loading results in shear stresses so high that the wear-reducing coating breaks off from the die. Consequently, the much cheaper hot working steel 1.2343 is still primarily used. Mandrels for alloy steel tube production are also made in the steels 1.2343 and 1.2365 (H10 or T20810). They usually have conical shanks. The mandrel life is similar to the die life of approximately 400 extrusions, helped by the internal and external cooling.

Extrusion Tooling for the Production of Steel Sections. Obviously, the high extrusion temperatures used allow only the production of simple steel profile cross sections by extrusion. The focus of profile production is therefore on solid sections. At the same time, hollow sections with simple cross-sectional geometry can be produced using profiled mandrels. In certain cases, it is also possible to extrude over a profiled mandrel tip. Intricate profile cross sections cannot be produced.

Usually, single-cavity extrusion is carried out. This does not exclude multicavity extrusion of up to six profiles for small cross sections. Long conical entries, as with round die apertures for the production of tubes, cannot be produced. Only limited material flow control can be achieved using angled and heavily rounded entry areas, as seen in Fig. 7.24 and 7.79. This also applies to the equalization of the material flow in the die aperture by bearings of different lengths. This method of control, which works well for the extrusion of aluminum sections, has practically no effect because of the low friction from the glass lubrication. Consequently, large variations in cross-sectional geometry must be avoided in the design of steel profiles, because the resultant variations in the material flow can be almost impossible to balance.

Short lengths—rarely over 15 m—are usually extruded to limit the high thermomechanical stressing of the tooling. In spite of this and the related short contact time, the die aperture can close in from the front of the extrusion to the back as a result of plastic deformation. The hot die material in the entry area of the die begins to flow into the die aperture, as seen, for example, in the die aperture area of dies for the production of copper profiles in Fig. 7.75. The shape-producing areas of a die do not deform uniformly. The projecting regions in the die aperture that are partly surrounded by the flowing material are particularly affected. This can clearly be seen in Fig. 7.24 and 7.79. Hot working tool steels only have a fraction of their hot strength at these high working temperatures.

Naturally, the producer of extruded steel sections puts considerable effort into increasing the service life of the extrusion tools. The profile dies are also more sensitive to high thermomechanical stresses than tube extrusion dies. In extensive studies [Bra 66], dies in numerous classical hot working steels, austenitic hot working steels, and cobalt, nickel, and molybdenum hot working materials were tested.

The best results of these hot working materials were obtained with the molybdenum material titanium-zirconium-molybdenum (TZM) in the precipitation-hardened condition. The service life of the experimental dies could be extended to well over 100 extrusions without reworking. At the same time, there was no economic advantage over hot working steel dies. More economic is a die in cast steel 1.2343. This hot working steel is inexpensive, easily machined, and has a relatively good thermal conductivity. The production of the die follows the route described previously. If the die aperture has deformed under high thermomechanical stresses after one to three extrusions, it can be brought back to a suitable condition for production by welding and then erosion and mechanical machining [Lau 76].

7.5 Extrusion Tools for Indirect Shape Production, Auxiliary and Support Tooling

Extrusion tools for indirect shape forming as well as the associated auxiliary and support tooling are numerous and fulfill a wide range of applications. Table 7.5 gives an overview.

Extrusion tools for indirect shape forming are designed to be replaceable and are located in movable tool carriers, including the container housing, moving crosshead, piercing crosshead, cassette, and so on. The functions can be classified into:

- Tools that come into direct contact with the extruded material during the extrusion pro-

cess and are indirectly involved with the deformation. The tool life is limited and depends mainly on the deformation temperature and the extrusion load, F_{St}. Tool changing, for example, container replacement, must be carried out in the shortest time possible.

- Tooling that does not come into contact with the extruded material and has either a support or an auxiliary function. This includes the mantle and the liner holder. The extrusion stem, the bolsters, and the mandrel holder also come into this category. In addition to the supporting role, the container also has temperature-controlling tasks, including heating and cooling. These tasks are very important because they provide the possibility of keeping down the cost of the container, which is an expensive tool. A container design matched to this application is a requirement for the economic efficiency of the extrusion press.

A tooling set with a fixed dummy block for direct extrusion is shown in Fig. 7.80. It corresponds to the tool set for the extrusion of easy and moderately difficult-to-extrude aluminum alloys. A loose dummy block must be used for the extrusion of copper alloys.

The tool set in Fig. 7.81 is for the indirect extrusion of copper alloys. A cleaning stem with a cleaning block can also be used to remove the shell.

The tool set in Fig. 7.82 is for the direct tube extrusion of copper alloys. A cleaning block to remove the shell is also used.

Figure 7.83 shows a tool set for the indirect extrusion of aluminum alloy tubes.

Tool sets for direct tube extrusion, as also shown in Fig. 7.1, differ from the usual tooling for direct extrusion only in the mandrel and the resultant changes in the stem and the dummy block. This applies to both direct and indirect extrusion. While in indirect tube extrusion a sealing tool is preferred for copper alloys, a press with a sealing stem is usually used for aluminum alloys, as shown in Fig. 7.8. DIN 24540 provides a reliable basis for the design and dimensioning of the extrusion tools for direct extrusion and direct tube extrusion, as already mentioned in section 7.2.1. The main dimensions of the tools, such as the container internal diameter, container length, extrusion stem, dummy block, and mandrel, are specified here. They are based on practical experience

Table 7.5 Overview of the direct and indirect extrusion tools for indirect shape forming

Tools for hot working on extrusion presses	Function for indirect shape forming	Extrusion press								
		Direct					Indirect			
		Rod		Rod and tube			Rod		Rod and tube	
		Al alloys	Cu alloys	Al alloys	Cu alloys	Steel	Al alloys	Cu alloys	Al alloys	Cu alloys
Solid extrusion stem	Indirect and supporting	■	■	■	■	■				
Hollow extrusion stem	Indirect and supporting			■	■	■				
Tool carrier stem	Indirect and supporting						■	■	■	■
Cleaning stem	Supporting							▨		▨
Sealing stem	Indirect and supporting						■		■	
Sealing tool	Indirect						▨	■	▨	■
Loose dummy block	Indirect	▨	■	■	■	■				
Fixed dummy block	Indirect	■		▨		■				
Loose sealing block	Indirect								■	
Fixed sealing block	Indirect						■			▨
Cleaning block	Supporting	■		■			■		■	
Combination dummy block and cleaning block	Indirect	▨		▨						

(continued)

(a) Resistance heating in container holder. Source: Groos

and have a direct relationship with the smallest container diameter that is obtained with a specific pressure (press power relative to the container cross section) of 1000 N/mm^2 at the maximum possible extrusion press load. The container length is five times the container internal diameter for p_i = 1000 N/mm^2, as recommended in DIN 24540. There is no data for extrusion tooling for indirect extrusion and indirect tube extrusion in DIN 24540. The design

Table 7.5   Continued

Tools for hot working on extrusion presses	Function for indirect shape forming	Extrusion press								
		Direct					Indirect			
		Rod		Rod and tube			Rod		Rod and tube	
		Al alloys	Cu alloys	Al alloys	Cu alloys	Steel	Al alloys	Cu alloys	Al alloys	Cu alloys
Container without heating(a)	Indirect and supporting	Standard	Not used	Not used	Not used	Not used	Not used	Not used	Not used	Not used
Container with resistance heating	Indirect and supporting	Infrequent	Infrequent	Infrequent	Infrequent	Infrequent	Infrequent	Infrequent	Infrequent	Infrequent
Container with resistance heating and cooling	Indirect and supporting	Infrequent	Infrequent	Standard	Standard	Infrequent	Standard	Standard	Standard	Standard
Container with induction heating	Indirect and supporting	Infrequent	Standard	Infrequent	Standard	Infrequent	Infrequent	Infrequent	Infrequent	Infrequent
Container with induction heating and cooling	Indirect and supporting	Infrequent	Infrequent	Infrequent	Infrequent	Infrequent	Infrequent	Infrequent	Infrequent	Infrequent
Design		Standard			Infrequent				Not used	

(a) Resistance heating in container holder. Source: Groos

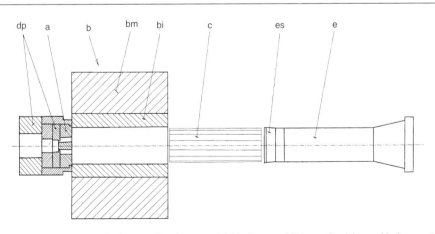

dp = support tooling; a = die; b = container; bm = mantel; bi = liner; c = billet; es = fixed dummy block; e = extrusion stem

Fig. 7.80 Complete tool set for direct extrusion of aluminum alloys. Source: Groos

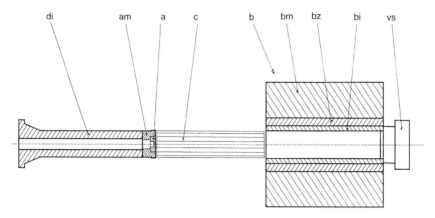

di = indirect extrusion stem; am = die block; a = die holder; c = billet; b = container; bm = mantel; bz = liner holder; bi = liner; vs = sealing tool

Fig. 7.81 Complete tool set for indirect extrusion of copper alloys. Source: Groos

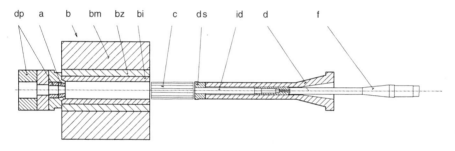

dp = support tooling; a = die; b = container; bm = mantel; bz = liner holder; bi = liner; c = billet; ds = loose dummy block; ld = mandrel; d = extrusion stem; f = mandrel holder

Fig. 7.82 Complete tool set for direct tube extrusion of copper alloys. Source: Groos

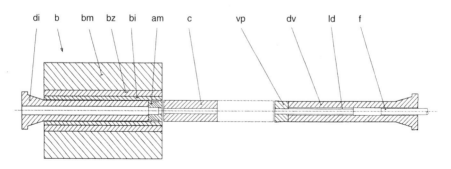

di = indirect extrusion stem; b = container; bm = mantle; bz = liner holder; bi = liner; am = die block; c = billet; vp = sealing block; dv = sealing stem; ld = piercing mandrel; f = mandrel holder

Fig. 7.83 Complete tool set for indirect tube extrusion of aluminum alloys. Source: Groos

and dimensioning of indirect-extrusion tooling is based on the bore of the hollow stem. The smallest container diameter with a specific pressure of 710 N/mm^2 gives an extrusion stem bore sufficient to ensure economic wire production of copper alloys such as brasses. The container length is given as 6.3 times the container internal diameter for p_i = 710 N/mm^2.

The resultant billet length has proved successful on a number of indirect-extrusion presses.

7.5.1 Mandrel Holder and Mandrel Cooling

The schematic drawing of different mandrel mountings in Fig. 7.84 shows the possible basic mandrel designs obtained by adapting the mandrel holder.

The mandrel mounting, consisting of the mandrel holder and the piercer bar, positions and locates the mandrel needed for the production of seamless tube and hollow sections, as shown in Fig. 7.25. It joins the mandrel with the piercer system or with the mandrel mover of the extrusion press. The mandrel that is directly involved in the deformation has a limited life because of its function in the die area at high deformation temperatures. In addition, the wide range of extruded products requires a large number of mandrels of very different shapes and sizes. To minimize the downtime when changing tooling, the method of fixing must be selected to enable rapid mandrel changing.

The dimensions of the mandrel holder are determined by the size of the stem bore and by the piercer or mover stroke. The diameter of the production-specific mandrel determines the size of the dummy block bore. Experience has shown that the guiding of the mandrel holder in the extrusion stem bore must have sufficient clearance. It should be located at the front end of the mandrel holder. In addition, the mandrel holder must be secured to prevent loosening during the screwing in and out of the mandrel into the mandrel holder. In order to speed up the screwing in and out of the mandrel, the mandrel rotation system is fitted with a drive that can also be used for positioning. The current methods of fixing the mandrel to the mandrel holder are:

- Parallel threads with double fit (used most often)
- Taper threads with double fit (not often seen)
- Bayonet lock (expensive and not suitable for transferring large loads)
- Mandrel with a fit and a shoulder as well as a threaded sleeve with a double fit (suitable for small mandrels)

Care should also be taken to ensure that the forces developed do not damage either the mandrel holder or the piercer bar in the piercer cross head. Failure of a mandrel is preferred to damage to the expensive mandrel holder and piecer bar. The stresses developed during the extrusion process make it necessary to use high-strength steels similar to those used for the mandrels for the mandrel holder. Extremely high stresses can develop in the interface between the mandrel and the mandrel holder in the tube extrusion of aluminum and magnesium alloys over large stationary mandrels. The resultant high tensile stresses on the mandrel and its holder require special attention. In this case, monitoring of the forces that occur during extrusion within the tube press can be used. With small- and medium-sized mandrels, the mandrel holder is se-

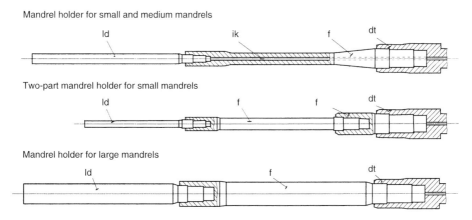

Mandrel holder for small and medium mandrels

Two-part mandrel holder for small mandrels

Mandrel holder for large mandrels

ld = mandrel; f = mandrel holder; dt = mandrel holder carrier; ik = internal cooling

Fig. 7.84 Standard mandrel holders for mandrels of different sizes. Source: Groos

cure against damage because of the steps in the dimensions.

The design of the mandrel holder must be matched to the dimensions, the shape, and the material of the connecting components to ensure that the mandrel holder is less highly stressed than the mandrel. The piercer bar is part of the piercing system and is not as highly stressed as the mandrel holder. The threaded connections must be reliable. The threads must not loosen or seize. To achieve an acceptable service life and reliability in operation, all influences, including notches, turning marks, and rough surfaces, that could result in fatigue failure must be avoided. The shape and positional tolerance according to DIN 7184 in terms of straightness, squareness, concentricity/coaxiality, and runout must be maintained to tight limits.

For tube extrusion with mandrels according to Fig. 7.82, a single extrusion stem with a bore that is sized for a suitable mandrel holder suffices for one container bore. The mandrel holder shown in Fig. 7.84 is suitable for use with most mandrels with different dimensions. Monitoring the tensile and compression stresses in the mandrel during piercing and tube extrusion also protects the mandrel holder against overloading. Mandrel holders are usually one piece. Only when large and small tubes are extruded on a tube press can it be advisable to use a two-piece mandrel holder, as shown in Fig. 7.84. This multipart design enables the tool cost to be reduced and the tool changing to be less involved.

External mandrel cooling is used on vertical tube presses with small mandrels. On horizontal tube presses, there is the risk that the horizontally located mandrel is not uniformly cooled on the surface and thus bends. In addition, it is also possible for thermal stress cracks to form on the mandrel surface after a relative short time as a consequence of exceeding the resistance of the hot working steel to temperature fluctuations (Fig. 7.119). Internal cooling of the mandrel, as depicted in Fig. 7.25, is standard technology in the extrusion of copper alloys. The cooling must be the most effective in the area of the deformation zone of the mandrel or mandrel tip. The cooling medium is fed into the front portion of the mandrel through the cooling tube. The return flow takes place between the cooling tube external diameter and the bore of the mandrel and the mandrel holder, which is axially bored to allow internal cooling of the mandrel. This must be large enough for the centrally aligned internal cooling tube and for sufficient feed and return of the cooling medium. The internal bore of the mandrel must be dead center to ensure that thermal influences do not affect the central location of the mandrel during production. The cooling tube must be fitted with plug fittings for rapid tool changing and be centrally located. The piercer bar, which is connected to the cooling system, also has a tube plug fitting. The cooling medium is treated and heated water in a closed circuit. In addition to the cooling and heating function, care must be taken to ensure that no cooling water remains in the tube and the tooling before changing a mandrel. The mandrel cooling system should be as close to the press as possible in an accessible cellar.

7.5.2 Dummy and Cleaning Blocks for Round and Oval (Rectangular Billet) Containers

For direct extrusion, the following are used:

- Loose dummy block
- Fixed dummy block
- Combination dummy and cleaning block

For indirect extrusion, the following are used:

- Die block (single piece for aluminum alloy extrusion, as shown in Fig. 7.83, and multipart with inserted die for copper alloy extrusion)
- Sealing block that seals the container bore

Only the most common block designs are discussed because of the wide range of dummy blocks and cleaning blocks used.

7.5.2.1 Dummy and Cleaning Blocks for Direct Extrusion

Loose dummy blocks are always used with a shell for extrusion. The dummy block thickness is based on a value of 0.5 to 0.7 times the container bore. Both the extrusion temperature and the extrusion load transfer to the stem influence the thickness of the dummy block, and this must be taken into account. The diameter of the front land determines the shell thickness during extrusion. The thickness of the shell itself depends on the billet quality. The length of the front land is between 0.25 and 0.4 times the dummy block thickness and depends on the material being extruded. After each extrusion, the loose dummy block must be separated from the discard and the shell, and consequently, four to six dummy blocks must be in circulation, as described in section 6.1.1.3 "Auxiliary Equipment for Direct Extrusion."

Fixed dummy blocks, whether for round billets or billets with an oval cross section, be divided into two functional types: expanding or solid. They vary considerably in design. The expanding fixed dummy block is used exclusively for the extrusion of easy and moderately difficult-to-extrude aluminum alloys. In the extrusion of aluminum alloys, the residual material layer in the container bore is shaved off during the return of the previously used solid fixed dummy block. A ring of the shell then forms behind the land. As extrusion continues, a correspondingly large number of shell rings form that result in problems if they are not removed. This resulted in the development of different expanding fixed dummy blocks in one-piece and multipiece designs. In order to avoid the undesirable shell ring, the front external diameter of the fixed dummy block must be larger during extrusion than on the return. In the single-piece design, the front surface of the block is designed so that the outer diameter expands under the extrusion load. This increase in the external diameter must take place in the elastic range of the dummy block material. Sufficient external diameter expansion can be achieved with a suitable shape and no critical notch effects, for example, from the machining. This solution is associated with a larger discard because of the machined profile of the front face. The multipart design in Fig. 7.85 enables a flat face with no machined profile to be used. The desired fixed dummy block effect of the external diameter being smaller during the return is achieved relatively successfully by a conical insert and a matched external ring. However, the individual components must be matched to give an acceptable service life in production. Incorrect mechanical properties in the conical components can reduce the life of the dummy block considerably. The fixed dummy block in the multipart design is used almost exclusively in the extrusion of aluminum alloys. The solid fixed dummy block is always one piece. It is used for the extrusion of copper alloys with a low extrudability without a shell, particularly tube extrusion and for steel extrusion. While the front surface is conical for copper alloys, flat front surfaces with large radii to the external diameter are used for steel.

Expanding and solidified dummy blocks

Expanding fixed dummy block

epi epa sp   e   ha

Solid fixed dummy block

es   e   ha   ld   es   e   ha

epi = internal piece; epa = external piece; sp = clearance;
e = extrusion stem; ha = retaining bar; es = fixed dummy block;
ld = mandrel

(a)

(b)

Fig. 7.85 (a) Schematic design of a fixed dummy block. Source: Groos. (b) Photograph of a multipart fixed dummy block. Source: CLECIM

The cleaning blocks are ring shaped and have the same main external dimensions as the loose dummy blocks. This is necessary because of the common recycling in the auxiliary system. The external diameter is dimensioned so that the shell can be removed completely and reliably from the container liner. Often, it is slightly oversized. In this case, it must have a diagonal slit in order to elastically conform to the liner wall that must be cleaned like a spring (Fig. 7.86).

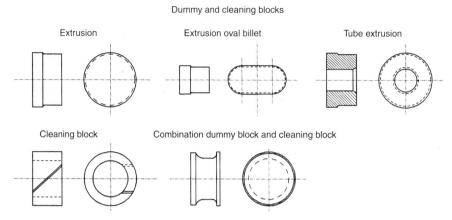

Fig. 7.86 Schematic drawings of typical loose dummy blocks and cleaning blocks. Source: Groos

The combined dummy block and cleaning block is preferentially used when the shell volume is small and can be removed from the shell chamber without difficulty (Fig. 7.87). This is the case with short billets for the extrusion of tubes. Guiding the mandrel through the block and locating it in the center of the container bore gives the optimal requirements for central piercing of the billet. The container bore and the combination dummy and cleaning block must be in good condition. Wear that impairs the bore geometry is unacceptable. In particular, the combination dummy block and cleaning block can be successfully used with thin shells. Problems occur when the shell volume in the shell chamber is too severely compacted, and removal of the shell from the block becomes difficult. The time needed to clean the shell chamber is then too long.

A big advantage of the combination dummy and cleaning block is the simplified operation of the press. The time and manipulation requirement as well as the cleaning time needed to use a separate cleaning block are eliminated, as seen in the operating sequence in Chapter 6.

7.5.2.2 Dummy Blocks and Cleaning Blocks for Indirect Extrusion

The loose dummy block acts as the die block or the sealing block for the sealing stem, as seen in Fig. 7.83. The loose die block is preferred for the indirect extrusion of copper alloys and aluminum alloys (Fig. 7.88). The die block thickness depends on the size of the die, the die support needed, and the size of the bore in the die-carrying stem, which determines the space available for the emerging extruded product.

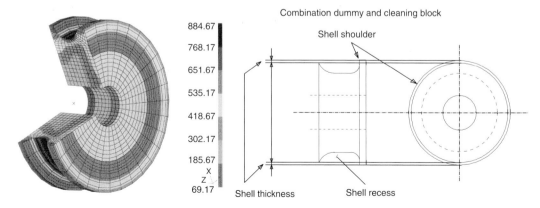

Fig. 7.87 Finite element study (Left); (Source: Schloemanna) and sketch (right) of a combination dummy and cleaning block for tube extrusion. The size and shape of the shell chamber produce stress concentrations that must be limited. In this example, the maximum equivalent stress at the root of the shell chamber is approximately 850 N/mm².

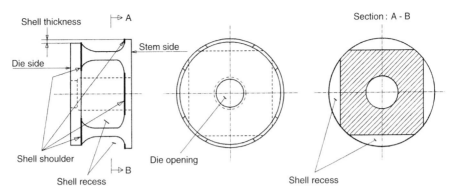

Fig. 7.88 Sketch of a combination die and cleaning block for extrusion of aluminum alloys. Source: Groos

Figures 7.2 and 7.9 show this clearly. Both the deformation temperature and the extrusion load transfer onto the hollow tool carrier stem (extrusion stem) influence the thickness of the die block, which is important for the quality of the extruded product and for the service life of the tooling, and therefore must be taken into consideration. The diameter of the front land determines the thickness of the shell in indirect extrusion. The thickness of the shell itself depends on the quality of the billet surface, which must be good in indirect extrusion for process technological reasons. The length of the front land depends on the material being extruded. The thickness of the sealing block corresponds to the thickness of a loose dummy block used in direct extrusion. The number (one or two) of the die blocks (die holder) in use depends on the order size. Thus, two die blocks can be used. The productivity with two die blocks is increased because of the reduced dead cycle time during a production cycle. A single loose die block in indirect extrusion is practical only for small orders.

The fixed dummy block as a die block (die holder) is not used in the indirect extrusion of copper alloys. In the indirect extrusion of aluminum alloys, the use of fixed die blocks is, in contrast, widespread. The attachment to the hollow tool carrier stem (hollow stem) represents a weak point and results in additional stress concentrations in the highly stressed tooling. Also, the resultant shell ring in the die block area must be removed within the press. However, the auxiliary systems are less expensive because the circulation system for the die block is not required.

The combined die and cleaning block is used in the indirect extrusion of aluminum alloys.

The resultant small shell volume of the premachined billets can be collected in the shell chamber of the die block. In the indirect extrusion of copper alloys, the combination die and cleaning block is preferred when small shell volumes occur. The separate cleaning block is required in copper alloy extrusion when long billets are extruded and a thick shell is produced. The shell volume is relatively large because of the long billets. The shell then must be removed in an additional operation. The combination die and cleaning block do not differ from the cleaning discs used in direct extrusion.

7.5.3 Extrusion Stems for Round and Oval Billet Containers

For direct extrusion, the following are used:

- Extrusion stem as a solid stem for the extrusion of round billets
- Extrusion stem as a solid stem for the extrusion of rectangular billets (billets with an oval cross section)
- Extrusion stem as a hollow stem for tube extrusion

For indirect extrusion, the following are used:

- Die carrier stem (hollow stem) for extrusion and tube extrusion
- Sealing stem to seal the container bore
- Cleaning stem to remove the shell from the container bore

Because the method of locating the stem depends on the press manufacturer, different systems are met in practice. The stem location is designed as a quick-fit connection for rapid

Fig. 7.89 Extrusion stem with an oval cross section (rectangular billet stem) and a fixed pad in production. Source: SMS Schloemann

tooling changes. In addition, the foot of the stem must be self-centering to ensure a reproducible central location of the tooling with each other on stem changing. All fatigue-affecting factors, including stress concentrations from notches and damage on the stem surface, must be avoided to achieve an acceptable service life. The shape and length tolerances for the tooling according to DIN 7184 for the straightness, squareness, concentricity/coaxiality, and runout must be held to tight tolerances. The tolerances for extrusion with a loose dummy block are not as tight as for extrusion with a fixed dummy

block. The highest demands on accuracy are for tube extrusion.

7.5.3.1 Extrusion Stems for Direct Extrusion

In direct extrusion, stems are used that must be suitable for a specific press load to a maximum of 1000 N/mm². They do not take any direct role in the hot working process.

If a compressive stress as high as 1200 N/mm² occurs in the extrusion stem in plants extruding high-strength materials, then specific demands must be placed on the material, design, and manufacture. For safety reasons, a compressive stress of 1200 N/mm² should not be exceeded. The solid stem for the extrusion of billets with oval cross sections (rectangular billets) can be loaded in the shaft area up to a maximum of 710 N/mm² (Fig. 7.89).

The design of the transition from the shank of the extrusion stem to the foot influences the mechanical properties of the extrusion stem. The maximum equivalent stress, $\sigma_v = 1200$ N/mm² according to the von Mises theory, that occurs at the stem foot (Fig. 7.90) illustrates the highly stressed critical region of the foot of this stem (from a finite element modeling, or FEM study). Because extrusion stems can have rather severe transitions from the shank to the foot, as seen in Fig. 7.91, dangerous stress concentrations can result.

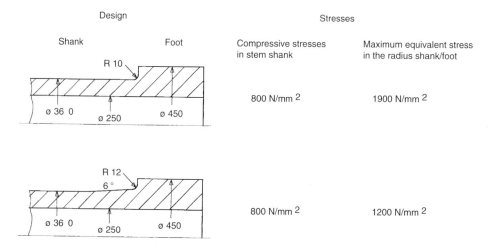

Fig. 7.90 Equivalent stresses at the transition to the stem foot of an extrusion stem for indirect extrusion. Source: SMS Schlomann

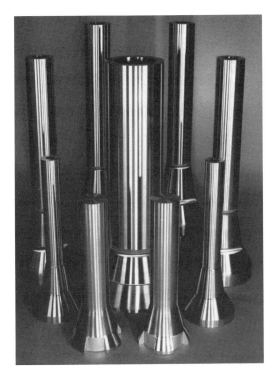

Fig. 7.91 Solid and hollow stems for direct extrusion. Source: Schmidt + Clemens

7.5.3.2 Extrusion Stems for Indirect Extrusion

In indirect extrusion, the advantage of using larger and longer billets for the same press power is limited by the hollow stem that must withstand the extrusion load.

The extrusion stem, also referred to as the die carrier stem, must have an internal bore for the passage of the extruded material in indirect extrusion. The cross-sectional area of the hollow stem should not be stressed higher than 900 N/mm^2 with the usual hot working tool steels. Stresses up to 1100 N/mm^2 are possible with austenitic hot working steels.

7.5.3.3 Calculations and Dimensions for Extrusion Stems

The dimensioning of the shank of the extrusion stem is determined by:

- Billet dimensions in extrusion (solid stem)
- Required bore of the hollow stem for the extruded product in indirect extrusion
- Maximum mandrel dimension for tube extrusion (hollow stem)

The billet size and the method of stem location are the controlling factors for the dimensions of the stem foot. Strength and stability calculations must be carried out for deviations from the normal cases. The extrusion stem is a tool that is loaded uniaxially in compression. Compared to the free end, the stem shank is securely clamped and has a significantly larger diameter. The extrusion load is applied through the dummy block or the die block by the front face of the stem shank onto the billet. It is assumed for the stability calculation that the front face of the stem is pinned and acts as a slip face. The stem foot is clamped.

The stem shank measurements for direct extrusion are standardized for normal applications (DIN 24540 part 2). The stem shank dimensions for indirect extrusion are derived from the standard DIN 24540 part 2. Table 7.6 shows the stem dimensions for indirect extrusion as a function of the specific stress.

The stem loaded in compression by the extrusion load is relatively long compared to the cross section. Therefore, it may be in an unstable equilibrium position, with the risk of bending or buckling, as shown in Fig. 7.92. Off-center extrusion loads with nonaligned extrusion tooling develop transverse forces that load the extrusion stem in bending. The foot of the extrusion stem is particularly at risk with highly stressed extrusion stems. An FEM stress analysis is advisable for safe dimensioning.

The stem loading in extrusion shown schematically in Fig. 7.92 results in Euler's buckling type 3 (effective length $L_k = 0.7L$). The maximum stresses occur at the start of extrusion when the maximum press power can be reached. Usually, the billets have an external diameter that is $x\%$ smaller than the container diameter (DIN 24540). Consequently, the center of the billet in the container bore is approximately $x/2\%$ below the press center, which should coincide with the axis of the container. This eccentricity of the billet reduces as the extrusion load increases during upsetting. The extrusion load acts with an eccentricity, e, on the extrusion stem, which, for safety reasons, should be assumed to be 25% of the billet clearance. With this assumption, values of 3 to 4 mm are achieved with current billet dimensions. The following factors must be held to tight limits:

- Alignment errors between the container and the stem

Table 7.6 Dimensions of extrusion stems for indirect extrusion for specific press pressures

		Stem dimensions and stem loads						
		Press capacity, MN						
		12.5–14	16–18	20–22.5	25–28	31.5–36	40–45	50–56
					Shank length, mm			
Specific extrusion pressure, N/mm²		1000	1120	1250	1400	1600	1800	2000
315	Outside diameter, mm	230	259	293	328	373	417	467
	Inside diameter, mm	175	195	220	245	280	310	350
	Compressive stress, N/mm²	800	789	765	750	744	737	746
400	Outside diameter, mm	206	230	259	293	328	373	415
	Inside diameter, mm	145	160	180	205	230	265	290
	Compressive stress, N/mm²	836	840	826	814	827	801	809
500	Outside diameter, mm	185	206	230	259	293	328	373
	Inside diameter, mm	115	125	140	160	180	200	225
	Compressive stress, N/mm²	849	855	860	859	846	848	806
630	Outside diameter, mm	165	185	206	230	259	293	328
	Inside diameter, mm	85	95	105	115	130	150	165
	Compressive stress, N/mm²	891	901	912	899	901	904	887
710	Outside diameter, mm	155	175	195	219	244	274	308
	Inside diameter, mm	65	70	80	90	100	110	125
	Compressive stress, N/mm²	900	890	906	895	913	910	900

Source: Groos

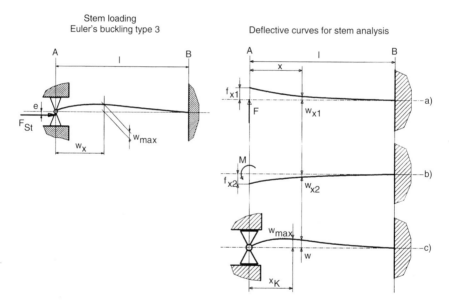

Stem loading
Euler's buckling type 3

Deflective curves for stem analysis

Fig. 7.92 Deflection curves for buckling. Source: Groos

- Squareness of the billet end faces
- Structural homogeneity of the billet
- Uniformity of the temperature over the billet cross section
- Billet clearance in the container

The eccentric forces, which depend on the operational conditions, are used to calculate the buckling of the extrusion stem. The geometrically possible eccentricity at full extrusion load is always less than 25% of the billet clearance. Thus, the recommended values for the calcu-

lation give an additional degree of safety for the stem.

The stability calculation is derived as follows.

For given dimensions and loadings, the transverse force, F, in the most unfavorable case with an eccentricity, e, is calculated. Starting from a cantilever clamped at one end, the calculation of statistically indeterminate systems with the solution for simple statistically indeterminate systems [Gie 95] as well as the formula for the corresponding deflection line [Dub

86] gives useable results for the extrusion stem, corresponding to the deflection lines a, b, and c in Fig. 7.92:

$$w_{x1} = -\frac{F \times l^3}{6 \times E \times I_y} \times \left[2 - 3\frac{x}{l} + \left(\frac{x}{l}\right)^3\right]$$

$$w_{x2} = \frac{M \times l^2}{2 \times E \times I_y} \times \left[1 - 2\frac{x}{l} + \left(\frac{x}{l}\right)^2\right]$$

The deflection line w for buckling loading F with the eccentricity e, that is, $M = F \times e$, is the addition of $w_{x1} + w_{x2}$:

$$w = w_{x1} + w_{x2} = -\frac{F \times l^3}{6 \times E \times I_y}$$

$$\times \left[2 - 3\frac{x}{l} + \left(\frac{x}{l}\right)^3\right] + \frac{M \times l^2}{2 \times E \times I_y}$$

$$\times \left[1 - 2\frac{x}{l} + \left(\frac{x}{l}\right)^2\right]$$

For a centrally guided buckling beam, $wA = 0$ and $x = 0$. The resultant transverse force $Q = F$ is:

$$F = \frac{3 \times F_{St} \times e}{2 \times l}$$

The resultant maximum deflection, w_{max}, is given by:

$$w_{max} = \frac{F_{St} \times e \times l^2}{27 \times E \times I_y}$$

Provided the stem dimensions for direct extrusion match the requirements of DIN 24540, and those for indirect extrusion follow Table 7.6, then a stability analysis is not required. The temperature influence on the stem from the billet is reduced by the dummy block in direct extrusion or by the die block (die holder) in indirect extrusion. The temperature influence from the container is not very high. Temperature measurements on the stem of an indirect extrusion press in the indirect extrusion of aluminum alloys gave approximately 300 °C on the end face. The temperature of the stem shank at a distance of one-third of the stem length from the front face was approximately 200 °C and approximately 100 °C at the stem foot. In the indirect extrusion of copper alloys, stem shank shaft temperatures were measured at 360 °C at the front face, 320 °C at one-third of the stem length, and approximately 290 °C at the stem foot. No higher temperature was detected in the stem bore as a result of the passage of the extruded material. A definite temperature decrease develops from the front face toward the stem foot, depending on the operating conditions. In any case, the temperature of the stem in indirect extrusion should be taken into account. Basically, the stem and, in particular, the die carrier stem should be preheated to avoid damage to the stem.

The maximum buckling load occurs at one-third of the buckling length from the front face. This region is unlikely to be overheated by the working temperature. Thus, there is no significant decrease in strength. Failures from acceptable buckling loading are not known. Failures that have occurred are almost always attributable to unacceptable stress concentrations, thermal shocks from the use of cold stems in the press at working temperature, unacceptable transverse loads from operational defects, and production errors. In addition, high thermal stress fluctuations result in surface cracking.

7.5.3.4 Examples of Stem Calculations for Direct and Indirect Extrusion

Figure 7.93 shows typical extrusion stems.
Example 1: Solid Stem for a 1000 N/mm² Container for a 31.5 MN Direct-Extrusion Press.

Material parameters

Material	1.2344 (X40CrMoV5.1)
Strength	1700 N/mm²
E modulus	210,000 N/mm² (room temperature)
	195,000 N/mm² (350 °C)

Dimensions

Stem length	1300 mm
Shank diameter	195 mm

Strength Analysis. The actual extrusion load differs in practice from the nominal press load. It is usually higher. Compared to the nominal press load of 31.5 MN, the actual load can be 32.29 MN, which is an increase of 2.5% in the press load. Consequently, the compressive stress on a solid stem with a diameter of 195 mm is not equal to 1055 N/mm², as given in DIN 24540, but:

$$\sigma_D = \frac{3.229 \text{ N} \times 10^7 \times 4}{195^2 \text{ mm}^2 \times \pi} \approx 1081 \text{ N/mm}^2$$

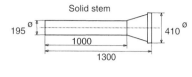

1) Extrusion stem for the extrusion of wire, bar, and sections

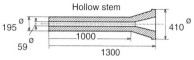

2) Extrusion stem for rod and tube extrusion for the extrusion of tubes using mandrels. The stem bore determines the largest mandrel.

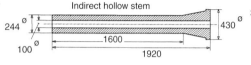

3) Extrusion stem (die carrier stem) for indirect extrusion. The stem bore determines the largest extruded product cross section.

Fig. 7.93 Typical extrusion stems

With a minimum yield strength of 1700 N/mm^2 for the stem material 1.2344, the maximum permitted loading is:

$$\sigma_{0.8} = 1700 \text{ N/mm}^2 \times 0.8 = 1360 \text{ N/mm}^2$$

The safety factor is then:

$$S_D = \frac{1360 \text{ N/mm}^2}{1081 \text{ N/mm}^2} = 1.26$$

Stability analysis is not necessary in this case but is given as an example for stem analysis. Under the assumptions and dimensions given earlier, for the worst case, the transverse force F with an eccentricity of 3 mm is given by:

$$F = \frac{3 \times 3.229 \text{ N} \times 10^7 \times 3 \text{ mm}}{2 \times 1300 \text{ mm}} = 111.8 \text{ kN}$$

The resultant maximum deflection, w_{max} is:

$$w_{max} = \frac{3.229 \text{ N} \times 10^7 \times 3 \text{ mm} \times 1300^2 \text{ mm}^2}{27 \times 1.95 \text{ N/mm}^2 \times 10^5 \times 7.098 \text{ mm}^4 \times 10^7}$$
$$= 0.438 \text{ mm}$$

Stresses can be calculated as:

$$\sigma_D = \frac{3.229 \text{ N} \times 10^7}{2.986 \text{ mm}^2 \times 10^4} = 1081 \text{ N/mm}^2$$

$$\sigma_B = \frac{3.229 \text{ N} \times 10^7 \times (3 \text{ mm} + 0.438 \text{ mm})}{7.28 \text{ mm}^3 \times 10^5}$$
$$= 152.49 \text{ N/mm}^2$$

$$\sigma_{max} = 1081 \text{ N/mm}^2 + 152.49 \text{ N/mm}^2$$
$$= 1233 \text{ N/mm}^2$$

The safety factor [Dub 86] can be calculated as:

$$S_\sigma = \frac{1360 \text{ N/mm}^2}{1233 \text{ N/mm}^2} = 1.103$$

$$S_K =$$
$$\frac{\pi^2 \times 2 \times 1.95 \text{ N/mm}^2 \times 10^5 \times 7.098 \text{ mm}^4 \times 10^7}{3.229 \text{ N} \times 10^7 \times 1300^2 \text{ mm}^2}$$
$$= 5007$$

Buckling length can be calculated as:

$$l_K =$$
$$\sqrt{\pi^2 \times 2 \times \frac{1.95 \text{ N/mm}^2 \times 10^5 \times 7.098 \text{ mm}^4 \times 10^7}{3.229 \text{ N} \times 10^7}}$$
$$= 2909 \text{ mm}$$

$$l_{perm} = \sqrt{\frac{2909^2 \text{ mm}^2}{5007}} = 1300 \text{ mm}$$

Example 2: Hollow Stem for a 1000 N/mm^2 Container for a 31.5 MN Direct Tube Press.

Material parameters

Material	1.2344 (X40CrMoV5.1)
Strength	1700 N/mm^2
E modulus	210,000 N.mm^2 (room temperature)
	195,000 N/mm^2 (350 °C)

Dimensions

Stem length	1300 mm
Stem shank diameter	195 mm
Stem bore diameter	59 mm

Strength Analysis. The actual extrusion load differs in practice from the nominal press load. It is usually higher. Compared to the nominal press load of 31.5 MN, the actual load can be 32.29 MN, which is an increase of 2.5% in the press load. Consequently, the compressive stress on a hollow stem with a diameter of 195 mm and a bore of 59 mm is not equal to 1161 N/mm^2, as given in DIN 24540, but:

$$\sigma = \frac{3.229 \text{ N} \times 10^7 \times 4}{(195^2 - 59^2)mm^2 \times \pi} = 1190 \text{ N/mm}^2$$

With a minimum yield strength of 1700 N/mm^2 for the stem material 1.2344, the maximum permitted loading is:

$$\sigma_{0.8} = 1700 \text{ N/mm}^2 \times 0.8 = 1360 \text{ N/mm}^2$$

The safety factor is then:

$$S = \frac{1360 \text{ N/mm}^2}{1190 \text{ N/mm}^2} = 1.14$$

Stability analysis is not necessary in this case but is given as an example for stem analysis. Under the assumptions and dimensions given earlier, for the worst case, the transverse force F with an eccentricity of 3 mm is given by:

$$F = \frac{3 \times 3.229 \text{ N} \times 10^7 \times 3 \text{ mm}}{2 \times 1300 \text{ mm}} = 111.8 \text{ kN}$$

The resultant maximum deflection, w_{max}, is:

$$w_{max} =$$
$$\frac{3.229 \text{ N} \times 10^7 \times 3 \text{ mm} \times 1300^2 \text{ mm}^2}{27 \times 1.95 \text{ N/mm}^2 \times 10^5 \times 7.038 \text{ mm}^4 \times 10^7}$$
$$= 0.442 \text{ mm}$$

Stresses can be calculated as:

$$\sigma_D = \frac{3.229 \text{ N} \times 10^7}{2.7310 \text{ mm}^2 \times 10^4} = 1190 \text{ N/mm}^2$$

$$\sigma_B = \frac{3.229 \text{ N} \times 10^7 \times (3 \text{ mm} + 0.442 \text{ mm})}{7.219 \text{ mm}^3 \times 10^5}$$
$$= 153.958 \text{ N/mm}^2$$

$$\sigma_{max} = 1190 \text{ N/mm}^2 + 153.985 \text{ N/mm}^2$$
$$= 1344 \text{ N/mm}^2$$

The safety factor can be calculated as:

$$S_\sigma = \frac{1360 \text{ N/mm}^2}{1344 \text{ N/mm}^2} = 1.012 \text{ N/mm}^2$$

$$S_K =$$
$$\frac{\pi^2 \times 2 \times 1.95 \text{ N/mm}^2 \times 10^5 \times 7.038 \text{ mm}^4 \times 10^7}{3.229 \text{ N} \times 10^7 \times 1300^2 \text{ mm}^2}$$
$$= 4.964$$

Buckling length can be calculated as:

$$l_K =$$
$$\sqrt{\pi^2 \times 2 \times \frac{1.95 \text{ N/mm}^2 \times 10^5 \times 7.038 \text{ mm}^4 \times 10^7}{3.229 \text{ N} \times 10^7}}$$
$$= 2896 \text{ mm}$$

$$l_{perm} = \frac{2896^2 \text{ mm}^2}{4.964} = 1300 \text{ mm}$$

Example 3: Hollow Stem for a 710 N/mm² Container for a 35.5 MN Indirect Extrusion Press.

Material parameters	
Material	1.2343 (X38CrMoV5.1)
Strength	1600 N/mm^2
E modulus	210,000 N/mm^2 (room temperature)
	195,000 N/mm^2 (350 °C)

Dimensions	
Stem length	1920 mm
Shank diameter	244 mm
Stem bore diameter	100 mm

Strength Analysis. The actual extrusion load differs in practice from the nominal press load. It is usually higher. Compared to the nominal press load of 35.5 MN, the actual load can be 35.69 MN, which is an increase of approximately 0.5% in the press load. Consequently, the compressive stress on a solid stem with a diameter of 244 mm and a bore of 10 mm is not equal to 913 N/mm^2, as given in DIN 24540, but:

$$\sigma_D = \frac{3.569 \text{ N} \times 10^7 \times 4}{(244^2 - 100^2)mm^2 \times \pi} = 917 \text{ N/mm}^2$$

With a minimum yield strength of 1600 N/mm^2 for the stem material 2343, the maximum permitted loading is:

$$\sigma_{0.8} = 1600 \text{ N/mm}^2 \times 0.8 = 1280 \text{ N/mm}^2$$

The safety factor is then:

$$S = \frac{1280 \text{ N/mm}^2}{917 \text{ N/mm}^2} = 1.4$$

Stability analysis is not necessary in this case but is given as an example for stem analysis. Under the assumptions and dimensions given earlier, for the worst case, the transverse force F with an eccentricity of 3 mm is given by:

$$F = \frac{3 \times 3.569 \text{ N} \times 10^7 \times 3 \text{ mm}}{2 \times 1920 \text{ mm}} = 83.65 \text{ kN}$$

The resultant maximum deflection, w_{max}, is:

$$w_{max} = \frac{3.569 \text{ N} \times 10^7 \times 3 \text{ mm} \times 1920^2 \text{ mm}^2}{27 \times 1.95 \text{ N/mm}^2 \times 10^5 \times 1.691 \text{ mm}^4 \times 10^8} = 0.443 \text{ mm}$$

Stresses can be calculated as:

$$\sigma_D = \frac{3.569 \text{ N} \times 10^7}{3.891 \text{ mm}^2 \times 10^4} = 917 \text{ N/mm}^2$$

$$\sigma_B = \frac{3.569 \text{ N} \times 10^7 \times (3 \text{ mm} + 0.443 \text{ mm})}{1.386 \text{ mm}^3 \times 10^6}$$
$$= 88.658 \text{ N/mm}^2$$

$$\sigma_{max} = 917 \text{ N/mm}^2 + 88.658 \text{ N/mm}^2$$
$$= 1006 \text{ N/mm}^2$$

The safety factor can be calculated as:

$$S_\sigma = \frac{1280 \text{ N/mm}^2}{1006 \text{ N/mm}^2} = 1.272$$

$$S_K = \frac{\pi^2 \times 2 \times 1.95 \text{ N/mm}^2 \times 10^5 \times 1.691 \text{ mm}^4 \times 10^8}{3.569 \text{ N} \times 10^7 \times 1920^2 \text{ mm}^2}$$
$$= 4.947$$

Buckling length can be calculated as:

$$l_K = \sqrt{\pi^2 \times 2 \times \frac{1.95 \text{ N/mm}^2 \times 10^5 \times 1.691 \text{ mm}^4 \times 10^7}{3.569 \text{ N} \times 10^7}}$$
$$= 4271 \text{ mm}$$

$$l_{perm} = \sqrt{\frac{4271^2 \text{ mm}^2}{4.947}} = 1920 \text{ mm}$$

7.5.3.5 Thermomechanical Stressing of Stems during Extrusion

The invention of the dummy block by Alexander Dick at the end of the 19th century provided the breakthrough for extrusion for industrial applications. A high deformation temperature of the extruded material is always a problem for the extrusion tooling if the extrusion cycle is long. This can occur with copper alloys and low-extrudability aluminum alloys in both direct and indirect extrusion. The relationship of extrusion time to the dead cycle time gives an indication of the risk of the stem front face losing strength by tempering. Under extreme conditions (extrusion pressure and temperature), the stem shank can directly upset at the front face. It is then standard practice to correct the stem by reworking. Until now, this has not resulted in any serious failures. However, because the economics of the production in the extrusion plant are impaired, the design and the selection of the extrusion stem material must take this situation into account.

The heat treated hot working steel must have a tempering resistance suitable for the operational conditions. The maximum possible stem cross section should always be used to reduce the stem loading.

7.5.4 Temperature-Related Maintenance and Handling of Extrusion Tooling

An important requirement for a normal service life of the extrusion tooling is slow heating. Tooling that has not been preheated is subjected to a thermal shock that will ultimately lead to failure. Cracks and failure of tooling can often be related back to inadequate heating. Preheating the tooling increases the thermal conductivity and the material toughness. The risk of cracking from excessive temperature gradients is then removed. The stem should be pushed into the container during downtime. It will then retain its temperature.

Extrusion dies, dummy blocks, extrusion stems, and mandrels in conventional hot working steels must be through-heated. This is essential for tooling with large volumes or cross sections. The preheat temperature in the tool oven should be in the range of 350 to 400 °C. Dies in nickel- and cobalt-base alloys must be preheated to 450 to 500 °C. If the stem is changed, then a preheated stem should be available.

The cooling of the removed tooling should be carried out slowly in a suitable environment. Stresses develop with incorrect heating and cooling. From experience, there is the risk that in an environment that is too cold, thermal stresses can develop in the tool that will result in fracture several days or weeks later. Thermal stresses in removed tooling are increased still further if the hot tool is subjected to the factory air. Areas with air currents should definitely be avoided, because this prevents uniform cooling, and cracks can easily develop.

At the end of a program or when a tool is changed, it must be placed in a heated holding station. Here, it is held at a temperature of 350 to 400 °C for 2 to 6 h, depending on the cross section. A slow temperature decrease of approximately 30 °C (50 °F) per hour is beneficial to the tool and is an important requirement for a long life. Stems and mandrels should not be placed flat but heated or cooled in a standing or hanging position. To avoid thermal shock, cooling by air or a mixture of air and water can only be carried out during production. Heated water should be used for the mandrel internal cooling. Overcooling should be avoided at all costs. The temperature drop from intensive cooling should not exceed 100 °C. These considerations also apply to the temperature-related operational maintenance and handling of containers. The fracture surface of an extrusion stem (Fig. 7.94) with an external diameter of 254 mm and a bore of 59 mm was located approximately 150 mm from the front face. The failure occurred after approximately 3800 extrusions, because the stem had been loaded cold and was not preheated. The deformation temperatures for the indirect extrusion were in the range of 750 to 900 °C for different extruded materials with different extrusion programs. The temperature of the container liner was between 500 and 600 °C.

7.5.5 Containers

The requirements for containers are a long life, operational reliability, low maintenance, and rapid container changing, as well as low investment costs and high productivity.

The size of the container can be immense (Fig. 7.95). For a 125 MN extrusion press, an external diameter of 2100 mm is necessary, and the length is 2000 mm, given a weight of 50 tonnes for the container. The production is relatively difficult, because of the size of the individual container components.

Additional technological functions of the extrusion tool container are becoming increasingly important to improve the extrusion process. The temperature-controlled container, with a combination of heating and cooling, is suited for the extrusion of aluminum alloys with a constant exit temperature.

7.5.5.1 Container Construction

There are different container constructions, depending on the application of the container

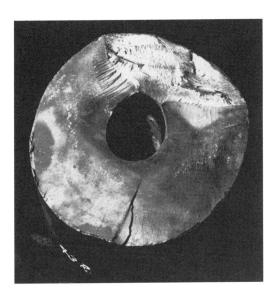

Fig. 7.94 Failed extrusion stem for indirect extrusion. Source: SMS Schloemann

Fig. 7.95 Container with oval bore for direct extrusion of aluminum alloys for a 75 MN extrusion press. Source: Alusuisse

(Fig. 7.96). The round billet is standard and, to a certain extent, the prerequisite for extrusion. Solid or hollow billets can be used. The billet with an oval cross section (rectangular billet) is the exception. It is used for aluminum alloys with a high and moderate extrudability. The necessary extrusion pressure in the container requires a two-part or three-part design to withstand the large stresses. The four-part design is required for extrusion pressures above 1250 N/mm^2 in the container. The stress-related dimensioning, including the shrink-fit, design, and materials selection, is determined from stress analysis. In special cases and in the case of rectangular billet containers, the stresses must be analyzed by FEM stress studies. The extruded material-dependent deformation temperature influences the method of heating. Cooling is necessary in high temperature regions. The internal components of the container in the center, in particular, are subjected to a buildup of heat. If temperature control of the container is necessary for technological reasons, a controlled combination heating and cooling system that is effective in different locations is necessary. The wear on the free surface of the liner at high billet temperatures, combined with high extrusion pressures, must be taken into account in materials selection. The spatial location of the container must be stable in the press, independent of the working temperature. In other words, a central operation of the mandrel, stem, dummy block, container, and die must be guaranteed for every operational state. A risk of axial movement of the liner can be prevented by machining shoulders into the liner.

The following suggestions and technical data should be considered as guidelines for the design and construction of containers for extrusion.

Standardization of extrusion tooling is based on many years' practical experience with design and manufacture in extrusion plants. The most important technical data can be taken from DIN 24540. This gives the main dimensions of the tooling for direct-extrusion presses from 5 to 125 MN. The container bores mentioned for rectangular billets require a specific design for the container as a whole.

Container internal pressure depends on the extruded material. The values vary from a specific extrusion pressure, F_{St}/A_0, of 315 to 1000 N/mm^2. Higher values require special designs.

Container internal bore is derived from the relative specific pressure needed to extrude the different materials and the size of the press. The range covers values of 80 to 710 mm diameter for round container bores for extrusion presses from 5 to 125 MN.

Container length is not of fundamental importance for the design and construction of the container. The container length must be restricted because of the operational safety of the extrusion stem (risk of buckling). The relevant data in DIN 24540 are values based on experience. The container length is an important economic factor and is optimized for special cases, for example, the standard extrusion of aluminum alloys and indirect extrusion.

The two-part round billet container is used for internal pressures up to 630 N/mm^2. Container heating in the housing is sufficient for

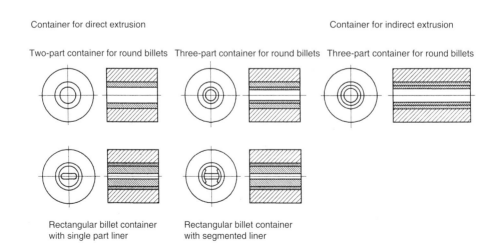

Container for direct extrusion   Container for indirect extrusion

Two-part container for round billets   Three-part container for round billets   Three-part container for round billets

Rectangular billet container with single part liner

Rectangular billet container with segmented liner

Fig. 7.96 Schematic design of different containers. Source: Groos

materials that are extruded at temperatures below 500 °C. This does not apply to products that require temperature control within the container. In the extrusion of seamless tubes, the cross section of the mandrel must be taken into account in the calculation of the internal pressure.

Three-part round billet container designs are required for internal pressures above 630 N/mm^2. As a rule, internal pressures over 630 N/mm^2 occur in tube extrusion. Internally cooled containers must be used for materials with extrusion temperatures over 600 °C. They should be three-part even with internal pressures below 630 N/mm^2 because of the higher stresses in the area of the cooling grooves.

The three-part rectangular billet container design should be preferred to the two-part design, that is still found, to achieve a higher life. A segmented internal liner is rarely used because of the high production costs.

Hot working requires a process-related tool temperature in the container. A specific temperature is required, depending on the material being extruded. Additional deformation and friction heat is produced during the extrusion process. Heating and cooling systems, which can also be combined, are therefore necessary.

Containers for indirect extrusion differ from those for direct extrusion only in the longer container length. In addition, only three-part round billet containers are used for indirect extrusion. The two-part design is rarely used because of the cooling needed for temperature control, even for the extrusion of aluminum.

The design of the container is determined by the production program in the extrusion plant. This results in different constructions that only permit a limited number of individual dimensions and features. The most important design considerations include the following.

The hot-working material depends on the extruded material and the extrusion temperature.

The heating system is usually installed in the container mantle. Induction heating is used less frequently than resistance heating. The resistance heating can be divided into several heating zones. With rectangular billet containers, heating elements are installed in the wide side, the thick-wall part. Resistance heating is also installed outside the container in the container holder.

The cooling system is fitted on the external diameter of the liner holder within a three-part container.

In a combined heating and cooling system with temperature control, a localized temperature buildup can be prevented by cooling.

The location and method of holding in the tool holder (container holder) requires that there are no critical notches in the components. The central location of the container should be maintained independent of the actual working temperature during the production period. Fast container changing times must be provided by a quick connection. The heating and cooling system also must be capable of being changed quickly.

Maintaining the interference fit is essential. If axial movement of the liner and sometimes the liner holder occur, then these must be fitted with a shoulder at the end against the direction of slip. The shape of the shoulder must be designed so that stress concentrations from the notch effect are minimal.

The liner with oval bore is usually one piece and only rarely designed as segments.

Containers for the Extrusion of Materials in the Range of 0 to 300 °C. Containers that operate in this temperature range are only subjected to low thermal stresses. They are used for cold extrusion, the extrusion of lead and tin alloys, and the extrusion of zinc alloys. In most cases, the normal tools do not correspond to DIN 24540 because of their special designs, which meet the individual operational requirements.

In cold extrusion, specific extrusion pressures of approximately 1400 N/mm^2 and higher are common. These pressures can only be withstood by four-part containers. They are used without heating, and the design length of the container is relatively short because of the extreme stem loading.

Extrusion presses for the deformation of lead alloys operate with specific stem pressures above 160 N/mm^2. Presses with 5 to 16 MN stem load are used for the production of lead tubes with a charge of 250 to 1800 kg. The containers are heated or cooled, depending on the operational phase. The two-piece containers have a long length and are special designs that are sometimes fitted with steam heating and hot water cooling (80 °C). Cable sheathing presses for lead alloys operate with specific pressures between 325 and 550 N/mm^2. The charge weights fall between 135 and 1000 kg. Cable sheathing presses have press loads of 6 to 30 MN. The vertical operating presses are very tall. The horizontal presses operate with two containers and two extrusion stems. Profiles, rod, and tubes in tin and lead alloys are produced for the chemical industry on presses with powers in the range of 5 MN. The containers for solder wire extrusion have specific pressures up to 630 N/mm^2. They are small presses with a maximum press power of approximately 2.5 MN (see the section "Extrusion of Tin- and Lead-Base Soft Solders" in Chapter 5).

The extrusion of zinc alloys requires specific pressures of 800 to 1000 N/mm^2 and temperatures of 200 to 350 °C, depending on the material. Smaller extrusion presses up to 10 MN press power are used. Because these extruded products in the form of tube, section, and wire have a limited application, only a few presses are in operation. The containers for the zinc alloys can be designed according to DIN 24540.

Containers for the Extrusion of Materials with Deformation Temperatures of 300 to 600 °C. This family of containers, which is almost exclusively used for the extrusion of magnesium and aluminum alloys, is found in over 70% of all extrusion plants. The tooling and the containers basically correspond to the standard DIN 24540. Large extrusion presses from 80 to 200 MN press power are only found in aluminum extrusion plants. Conventional hot working steels can cope with the thermal stressing of the container that results from the deformation temperature. While deformation temperatures of 250 to 450 °C and pressures up to 400 N/mm^2 are necessary in the extrusion of magnesium alloys, the deformation temperatures in the extrusion of aluminum alloys are between 350 and 530 °C. The deformation pressures require specific press pressures up to 1000 N/mm^2. The shearing of the billet at the container wall can be significantly more than 50% of the extrusion load needed, depending on the length of the billet. In direct extrusion, round and occasionally rectangular billets are used. In indirect extrusion, only round billet containers are used that are usually designed for long billets.

The round billet container is often designed without heating for the aluminum alloys with high extrudability. In this case, the heating is located in the container housing in standard presses. The distance between the columns must be sufficiently large for the removal and replacing of a container. The dimensions of the press cross section are therefore determined by the external diameter of the container. The advantage of round billet containers without heating is obviously the smaller external diameter. Consequently, the investment costs for the container and for the standard extrusion press, which can be more compact, are significantly lower. Round billet containers with heating are always needed if higher technological requirements are placed on the extrusion process. In the extrusion of aluminum alloys with moderate and low extrudability, the heating is preferably located as resistance heating in the container mantle. Temperature-controlled containers that include combined heating and cooling systems are well suited for the extrusion process. These are particularly important for the quality of the product in indirect extrusion. Rectangular billet containers are also fitted with resistance heating (Fig. 7.97).

However, recent developments have replaced the expensive rectangular billet container with spreader feeder chambers for round billet con-

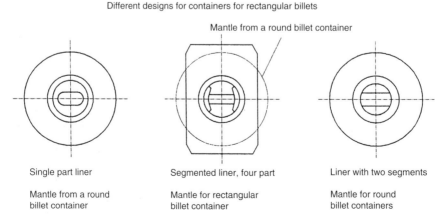

Different designs for containers for rectangular billets

Mantle from a round billet container

Single part liner

Mantle from a round billet container

Segmented liner, four part

Mantle for rectangular billet container

Liner with two segments

Mantle for round billet containers

Fig. 7.97 Rectangular billet containers with different segment arrangements for the liner. Source: Groos

tainers. These so-called spreaders enable flat profiles to be produced from round billet containers that have widths close to those from rectangular billet containers, as described in the section about spreader chambers in this Chapter. The widely used single-piece liner with a rectangular bore has a very limited life. This design should not be used with extrusion pressures over 560 N/mm². The dimensions given in DIN 24540 part 2 correspond to this design. The four-part segmented design was developed by the Loewy Construction Company in the United States in 1954. It also gives an acceptable service life at higher extrusion pressures. However, this expensive design is associated with high production costs. The extent to which two segment liners, a design from Edelstahlwerke Buderus AG for an extrusion plant in the United States, has proved successful is not known. Apart from the difficulties associated with securing the two segments, it is a solution that is economic from the production costs and appears practical from the technical point of view.

Containers for the Extrusion of Materials with Deformation Temperatures from 600 to 1300 °C.

Only round billets are used for containers in this temperature range for direct and indirect extrusion. The dimensions of the containers correspond to the standard DIN 24540 for extrusion tooling. Rod and tube extrusion presses for copper alloys have press powers between 5 and 80 MN. Extrusion presses for the production of brass products, including wire and bar, are often indirect presses. Containers for deformation temperatures over 600 °C without a suitable temperature control to prevent overheating cannot be justified today and are also uneconomic. If the container can be cooled, particularly with rapid billet throughputs, and if the liner is made from an age-hardening austenitic tool steel similar to 1.2779 with a high hot strength, then high billet temperatures can be accommodated. Whereas, for the extrusion of copper-zinc alloys, temperatures of 650 to 750 °C and pressures up to 800 N/mm² are required, the extrusion temperatures for copper alloys are between 800 and 900 °C. The pressures can reach 1000 N/mm². Because extrusion is normally carried out with a shell, billet shearing of the copper alloy occurs close to the container liner wall. This requires 10% of the extrusion load. Indirect extrusion of copper alloys is mainly restricted to copper-zinc alloys. In this case, the container

must be equipped with a combined heating and cooling system, because of the long billet and the rapid billet throughput. The round billet containers must be three-part designs. If the liner is made from high hot strength austenitic tool steel, it must have a thin wall because of the poor thermal conductivity and the higher thermal expansion. If only tubes are extruded, then short, round billet containers can be used. In this case, the rod and tube press can operate with a correspondingly shorter stroke.

The thermomechanical stressing of the container family described here has always been a problem that demanded a solution. The liner is heated above the limit of the tool material by the high billet temperatures. The maximum tempering temperature of the liner material is exceeded, leading to a rapid loss in strength. The extrusion loads then result in plastic deformation. The shrink-fit then disappears and loses its function. Cooling of the liner wall between cycles with a reduced press output and frequent turning of the container, that is, moving the stem face to the die face, can no longer be accepted because of the poor productivity. The life of the container is unsatisfactory in spite of these measures. A technically and economically usable design to avoid overheating of thermally highly stressed round billet containers is the integrated heating and cooling system. This applies to the extrusion of materials with high deformation temperatures, which includes copper alloys. The internal cooling does result in a weakening of the contact faces of the interference-fit liner holder/mantle. The surface of the outside diameter of the liner holder is reduced by the cooling channels. This should not have an unacceptable effect on the interference fit. Even so, the cooling grooves (Fig. 7.98) on the outside diameter of the liner holder naturally act as stress concentrations. Cooling and interference surfaces must be balanced in the design of the container together with minimization of the notch effect.

Titanium alloys are lubricated with glass, similar to iron alloys. The billet friction is therefore low. The glass film reduces the heat transfer from the extruded material to the tooling. For the extrusion of iron alloys and nickel alloys, only round billets for direct extrusion are used. Tube production dominates. The dimensions of the container largely follow the standard for extrusion tooling, DIN 24540. Rod and tube presses in the size range of 16 to 110 MN are mainly used. The thermal stressing of

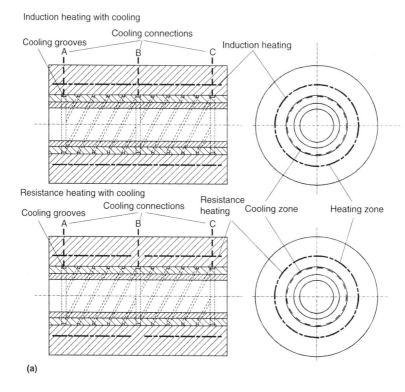

Induction heating with cooling

Cooling grooves
Cooling connections
A — B — C
Induction heating

Resistance heating with cooling

Cooling grooves
Cooling connections
A — B — C
Resistance heating
Cooling zone
Heating zone

(a)

A, B, and C: either inlet or outlet for the zone cooling, depending on requirements.
Induction heating uniform temperature input over the entire container length, depending
on the requirements. Resistance heating in two or more zones independently from each
other, depending on requirements.

(b)

Fig. 7.98 (a) Combination heating and cooling system. Source: Groos. (b) Liner holder with cooling grooves. Source: Böhler

the containers at deformation temperatures over 1000 °C requires special measures to achieve an acceptable life. High extrusion speeds are usually used in the high-temperature range. The contact time with the tooling by the hot extruded material is then short. In addition, the insulating effect of the glass lubricant in the container helps prevent overheating of the die, liner, and dummy block. The billet friction is very low. The method of lubrication, whether with glass or, more rarely, an oil-graphite salt mixture, has little effect on the magnitude of the billet friction. The specific extrusion pressures required are often in the range of 1000 N/mm^2. Integrated cooling in the container is not used. Thin-wall liners, which have a limited life as a wear component, are used successfully. They are not shrink-fitted in the conventional way and can be quickly changed. They protect the containers from excessive temperature.

7.5.5.2 Thermomechanical Stressing of the Container during Extrusion

The thermomechanical stressing during press operation results in an extremely complex set of circumstances in the container that is characterized by considerable interactions. The magnitude of the thermal and mechanical stresses in the container is often at the upper limit of conventional hot working materials. This results in a limited life for the liner and ultimately for the container.

The mechanical stressing of the container is best illustrated using:

- Containers with round bores
- Containers for the extrusion of materials that require an extrusion pressure below 1000 N/mm^2
- Containers free from dangerous notches in their design and manufacture. The stresses that can result from unavoidable heater holes, shoulders, and slots must be held within acceptable limits because of stress concentrations.

The mechanical stresses result from:

- Specific pressure during extrusion
- Externally applied sealing force from the container movement that corresponds to the contact force between the container and the die or the die holder
- Friction and shearing between the billet and the liner wall

- Interference forces on the container components, that is, the compressive stresses on the liner and liner holder and the tensile stresses on the mantle

The analysis of the mechanical stresses on the container should also consider the container sealing forces and the friction and shear forces that develop during extrusion. These forces, which should not be underestimated, act in the axial direction. The resultant three-axis stress state must be taken into account.

The thermal stresses result in more complex problems. They arise from:

- Local overheating
- High billet throughputs with billet temperatures over 600 °C
- Short billets with billet temperatures over 600 °C
- Too rapid heating and cooling when changing containers

The thermal stresses can be withstood if, during production:

- A maximum temperature well below the tempering temperature of the hot working steels used for manufacture can be held at all locations within the container.
- A reliable heating and cooling system within the container is available for temperature control that can demonstrably maintain the specified working temperature without an unacceptable buildup of heat in the central area of the container.
- Only a preheated container is used when the tooling is changed, and the removed container is cooled slowly under a thermal protection cover.

Unacceptable thermal conditions occur:

- When, during production, materials with extrusion temperatures over 600 °C are extruded without a heating and cooling system, that is, without a reliably operating thermal control, in this case, without cooling
- When the resultant temperature exposure results in an unacceptable heat buildup in the central region of the container
- When there is excessive cooling of the container from the outside

In the extrusion of materials with deformation temperatures over 600 °C, there exists an extremely unequal temperature distribution within the container. In the axial direction, temperature differences of up to 200 °C occur. This results in a buildup of heat, depending on the billet length, temperature, and press throughput. In direct operating extrusion presses, this occurs approximately one-third to one-fourth of the container length from the die (Fig. 7.99), and in indirect operating presses, in front of the sealing tool. The radial temperature differences in the container are not important. They develop from the horizontal location of the container in the extrusion press. The thermal center point is slightly above the center of the press.

Temperature differences over the length of the container are required for isothermal extrusion. Radial temperature differences in the container in large extrusion presses can result in asymmetrical flow of the extruded material. In these cases, the temperature control in the container or the die must be corrected.

7.5.5.3   Container Heating and Cooling

The extensively used resistance and induction heating systems have currently reached a level of technology that can meet different requirements according to the application.

Today, resistance heating is preferred for heating containers for the extrusion of aluminum alloys. This prevents the formation of hot spots by sensitive temperature measurements with thermocouples on the outside diameter of the liner and by effective temperature control. Hot spots (Fig. 7.99, 7.100), with temperatures that reach or even exceed the tempering temperature of the hot working steels, reduce the hot strength over a period of time and thus shorten the life of the container. The container housing is internally insulated to reduce heat losses. The insulation is provided with additional heat-reflecting sheets that face the container surface. A resistance heating system in the container housing is located between the reflective sheets and the container mantle surface. The only container faces that directly lose heat are the end faces.

The heating power required depends primarily on the desired rate of heating. The heating power needed during production to maintain the operating temperature is small. It depends on the effectiveness of the insulation and the heat radiation from the exposed surfaces. A heating station independent of the extrusion press that is also suitable as a holding station is useful and should be considered as essential.

Temperature distribution in the container for the direct extrusion of copper
Container with induction heating without cooling

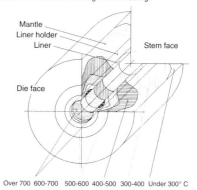

Over 700   600-700   500-600   400-500   300-400   Under 300° C

Container temperature across the container length, °C

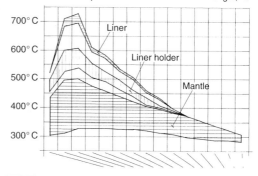

Liner internal diameter	530	715	730	615	585	540	505	465	430	400	370	355	340	325	305
Liner external diameter	520	680	690	595	565	530	495	455	425	395	370	355	340	325	305
Liner holder internal diameter	495	500	615	555	525	495	470	440	415	390	370	350	340	320	305
Liner holder external diameter	460	530	540	505	485	460	410	420	400	380	365	350	335	320	305
Mantle internal diameter	440	490	500	475	450	440	425	405	380	375	360	345	330	320	305
Mantle external diameter	300	315	325	325	325	325	320	320	315	310	305	300	290	280	270

Fig. 7.99 Temperatures distribution in the container without cooling after 2h production. The table lists the measured local temperature (°C) at the internal and external diameter of the container components. Source: Groos

It can also be used for slow cooling of removed containers. The heating power depends on:

- Operating temperature, taking into account the process technology requirements
- Container surface, both the exposed and the insulated areas

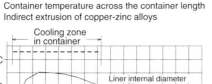

Container temperature across the container length
Indirect extrusion of copper-zinc alloys

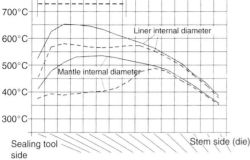

Without cooling

Liner internal diameter	530	625	655	650	640	630	620	600	580	560	535	510	470	430	380
Mantle internal diameter	415	475	510	530	535	535	530	520	510	496	480	450	425	390	360

With cooling

Liner internal diameter	455	565	585	575	565	560	565	575	575	550	525	500	465	420	365
Mantle internal diameter	380	390	385	390	400	400	420	440	465	480	470	445	420	385	350

Fig. 7.100 Temperature at the internal liner bore and the mantle internal diameter measured on a container with cooling (broken line) and without cooling (solid line). Source: Groos

- Rate of heating, which should not exceed 40 °C/h. A much lower value can be maintained by using a separate heating station outside the press.
- Number of heating elements, which, in the case of resistance heating, are heating cartridges or heating tubes in various designs, or the number of heating rods in induction heating
- Spatial location of the heating

With increasing throughputs, particularly for copper alloy extrusion, container cooling is required. The increase in productivity, especially in indirect extrusion for copper alloys, results in overheating of the liner if cooling is not available. The deformation heat builds up so that the tempering temperature of the container liner material is exceeded. Excessive contact time between the hot billet and the liner occurs when the extrusion time predominates in relation to the dead cycle time. Without container cooling, the economy of the modern high-throughput indirect-extrusion press cannot be used.

Many years' experience with water cooling in the stationary piercing containers of vertical piercing presses for steel blanks guarantees a successful operation. In horizontal presses with moving containers, this type of water cooling cannot be installed without operational disadvantages and risks. The horizontal design for cooling water as well as its supply and removal is difficult, and the safety of the operating personnel and the plant must take priority. Over time, cooling with compressed air was developed with good results by Schloemann. A computer program to simulate different operating conditions in hot extrusion was developed. The simulated temperature fields in the container correspond to the actual conditions during production. The first air cooling for an induction-heated container located in the liner holder/mantle region was used with good results in a 45 MN rod and tube press for indirect extrusion of copper alloys in approximately 1980 in the United States. The initially low liner life was considerably extended by air cooling. A short time later, air cooling combined with resistance heating was used on an indirect 35 MN extrusion press for aluminum alloys. For process technical reasons, the temperature in the container had to be held constant within 20 °C. Successful experiences were also obtained by Sumitomo Light Metals in Japan.

The design of the heating depends on the heating power required and the required operating temperature. In addition, the operational requirements for service, repair, and maintenance must be considered. The heating elements for a resistance heating system with standard heating power can be installed in the container if one or more heating zones are used. If the heating must be installed in the container housing, the heating power is restricted with short container housings. Heating rods installed in the container mantle for induction heating or resistance heating should be located as close as possible to the container bore without being in a critical zone in terms of the container stresses. For strength reasons, the distance between the heater holes should be at least 2.5 times the diameter of the holes. Zone heating is not possible with induction heating. Resistance heating is less suitable than induction heating for operating temperatures over 500 °C.

Resistance Heating for Containers. Resistance heating was used relatively early for heating containers. Initially, it was installed in the container housing and divided into different zones to give localized heating. However, the exposed heating wire oxidized and was susceptible to damage in the harsh working conditions. This resulted in the development of heating elements that encapsulated the heating wire and thus protected it from oxidation and mechanical effects. These are referred to as tubular elements and heating cartridges.

The tubular heating elements have a relatively small external diameter. The thin heating wire in Cr-Ni-Fe is embedded in magnesium oxide in an airtight alloy steel tube. Heating elements with tube diameters of 8 mm are fitted to the container housing. Heating elements with tube diameters of 12 mm are fitted as plug-in elements in heating holes of 42 mm in the container mantle. With the large clearance between the tubular heating elements and the heater hole in the container, the surface temperature of the heating elements must be very high, up to 800 °C. Increasingly, therefore, heating cartridges are being used for container heating. Macrotubes (heating cartridges) can be considered as larger tubular heating elements. They are fitted with a thicker heater wire and have an outside diameter of 31.5 mm within narrow tolerances [Eck 97].

The efficiency of resistance heating is determined by the efficiency of the heat transfer. Heating cartridges located directly in the container are the best for thermal balance. Resistance heating is also the most suited for an effective temperature control. An almost constant temperature or a predetermined temperature profile over the container length can be achieved with a combination of resistance heating with integrated cooling.

The smaller the gap between the cartridge diameter and the bore, the higher the heat transfer efficiency. The division of a container into six controlled zones, as shown in Fig. 7.101, by the use of a combined heating and cooling system is advantageous. The location of three thermocouples—in the upper region on the die side, in the center, and on the stem side—and three additional opposing thermocouples in the lower region, each measuring on the external diameter of the liner, provides good monitoring of the container. Each heating zone has a temperature probe. To protect against overheating of the heating cartridges, an additional thermocouple is often installed close to a heating cartridge in the central region. The heating connection must be designed for both the die side and the stem side. The time needed to disconnect and reconnect the measuring and heating cables to the container is relatively short when changing the tooling, compared to induction heating (Fig. 7.102).

Locating a resistance heating system in the container housing is less effective but is sufficient in specific applications (Fig. 7.103). Be-

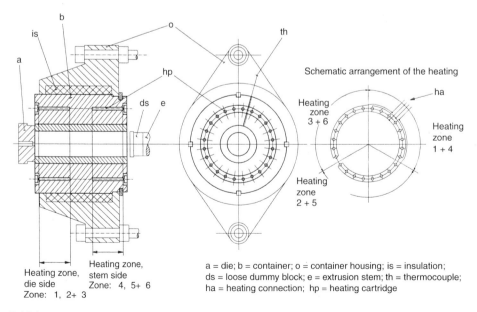

Schematic arrangement of the heating

Heating zone 3 + 6

Heating zone 1 + 4

Heating zone 2 + 5

Heating zone, die side Zone: 1, 2+ 3

Heating zone, stem side Zone: 4, 5+ 6

a = die; b = container; o = container housing; is = insulation; ds = loose dummy block; e = extrusion stem; th = thermocouple; ha = heating connection; hp = heating cartridge

Fig. 7.101 Schematic arrangement of six-zone resistance heating in a container. Source: Groos

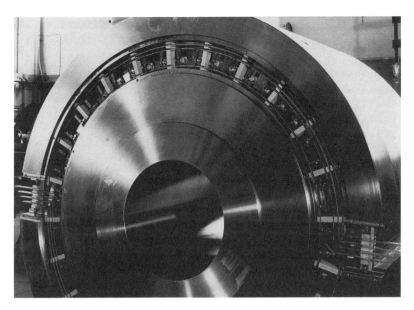

Fig. 7.102 Four-zone heating with quick heating connection. Source: Marx

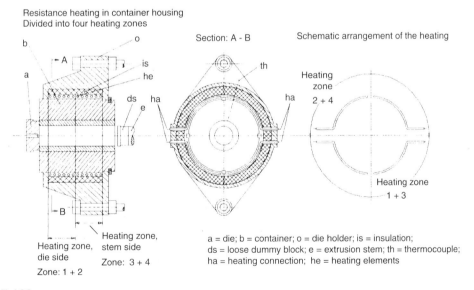

Fig. 7.103 Schematic arrangement of four-zone resistance in the container housing. Source: Groos

cause no heater holes are required in the container mantle, the external diameter of the container is smaller than with a container with integrated heating. The container is therefore less expensive. Container changing without heating connections requires less time. The replacement of defective heating elements is relatively simple. Before a new container is loaded, it should be preheated to the working temperature in a special heating station. For prolonged downtime, a transportable additional resistance heater for the liner bore is useful. However, temperature control of the container by resistance heating in the container housing is not possible.

Recent Developments in Resistance Heating of Containers

Wolfgang Eckenbach*

The requirements of the extrusion plant for temperature-controlled containers have increased considerably over recent years. On one hand, the billet and billet diameter have increased in length and size, and on the other, the extruded materials are more diverse. The extrusion speed and the associated dwell time in the container have also changed. Various heating and, to an increasing extent, cooling systems have been used to compensate for the different temperature distributions. These enable the initial temperature at the start of production to be set and can have an effect on the necessary temperature equalization.

Intelligent heating systems are needed in combination with suitable cooling systems to more closely reach the aim of a linear temperature profile in the container. Approximately 10 years ago, an intensive exchange of experience between the press manufacturer, heating manufacturer, tool supplier, and the plant operator began in order to find a common solution. The solution was integrated process-controlled multizone heating with superimposed zone cooling. To achieve this end, it was first necessary to find an alternative to induction heating and to investigate the possibilities of liner holder cooling. Resistance heating was developed with spiral flat wire embedded in a highly compacted soft ceramic that was stretch reduced and that gave optimal heat transfer [Marx] [Eck 97]. While old ceramic designs with a mantle temperature of 750 °C and a wire coil surface temperature an additional 300 °C higher, that is, approximately 1050 °C, were operating at the limit of their load, the highly compacted soft ceramic cartridges could be operated approximately 80 to 150 °C higher.

This extremely favorable temperature difference enabled a surface thermal load of up to 6 W/cm^2 to be developed on the cartridge, and the wall spacing between the bore and the car-

tridge to be increased to 0.7 mm in diameter. Baking on of the cartridges is then largely eliminated, and the removal and installation can be carried out without problems. This replacement for pure induction heating with significantly simpler assembly and maintenance conditions was then further developed. The next stage was fitting containers with cartridges of different heating power and length on different pitch circles. These systems were replaced with heating cartridges with integrated multiple heating zones. Today, there are cartridges on the market with up to three zones that can be positioned where required in the container. The arrangement of individual groups can be flexible, and they can be operated separately or together [Marx] [Eck 97].

In addition to zone heating systems, zone cooling systems have been developed. Heating and cooling zones in containers can then be arranged so that specified container temperatures are possible over the length of the container. The air cooling has been refined to three-zone cooling. The container temperature can be maintained in a specified range by automatic control of the heating and cooling zones, using temperature measurements at numerous measurement points.

7.6 Induction Heating for Containers

The first induction heating systems for containers were developed by Schloemann in approximately 1930. They were installed in the container mantle. While resistance heating was used from an early date for container heating in the United States, induction heating was preferred in Europe. It still has advantages today (Fig. 7.104).

In induction heating, the heat is directly produced in the area surrounding the heating bars in the container mantle. The copper bars are surrounded by an efficient thermal insulation that must not be hygroscopic. The bars are joined at the end by welded straps to form a coil. It is powered by a low-voltage and high-amperage alternating current from a transformer with a condenser battery. An independent heating station or heat-retaining chamber is used to prevent moisture from forming in the container during downtime. Induction heating is used for high operating temperatures. A constant temperature is not achieved over the container length because of the heat losses from the con-

---

*Recent Developments in Resistance Heating of Containers, Wolfgaug Eckenbach

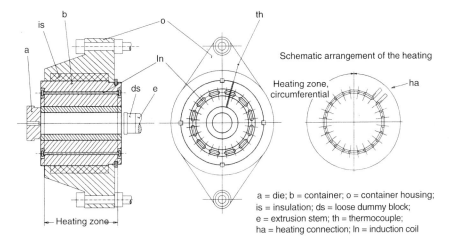

a = die; b = container; o = container housing;
is = insulation; ds = loose dummy block;
e = extrusion stem; th = thermocouple;
ha = heating connection; ln = induction coil

Fig. 7.104 Schematic arrangement of induction heating in a container. Source: Groos

tainer end faces. The inevitable heat buildup in the middle of the container can be reduced by internal container cooling. A specified temperature profile similar to that with resistance heating cannot be achieved with induction heating and integrated cooling.

7.6.1 Combined Container Heating and Cooling System

An understanding of the temperature distribution in the different zones of the container is essential for the design and control of an effective combination heating and cooling system. The temperature fields in the container must be maintained constant, and overheating in the center must be excluded. The use of cooling cannot be avoided. The combined heating and cooling systems (Fig. 7.98) are very important for the economics and product quality in the extrusion plant and should therefore be standard.

A constant temperature over the container length can only be achieved to a limited extent, because of the exposed container end faces. There is no suitable thermal insulation available for the container end faces. Heat buildup within the container can be partly reduced by dividing the heating into zones. An effective method of countering the buildup of heat in the middle region of the container is the cooling of the hotter zones.

In hot working, there is a wide range of methods used for cooling the tooling. Of the most common cooling media, including water, cooling oil, air-water mixture, and air, cooling

with air has proved to be best suited for containers. The necessary cooling intensity requires compressed air. Working with compressed air in the plant is simple, environmentally friendly, and safe. The cooling intensity of the compressed air can be varied by the pressure. It can be precisely fed locally into the hotter zones, which is advantageous for the different temperatures in the container. The hot exhaust air is taken away so that there is no detrimental effect on the surroundings. Cooling with compressed air is suitable, because the tool material being cooled is protected. Figure 7.98 shows the cooling grooves of a liner holder and the cooling in a container.

The combination of resistance heating and compressed air cooling is now the best-suited technology for a temperature-controlled container. The resistance heating must be divided into several zones, and the cooling must be locally adjustable. It must be possible to vary and alternate the supply and exhaust of the cooling compressed air over the container length. At least six thermocouples in suitable locations in the container are required for the monitoring and control of a combined heating and cooling system. If aluminum alloys are extruded, it is economic to operate with an individual temperature profile matched to the particular deformation conditions. The heating and cooling systems described have proved successful in practical operation. They are of fundamental importance for the further development of the process technology. The temperature losses in the area of the container end faces are low and can be ignored in practice. They only influence the extrusion process over a length of 100 to 150 mm from the end face, depending on the size of the press.

Compressed air cooling is also advantageous for containers heated by induction. In the extrusion of copper alloys, the combination of induction heating and compressed air cooling is necessary. The service life of the container liner can be significantly improved by reducing the heat buildup in the central region of the container, using compressed air. This reduces tooling costs significantly, and thus, downtime for container changing occurs less often. Three thermocouples located at suitable positions in the container are used for the monitoring and control of the induction heating and cooling system. Containers for copper extrusion with induction heating can be retrofitted with compressed air cooling. Retrofitting of compressed air cooling for aluminum extrusion is less beneficial. It cannot guarantee the desired temperature control with induction-heated containers.

7.7 Design, Calculation, and Dimensioning of Containers

The standard multipart container is subjected to three-dimensional variable and superimposed forces during the extrusion cycle. Basically, these are:

- Radial and tangential deformation stresses during extrusion
- Axial tangential and shear forces during the direct-extrusion process
- Radial, tangential, and axial residual stresses produced by the shrink-fitting process
- Axial sealing forces between the container and the die in direct extrusion
- Axial container moving force in the extrusion direction in indirect extrusion

The deformation forces shown in Fig. 7.105 stress the container between 0 and the maximum stem load, $F_{St\ max}$. The shrink-fitting stresses in the container are superimposed on the deformation loads. As a result of the superimposition, the liner of a two-part and the liner and the liner holder of a three-piece container are dynamically loaded in the tension/compression range, whereas the container mantle is always subjected to dynamic fluctuating tensile loads. The frequency of the dynamic stressing depends on the number of extrusion cycles per unit time. If, however, only slow stem speeds are possible for the deformation of an extruded material, as, for example, with the aluminum alloys with low extrudability, the dynamic loading of the container can be considered to be cyclic creep loading. Hot working steels that are subjected to creep loading can be subjected to plastic deformation if the creep strength is exceeded, which is referred to as material creep.

Both the optimal design of a container and the use of the correct hot working tool steels are important. Container mantles manufactured in the hot working steels 1.2323 and 1.2714 exhibit significant strength losses, apparently caused by production-related long-term tempering under thermal stresses. Incorrect preheating with excessive temperature gradients in the container mantle can also contribute to this. As a result of the loss in strength, the container mantles can no longer elastically withstand the forces developed during the extrusion process. The problem was solved by the use of the more temper-resistant hot working steel 1.2343 instead of the previously used less temper-resistant hot working steels.

The container design should be as simple as possible, with extensive avoidance of design details that produce stress concentrations. Notch-induced stress concentrations in the container mantle region can result in a fatigue failure. Notch-acting areas cannot always be completely avoided in container design. Points to consider are:

- Heating and thermocouple holes in the mantle and the liner holder
- Keyways in the mantle to hold and locate the container
- Blends at the cylindrical shoulders on the liner, liner holder, and/or mantle
- Cooling grooves in the liner holder mantle face

Consideration should also be given to the fact that coarse machining marks on the mating surfaces of the container components and the surface of the container mantle can result in high stress concentrations. Unacceptably high stress peaks should be avoided. In addition, the shape and positional tolerances according to DIN 7184 must be maintained in terms of straightness, angularity, concentricity/coaxiality, and runout. This applies to the mating surfaces of the individual container components and, equally, for the alignment accuracy of the

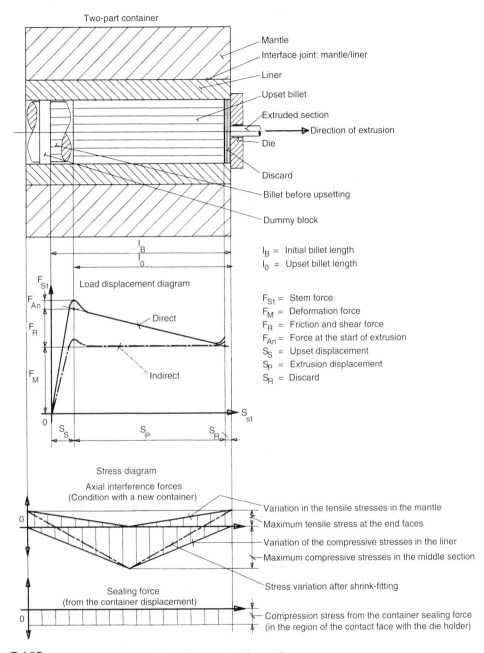

Fig. 7.105 Stresses in a two-part container during extrusion. Source: Groos

extrusion tooling within the extrusion press, where the container plays a decisive role. For rapid installation and removal of the container, the container housing is fitted with a quick-fit connection that is also suitable for the positioning and transfer of the container sealing forces. Very demanding design analysis is required when a heating or combined heating and cool-

ing system must be integrated into the container.

After the operating program has been established, the estimates of the maximum extrusion pressure and the maximum thermal stresses are the important factors in the initial design of the container. Tables 7.7 and 7.8 give corresponding material-dependent data for containers with

Table 7.7 Working conditions for containers operating without cooling

Material and specific method	Temperature(a), °C	Extrusion pressure, N/mm²	Friction/shearing	Evaluation(b)	Comments(c)
Easily extruded aluminum alloys	500	0–630	Moderate	High possibility	Favorable
Moderately difficult aluminum alloys	500	630–800	Moderate to high	High possibility	Favorable
Moderately difficult aluminum alloys, indirect	450	400–630	Not present	High possibility	Increases difficulty
Difficult-to-extrude aluminum alloys	500	800–1000	High	Possible	Favorable
Difficult-to-extrude aluminum alloys, indirect	450	630–710	Not present	High possibility	Increases difficulty
Easily extruded copper alloys	600	630	Low	Limited	Favorable
Easily extruded copper alloys, indirect	600	400–630	Not present	Limited	Favorable
Moderately difficult copper alloys	650	630–800	Low	Questionable	Increases difficulty
Difficult-to-extrude copper alloys	700	800–1000	Low to moderate	Questionable	Difficult
Easily extruded iron alloys	550(d)	630–800	Minimum(e)	Possible	Difficult
Difficult-to-extrude iron alloys	600(d)	800–1250	Minimum(e)	Limited	Very difficult
Nickel alloys	650(d)	800–1250	Low(e)	Questionable	Very difficult

(a) Maximum container temperature in the liner in direct extrusion. With temperature monitoring. (b) Estimation of the possibility of design using classical elasticity theory. (c) Comments on the operating conditions. (d) Short extrusion times and glass lubrication largely prevent overheating. (e) Dependent on the lubrication. Source: Groos

Table 7.8 Working conditions for containers operating with cooling

Material-specific method	Temperature(a), °C	Extrusion pressure, N/mm²	Friction/shearing	Evaluation(b)	Comments(c)
Easily extruded aluminum alloys	500	0–630	Moderate	Possible	Favorable
Moderately difficult aluminum alloys	500	630–800	Moderate to high	Possible	Favorable
Moderately difficult aluminum alloys, indirect	450	400–630	Not present	High possibility	Increases difficulty
Difficult-to-extrude aluminum alloys	500	800–1000	High	Possible	Favorable
Difficult-to-extrude aluminum alloys indirect	450	630–710	Not present	High possibility	Increases difficulty
Easily extruded copper alloys	500	630	Low	Possible	Favorable
Easily extruded copper alloys, indirect	500	400–630	Not present	Possible	Favorable
Moderately difficult copper alloys	550	630–800	Low	Limited	Increases difficulty
Difficult-to-extrude copper alloys	600	800–1000	Low to moderate	Limited	Difficult
Easily extruded iron alloys	500	630–800	Minimum(d)	Possible	Difficult
Difficult-to-extrude iron alloys	500	800–1250	Minimum(d)	Possible	Very difficult
Nickel alloys	600	800–1250	Low(d)	Limited	Very difficult

(a) Maximum container temperature in the liner in direct and indirect extrusion. Temperature control using a combined heating and cooling system. (b) Estimation on the possibility of design using classical elasticity. (c) Comments on the operating conditions. (d) Dependent on lubrication. Source: Groos

and without cooling. The container can be provisionally designed using these stress parameters. Table 7.18 in section 7.17 helps to select the material for the container as a function of the material being extruded. The final analysis of the container—usually following the classic elastic theory—follows the optimization of the initial dimensions. The analytical results enable corrections to be made to avoid excessive stresses. A fatigue life calculation using the expected load collective of the container, which must be obtained from the actual thermal and mechanical stresses over a long period of time on a similar container, is the final stage of the design process. The subsequent operational steps are followed for the design of a new container as well as a new development in the context of DIN 24540:

1 Determine the extrusion program as the starting point

2 Estimate the maximum extrusion pressure and the maximum temperature
3 Preliminary design of the container, based on values from experience or assumptions for a new design with preliminary determination of the dimensions and material of the container
4 Accurate calculation of the container, with subsequent optimization of the preliminary container design using the results
5 Estimate the fatigue life of the new container using the load collective from the operational program

A container is not continuously thermomechanically stressed to its maximum. More often, the extrusion load required varies according to the production requirements, between 65 and 90% of the maximum load of the extrusion press. The thermal stressing also depends on the relation between the time needed for the actual deformation and the total time of the extrusion process. Some information is given in Table 7.9. The pure extrusion times given in the table, which vary significantly depending on the material being extruded, also demonstrate that it is not advisable to universally use containers for mixed-extrusion programs, which has occasionally occurred in the past. For example, if aluminum alloys and copper alloys were extruded from the same container, which would result in quality problems, these containers would always have to be designed for the maximum thermomechanical stresses. They would then be expensive and uneconomic.

It is important to adhere to the design- and manufacture-related operating conditions as well as the safety considerations to ensure the extended operational availability of a container. For safety reasons, the following exceptional operating conditions must be avoided:

- Heat buildup
- Sticking billets in the container, that is, insufficient maximum press load to extrude the billet
- Overloading in the hydraulic system, resulting from incorrect setting or safety valves
- Overloading as a result of unacceptably high extrusion pressures by the use of mandrels with excessive cross sections in tube extrusion
- Excessive temperature gradients during heating or cooling of containers
- Misalignment between the extrusion tooling

The FEM analysis in Fig. 7.106 shows the variation in the equivalent stresses, σ_v, in the components of two three-part containers, with the high stresses around the heater holes in the case of the round billet container as well as around the asymmetrical liner in the rectangular billet container (oval cross section). Stress concentrations and thus crack-susceptible areas can be avoided by design measures, including, for example, fillets on keyways, increased distance between holes in groups of holes, and overall notch-free design. The FEM studies enable optimal designs for the manufacture of containers to be realized.

For a long time, little importance was attached to the axial stresses. Experience has shown that the axial forces on the container should not be completely ignored. The following axial forces can act on the container:

- Friction and shear forces on the liner wall during direct extrusion
- Axial forces developed during the shrink-fitting of the container components
- Container moving force involved in indirect extrusion, resulting from the displacement force in the extrusion direction
- Container sealing force against the die and/or die holder in direct extrusion

The friction and shear forces operating in direct extrusion can be obtained from a plot of the extrusion load against the ram displacement, as seen in Fig. 7.105.

In the direct extrusion of aluminum alloys, the magnitude of the friction and shear forces is between 30 and 60% of the maximum force, $F_{St\ max}$, and in the direct extrusion of copper alloys, 5 to 30%. At the start of the deformation of the billet, these forces are at a maximum, and the axial loads on the container are particularly high during this phase of the extrusion process. However, they continually decrease

Table 7.9   Factors that affect the material-dependent design of containers

Extruded material	Temperature(a), °C	Specific extrusion pressure, $p_{St} = F_{St}/A_0$, N/mm²	Extrusion time as a percentage of cycle time(b)	Friction and shearing at the liner wall(c)
Easily extruded aluminum alloys	<550	<630	80	Moderate
Moderately difficult aluminum alloys	<550	630–800	85	Moderate to high
Moderately difficult aluminum alloys, indirect	<450	400–630	80	Not present
Difficult-to-extrude aluminum alloys	<550	800–1000	95	High
Difficult-to-extrude aluminum alloys, indirect	<450	630–710	85	Not present
Easily extruded copper alloys	<800	<630	65	Low
Easily extruded copper alloys, indirect	<750	400–630	60	Not present
Moderately difficult copper alloys	<900	630–800	50	Low
Difficult-to-extrude copper alloys	<1000	800–1000	20	Low to moderate
Easily extruded iron alloys	<1200	630–800	10	Negligible(d)
Difficult-to-extrude iron alloys	<1200	800–1250	10	Negligible(e)
Nickel alloys	<1200	800–1250	20	Low to moderate

(a) Maximum billet temperature. (b) Average values. (c) Does not apply to indirect extrusion. (d) For carbon steels using oil-graphite-salt lubrication. (e) For carbon steels with glass lubrication. Source: Groos

Three-part container

(a)

(b)

Fig. 7.106 Variation in equivalent stresses in (a) a three-part round billet container and (b) a three-part rectangular billet container. The stress concentrations (light) at the heating holes in the mantle and the high stresses (light) at the side faces of the bore of the rectangular billet container can clearly be seen. Source: SMS Schloemann

with the reduction in billet length, l_R, until the stem load, F_{St}, starts to increase at the start of the extrusion of the deformation zone and the dead metal zone.

The following example gives an indication of the magnitude of these forces. An aluminum alloy with a high extrudability is extruded on a direct-extrusion press with a maximum press power, $F_{St\ max}$, of 25 MN. The container internal diameter is 225 mm, and the length of the billet prior to upsetting is 950 mm. A load displacement diagram was plotted to determine the friction and shear forces (F_R). This indicated

that for the maximum friction and shear force, F_R is 30% of $F_{St\ max}$. Then:

$$F_R = 0.3 \times 25 = 7.5\ \text{MN}$$

If the friction and shear forces are 60% of the maximum extrusion load, then 15 MN, almost two-thirds of $F_{St\ max}$, is required to overcome $F_{R\ max}$ at the start of extrusion. The container sealing load in direct extrusion has a value of 12.5% of $F_{St\ max}$ on many extrusion presses. It can be transmitted to the tool holder of the extrusion press by the friction between the fitted faces of the interference interface.

The container sealing forces thus load the container axially. For the direct-extrusion press with 25 MN maximum extrusion load mentioned previously, these forces are 3.13 MN. This force is transferred to the tool holder of the extrusion press.

Axial interference-fit-associated forces result from the manufacture of the interference fit of multipart containers. The liner fitted with or without a liner holder into the container mantle heats up while the container mantle cools. After a specific time for temperature equalization, the first contact between the interface surface of the liner with the interface surface of the mantle of the liner holder occurs in the location of the mantle end faces, because the mantle end faces radiate additional heat and thus cool more quickly than the core. Consequently, the first interference fit occurs in this region, whereby the liner is practically clamped at its ends. In the hotter core of the mantle the liner absorbs more heat and tries to increase in length. However, this is prevented by the clamped ends. The liner is then subjected to thermal compressive stresses that frequently result in plastic upsetting, with increases in wall thickness in the area of the middle of the liner. The associated reduction in the liner bore must be removed at the end of the interference-fitting process by machining. During the removal of worn liners, there is an increase in length of these liners for all hot working materials, in particular with austenitic hot working steels because of the high thermal expansion. This shows that liners are subjected to axial compressive stresses even after complete cooling of the container. These prestresses are contained, provided the containers are only elastically stressed by moderate thermomechanical stresses. However, with high thermomechanical stresses such as those experienced in the extrusion of copper, the liner partly undergoes plastic deformation during the extrusion process. This changes the prestress state produced by the shrink-fitting in the container. At the same time, the liner is again subjected to compressive stresses, because it wants to expand under the high thermomechanical stresses, but this is prevented by the interference fit. The mantle is only slightly loaded by tensile stresses from the interference fit because of the significantly larger volume.

The axial forces developed in the container during cooling after shrink-fitting can only be approximately determined. With hot working steels with equal coefficients of thermal expansion, the axial length change, for example, of the liner relative to the mandrel is in the range of 0.01 to 0.04% depending on the shrinkage forces and the length of the container. The resultant axial stresses are superimposed on the radial and tangential stresses in the liner in the static and working conditions. Over time, the original prestresses in the container from the shrink-fitting can change radially and axially because of temperature differences between the container components as a result of heating and cooling as well as the fluctuating working conditions. According to these considerations as well as practical experience, the interference fit is lost when:

- The operating temperature exceeds 600 °C, that is, over the tempering temperature of the hot working steels used.
- The container mantle under the applied container sealing load is heated too quickly, that is, with an excessive temperature gradient.
- Significantly hotter billets are extruded in a cold container.

A billet heated to the extrusion temperature and upset in a container that is too cold raises the temperature of the liner, which then wants to expand according to the temperature but is prevented by the container mantle or the liner holder. If it is then thermomechanically over-stressed, the function of the original interference stresses is reduced.

To summarize, the analysis of the axial loads on the container reveals a varied stress situation. The axial forces have very different orders of magnitude, depending on the deformation conditions for the extruded material under consideration, and cannot be fully determined. It is recommended that the axial forces developed by interference stresses acting on the container, the friction/shear forces, and the container sealing forces be taken into account, with the help of Table 7.10.

From this, the axial loading of the container in a direct-extrusion press for the extrusion of copper alloys is given by the axial stress:

$$\sigma_z = 0.35 \times p_i + 0.35 \times p_s$$

These values are reasonably close enough to reality for the determination of the equivalent stresses in the container, as shown by the calculation examples in section 7.10.

The manufacturers of containers have considerably improved and standardized the classical methods of calculation. Today, multipart containers can be analyzed in minutes by using computer programs using classical elasticity theory from the specified data. There have also been many efforts to mathematically determine the elastic/plastic behavior of containers and their components subjected to high thermomechanical stresses. However, practical experience has shown that the method of classical elasticity theory using the safety factors k in the section "Static- and Elastic-Based Analysis and Dimensioning of Containers Loaded in Three Dimensions" in this Chapter usually suffices for the design of containers not subjected to extremely high thermomechanical stresses. However, the elastic equilibrium conditions derived from the equilibrium analysis in the aforementioned section in the form of integral equations can only be fully integrated with simplified assumptions.

Table 7.10 Reference values for determining the axial forces on the container during extrusion

Application	Effective axial forces		Factors	
	Prestresses, p_s	Working stresses, p_i	p_S	p_i
Indirect-extrusion copper alloys	Interference-fit forces	. . .	0.5	. . .
Indirect-extrusion aluminum alloys	Interference-fit forces	. . .	0.5	. . .
Direct-extrusion copper alloys	Interference-fit forces	Friction/shear forces, container sealing forces	0.35	0.35
Direct-extrusion aluminum alloys	Interference-fit forces	Friction/shear forces, container sealing forces	0.35	0.65

Source: Groos

Static- and Elastic-Based Analysis and Dimensioning of Containers Loaded in Three Dimensions

Günther Sauer*

Even today, or at least in Germany, the container is usually statically designed on an elastic basis in spite of its creep/fatigue loading. The dimensioning uses the 0.2% proof hot yield stress ($R_{p0.2hot}$) of the hot working material used for the manufacture of the container. However, this is a material parameter in which a permanent deformation of the hot working material of 0.2% has already taken place. If the prestressed container was actually subjected to such a material loading during operation, the interference-fit stresses would be significantly reduced by creep. To avoid plastic deformation within the container, the manufacturers multiply the calculated equivalent stresses σ_v, by a safety factor, k, of the order 1.3 to 1.6 (in some cases, up to 2.0), depending on the operating conditions of the container:

$$k \times \sigma_v \leq R_{p0.2hot} \text{ or } \sigma_v \leq \frac{1}{k} \times R_{p0.2hot}$$

However, it should be remembered that the creep strength and the fatigue strength of the conventional hot working tool steels used to manufacture containers have very different values from the 0.2% hot proof stresses under the same thermomechanical loading, which can be illustrated by the example of the hot working steel 1.2343 frequently used for aluminum containers. This can clearly be seen in Fig. 7.107. The diagram shows that for the same heat treatment, the steel has a 0.2% hot proof stress of approximately 800 N/mm² but a 0.2% 100 h creep strength of approximately 400 N/mm², which is only 50% of the 0.2% hot proof stress. The dimensioning of a container made from this hot working steel with 50% of its 0.2% hot proof stress can be critical at high thermomechanical loading. In addition, Table 7.11 shows that at 500 °C, this steel has a tensile fatigue

*Static- and Elastic-Based Analysis and Dimensioning of Containers Loaded in Three Dimensions, Günther Sauer

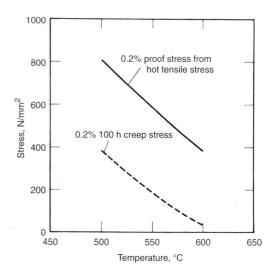

Fig. 7.107 Comparison of the 0.2% hot proof stress of the hot working tool steel 1.2343 measured in hot tensile tests between 500 and 600 °C, with the 0.2% 100 h creep stress in the same temperature region [Güm 81]

strength of 540 N/mm². It must be remembered that fatigue and creep of hot working steels under time-dependent thermomechanical stresses can smoothly merge together.

The values for the creep and tensile fatigue strength of the hot working tool steel 1.2343 at 500 °C can fall below the values reduced by the factor k. This can often be the cause of the liner slipping. This also applies to other hot working steels used for the manufacture of containers. The design should therefore take into account the plastic behavior of the container material under time-dependent thermomechanical stresses if the reduction of the interference-fit stresses is to be prevented or at least held within limits. This problem is helped by the previously described combined heating and cooling system. A locally targeted cooling over the container length can largely prevent or at least reduce thermal overstressing.

The static calculation of containers based on elastic theory is based on the equilibrium requirements of thick-wall hollow bodies. Because round billets are mainly extruded and containers with round bores are usually used, the equilibrium analysis required to determine the forces in the three axes can preferentially be carried out on a volume element with cylindrical coordinates r, t, and z.

The maximum radial, tangential, and axial stresses for the design of the container are combined to an equivalent stress using the von Mises yield criteria:

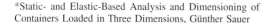

Table 7.11   Characteristic material parameters of hot working tool steels and a nickel-base hot working material measured at room temperature (RT) and at 500 °C under static and dynamic loading

Tool steel number	Abbreviation	$R_{m/RT}$, N/mm^2	$R_{m/600}$, N/mm^2	$R_{p0.2/500}$, N/mm^2	$R_{ZSch/500}$, N/mm^2	A_5, %
1.2343	X38CrMoV51	1511	1040	883	540	12
1.2344	X40CrMoV52	1619	1099	706	530	12
1.2365	X32CrMoV33	1354	883	638	441	8
1.2567	X30WCrV53	1511	1014	706	510	12
1.2581	X30WCrV93	1550	1099	903	530	8
1.2603	45CrMoW58	1452	952	706	481	12
1.4973	NiCr19CoMo	1315	1295	952	598	...

$R_{m/RT}$, tensile strength at room temperature; $R_{m/500}$, tensile strength at 500 °C; $R_{p0.2/500}$, 0.2% proof stress at 500 °C; $R_{ZSch/500}$, elevated-temperature tensile fatigue strength. Source: [Wan 72]

$$\sigma_v = \frac{1}{\sqrt{2}} \sqrt{(\sigma_t - \sigma_r)^2 + (\sigma_r - \sigma_z)^2 + (\sigma_t - \sigma_z)^2}$$

When designing the liner, liner holder, and the container mantle, experience-based internal and external diameters and interference fit form the starting point, and these are then adjusted according to the resultant equivalent stresses. The internal pressure, p_i, in the liner can be approximately set to the specific stem pressure.

The following symbols apply to the calculations:

d_{1i} = liner internal diameter
d_{2i} = liner holder internal diameter
d_{3i} = mantle internal diameter
d_{1a} = liner external diameter
d_{2a} = liner holder external diameter
d_{3a} = mantle external diameter
$u_n = (d_{na}/d_{ni})$ = diameter ratio, for example:
$u_1 = (d_{1a}/d_{1i})$; $u_2 = (d_{2a}/d_{2i})$; $u_3 = (d_{3a}/d_{3i})$; for three-part containers
F_{St} = extrusion load = stem load
A_0 = cross-sectional area of the liner bore
p_a = external pressure on the individual container components, for example, from the interference fits
p_{sn} = interference pressure between the individual container components
$p_{St} = F_{St}/A_0$ specific extrusion pressure = stem load/area of the container bore
p_i = internal pressure on the individual container components
σ_r = radial working or prestresses in the container as a result of the working pressure or the prestresses
σ_t = tangential or prestresses in the container as a result of the working pressure or the prestresses
σ_a = axial working and prestresses in the container

σ_{rges} = effective radial working stresses from the superimposition of the working and prestresses
σ_{tges} = effective tangential working stresses from the superimposition of the working and prestresses
σ_v = equivalent stresses from σ_{tges}, σ_{rges}, and σ_{zges}
E = Young's modulus
ε_t = relative expansion or compression of the individual container components under the effect of the working or interference forces
ε_s = relative interference fit

7.8   Design of a Single-Piece Container Loaded in Three Dimensions

The stress variation over the wall thickness on a single piece container is calculated as follows:

Container inner wall: $\sigma_{r(ri)} = -p$

$$\sigma_{t(ri)} = p_i \frac{u^2 + 1}{u^2 - 1}$$

Container outer wall: $\sigma_{t(ra)} = -0$

$$\sigma_{t(ra)} = p_{ri} \frac{2}{u^2 - 1} \left(\text{for } u = \frac{d_a}{d_i} \right)$$

The equivalent stresses are:

Container inner wall:

$$\sigma_{v(ri)} = \frac{1}{\sqrt{2}}$$
$$\sqrt{(\sigma_{t(ri)} - \sigma_{r(ri)})^2 + (\sigma_{r(ri)} - \sigma_z)^2 + (\sigma_z - \sigma_{t(ri)})^2}$$

Container outer wall:

$$\sigma_{v(ra)} = \frac{1}{\sqrt{2}}$$

$$\sqrt{(\sigma_{t(ra)} - \sigma_{r(ra)})^2 + (\sigma_{r(ra)} - \sigma_z)^2 + (\sigma_z - \sigma_{t(ra)})^2}$$

The maximum equivalent stress always occurs on the container inner wall.

7.9 Design of a Two-Part Container

7.9.1 Calculation of the Prestresses σ_r^x and σ_t^x Developed in a Two-Part Container by the Interference-Fit Forces

The interference pressure, p_s, between the liner and the mantle is obtained from:

$$p_s = \frac{E \times \varepsilon_s}{2} \times \frac{(u_3^2 - 1) \times (u_1^2 - 1)}{u^2 - 1}$$

The prestresses produced from the interference pressure, p_s, are calculated from:

For the liner inner wall:

$$\sigma_r^x(d_{1i}) = 0 \quad \sigma_t^x(d_{1i}) = -p_s \frac{2u_1^2}{u_1^2 - 1}$$

For the interface on the liner outer wall:

$$\sigma_r^x(d_{1a}) = -p_s \quad \sigma_t^x(d_{1a}) = -p_s \frac{u_1^2 + 1}{u_1^2 - 1}$$

For the interface on the mantle inner wall:

$$\sigma_r^x(d_{3i}) = -p_s \quad \sigma_t^x(d_{3i}) = p_s \frac{u_3^2 + 1}{u_3^2 - 1}$$

For the mantle external wall:

$$\sigma_r^x(d_{3a}) = 0 \quad \sigma_t^x(d_{3a}) = p_s \frac{2}{u_3^2 - 1}$$

7.9.1.1 Calculation of the Working Stresses σ_r^{xx} and σ_t^{xx} from the Extrusion Forces in a Two-Part Container

During extrusion, the deformation forces in the container bore, or rather the specific stem

pressure F_{St}/A_0, radially load the container with the working pressure, p_t. The resultant operational stresses, σ_r and σ_y, must to be obtained from the one-part container analysis. Accordingly:

For the liner wall of the container

$$\sigma_r^{xx}(d_{1i}) = -p_i \quad \sigma_t^{xx}(d_{1i}) = p_i \frac{u^2 + 1}{u^2 - 1}$$

For the interface d_{1a}/d_{3i} of the two-part container:

$$\sigma_r^{xx}\left(\frac{d_{1a}}{d_{3i}}\right) = -p_i \frac{u_3^2 - 1}{u^2 - 1} \quad \sigma_t^{xx}\left(\frac{d_{1a}}{d_{3i}}\right) = p_i \frac{u_3^2 + 1}{u^2 - 1}$$

For the container outer wall:

$$\sigma_r^{xx}(d_{3a}) = 0 \quad \sigma_t^{xx}(d_{3a}) = p_i \frac{2}{u^2 - 1}$$

The effective stresses in the container (the working stresses) are obtained from the addition of the operational stresses and the prestresses (additive superimposition).

7.9.1.2 Determining the Operating Stresses σ_r^{xxx} and σ_t^{xxx} by Addition (Additive Superimposition) of σ_r^x and σ_t^x and σ_r^{xx} and σ_t^{xx} in a Two-Part Container

Accordingly:

For the container inner wall:

$$\sigma_{r.}^{xxx}(d_{1i}) = -p_i$$

$$\sigma_t^{xxx}(d_{1i}) = p_i \frac{u^2 + 1}{u^2 - 1} - p_s \frac{2u_1^2}{u_1^2 - 1}$$

For the outer wall of the liner at the interface:

$$\sigma_r^{xxx}(d_{1a}) = -p_i \frac{u_3^2 - 1}{u^2 - 1} - p_s$$

$$\sigma_t^{xxx}(d_{1a}) = p_i \frac{u_3^2 + 1}{u^2 - 1} - p_s \frac{u_1^2 + 1}{u_1^2 - 1}$$

For the mantle inner wall at the interface:

$$\sigma_r^{xxx}(d_{3i}) = -p_i \frac{u_3^2 - 1}{u^2 - 1} - p_s$$

$$\sigma_t^{xxx}(d_{3i}) = p_i \frac{u_3^2 + 1}{u^2 - 1} + p_s \frac{u_3^2 + 1}{u_3^2 - 1}$$

For the container outer wall:

$$\sigma_r^{xxx}(d_{3a}) = 0 \quad \sigma_t^{xxx}(d_{3a}) = p_i \frac{2}{u^2 - 1} + p_s \frac{2}{u_3^2 - 1}$$

7.9.1.3 Calculation of the Equivalent Stress σ_v in a Two-Part Container

For the container inner wall (container liner bore)

$$\sigma_{v(d_{1i})} =$$
$$\frac{1}{\sqrt{2}} \sqrt{(\sigma_{t(d_{1i})} - \sigma_{r(d_{1i})})^2 + (\sigma_z - \sigma_{t(d_{1i})})^2 + (\sigma_z - \sigma_{r(d_{1i})})^2}$$

For the outer liner wall at the interface:

$$\sigma_{v(d_{1a})} =$$
$$\frac{1}{\sqrt{2}} \sqrt{(\sigma_{t(d_{1a})} - \sigma_{r(d_{1a})})^2 + (\sigma_z - \sigma_{t(d_{1a})})^2 + (\sigma_z - \sigma_{r(d_{1a})})^2}$$

For the inner wall of the mantle at the interface:

$$\sigma_{v(d_{3i})} =$$
$$\frac{1}{\sqrt{2}} \sqrt{(\sigma_{t(d_{3i})} - \sigma_{r(d_{3i})})^2 + (\sigma_z - \sigma_{t(d_{3i})})^2 + (\sigma_z - \sigma_{r(d_{3i})})^2}$$

For the external wall of the mantle:

$$\sigma_{v(d_{3a})} =$$
$$\frac{1}{\sqrt{2}} \sqrt{(\sigma_{t(d_{3a})} - \sigma_{r(d_{3a})})^2 + (\sigma_z - \sigma_{t(d_{3a})})^2 + (\sigma_z - \sigma_{r(d_{3a})})^2}$$

7.9.2 Design of a Three-Part Container

7.9.2.1 Calculation of the Prestresses σ_r^x and σ_t^x Developed by the Interference-Fit Forces in a Three-Part-Container

The interference-fit pressure, p_{s1}, between the liner and the liner holder is given by:

$$p_{s1} = \frac{E \times \varepsilon_{s1}}{2} \times \frac{(u_3^2 \times u_2^2 - 1) \times (u_1^2 - 1)}{u^2 - 1}$$

Under the effect of the interference pressure, p_{s1}, the following radial and tangential prestresses, σ_r^x and σ_t^x, occur in the container if the liner holder and container mantle are treated as one item:

For the liner wall:

$$\sigma_r^x(d_{1i}) = 0 \quad \sigma_t^x(d_{1i}) = -p_{s1} \frac{2u_1^2}{u_1^2 - 1}$$

For the interface 1 at the outside of the liner:

$$\sigma_r^x(d_{1a}) = -p_{s1} \quad \sigma_t^x(d_{1a}) = -p_{s1} \frac{u_1^2 + 1}{u_1^2 - 1}$$

For the interface 1 on the inner wall of the liner holder:

$$\sigma_r^x(d_{2i}) = -p_{s1} \quad \sigma_t^x(d_{2i}) = p_{s1} \frac{u_3^2 \times u_2^2 + 1}{u_3^2 \times u_2^2 - 1}$$

For the interface 2 of the outside wall of the liner holder with the inside wall of the mantle:

$$\sigma_r^x\left(\frac{d_{2a}}{d_{3i}}\right) = -p_{s1} \frac{u_3^2 - 1}{u_3^2 \times u_2^2 - 1}$$
$$\sigma_t^x\left(\frac{d_{2a}}{d_{3i}}\right) = p_{s1} \frac{u_3^2 + 1}{u_3^2 \times u_2^2 - 1}$$

For the outside wall of the mantle:

$$\sigma_r^x(d_{3a}) = 0 \quad \sigma_t^x(d_{3a}) = p_{s1} \frac{2}{u_3^2 \times u_2^2 - 1}$$

Under the effect of the interference pressure, p_{s2}, the following radial and tangential prestresses, σ_r^0 and σ_t^0, occur in the container if the liner and liner holder are treated as one item:

For the liner wall:

$$\sigma_r^0(d_{1i}) = 0 \quad \sigma_t^0(d_{1i}) = -p_{s2} \frac{2 \times u_2^2 \times u_1^2}{u_2^2 \times u_1^2 - 1}$$

For the interface 1 outside of the liner to the inside of the liner holder

$$\sigma_r^0\left(\frac{d_{1a}}{d_{2i}}\right) = -p_{s2} \frac{u_2^2 \times u_1^2 - u_2^2}{u_2^2 \times u_1^2 - 1}$$
$$\sigma_t^0\left(\frac{d_{1a}}{d_{2i}}\right) = -p_{s2} \frac{u_2^2 \times u_1^2 + u_2^2}{u_2^2 \times u_1^2 - 1}$$

For the interface 2 on the outer wall of the liner holder:

$$\sigma_r^0(d_{2a}) = -p_{s2} \quad \sigma_t^0(d_{2a}) = -p_{s2} \frac{u_2^2 \times u_1^2 + 1}{u_2^2 \times u_1^2 - 1}$$

For the interface 2 on the inside wall of the mantle:

$$\sigma_r^0(d_{3i}) = -p_{s2} \quad \sigma_t^0(d_{3i}) = -p_{s2}\frac{2}{u_3^2 - 1}$$

For the outside wall of the mantle:

$$\sigma_r^0(d_{3a}) = 0 \quad \sigma_t^0(d_{3a}) = p_{s2}\frac{2}{u_3^2 - 1}$$

7.9.2.2 Calculation of the Working Stresses σ_r^{xx} and σ_t^{xx} Resulting from Deformation Forces during Extrusion in a Three-Part Container

The specific stem pressure, F_{St}/A_0, loads the container inner wall radially with the operating pressure, p_i. This results in radial and tangential working stresses, σ_r^{xx} and σ_t^{xx}, in the container wall and can be calculated for a three-part container as follows:

For the internal wall of the container:

$$\sigma_r^{xx}(d_{1i}) = -p_i \quad \sigma_t^{xx}(d_{1i}) = p_i\frac{u^2 + 1}{u^2 - 1}$$

For the interface 1 between the liner and the liner holder:

$$\sigma_r^{xx}\left(\frac{d_{1a}}{d_{2i}}\right) = -p_i\frac{u_3^2 \times u_2^2 - 1}{u^2 - 1}$$

$$\sigma_t^{xx}\left(\frac{d_{1a}}{d_{2i}}\right) = p_i\frac{u_3^2 \times u_2^2 + 1}{u^2 - 1}$$

For the interface 2 between the liner holder and the mantle:

$$\sigma_r^{xx}\left(\frac{d_{2a}}{d_{3i}}\right) = -p_i\frac{u_3^2 - 1}{u^2 - 1} \quad \sigma_t^{xx}\left(\frac{d_{2a}}{d_{3i}}\right) = p_i\frac{u_3^2 + 1}{u^2 - 1}$$

For the outer wall of the mantle:

$$\sigma_r^{xx}(d_{3a}) = p_i\frac{d_{1i}^2}{d_{3a}^2 - d_{3a}^2}\left\{1 - \frac{d_{3a}^2}{d_{3a}^2}\right\} = 0$$

$$\sigma_t^{xx}(d_{3a}) = p_i\frac{2}{u^2 - 1}$$

7.9.2.3 Calculation of the Working Stresses σ_r^{xxx} and σ_t^{xxx} by the Addition of the Prestresses σ_r^x and σ_t^x, and σ_r^0 and σ_t^0, and the Operating Stresses σ_r^{xx} and σ_t^{xx} (Additive Superimposition) in the Three-Part Container

For the liner wall:

$$\sigma_r^{xxx}(d_{1i}) = -p_i \quad \sigma_t^{xxx}(d_{1i}) = p_i\frac{u^2 + 1}{u^2 - 1}$$

$$- p_{s1}\frac{2u_1^2}{u_1^2 - 1} - p_{s2}\frac{2 \times u_2^2 \times u_1^2}{u_2^2 \times u2_1^2 - 1}$$

For the interface 1 outside of the liner:

$$\sigma_r^{xxx}(d_{1a}) = -p_i\frac{u_3^2 \times u_2^2 - 1}{u^2 - 1}$$

$$- p_{s1} - p_{s2}\frac{u_2^2 \times u_1^2 - u_2^2}{u_2^2 \times u_1^2 - 1}$$

$$\sigma_t^{xxx}(d_{1a}) = p_i\frac{u_3^2 \times u_2^2 + 1}{u^2 - 1} - p_{s1}\frac{u_1^2 + 1}{u_1^2 - 1}$$

$$- p_{s2}\frac{u_2^2 \times u_1^2 + u_2^2}{u_2^2 \times u_1^2 - 1}$$

For the interface 1 inside wall of the liner holder:

$$\sigma_r^{xxx}(d_{2i}) = -p_i\frac{u_3^2 \times u_2^2 - 1}{u^2 - 1}$$

$$- p_{s1} - p_{s2}\frac{u_2^2 \times u_1^2 - u_2^2}{u_2^2 \times u_1^2 - 1}$$

$$\sigma_t^{xxx}(d_{2i}) = p_i\frac{u_3^2 \times u_2^2 + 1}{u^2 - 1} + p_{s1}\frac{u_3^2 \times u_2^2 + 1}{u_3^2 \times u_2^2 - 1}$$

$$- p_{s2}\frac{u_2^2 \times u_1^2 + u_2^2}{u_2^2 \times u_1^2 - 1}$$

For interface 2 outside wall of the liner holder:

$$\sigma_r^{xxx}(d_{2a}) = -p_i\frac{u_3^2 - 1}{u^2 - 1} - p_{s1}\frac{u_3^2 - 1}{u_3^2 \times u_2^2 - 1} - p_{s2}$$

$$\sigma_t^{xxx}(d_{2a}) = p_i\frac{u_3^2 + 1}{u^2 - 1} + p_{s1}\frac{u_3^2 + 1}{u_3^2 \times u_2^2 - 1}$$

$$- p_{s2}\frac{u_2^2 \times u_1^2 + 1}{u_2^2 \times u_1^2 - 1}$$

For interface 2 inside wall of the mantle:

$$\sigma_r^{xxx}(d_{3i}) = -p_i\frac{u_3^2 - 1}{u^2 - 1} - p_{s1}\frac{u_3^2 - 1}{u_3^2 \times u_2^2 - 1} - p_{s2}$$

$$\sigma_t^{xxx}(d_{3i}) = p_i\frac{u_3^2 + 1}{u^2 - 1} + p_{s1}\frac{u_3^2 + 1}{u_3^2 \times u_2^2 - 1}$$

$$+ p_{s2}\frac{2}{u_3^2 - 1}$$

For the outside of the mantle:

$$\sigma_r^{xxx}(d_{3a}) = 0$$

$$\sigma_t^{xxx}(d_{3a}) = p_i \frac{2}{u^2 - 1} + p_{s1} \frac{2}{u_3^2 \times u_2^2 - 1}$$
$$+ p_{s2} \frac{2}{u_3^2 - 1}$$

7.9.2.4 Calculation of the Equivalent Stresses, σ_v, in the Three-Part Container

For the inside wall of the container (liner bore):

$$\sigma_{v(d_{1i})} =$$
$$\frac{1}{\sqrt{2}} \sqrt{(\sigma_{t(d_{1i})} - \sigma_{r(d_{1i})})^2 + (\sigma_z - \sigma_{t(d_{1i})})^2 + (\sigma_z - \sigma_{r(d_{1i})})^2}$$

For the outside wall of the liner at the interface:

$$\sigma_{v(d_{1a})} =$$
$$\frac{1}{\sqrt{2}} \sqrt{(\sigma_{t(d_{1a})} - \sigma_{r(d_{1a})})^2 + (\sigma_z - \sigma_{t(d_{1a})})^2 + (\sigma_z - \sigma_{r(d_{1a})})^2}$$

For the inner wall of the liner holder at the interface:

$$\sigma_{v(d_{2i})} =$$
$$\frac{1}{\sqrt{2}} \sqrt{(\sigma_{t(d_{2i})} - \sigma_{r(d_{2i})})^2 + (\sigma_z - \sigma_{t(d_{2i})})^2 + (\sigma_z - \sigma_{r(d_{2i})})^2}$$

For the outer wall of the liner holder at the interface:

$$\sigma_{v(d_{2a})} =$$
$$\frac{1}{\sqrt{2}} \sqrt{(\sigma_{t(d_{2a})} - \sigma_{r(d_{2a})})^2 + (\sigma_z - \sigma_{t(d_{2a})})^2 + (\sigma_z - \sigma_{r(d_{2a})})^2}$$

For the inside wall of the mantle at the interface:

$$\sigma_{v(d_{3i})} =$$
$$\frac{1}{\sqrt{2}} \sqrt{(\sigma_{t(d_{3i})} - \sigma_{r(d_{3i})})^2 + (\sigma_z - \sigma_{t(d_{3i})})^2 + (\sigma_z - \sigma_{r(d_{3i})})^2}$$

For the outside wall of the mantle:

$$\sigma_{v(d_{3a})} =$$
$$\frac{1}{\sqrt{2}} \sqrt{(\sigma_{t(d_{3a})} - \sigma_{r(d_{3a})})^2 + (\sigma_z - \sigma_{t(d_{3a})})^2 + (\sigma_z - \sigma_{r(d_{3a})})^2}$$

7.10 Examples of Calculations for Different Containers, Their Stresses and Dimensions

Examples of the stresses and dimensioning of containers are given in this section. The two-part container described in section 7.10.1 is not very highly stressed in terms of the relatively low thermal and mechanical loads. The stresses fall in the elastic range of the hot working steels. In section 7.10.2, a comparable liner with a round bore is selected for the liner with an oval bore. Stress concentrations for a life estimate must be determined by FEM analysis. In section 7.10.3, the calculated stresses in a three-part container for copper alloys is described. The results show that the mechanical loading at high working temperatures necessitates further investigations for service life, particularly of the liner.

The influence of the axial load is clearly shown in the comparison in section 7.10.4. The working condition that arises from the plastic behavior of the material at the high temperatures of the container components is discussed in section 7.10.5.

The working conditions in hot working by extrusion vary considerably. Therefore, a detailed knowledge of the working parameters in a particular application is necessary for the design of a container. Basically, the maximum possible thermal and mechanical loads that can occur during production provide the starting point. Load records are therefore required. At working temperatures of 600 °C and above, the elastic limit of hot working steels is greatly exceeded. In this case, consideration must be given to the measures (cooling, special hot working steels) that will reduce material damage and thus increase the service life.

The calculated stresses are necessary to determine the life of a container.

7.10.1 Design of a Two-Part Container with a Round Bore for Aluminum Alloys

Two-part containers are usually used for the easy and moderately difficult-to-extrude aluminum alloys. In this example, the formulae for calculating the stresses are taken from section 7.9. The data for the calculation and the equivalent stresses, σ_v, for dimensioning the container and the selection of the hot working steel are given as follows.

7.10.1.1 Two-Part Container for a 25 MN Extrusion Press

Extruded Material. Easy and Moderately Difficult-to-extrude Aluminum Alloys:

Working temperature range of the extruded material	$<530\ °C$
Maximum container operating temperature	$<500\ °C$
Maximum extrusion press load, $F_{St\ max}$	25 MN
Maximum specific stem pressure, p_{St}	509 N/mm^2
Maximum radial pressure, p_i	356 N/mm^2
Modulus of elasticity, E	1.8×10^5 N/mm^2
Safety factor	1.25
Liner bore, d_{1i}	250 mm
Outsid diameter of the liner, d_{1a}	440 mm
Liner diameter ratio, u_1 $= d_{1a}/d_{1i}$	1.76
Mantle internal diameter, d_{3i}	440 mm
Mantle external diameter, d_{3a}	950 mm
Mantle diameter ratio, u_3 $= d_{3a}/d_{3i}$	2.16
Container diameter ratio, $u = d_{3a}/d_{1i}$	3.8
Relative interference fit, ε_s	1.8×10^{-3}
Equivalent stress liner bore, $\sigma_v(d_{1i})$	439 N/mm^2
Equivalent stress liner outside diameter, $\sigma_v(d_{1a})$	176 N/mm^2
Equivalent stress mantle internal diameter, $\sigma_v(d_{3i})$	422 N/mm^2
Equivalent stress mantle external diameter, $\sigma_v(d_{3a})$	104 N/mm^2

7.10.2 Calculation of a Three-Part Container with an Oval Bore for Aluminum Alloys

Containers with oval cross-sectional billets are more suited for the production of very wide flat sections than containers for round billets. The calculation of the stresses of a liner with an oval cross section, as well as the complete container, is similar to that for a liner with a round bore. The varying wall thickness of the liner—the thickest can be several times the thinnest—results in a very unequal shape influence under load. The resultant stress concentrations depend on the side ratio of the bore. The higher the side ratio, the greater the stress concentration. It occurs in the transition zone from the widest to the smallest side. A one-part liner with an oval bore is therefore not suited to withstand the required interference pressure uniformly distributed over the external circular diameter. The interference-fit stresses act more severely on the thinnest wall thickness of the liner. In contrast, the effect of the working pressure on the liner is less in the horizontal axis than in the vertical axis. To achieve an acceptable life for a one-piece liner of a container with an oval bore, the stress concentrations must be kept low. The narrow sides should be semicircles, and the ratio of the narrow to the wide side should not be much higher than 1 to 2. Liners with higher values (approximately 2.5) are in use.

As already mentioned, there is no method to calculate the stresses in containers with oval bores. The starting point is therefore a comparable round bore. Also, for machine design reasons, it is assumed for a specific press size that the outside diameter of the container is always the same for extrusion billets with round or oval cross sections. In order to be able to calculate the dimensions for a container with an oval bore, the liner with the oval bore is converted to a liner with a round bore. However, the resultant lower specific stem pressure, p_{St}, cannot be used in the comparative equations. Instead, the specific pressure p_{St} must be calculated for the container with the oval bore. The dimensions and interference fits for the container with the oval bore can then be determined from the stresses obtained by using the method described in section 7.10.1. The stress in the liner can be obtained by FEM analysis.

In the following design example, a container for aluminum alloys with high extrudability was chosen. With a side ratio of 1 to 2 and the dimensions for an oval bore, a stress concentration factor of approximately 2.5 must be assumed in the area of the semicircular narrow side. This value, based on experience, can be used for the dimensions assumed in the design example. The internal diameter of the liner, d_{1i}, is calculated from the circumference of the oval bore, as follows:

$$d_{1i} = [h \times \pi + 2(b - h)] \times \frac{1}{\pi}$$

$$= [160 \times \pi + 2(335 - 160)] \times \frac{1}{\pi} = 271 \text{ mm}$$

Accordingly, d_{1i} is taken to be 270 mm. The data for the calculation and the resultant equivalent stresses, σ_v, for the dimensioning of the container and the selection of the hot working steels are given as follows.

7.10.2.1 Three-Part Container for a 25 MN Extrusion Press

Extruded Material. Easy and Moderately Difficult-to-Extrude Aluminum Alloys:

Working temperature range of the extruded material	<530 °C
Maximum container operating temperature	<500 °C
Maximum extrusion press load, $F_{St\ max}$	25 MN
Maximum specific stem pressure, p_{St}	437 N/mm^2
Maximum radial pressure, p_i	306 N/mm^2
Modulus of elasticity, E	1.8×10^5 N/mm^2
Safety factor	1.6
Liner bore, d_{1i}	270 mm (160 × 335 mm)
Outside diameter of the liner, d_{1a}	425 mm
Liner diameter ratio, $u_1 = d_{1a}/d_{1i}$	1.58
Liner holder internal diameter, d_{2i}	425 mm
Liner holder external diameter, d_{2a}	560 mm
Liner holder diameter ratio, $u_2 = d_{2a}/d_{2i}$	1.31
Mantle internal diameter, d_{3i}	560 mm
Mantle external diameter, d_{3a}	950 mm
Mantle diameter ratio, $u_3 = d_{3a}/d_{3i}$	1.7
Container diameter ratio, $u = d_{3a}/d_{1i}$	3.52
Relative interference fit, ε_{s1} (liner/liner holder)	0.8×10^{-3}
Relative interference fit, ε_{s2} (liner + liner holder/mantle)	1.0×10^{-3}
Equivalent stress liner bore, $\sigma_v(d_{1i})$	475 N/mm^2
Equivalent stress liner outside diameter, $\sigma_v(d_{1a})$	211 N/mm^2
Equivalent stress liner holder inside diameter, $\sigma_v(d_{2i})$	314 N/mm^2
Equivalent stress liner holder outside diameter, $\sigma_v(d_{2a})$	187 N/mm^2
Equivalent stress mantle internal diameter, $\sigma_v(d_{3i})$	348 N/mm^2
Equivalent stress mantle external diameter, $\sigma_v(d_{3a})$	133 N/mm^2

The low equivalent stress at the inner wall of $\sigma_v = 475$ N/mm^2 only applies to a liner with a constant wall thickness. For a liner with an oval bore (side ratio of 1 to 2) there exist stress concentrations that are 2.5 times higher. Therefore, there are stress concentrations of almost 1200 N/mm^2. The working stress (collected load data) on a well-used extrusion press is 0.8 the maximum extrusion load. This gives an average stress of approximately 950 N/mm^2 for the liner with a flat bore. This value indicates that the service life will be relatively short.

7.10.3 Calculation of a Three-Part Container with a Round Bore for Copper Alloys

Three-part containers are required for copper alloys with a low extrudability. The formulae in section 7.9.2 form the basis for the calculation. Axial stresses are not taken into account. The results show, however, that overloading of the selected hot working steels occurs.

7.10.3.1 Three-Part Container for a 25 MN Extrusion Press

Extruded Material. Copper Alloys with a Low Extrudability.

Working temperature range of the extruded material	>600 °C
Maximum container operating temperature	<450 °C

Maximum extrusion press load, $F_{St\,max}$	25 MN
Maximum specific stem pressure, p_{St}	982 N/mm^2
Maximum radial pressure, p_i	688 N/mm^2
Modulus of elasticity, E	1.8×10^5 N/mm^2
Safety factor	1.25
Liner bore, d_i	180 mm
Outside diameter of the liner, d_{1a}	280 mm
Liner diameter ratio, $u_1 = d_{1a}/d_{1i}$	1.56
Liner holder internal diameter, d_{2i}	280 mm
Liner holder external diameter, d_{2a}	440 mm
Liner holder diameter ratio, $u_2 = d_{2a}/d_{2i}$	1.57
Mantle internal diameter, d_{3i}	440 mm
Mantle external diameter, d_{3a}	950 mm
Mantle diameter ratio, $u_3 = d_{3a}/d_{3i}$	2.16
Container diameter ratio, $u = d_{3a}/d_{1i}$	5.0
Relative interference fit, ε_{s1} (liner/liner holder)	1.8×10^{-3} mm
Relative interference fit, ε_{s2} (liner + liner holder/mantle)	1.4×10^{-3} mm
Equivalent stress liner bore, $\sigma_v(d_{1i})$	826 N/mm^2
Equivalent stress liner outside diameter, $\sigma_v(d_{1a})$	400 N/mm^2
Equivalent stress liner holder inside diameter, $\sigma_v(d_{2i})$	612 N/mm^2
Equivalent stress liner holder outside diameter, $\sigma_v(d_{2a})$	256 N/mm^2
Equivalent stress mantle internal diameter, $\sigma_v(d_{3i})$	467 N/mm^2
Equivalent stress mantle external diameter, $\sigma_v(d_{3a})$	114 N/mm^2

The results of the calculations in this case indicate stresses at which pure elastic behavior cannot be expected. Instead, the service life of the elastically/plastically stressed component must be verified using material data for the se-

lected hot working tool steels to determine whether the container is economically viable.

7.10.4 Influence of Axial Loading of the Container

The equivalent stress, σ_v, without the axial force from section 7.10.1 is referred to for the consideration of the effect of axial stresses.

Because axial stresses are present in a container in the rest condition and also occur during production, they should always be included in the calculations where there is concern. A pure mathematical calculation of the axial forces is not possible. For the stress state in the container, the effects that arise from the shrink-fitting process during manufacture as well as those that occur during production cannot be considered as fixed or stable values. They cannot be clearly defined in magnitude. Only the container sealing load is known. The actual axial force from the friction/shearing varies. It can be measured during the extrusion process. The axial force produced from shrink-fitting cannot be accurately determined. It depends on the circumstances and the influences that occur during shrink-fitting. In addition, the interference forces vary locally in the interface, depending on the container temperature. The interference pressure decreases during the life of a container. Therefore, the axial force produced by shrink-fitting must be estimated from experience. More information can be found in Fig. 7.105. In this example, the container is 1000 mm long. For direct extrusion with long billets, the factors for the prestress, $0.35 \times p_s$, is used to calculate the axial stresses, and for the working stress, $0.65 \times p_i$. The equivalent stress according to the von Mises criterion is used for the three-dimensional state.

In principle, the axial forces in the container produce compressive stresses.

The equivalent stress in this example at the bore of the liner when the axial stresses are taken into account are 10% higher than that calculated without the axial stresses. This resultant stress increase has a negative influence on the service life, which can be critical for the liner at high temperatures. However, the load on the container mantle increases only slightly, with a 2% higher stress at the inner wall.

The influence of the axial stresses in the container varies significantly. The operating strength of containers that from experience have an economic service life is not significantly reduced by the axial stresses. Table 7.12 shows the result of the calculation.

Although the prediction of the developed stresses includes relatively coarse simplifications and thus induces uncertainties into the calculation, axial forces should always be taken into account if the thermal and mechanical working stresses reach the limits of the hot-working steels.

7.10.5 Operating Conditions from Elastic/Plastic Behavior of the Tool Material under the Influence of the Thermomechanical Working Stresses

Containers are highly stressed both thermally and mechanically in extrusion. If the temperature and stress state in the thick-wall container sleeves results in localized plastic deformation, this first starts at the inner fibers of the liner. Complete plastic deformation of the liner and, in certain cases, of the liner holder and the mantle does not occur. Only in the area of the interference fit can partial plastic deformation of the internal wall of the liner holder occur to a limited extent. It can therefore be assumed that only localized plastic deformation of the liner occurs. Stress variations are developed at the internal and external diameter of the partially plastically deformed liner that hardly change from the elastic stress state in the central region of the liner wall as a result of creep. The radial stresses, on the other hand, are only slightly influenced in the middle region. This is shown in Dubbel [1986].

If there is a buildup of heat in the container from the high deformation temperature, the elastic limit can be exceeded, so that plastic deformation, and consequently work hardening,

can occur. If embrittlement and ultimately fatigue of the material, together with a reduction in the ductility, occur as a result of further high thermal and mechanical loading, then the consequence is the formation of a crack.

While the static stressing process damages the hot working material by creep, fatigue results from the number of load cycles. The creep and the fatigue damage results in permanent deformation and a reduction in the service life of the container [Ber 76/1-4].

The stresses in the container are determined by the calculations based on elasticity. On the other hand, the calculation on an elastic/plastic basis determines the service life. In addition to determining the temperature distribution within the container over a defined number of working cycles in a given time, approximately 10 to 20 cycles, the stresses must be determined after a stable operating state has been reached in order to determine the service life. It is possible to determine the service life of a container that has undergone plastic deformation by FEM analysis, using knowledge of the material parameters. The analysis of a rectangular billet container [Mit 97] serves as an example. A container for aluminum alloys with an operating temperature of approximately 500 °C is investigated. In this temperature range, creep damage dominates with the hot working steels used, X38 CrMoV5-1 and X2 NiCoMo 18-9-5. It is identified by fatigue tests at different load frequencies. A method of service life prediction is used with creep/fatigue interaction in which the nonelastic strains and strain rates must be known. They are obtained from the experimental simulation of creep tests with the hot working steels used.

Restrictions must be made because of the actual operating conditions in extrusion:

Table 7.12 Stress in the container

With and without axial force

		Local stresses(a), N/mm^2			
		Liner		Mantle	
Load condition and stress type	Stress component	Inner wall	External wall	Inner wall	External wall
Prestress, p_{s1}	Tangential, σ_t	-275	-182	144	51
Interference pressure	Radial, σ_r	0	-93	-93	0
	Axial, σ_z	48	48	-9	-9
Working stress, p_i	Tangential, σ_t	409	150	150	53
Working pressure	Radial, σ_r	-356	-97	-97	0
	Axial, σ_z	-17	-17	-17	-17
Equivalent stress without axial force (two-dimensional)	Working stress, σ_v	439	176	422	104
Equivalent stress with axial force (three-dimensional)	Working stress, σ_v	483	254	430	130

(a) Negative stresses are compressive. Source: Groos

Table 7.13 Hot working materials for production of extrusion tools for direct and indirect extrusion of nonferrous metals and steels

Material number	Abbreviation (commercial name)	Chemical composition (typical), %													CTE(a)	Liquidus temperature, °C
		C	Si	Mn	Co	Cr	Mo	Ni	V	W	Ti	Al	Zr/ZrO2	Other		
Hot working steels																
1.2311	40CrMnMo7	0.40	0.30	1.45	...	1.95	0.20	...	...	...	...	...	...	...	...	...
1.2323	48CrMoV67	0.45	0.25	0.75	...	1.50	0.70	...	0.30	...	...	...	...	...	...	1500
1.2343	X38CrMoV51	0.38	1.05	0.40	...	5.20	1.30	...	0.40	...	...	...	...	...	10	1500
1.2344	X40CrMoV51	0.40	1.05	0.40	...	5.20	1.40	...	1.00	...	...	...	...	...	10	1500
1.2365	X32CrMoV33	0.30	0.30	0.30	...	3.00	2.80	...	0.50	...	...	...	...	...	10	...
1.2367	X40WCrV53	0.37	0.40	0.40	...	5.00	3.00	...	0.60	...	...	...	...	...	...	...
1.2567	X30WCrV53	0.30	...	...	...	2.40	0.60	...	...	4.3	...	...	...	...	...	...
1.2581	X30WCrV93	0.30	...	...	...	2.60	0.35	...	0.40	8.5	...	...	...	...	...	...
1.2678	X45CoCrWV555	0.45	0.40	0.40	4.50	4.50	0.50	...	2.00	4.50	...	...	...	...	...	...
1.2713	55NiCrMoV6	0.55	0.30	0.60	...	0.70	0.30	1.70	0.10	...	...	...	...	...	...	...
1.2714	56NiCrMoV7	0.56	0.30	0.70	...	1.00	0.50	1.70	0.10	...	...	...	...	...	...	...
1.2758	X50WNiCrVCo121 2	0.50	1.40	0.60	1.65	4.00	0.70	11.50	1.10	12.00	...	...	...	...	...	...
1.2885	X32CrMoCoV333 2	0.32	...	...	3.00	3.00	2.80	...	0.60	...	...	...	...	...	...	...
1.2888	X20CoCrWMo109	0.20	0.25	0.50	9.50	8.50	2.20	...	...	6.80	...	...	...	...	...	...
Austenitic hot working steels																
1.2731	X50NiCrWV1313	0.50	1.35	0.70	...	13.00	...	13.00	1.30	1.30	...	...	...	B	18.5	1450
1.2758	X50WNiCrVCo121 2	0.50	1.40	0.60	1.70	4.00	0.70	11.50	1.10	12.50	2.10	...	...	...	...	...
1.2779	X6NiCrTi2615	0.05	1.00	2.00	...	15.00	1.30	25.50	0.30	...	2.10	...	...	B = 0.07	...	...
Cobalt-base alloys																
2.4979	CoC28MoNi	0.30	1.00	1.00	bal	28.00	5.50	2.25	...	...	...	...	...	...	...	...
	Stellite 4	0.90	...	...	bal	26.00	...	...	...	15.00	...	...	...	Nb	~13	1310
	Stellite 3	2.20	...	...	bal	30.00	...	...	...	16.00	...	...	...	...	...	...
2.9877	Stellite 6	1.10	...	...	bal	26.00	...	...	...	5.00	...	...	...	...	...	...
Nickel-base alloys																
2.4668	NiCr19NbMo	0.05	...	...	...	19.00	3.00	53.00	...	...	1.00	0.60	...	B, Fe	...	...
2.4973	NiCr19CoMo	0.08	...	...	11.00	19.00	10.00	bal	...	...	3.00	1.60	...	B, Fe 5.00	13.8	1320–1350
Molybdenum-base alloys																
	TZM	0.02	...	...	...	...	...	...	...	...	0.50	...	0.08	...	4.0	2610
	ZHM	0.08	...	...	...	...	...	...	...	...	0.14	...	0.72	Hf: 0.14	...	...
	MHC	0.13	...	...	...	...	...	...	...	...	1.50	...	...	1.50	...	...
Molybdenum-base metal-ceramic hot working materials																
	Cermotherm 2015	...	...	...	...	...	85.0	...	...	...	...	...	15.0 ZrO2	...	6.6	Sintered
Hard metals																
	G3 (GT3)	...	Co% 12 25–30	...	...	WC% 88 bal	...	...	(Ta, Nb) C 0–2.50 0–2.50	...	...	TiC max 1.00 1.00	...	...	6.3 7.0	Sintered
Ceramic hot working materials																
	Ziroca comp. 1027	...	%ZrO2 99.50	...	...	%SiO2 0.30	...	...	%HfO2 Trace	...	...	%Fe2O3 Trace	...	...	6.7	...
	Ziroca comp. 2016	...	...	...	...	...	...	...	...	...	...	...	...	...	7.0	Sintered

(a) CTE, cofficient of thermal expansion, 10^{-6}/K, room temperature to 1000 K

- The load cycle must be idealized.
- A ratio of the axial stem pressures to the radially acting internal pressure must be assumed.
- The container must be uniformly loaded over the entire length.
- The temperature is constant in the container (no temperature gradient).
- The interference pressure is uniform and constant over the full length.

Knowledge of the material characteristic parameters for the hot working steel used for the container components is necessary for a working-life determination. Because the material characteristic parameters are not generally available but are known by the producers of the hot working steels, the user of the container must rely on the data from the supplier. A working-life prognosis is necessary to evaluate the economic viability of the container once the operating conditions have been specified by the user.

An evaluation can indicate whether a working-life determination is necessary for a container that is subjected to plastic deformation, even if only slightly. The steel application lists 201 and 202 of the VDEh (German Steel Federation guidelines) give permissible stress magnitudes for the most important hot working steels under "Material Properties" [VDE 85].

The strength of a hot-working steel corresponding to the hot proof stress $R_{p0.2}$ is only valid for a brief temperature exposure. It does not apply from the mechanical viewpoint to the actual prolonged thermal exposure. This also applies to the technical elastic limit $R_{p0.01}$. The deformations that arise from prolonged loads by material flow have to be taken into account. A comparison of the upper stress limits of the common hot-working steels including 1.2343, 1.2344, and 1.2367 show that the technical elastic limit $R_{p0.01}$ is around 70 to 90% of the hot proof stress $R_{p0.2}$ independent of the temperature and that the creep stress for 1% elongation after 1000 h is of the order of 45 to 55% at 500 °C and between only 6 to 10% at 600 °C. The strength of the hot-working steels decreases further the longer the duration of the loading and the higher the working temperature. This fact is true, in particular, with experience in copper alloy extrusion plants. Consequently, the working life of liners operating at high temperatures is often less than 10,000 extrusions. This means that at 40 extrusions per

hour the operating life is 250 hours. Meanwhile, the service life of liners has been increased significantly by container cooling in the majority of applications.

7.11 Manufacture of Containers

The usefulness of a container depends to a large degree on the shape and positional tolerances in terms of straightness, angularity, concentricity, coaxiality and runout according to DIN 7184. The liner bore or the internal bore of containers with oval cross-sections (rectangular billet containers) based on the three datum planes, longitudinal axis = A, horizontal axis = B, and vertical axis = C, the following have to be ensured within tight tolerances:

- The end faces as contact faces are at a right angle to the inner bore so that there is no tilting of the tool when load is applied.
- The location of the container in the container holder can be reproduced. In other words, the centring keyways and the centring keys have to be parallel to the internal bore within tight tolerances.
- The liners and the mantle bore are cylindrical. The liners (which also include the mantle) must have constant wall thickness. There must be no eccentricity. A uniform interference pressure has to be guaranteed and a common centre provided for all containers used on an extrusion press.
- The tolerances for the production of the container should be related to the tolerances of the extrusion press. These include a runout accuracy of 0.15/1000 mm for the fixed dummy block, the runout for a tube press with a mandrel of 0.1/1000 mm, or, the runout for an extrusion press with a loose dummy block, for example, for brass wire, around 0.3/1000 mm.

The production of the interference joint in a container can vary whether two- or three-part construction. The machining of the rough shaped component (hollow blank) to the finished diameter dimension and the sequence of the shrink fitting depends on manufacturing capabilities. The interference value, which is the factor that determines the magnitude of the interference pressure at the interface, is the difference between the diameters of two hollow bodies that have to be fitted together. The interference value is given as an absolute value relative to the nominal value, or generally as a 0/00 (per thousand) value. The overvalue as the interference value is added to the actual value of the bore, and this gives the dimension of the external diameter of the sleeve that is to be fitted. It can also be calculated in the opposite way, starting from the actual value of the external diameter of the sleeve and machining the bore with the corresponding interference value. The same interference value is used for both manufacturing methods. The interference value addition therefore depends on whether the reference dimension taken from the opposing surface stems from a free hollow body or from a hollow body in which another has already been shrunk in. The sequence of fitting, whether from the inside to the outside or from the outside to the inside, must be taken into account.

Fitting from the inside to the outside is preferred. Starting from the bore, the actual value for shrink-fitting is determined from at least five measurements taken crosswise and distributed uniformly over the length. The external diameter of the liner to be fitted is then produced, taking into account the interference value. The material of the component determines the interference value. It must be calculated. After shrink-fitting, the internal bore of the container is remachined. This ensures that the internal bore is cylindrical and dimensionally correct.

The interference value for a two-part container is determined as follows. The external diameter of the liner is finish-machined according to the actual value of the bore of the finished mantle. The dimension of the external diameter of the liner is calculated from:

$$d_{2ib} = d_{2m} + (\varepsilon_{ibx}) \times d_{2m}$$

where d_{2ib} is the outside diameter of the liner, d_{2m} is the inside diameter of the mantle (actual value), and ε_{ibx} is the interference value for the liner (relative interference).

The interference value for a three-part container is determined as follows. After determining the actual value of the liner holder bore that has been produced with a provisional excess on the external diameter, the dimension for the external diameter of the liner is determined:

$$d_{2ib} = d_{2zb} + (\varepsilon_{iby}) \times d_{2zb}$$

where d_{2ib} is the outside diameter of the liner, d_{2zb} is the inside diameter of the liner holder

(actual value), and ε_{iby} is the interference value for the liner (relative interference).

The external diameter of the liner set, consisting of the liner holder and the liner, is finish-machined according to the actual value of the bore of the finished container mantle. The dimension for the external diameter of the liner set is determined as follows:

$$d_{3zb} = d_{3m} + (\varepsilon_{zbz}) \times d_{3m}$$

where d_{3zb} is the outside diameter of the liner set (liner holder), d_{3m} is the inside diameter of the mantle (actual value), and ε_{zbz} is the interference value for the liner holder with the fitted liner (relative interference).

7.12 Container Operation

Careful consideration must be given to the container working temperature, which is important for the press operation. The working temperature must be reached before extrusion commences. The heating rate must not exceed the maximum of 60 °C (108 °F) per hour. With faster heating, there is the risk that the container will not be uniformly heated. The function of the interference fit cannot then be guaranteed. The liner is then overstressed and/or slips. If the container is heated in the press, it should not be sealed against the tool stack, to avoid liner slip.

Both ends of the container bore should be closed during prolonged downtime. This prevents the temperature of the liner from falling below the temperature of the mantle. Standard practice is to close the bore at one end, with the stem and the die set at the other end—without the container sealing load. The interference forces are reduced significantly, even with a temperature difference of only 50 °C (90 °F) between the mantle and the liner. The result is that the safe equivalent stress is exceeded during production. In addition, the action of the container sealing force can result in liner slip.

If a "sticker" occurs (a billet seized in the container), it should be removed from the container as quickly as possible, particularly if the billet temperature exceeds 550 °C. The life of the liner and, in some cases, the liner holder can be significantly reduced by such a mishap.

The location of the container in the press must be central and aligned with the stem. It is particularly important with rod and tube presses (integral piercer) and extrusion presses with fixed dummy blocks to maintain the tooling alignment accuracy specified by the manufacturer. With short-stroke presses, accurate central location of the container is also required. The central location of the tooling to each other is important for both safety and also for process technical requirements.

7.13 Maintenance of Containers

The design drawing, with the associated manufacturing specifications, shrinkage specifications, and production protocol, is needed for the maintenance of containers.

Defect prevention should be the main focus for the maintenance of containers. The operating and maintenance personnel should be trained accordingly.

Attention should be paid to:

- Heating and cooling of containers should follow the guidelines of the manufacturer.
- Stickers are billets in the container that cannot be extruded. They must be immediately removed from the container if the billet temperature exceeds 550 °C. Heat transfer to the liner takes place particularly quickly and intensively in the upset condition.
- Temperature control matched to the production and monitored for protection of the container is recommended for quality reasons for aluminum alloys and is necessary for copper alloys. Intensive cooling of the critical zones within the container is essential for extrusion temperatures over 600 °C.
- Clean contact faces between the extrusion tools (dies, die holder, and hollow dies) and the end face of the liner are necessary.
- Alignment of the extrusion stem to the container must be ensured. Alignment errors can easily result in damage to the liner wall in the container.
- Air inclusions within the container must be avoided. The explosive release of the highly compressed air in the area of the die and the container liner can result in damage to the tooling.

The replacement of worn liners is an essential procedure in the maintenance of containers. When this takes place, the condition of the entire container must be assessed and, if necessary, repairs carried out.

Condition monitoring of the complete container and the procedure for liner replacement include:

1. The number of extrusions at the average operating temperature, extrusion time, the number of stickers at the billet temperature x °C, and the delay before removal from the container
2. The state of the liner close to the end faces and in the bore
3. Dropping out of old liners. If they cannot be dropped out because of bulging in the middle, then removal by machining is necessary.
4. Actual bore of the liner holder or the mantle at room temperature at intervals of 100 mm, crosswise. With a three-part design, subsequent control of the interference joint mantle/liner holder by ultrasonic inspection is necessary.
5. Monitoring the mechanical properties of the liner holder and/or the mantle
6. Control of the centering and locking faces on the mantle external diameter for wear. Mating parts should also be inspected. Any damage should be repaired according to the drawing.
7. Remachining of the bore of the liner holder or the mantle, corresponding to the shape and dimensional tolerances
8. Machine the external diameter of the new liner to the resultant dimensions of the new bore with the shrinkage additions.
9. Shrink-fitting of the liner
10. Finish-machining of the liner after shrink-fitting to the shape and dimensional tolerances
11. Condition and functional control of the heating, with repair if necessary

The operating procedure should be documented. The most important data can then be used to improve the working life and possibly bring about a future cost reduction.

Hot Working Materials for the Manufacture of Extrusion Tooling

Günther Sauer*

Every extruded material has its individual deformation conditions. The extrusion tooling is, accordingly, subjected to different degrees of thermomechanical and tribological stresses. The direction of extrusion is the main loading direction, but the mechanical stresses are multidirectional, particularly in hollow dies. Hot working materials for the manufacture of extrusion tooling should therefore have the best direction-independent parameters, with a good ability to withstand thermal, tribological, and mechanical loading, that is, largely isotropic properties. The resultant requirements are described in section 7.1.2.

The economic viability of an extrusion tool depends extensively on the hot working materials used for manufacture, their heat treatment, and, in some cases, the surface treatment as well as the design. The hot working materials available can be used individually for the manufacture of extrusion tooling, depending on the extruded material-dependent deformation conditions. However, it is not possible to combine all the properties needed for hot working into one hot working material. Advantages in one area result in disadvantages in others. For example, tool materials with high hot strengths are usually less tough and therefore must be protected from high tensile stresses during deformation by shrinking into a metallic die holder.

As usual, most extrusion tooling is manufactured from hot working steels. Tooling made in hot working tool steels has good throughputs for the extrusion of materials with deformation temperatures up to a maximum of 50 °C (90 °F) below the tempering temperature of the tool material. This condition principally covers the extrusion of tin- and lead-base alloys, those based on zinc and magnesium, up to aluminum alloys. The focal point for the application of the classic hot working steels is the tooling for the

hot working of aluminum alloys. However, these hot working steels can also give good results at even higher thermomechanical loads at extrusion temperatures up to 700 °C for direct deformation, for example, the extrusion of specific copper-zinc alloys. However, the working temperatures are then approximately 100 °C over the maximum tempering temperature, so that these extrusion tools lose strength as a function of their working life. Localized plastic deformation and softening of the tool steel is therefore to be expected after a certain working period, as shown in Fig. 7.109. Hot working tool steels are not suitable for tooling that is directly involved in deformation at temperatures above 700 °C. These conditions occur, for example, in the extrusion of difficult-to-extrude copper alloys and steels. In these cases, austenitic steels and high hot strength materials based on cobalt, molybdenum, and nickel are used in addition to metal-ceramic and pure ceramic hot working materials.

Problems occur with larger porthole dies for the extrusion of low-alloyed aluminum alloys, including AlMgSi0.5 and AlMgSi0.7, with the buildup of heat in the center after a specific number of extrusions as a result of inadequate heat extraction. In the location of the hot spot, the tool temperature increases close to the tempering temperature of the hot working tool steel. A loss in strength then occurs as a result of tempering, along with significant plastic deformation. In these cases, even with aluminum tooling, the high-quality classic hot working steels similar to 1.2367 reach their natural limitations. In addition, relatively slow extrusion speeds must be used because of the heat buildup. A solution could be provided by:

- Specific tool cooling to avoid a buildup of heat, as is currently possible with containers
- Application of temper-resistant hot working steels, for example, produced by powder metallurgy and forging

The hot working tool steels based on CrMoV that were developed in the middle of the 20th century have proved exceedingly beneficial for the manufacture of aluminum extrusion tooling. Detailed improvements in terms of degree of purity, fine tuning of the alloying elements, structural homogeneity, and isotropy have resulted in marked quality improvements in this steel family.

The hot working materials used for extrusion tooling are shown in Table 7.13. Section 7.17

*Hot Working Materials for the Manufacture of Extrusion Tooling, Günther Sauer

Shape and positional tolerances to DIN 7184

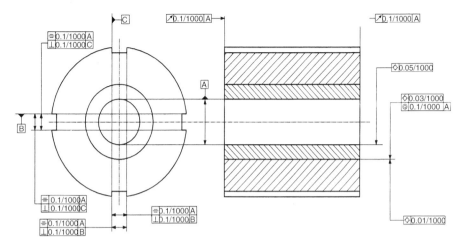

Fig. 7.108 Manufaturing data for containers. Source: Groos

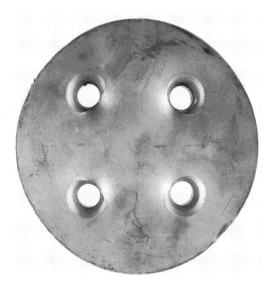

Fig. 7.109 Four-cavity extrusion die for brass wire. The billet-facing side of the die has deformed from center towards the die apertures as a result of the thermomechanical overstressing of the tool steel. Source: Wieland-Werke AG

covers their application for the different extrusion tooling which includes the following tables:

- Table 7.16: Hot working materials for direct deformation extrusion tooling
- Table 7.17: Hot working materials for indirect deformation extrusion tooling as well as auxiliary and support tools
- Table 7.18: Hot working materials for extrusion containers

7.14   Hot Working Steels

7.14.1   Classic Hot Working Steels

The expression *hot working tool steels* covers all alloyed steels used for the manufacture of tooling for the hot working of metallic materials where the working temperature is over 200 °C. They belong to the classification of tool steels and are used in the heat treated condition with initial strengths of between 1100 and 1800 N/mm^2. The high thermal loading of the extrusion tooling necessitates a high tempering resistance in the material used for their manufacture. The tempering resistance of a hot working steel is one of the decisive criteria for the selection of a tool material for specific extrusion conditions. An adequate tempering resistance of the tooling material is particularly important for extrusion tools that come into direct contact with the extruded material. The alloying elements promote the properties of the hot working steels in different ways, although their effect must take into account the interaction with each other:

- Carbon provides the basic requirement for the hardenability of the steel. It forms carbides and special carbides with the most important alloying elements for hot working steels. Carbides primarily control the hot strength, the tempering resistance, and the wear resistance of the hot working steels.

- Increasing silicon content increases the yield strength and the fracture strength but also reduces the toughness of the hot working steels.
- Manganese reduces the critical cooling rate and, even in small quantities, promotes the hardenability and the ability to through-harden. Manganese also displaces the pearlite point to the left in the iron-carbon diagram.
- Nickel promotes the through-hardening and the hot strength of the hot working steels without significantly reducing the toughness. In addition, similar to manganese, it reduces the critical cooling rate and acts as a grain refiner. Nickel does not form any carbides and tends toward temper embrittlement. This tendency can be compensated by other elements.
- Chromium is the most important alloying element in tool steels. It reduces the critical cooling rate and, together with carbon, controls the hardness and thus the strength as well as the wear resistance. Chromium promotes the hardenability, that is, the ability of the tool steel to through-harden even with thicker cross sections. It also improves the temper resistance of the hot working steel at the higher working temperatures.
- Cobalt significantly increases the hot strength of the hot working steels. However, it also increases the critical cooling rate. Cobalt-alloyed hot working steels therefore belong to the hot working steels subjected to the highest thermomechanical loads.
- Molybdenum forms special carbides and therefore increases the hot strength and the fatigue strength. Even in small quantities, molybdenum is the most important alloying element against temper embrittlement. In addition, it has a very strong influence on the through-hardenability of steel and has a favorable influence on the toughness properties of hot working steels. It is therefore one of the most valuable alloying elements.
- Vanadium forms very temperature-resistant special carbides and preferentially promotes secondary hardness at higher tempering temperatures through the precipitation of V_4C_3. These carbides only start to coagulate above 600 °C, resulting in significant losses in hardness and strength.

- Tungsten forms the low-solubility carbide $(FeW)_6C$. The alloying element plays a significant role in secondary hardening by carbide precipitation at high tempering temperatures. In addition, tungsten promotes fine grains in hot working steels and improves the hot strength as well as the wear resistance.

The majority of hot working steels with special carbide-forming elements are capable of secondary hardening under suitable tempering conditions. This is precipitation hardening. While the strength (hardness) falls with increasing tempering temperature because of iron carbide precipitation, it increases significantly with certain hot working steels above 450 to 550 °C by the precipitation of special carbides in the martensitic matrix of the steel and the breakdown of the residual austenite. As shown in Fig. 7.110, a hardness or strength maximum occurs that falls again after exceeding this temperature range. The special carbides mentioned are difficult to dissolve but also precipitate

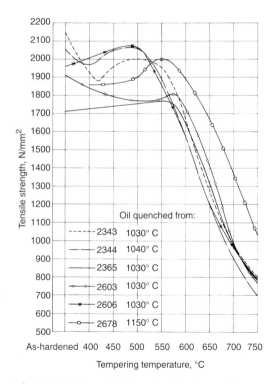

Fig. 7.110 Tempering curves for different secondary age-hardening hot working steels, primarily CrMo alloyed. The hot working steels 1.2603 and 1.2606 are rarely used for extrusion tools. (The points on the curves were taken from various literature references.)

slowly in the martensitic matrix. A particularly high volume of carbides needs to be dissolved to achieve a high tempering resistance, that is, the degree of carbide solubility determines the maximum strength that can be achieved during tempering as well as the tempering resistance. The hardening temperature must be correspondingly high; however, excessively high hardening temperatures must be avoided, because this would result in grain coarsening and thus affect the toughness of the hot working steel.

If the tempering temperature is significantly exceeded, the hot working steel softens to an increasing extent and starts to creep and flow under the influence of the extrusion forces, as can be seen in Fig. 7.109, which shows a thermomechanically overloaded four-cavity extrusion die for the production of brass wire. The loading on the material of an extrusion tool during the press cycle is given in Table 7.14.

Extrusion tooling is subjected to temperatures that frequently fall in the crystal recovery range of the tool material. The duration of the loading in the extrusion cycle depends primarily on the possible extrusion speeds and can thus range from 10 s to approximately 20 min. Accordingly, with short extrusion times, the loading can be referred to as fatigue, and with longer times, as periodically interrupted creep loading, because with long loading times, time-dependent changes can occur in the tool material under thermal and mechanical stresses.

Table 7.11 gives characteristic values for the dynamic behavior of different hot working steels in the tensile fatigue range at a temperature of 500 °C compared to the static 0.2% hot proof stress [Wan 72]. A similar comparison is shown in Fig. 7.107 for the 0.2% 100 h creep limit for the hot working steel 1.2343 compared

to the static 0.2% hot proof stress in a temperature range of 500 to 600 °C [Güm 81].

The 0.2% proof stress of hot working steel decreases in the crystal recovery range with increasing load duration. The dependence of the creep strength on the hardened and tempered strength of the hot working steel is shown in Fig. 7.111 for several different heat treated hot working steels [Güm 81, Hab 77]. The creep strength of the tool material is responsible for the shape and dimensional stability of an extrusion tool. Exceeding this value results in plastic

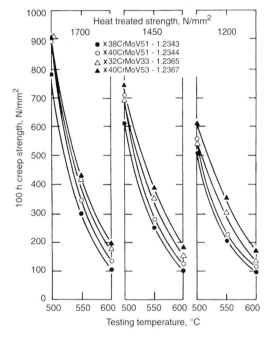

Fig. 7.111 Dependence of the creep strength of various hot working steels on the testing temperature at various heat treated strengths [Güm 81]

Table 7.14 Fluctuating loads on tool materials during the extrusion cycle that cause creep fatigue, oxidation, or wear

Thermomechanical	Thermal
• Fluctuating compressive forces during the extrusion cycle • Fluctuating tensile forces during the extrusion cycle • Fluctuating bending forces in the extrusion cycle • Alternating stress concentrations at unavoidable notches in the shape-forming die aperture	• Fluctuating thermal stresses in the extrusion cycle • Fluctuating temperature-related forces in the extrusion cycle
Chemical	**Tribological**
• Oxidation on heating • Heat retention and cooling in the surrounding medium • Grain-boundary attack of hot-working steels by tin- and copper-containing low-melting-point phases in the extruded material, with melting points below the deformation temperature	• Wear on the tool working surfaces during extrusion resulting from adhesion and abrasion by the flowing extruded material

Source: [Ber 82]

deformation in the shape-forming areas of the tool.

With inserted dies, the die body in hot working steel prestressed by the shrink-fitting of the insert is subjected to a permanent creep loading in the working condition that can loosen the composite.

Under thermomechanical creep loading, steels susceptible to deformation exhibit a deformation process similar to that shown in Fig. 7.112 for the hot working steel 1.2343 at a temperature of 500 °C and different loads. After high initial values, the creep rate decreases after a specific load duration as a result of work hardening of the steel. The creep rate remains practically constant for a specific time with increasing total elongation and then rapidly increases again. This increase is attributed to the softening process in the steel that occurs after extensive thermomechanical loading. The creep process of steel up to failure is correspondingly divided into three regions: the primary creep region, the secondary creep region, and the tertiary creep region. In order to avoid failure after a relatively short load duration, hot working steels should accordingly have a maximum possible secondary creep range; that is, in this creep phase, the creep rate should be as low as

possible [Ber 82, Ber 76]. This requirement is not met by all hot working steels, as can clearly be seen in the time elongation curve in Fig. 7.113 for the steel 1.2567. The hot working steel 1.2365 exhibits a similar behavior at a working temperature of 500 °C, depending on its heat treated strength. This is shown in Fig. 7.114 by the time elongation curves for this steel at different heat treated strengths. These hot working steels also exhibit creep embrittlement with increasing strength, and there is a close relationship between creep embrittlement and hot embrittlement of steel [Ber 82].

These embrittlement mechanisms become more effective with increasing heat treated strength. In addition, steels that are less susceptible to hot embrittlement are also less susceptible to creep embrittlement. However, creep embrittlement commences at temperatures of approximately 100 °C lower than hot embrittlement. This material-specific behavior of hot working steels must be taken into account in selection, along with the extrusion tool loading. Extrusion tools that tend toward plastic deformation as a consequence of the thermomechanical stresses can unexpectedly fail from creep embrittlement.

The creep behavior of hot working steels can be favorably influenced by the special carbide-

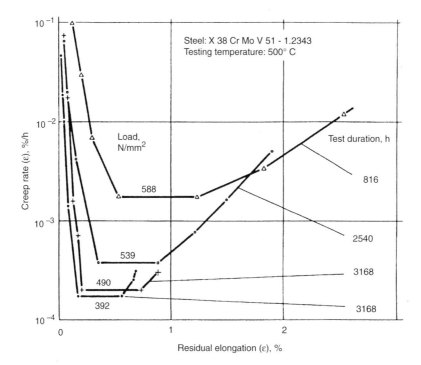

Fig. 7.112 Creep behavior of the hot working steel 1.2343 under different loads and creep rates as a function of creep elongation. The diagram shows the three creep phases: primary creep, secondary creep, and tertiary creep [Ber 76]

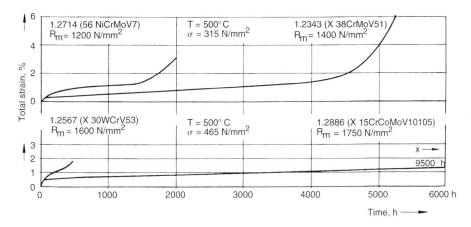

Fig. 7.113 Creep elongation curves for the hot working steels 1.2714, 1.2343, 1.2567, and 1.2886. The different steels exhibit ductile and brittle creep behavior [Ber 76]

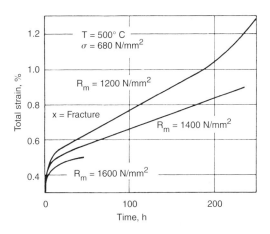

Fig. 7.114 Dependence of the creep behavior of the hot working steel 1.2365 on its heat treated strength [Ber 76]

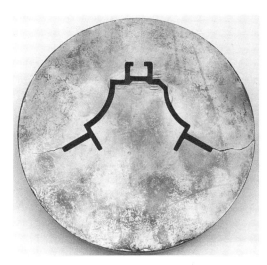

Fig. 7.115 Billet side of on extrusion die for the production of a brass section that has cracked at a critical cross section of the die aperture. Source: Wieland-Werke AG

forming alloying elements, including molybdenum, vanadium, and tungsten. Finally, it should be remembered that many hot working steels can creep even at temperatures below 500 °C. Tool working temperatures of 500 °C are significantly exceeded in the extrusion of iron and copper alloys and also even in the extrusion of aluminum alloys in hollow section dies.

The optimal output of an extrusion tool depends primarily on the hot toughness of the tool material and secondly on the initial strength. Toughness implies the resistance of the material against the formation and propagation of cracks. Crack susceptibility can, for example, occur at sharp corners in die apertures (Fig. 7.115). For these reasons, the hardened and tempered strength of a hot working steel is spe-

cifically selected to be a value that ensures sufficient hot toughness and prevents cracks or failures from occurring. A high hot toughness enables the hot working steel to reduce localized stress concentrations by limited flow without fracture. However, when determining the heat treated strength, some loss in wear resistance of the hot working steel must be allowed for compared to a higher heat treated strength, although a high hot toughness of a hot working steel permits a higher initial strength.

A hot working steel with a high hot toughness and a simultaneous high initial strength provides the greatest security against cracks usually caused by notch-related stress concentrations from the mechanical loading.

Basically, the toughness decreases with increasing initial strength, as shown in Fig. 7.116, by the notch impact values as a function of the tensile strength. Figure 7.116 also gives the dependence of the toughness on the direction of working of the hot working steel; that is, the toughness values are better in the forging direction than in the transverse direction. During forging, elongated crystal segregations and sulfides reduce the toughness in the transverse direction.

The material characteristic parameters, particularly the hot toughness, of certain hot working steels can be significantly improved by reducing the sulfur content and by optimal balancing of the alloying elements with each other. Reducing the carbon content in hot working steels with chromium contents of approximately 5% by weight, for example 1.2343, 1.2344, and 1.2367, gave a definite improvement in the hot toughness in general and in the transverse direction in particular. The tempering

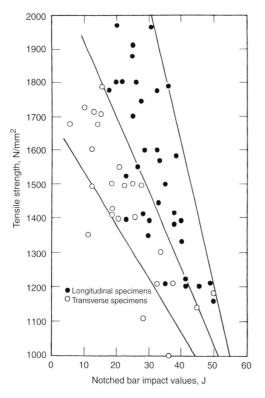

Fig. 7.116 Notched bar impact values for the hot working steel 1.2344 as a function of its tensile strength
[Hab 81]

resistance of the steels did fall above 500 °C but only slightly [Kre 78]. The carbon reduction resulted, in particular, in a reduction in the segregation tendency of the hot working steel and thus to less microsegregation by chromium, molybdenum, and vanadium [Dez 71]. This improves the transverse toughness to some extent. The silicon content also influences the susceptibility to segregation. Consequently, the transverse toughness is also improved by its reduction. One example is the steel 1.2367, which, for a long time, was not readily used for the manufacture of hollow section dies for the extrusion of low-alloyed aluminum alloys in spite of its good initial strength, because of the modest toughness values. The optimization described has changed this. The same thing applies to the hot working steel 1.2885, which, after optimization, has proved to have excellent temper resistance and thus shape stability in the hot spots of large hollow dies for the production of aluminum profiles.

Hot working steels have a tendency for hot embrittlement in the temperature range of 500 to 650 °C, depending on the chemical composition, manufacturing conditions, heat treated strength, and heat treatment. In this temperature range, there is a significant loss in ductility.

High hardening temperatures and cooling rates that are too slow can result in a considerable loss in toughness after austenitizing; for example, raising the hardening temperature does increase the fracture strength and the tempering resistance but also reduces the toughness.

A measure of the toughness of hot working steels is often the reduction in area at fracture, but primarily the notch impact strength. There is a close relationship between the reduction in area at fracture and the toughness of the hot working steel [Hab 81]. Figure 7.117 compares the hot reduction in area at fracture of various hot working steels of different compositions that were hardened and tempered to a strength of 1500 N/mm^2 at a testing temperature of 600 °C. The hot working steels 1.2365 and 1.2567 exhibit a clear tendency to hot embrittlement. The same results can be seen in Fig. 7.118 comparing the reduction in area at fracture of the steel 1.2567 with that of the hot working steel 1.2343 at testing temperatures up to 650 °C. The hot toughness of the hot working steel 1.2567 reveals hot embrittlement above 500 °C. Normally, the toughness of a hot working steel increases with temperature, as can clearly be seen in Fig. 7.118 for the steel 1.2343. How-

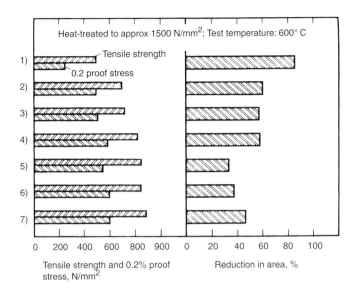

Fig. 7.117 Comparison of hot strength with reduction in area as an indication of the hot strength of the following hot working steels at a testing temperature of 600 °C. 1:1.2714 = 56 NiCrMo7; 2: 1.2343 = X38 CrMoV51; 3: 1.2344 = X40 CrMoV51; 4: 1.2367 = X40 CrMoV53; 5: 1.2365 = X32 CrMoV33; 6: 1.2567 = X30 WCrV53; 7: 1.2888 = X20CoCrWMo109 [Güm 81]

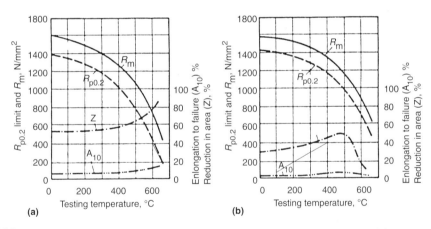

Fig. 7.118 Comparison of the hot strength and hot toughness of the hot working steels (a) 1.2343 and (b) 1.2567 [Bar 81]

ever with the steel 1.2567, the increase in hot toughness changes into a rapid loss in hot toughness above 500 °C. In principle, however, the hot toughness of the hot working steels increases with temperature, which is important for the thorough preheating of the extrusion tooling before use.

Extrusion tooling for direct forming subjected to permanent temperature fatigue loading at high deformation temperatures during the extrusion cycle frequently fails by hot crack formation. The hot stress cracks extend as a network over the tool surface, as shown in Fig. 7.119 on an extrusion mandrel, resulting in premature failure. This network of thermal cracks is caused by fluctuating tensile/compressive stresses in the working surfaces of the extrusion tooling. They develop from the temperature differences that occur during the extrusion cycle between the tool surface and the core material below it. This fluctuating loading in the tension compression range is particularly harmful in thermally highly loaded tools that are externally cooled between the individual extrusions. This method of cooling cannot always be avoided under certain working conditions in order to

Fig. 7.119 Hot cracking network on the working surface of a tapered extrusion mandrel in the hot working steel 1.2367 for the production of copper tubes, resulting from the fluctuating tensile and compressive stresses. Copper that has welded to the mandrel surface can be seen in the lower right and left areas of the photograph. Source: Wieland–Werke AG

avoid heating the tool material well above the tempering temperature. During cooling, the surface of the tool will assume a smaller volume than the core cross section of the tool, because of the lower temperature. This results in tensile thermal stresses in the working surface of the tool. During extrusion, the working surface is reheated to a higher temperature than the tool core cross section. This results in compressive thermal stresses in the working surface. If these fluctuating stresses in the tension/compression range exceed the elastic limit of the hot working material, then plastic deformation occurs, and this ultimately results in the formation of a typical hot crack network on the surface of the tool. The effect of the fluctuating temperature is particularly severe with hot working steels with low thermal conductivity. However, in spite of the use of the CrMoV steels with better thermal conductivity, hot cracking from rapid temperature fluctuations during the extrusion cycle at high deformation temperatures cannot always be prevented. In this context, there is no hot working steel completely resistant to temperature fluctuations. However, the working life of extrusion tooling subjected to temperature fluctuations can be optimized by careful balancing of the material properties responsible for the ability to resist temperature fluctuations, including hot flow stress, hot strength, hot toughness, and temper resistance, through the heat treatment. Experimental results have indicated

that hot cracks are comparable to fatigue cracks under mechanical/dynamic loads. Therefore, procedures that increase the fatigue strength of hot working steels should also improve the resistance to thermal cracking. The purity and homogeneity of the hot working material and, in particular, the heat treatment selected for a specific loading application are important to achieve a good relationship between the hot strength and the hot toughness [Güm 81].

The hot wear resistance of the hot working steel is very important for the shape-producing tooling and the container liner. Wear is characterized by material loss, and adhesive and abrasive wear as well as fatigue wear can occur on the working surfaces of the tool, for example, on mandrel surfaces. This wear impairs, in particular, the shape-producing regions of extrusion tools used to produce tubes and section to the finished dimensions. Even slight wear of the tool working surface can have an extremely negative influence on the material flow. Consequently, hot working steels used for the manufacture of these tools should have the optimal high wear resistance. The working temperature plays a role in this requirement, because semifinished products in materials extruded at high temperatures are not normally finish-extruded.

In terms of wear, the compatibility of the friction partners hot working steel and extruded material can be improved by surface treatment of the extrusion tooling, in which the chemical composition of the tool surface is changed. Nitriding is a well-proven process in this respect. Recently, there has been some initial success with chemical vapor deposition (CVD)-applied surface coatings. With these processes, the tool surface is further hardened or coated, which significantly improves the wear resistance. The tool working life is then considerably improved.

The results from wear studies using hot torsion tests with the friction partners extruded material/hot working steel for different extruded material are shown in Fig. 7.120 and 7.121. The increase in the wear depends on the extruded material, the working temperature, and the duration of loading.

During the extrusion process, reactions can occur between the extruded material and the tool material, including:

- Tribological reactions by adhesion, resulting in welding under pressure and temperature of the extruded material to the tool working surface
- Chemical reaction by corrosion attack of the extruded material at the grain boundaries of the hot working steel

The tool working surfaces usually deteriorate rapidly from adhesion as a result of the welding, as does the surface of the semifinished product after a certain production time. Of all the materials extruded, aluminum alloys in particular tend to weld to the tool steel. However, because aluminum alloys can be extruded at relatively low temperatures, the welding of the extruded material to the tool working surface can be reduced by a surface treatment, for example, nitriding. The welding cannot, however, be prevented. In contrast, the shape-forming extrusion tool areas for the extrusion of copper alloys are lubricated so that welding of the copper alloy to the tool working surface does not occur.

Under certain conditions, corrosion attack by the extruded material at the grain boundaries of the hot working steel on the tool working surfaces can take place during extrusion. This attack is a specific form of stress-corrosion cracking in which the liquid extruded material or a low-melting-point phase penetrates into the grain boundaries of the hot working material under tension, as can be seen in Fig. 7.122. Container liners are particularly affected by this type of corrosion attack, because they are subjected to tensile stress peaks in the bore during the extrusion cycle. This corrosion attack occurs basically under the following conditions:

- The extruded material or a low-melting-point phase must be soluble in iron, for example, tin and copper, and the liquidus temperature must be exceeded during the deformation.
- The wetted surfaces of the hot working steel must be subjected to tensile stresses above a critical value.

If these conditions are fulfilled, the liquid extruded material rapidly attacks the grain bound-

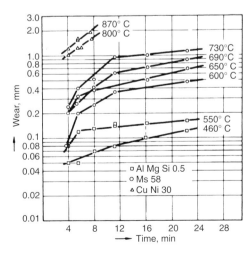

Fig. 7.120 Time-dependent wear rates from hot torsion tests for the hot working steel 1.2779 as the rotating steel heated to 550 °C and the extruded materials Al-MgSi0.5, CuZn42 and CuNi30 heated to the deformation temperature [Schi 82]

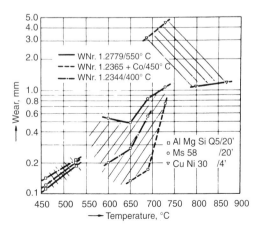

Fig. 7.121 Wear rates of the hot working steels used after 20 min test duration, corresponding to Fig. 7.130 as a function of the deformation temperatures of the three extruded materials used [Schi 82]

Fig. 7.122 Solder fracture in the liner of the container of an aluminum extrusion press with a 250 mm bore after a large number of extrusions with the bearing material AlSn6Cu1. The liner was manufactured in the hot working steel 1.2306. Source: VAW

aries of the hot working steel. It rapidly penetrates along the grain boundary into the tool material. Intercrystalline failure of the hot working steel then occurs under tensile stresses, because liquid metals cannot withstand any tensile forces. This special case of intercrystalline stress corrosion is also referred to as solder cracking. The risk of solder cracking increases with the temperature of the tool material. There is practically no remedy against the susceptibility to solder cracking. Higher chromium and silicon contents in the hot working steels do reduce the susceptibility to solder cracking, but this material defect can only be prevented by reducing the deformation temperature below the liquidus temperature of the extruded material by the selection of a suitable extrusion process.

The production methods for hot working steels have been significantly improved by secondary metallurgy and electroslag refining (ESR).

In the melt treatment using secondary metallurgy, for example, with argon injection, the melt is purified to give significant reductions in elongated manganese sulfide and segregation bands, improving the transverse toughness values.

In the ESR process, the steel is remelted in an arc furnace and solidified after the passage of a refining slag in a water-cooled mold. Figure 7.123 shows the difference in structure between a conventionally cast ingot preferentially solidified with columnar crystals transverse to the axis, and an ingot remelted by ESR, which has solidified with a significantly finer and more uniform grain size. The material parameters are more uniform and less orientation dependent. The ESR-remelted steels are more expensive and therefore used for complicated hollow dies.

The success of both processes has resulted in a qualitative division between the hot working steels according to the method of manufacture. Hot working steels that only receive the secondary metallurgy process during manufacture to obtain a higher microscopic purity are considered by the extrusion plant as fine-grade steels, and those that are additionally remelted with the ESR process as extra-fine grade.

Based on this classification, fine-grade steels are used for the manufacture of extrusion tooling subjected to moderately high thermomechanical stresses and extra-fine grade is used for the manufacture of extrusion tooling subjected to high thermomechanical stresses, for example, aluminum hollow dies.

The blank ingots are forged after diffusion heat treatment. Sawn blanks from forged round bars—particularly in the extra-fine grade—are suitable for the manufacture of dies. If the best possible transverse toughness values are required, then three-dimensionally forged blanks must be used.

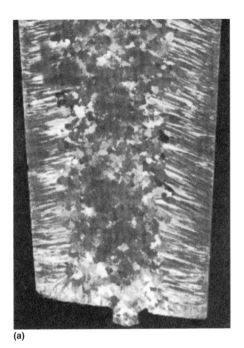

(a)

(b)

Fig. 7.123 Longitudinal cross section of (a) a conventionally produced and (b) an electroslag refining-produced cast billet [Bar 81]

7.14.1.1 Hardening and Tempering of the Classic Hot Working Steels

Extrusion tools made from hot working steels are given the ability to withstand the thermo-mechanical stresses in extrusion by suitable heat treatment. Of all the processing steps in the tool manufacture, heat treatment of the tool is the most important. It has a decisive influence on the behavior of the extrusion tool in service. While extrusion dies currently are usually made from heat treated steel blanks, hollow section dies are usually rough-machined from annealed hot working steels.

Initially, the steel blank or the rough-machined tool must be carefully thermally stress relieved for hardening before heating. The preheating itself should be carried out uniformly over the tool cross section with a moderate heating rate to avoid high thermal stresses. The loads developed in the die from the thermal stresses during heating can result in permanent shape changes in the tool and lead to cracking. The heating of the extrusion tool to the austenitizing temperature is therefore carried out in stages, as shown in Fig. 7.124.

The hot working steel is held for 20 min at temperature for austenitizing of up to 20 mm thick cross sections. Larger cross sections require an additional heating time of 4 min for each 10 mm increase in thickness. If the holding time is too short or the austenitizing temperature too low, the hot strength and the temper resistance is reduced as a result of insufficient carbide dissolution. On the other hand, the holding period should not be too long, to avoid grain coarsening. With large cross-sectional variations in the tool design, care must be taken because smaller cross sections heat more quickly.

The cooling from the austenitizing temperature must be quick enough to minimize the formation of bainite. Bainite becomes brittle on tempering and thus increases the risk of cracking. At the same time, the formation of high thermal stresses from accelerated cooling should be avoided. Martempering, which has been used up to now, has the advantage that the tendency for carbide precipitates on the austenite grain boundaries is suppressed by a relatively fast cooling to temperatures below the pearlite stage. However, the salt baths used are not environmentally friendly from today's viewpoint. The modern hardening shop operates with chamber furnaces in which the product being hardened is raised to the austenitizing temperature in a positive-pressure nitrogen atmosphere. Hardening is carried out by blowing vaporizing liquid nitrogen into the furnace chamber.

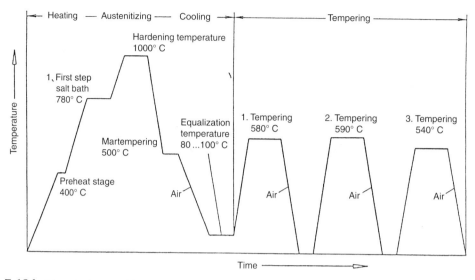

Fig. 7.124 Schematic diagram of the salt bath heat treatment sequence for hardening the hot working steel 1.2343 [Ame 71]

Further cooling in air can only be carried out after the extrusion tooling has completely reached the quenching temperature. Before reheating for tempering, the extrusion tool should be held for some time at an equalization temperature of 80 to 100 °C. As described in Fig. 7.124, this is followed by three tempering temperatures each of 4 to 6 h holding time and the temperature sequence of 580, 590, and 540 °C. Tempering also requires thorough through-heating with moderate heating rates to avoid detrimental thermal stresses. This also applies in reverse to the cooling phase. This should take place in absolutely still air and last at least 2 h or longer. Three-staged tempering should result in the following effects in the hot working steel:

- Secondary hardening
- Thermal stress relieving
- Transformation of the residual austenite in the steel structure into martensite or bainite
- An increase in the toughness of the hot working steel from the third tempering stage

The transformation of residual austenite in the tool material can result in dimensional changes from stresses within the extrusion tool, because the transformed structure has a different volume than the austenite. These dimensional changes in the shape-forming areas of the tool can be removed during the final production. In contrast, a residual austenite transformation when the tool is used in production can result in production problems associated with dimensional changes. Because hot working steels do not have large quantities of residual austenite, the reduction of residual austenite by tempering suffices.

7.14.1.2 Machining of Hardened and Tempered Hot Working Steels

The manufacturing cost of an extrusion tool, which is the most important production item in the extrusion plant, influences the economic success. The extrusion plant therefore requires the tool maker to use the most economic modern production methods.

The introduction of spark erosion machining of extrusion tool blanks for the production of the die aperture has resulted in significant reductions in the production times and hence the costs. Cutting out the die aperture from the heat treated material using wire erosion can replace sawing from the unheated die blank and sink erosion to the final dimensions after heat treatment. The spark erosion machining influences the newly formed surface of the hot working steels that will subsequently form the tool working surfaces in the die aperture as a function of the cutting rate. For this reason, the effect on the hot working steels at these cut surfaces is of considerable importance.

Figures 7.125 and 7.126 show the changes in the machined hot working steel surfaces resulting from spark erosion machining. A molten zone forms on the surface, and beneath this, a

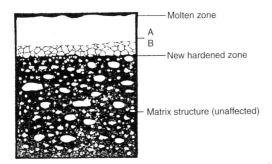

Fig. 7.125 Schematic diagram showing the influence of the erosion conditions on the structure of the cut surface [Kra 89]

Fig. 7.126 Degenerated surface approximately 200 μm thick in the region of a surface produced by high–power electroerosion of the heat treated hot working steel 1.2343. Source: VAW

heat-affected zone that extends to the unaffected matrix structure. The molten phase reacts with the dielectric used. Paraffin results in the carburization of the cut surfaces, and water as the dielectric during wire erosion with high power readily results in surface cracks from the release of high type-one internal stresses in the so-called white layer. The width of the molten zone and the heat-affected zone depends on the set current density for a constant dielectric. Investigations show that with constant erosion conditions, the impairment of the surface is more severe with water than with paraffin [Kra 89].

The condition of the tool working surfaces determines the surface quality of the extruded semifinished product, and the presence of a degraded hot working steel structure affects the working life of the extrusion tool, as shown in Fig. 7.126. The toughness of the hot working steel is also considerably reduced in the affected region. In the die apertures, the stress concentrations from notches can rapidly lead to cracks [Kra 89]. Therefore, spark erosion with high power must be followed by one or two spark erosion skim cuts at low power.

7.14.1.3 Surface Heat Treatment of Extrusion Tools in Classic Hot Working Steels

Aluminum bars extruded through nitrided tools exhibit a significantly more uniform and smooth surface as well as better dimensional and shape accuracy. The tool surfaces attain a significant increase in hardness from the diffusion of nitrogen and, depending on the composition of the hot working steel, can reach 1200 HV1 [Sar 67, Eys 67].

Today, all extrusion dies for lead, magnesium, and aluminum alloys are nitrided as a matter of course. Nitriding in an ammonia gas flow is the main competition to salt bath nitriding because it produces the same results as salt bath nitriding [Hub 80]. In particular, both processes are capable of ensuring defect-free nitriding, even in very narrow tool gaps, which is a very important requirement for the nitriding of section dies. Nitriding in the salt bath takes place at temperatures of 570 °C, and in the ammonia gas current at 520 to 540 °C. Both nitriding temperature ranges are below the maximum tempering temperature of the hot working steel. Tool distortion is therefore excluded. The nitriding times are 90 to 120 min in the salt bath and up to 240 min at 520 to 540 °C and up to 300 min at 520 °C in the gas current.

The nitrided surface zone of the hot working steel is characterized by the compound zone and the diffusion zone, as described by Sauer [1967] with micrographs. While the compound zone of ε-FeN should only be a few micrometers thick for stress reasons, the thickness of the diffusion zone should be 130 to 160 μm, depending on the composition of the hot working steel.

The deformation temperatures in the shape-producing die areas enable the nitrogen to diffuse from the diffusion zone into the interior of the tool material after the tool has been used for a specific time. As a consequence, the surface hardness decreases, as shown by hardness-against-depth curves [Sar 67]. These processes occur particularly in aluminum extrusion tools and especially in hollow dies because of the higher deformation temperatures. This is associated with a reduction in the surface quality of the extrusion, which continues to deteriorate. The die must be renitrided to regain the old capacity. In the production of aluminum semi-finished products, the following program, based on experience, is typically followed:

- After the first nitriding, approximately 40 to 50 extrusions
- After the second nitriding, approximately 60 to 80 extrusions
- After the third nitriding, approximately 80 to 100 extrusions
- After the fourth nitriding, approximately 100 to 140 extrusions
- After the fifth nitriding, until the die fails

During renitriding, the compound zone naturally increases in thickness. This is one of the reasons why the compound zone should only be a few micrometers thick after the first nitriding.

Extrusion tooling coated by CVD with titanium and chromium carbide as well as aluminum oxide provides a significantly longer working life than nitriding (Fig. 7.127). These coatings are extremely wear resistant. The surface finish of the treated tool does not deteriorate like nitrided surfaces, even after a large number of extrusions. In addition, it is not necessary to clean the die of aluminum when an order has been completed. Instead, for example, a hollow die can remain full of aluminum, provided the start of extrusion of a new order will not impair the shape-producing capability of the die.

The disadvantage of these coating processes is the high coating temperature of over 1000 °C. The extrusion tools can therefore only be heat treated after the CVD coating, with the tool to be hardened heated to the coating temperature and then tempered from this temperature. This can give distortion problems with larger tools.

7.14.2 Austenitic Hot Working Steels

Thermomechanical stresses that are too high for the classic hot working steels in hot extrusion require the application of higher hot strength hot working steels. The high-temperature austenitic hot working steels should first be considered. These do have naturally lower mechanical properties; however, they can be substantially work hardened if the steel is thermally stressed below its recrystallization temperature. The increase in the flow stress due to work

Fig. 7.127 Left, chemical vapor deposition (CVD)-coated aluminum extrusion dies. Right, demanding heat exchanger sections in AlMgSi0.5 produced with CVD–coated dies. Source: WEFA Singen Gmbh

hardening is only slightly lost at temperatures below the recrystallization temperature, for example, in the recovery region, but reduced completely by recrystallization. For this reason, manufacturers of semifinished products are interested in work-hardened high-temperature tool steels with high recrystallization temperatures. Austenitic steels fulfill this requirement. The addition of the high-melting-point alloying elements molybdenum, vanadium, and tungsten can increase the recrystallization temperature even further by precipitation hardening. The comparison of the 0.2% hot proof stress of the two hot working steels 1.2344 and 1.2779 in Fig. 7.128 clearly shows that the austenitic hot working steel can withstand higher thermal stresses. While the tool steel 1.2344 has practically no measurable hot proof stress at a testing temperature of 700 °C, the austenitic tool steel 1.2779 proof stress is still approximately 350 N/mm² at the same temperature. Typical examples of these hot working steels are the austenitic steels 1.2731, 1.2758, and 1.2779 given in Tables 7.13 and 7.15.

These austenitic steels are characterized by a high hot strength and resistance to temperature fluctuations. The steel 1.2731 has also proved successful for the exhaust valves of combustion engines as well as a hot working material for highly stressed extrusion dies. The material is completely austenitic and, unlike the usual hot working steels, there is no austenite/martensite transformation in any heat treatment. Therefore, there are neither any transformation stresses nor any transformation-associated dimensional changes. However, under high and prolonged thermal stresses, slight dimensional changes

can occur by shrinkage as a consequence of precipitation processes. When used in the "hammer hard" forged condition, the strength of the steels can be increased to 1100 to 1200 N/mm².

Largely uniform material properties across a blank volume can be achieved by precipitation hardening. This can take place if sufficient carbides in the matrix can be dissolved by solution heat treatment. This is possible with the hot working steels 1.2578 and 1.2779 but less so with the steel 1.2731. Naturally, the first two steels mentioned can also be brought to a usable strength range by hot work hardening. If necessary, the increase in strength from precipitation hardening can be further increased by a thermomechanical treatment of the steel by hotworking below the recrystallization temperature after the solution heat treatment. This increases the number of dislocations in the material lattice. These lattice defects act as preferential nuclei for the carbide precipitates during the secondary hardening.

The creep/fatigue behavior of the austenitic tool steels also depends strongly on the heat treatment. In general, under the same optimal age-hardening conditions, the creep strength increases with the magnitude of the solution heat treatment temperature at the expense of the creep ductility. However, as the solution heat treatment temperature is raised, the grain size also increases. This opposing tendency in terms of the desired material properties results in compromises having to be made in commercial heat treatment.

Austenitic hot working steels have proved successful in certain extrusion tooling applica-

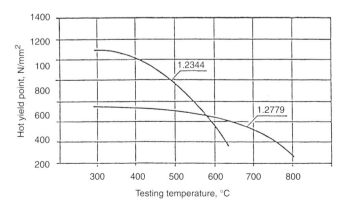

Fig. 7.128 Comparison of the 0.2% hot proof stress of the classic hot working steel 1.2344 with the austenitic hot working steel 1.2779 [Kor 95]

Table 7.15 Hot working steels for extrusion tools for the direct and indirect extrusion of aluminum and copper alloys

Material No.	Abbreviation	Nominal composition, wt%							
		C	Co	Cr	Mo	Ni	V	W	Ti
1.2311	40CrMnMo7	0.40	...	2.00	0.20	...	...	...	...
1.2323	48CrMoV51	0.45	...	1.45	0.75	...	0.30	...	...
1.2713	55NiCrMoV6	0.55	...	0.70	0.30	1.65	0.10	...	...
1.2714	56NiCrMoV7	0.55	...	1.10	0.50	1.65	0.10	...	...
1.2343	X38CrMoV51	0.38	...	5.20	1.25	...	0.40	...	...
1.2344	X40CrMoV51	0.40	...	5.20	1.35	...	1.00	...	...
1.2365	X32CrMoV33	0.32	...	3.00	2.80	...	0.55	...	...
1.2367	X40CrMoV53	0.38	...	5.00	3.00	...	0.55	...	...
1.2567	X30WCrV53	0.30	...	2.35	0.60	...	...	4.25	...
1.2581	X30WCrV93	0.30	...	2.65	0.35	...	...	8.50	...
1.2678	X45CoCrWV555	0.45	4.50	4.50	0.50	...	2.00	4.50	...
1.2885	X32CrMoCoV333	0.32	2.80	3.00	2.80	...	0.60	...	...
1.2889	X45CoCrMoV553	0.45	4.50	4.50	3.00	...	2.00	...	...
1.2731	X50NiCrWV1313	0.50	...	13.00	...	13.0	1.30	1.30	...
1.2758	X50WNiCrVCo1212	0.50	1.70	4.00	0.70	11.5	1.10	12.50	...
1.2779	X60NiCrTi2615	0.05	...	15.00	1.30	25.5	0.30	...	2.10 + B

Source: [Kor 95]

tions to overcome higher thermomechanical loading, for example, as the material for container liners for copper alloy extrusion and as dies or die inserts for copper tube and copper sections as well as dummy blocks. The extrusion of brass alloys with low zinc contents (Tombak) only became economic with the use of dummy blocks in the austenitic steel 1.2779 [Kor 97]. However, austenitic steels have high coefficients of expansion, a property that must be taken into account when determining the interference fit for shrink-fitting an austenitic liner into the hot working steel liner holder of a copper alloy container.

7.14.3 Classification of Hot Working Steels

Hot working steels for extrusion tools are specified in the steel application list of VDEh 201 for extrusion tools for copper alloys as well as in 202 for extrusion tools for magnesium and aluminum alloys. The most important ones are given in Table 7.15. They can be classified into five groups.

Low-alloy tool steels in the first group are used for extrusion tools that only have indirect contact with the extruded material, for example, support tools. The more highly CrMoV-alloyed tool steels in the second group are mainly used for the manufacture of extrusion tools for hot working aluminum alloys that come into direct contact with the extruded material. They are also used to a limited extent for extrusion dies

for hot extrusion of copper-zinc alloys. Hot working steels in the third group, based on WCrMo, are used for extrusion tools for the hot working of copper alloys. They have very good wear properties but poor thermal conductivity, a property that promotes hot spots, particularly on the surface of extrusion mandrels. Therefore, these tool steels have lost their importance. Cobalt-containing hot working steels of the fourth group have good high-temperature strengths and are therefore used for extrusion tools subjected to high thermomechanical stresses, including the extrusion of copper alloys but also the center of the shape-producing areas of large aluminum hollow sections. Finally, the austenitic-based hot working steels in the fifth group have better temper resistance than those listed previously. They are suitable mainly as the material for extrusion tools for copper alloy extrusion. They have proved particularly suitable for die inserts.

The quality of the hot working steels in Germany is governed by the following standards. These can be used to supply specifications for the materials for specific requirements of extrusion tools. The standards include:

- DIN 50 115 "Testing of Metallic Materials," notch impact bending tests
- Steel application list 201, materials for tools for tube and rod extrusion of copper and copper alloys
- Steel application list 202, materials for tools for tube and rod extrusion of aluminum and aluminum alloys

- Steel-Iron Test Sheet 1314, impact bending specimens, description, and specimen preparation
- Steel-Iron Test Sheet 1921, ultrasonic inspection of forged blanks
- EN 10 204, Method of inspection description
- DIN 17 350, tool steels, technical supply specifications
- ASTM E 112-77, standard procedures to estimate the average grain size of metals
- SEP 1614, microscopic testing of hot working steels using structure example series for the evaluation of annealed hot working steels
- DGM, technical supply guidelines for hot working materials for the manufacture of extrusion tools for the hot working of aluminum alloys

7.15 Special Materials

High-temperature-resistant special materials, including cobalt, molybdenum, and nickel alloys as well as hard metals, metal ceramics, and pure ceramic hot working materials, have been important tool materials for many years in addition to the classic and austenitic hot working steels described previously. They are listed in detail in Table 7.13.

Special materials that can withstand high thermomechanical loads can generally be used only in certain applications and not universally. Their application is usually limited to individual cases where they have proved very successful. The tool materials generally possess a high hot strength as well as a high hot wear resistance but predominantly low toughness, so that support is needed from die bodies in high-grade hot working steels. They are therefore shrunk into die holders.

7.15.1 Cobalt Alloys

Of all the high-temperature cobalt alloys, forged stellite in the form of a die insert has proved particularly suitable for extrusion dies for extrusion temperatures from 800 to 1000 °C. This is clearly shown in the comparison with the high-temperature austenitic steels shown in Fig. 7.129. Forged stellite has a better toughness than cast stellite. Nevertheless, the majority of stellite is used in the cast condition. In contrast, stellite 6 (Table 7.14) is produced by

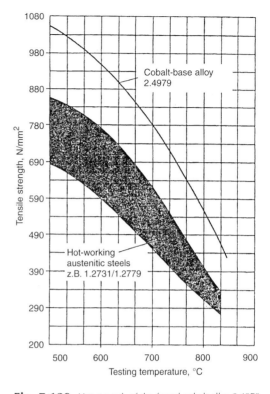

Fig. 7.129 Hot strength of the forged cobalt alloy 2.4979 compared to the hot-temperature austenitic steels. Source: Buderus Edelstahl

powder metallurgy and forged after a hot isostatic pressing process. Similar to nickel alloys, cobalt materials use the fact that face-centered cubic solid solutions possess better hot strength properties than body-centered cubic solid solutions, because of the elevated recovery and recrystallization temperatures and the resultant marked reduction in the diffusion capabilities. This hot strength basis can be further improved by carbide precipitates. For this reason, high-melting-point carbide-forming elements, including chromium, molybdenum, vanadium, and tungsten, are added in various amounts as alloying elements to cobalt alloys. Cobalt itself does not form carbides. Precipitation hardening is developed by solution heat treatment at approximately 1070 °C, quenching in oil or a hot bath, and then age hardening at approximately 750 °C. The resultant fine carbide precipitates hinder dislocation movement as long as they remain finely dispersed in the material structure. Above a temperature of 1000 °C, the precipitated particles coagulate and lose their locking effect on the dislocations. Consequently, cobalt alloys can only be used up to a maximum of 1000 °C [Kor 97].

7.15.2 Molybdenum Alloys

While high-temperature cobalt and nickel alloys can withstand deformation temperatures up to 1000 °C, hot working materials based on high-melting-point materials must be used at temperatures above 1000 °C to achieve an acceptable tool life. The technically interesting metals in this family include materials based on alloys of the body-centered cubic molybdenum with a liquidus of 2620 °C. No lattice transformations occur on heating, and consequently, molybdenum-base alloys can withstand temperatures up to 1500 °C. According to Table 7.13, the thermal expansion is lower than all other hot working materials for extrusion dies. This complicates the shrink-fitting of die inserts into die holders. The thermal conductivity of this material is higher.

Its resistance to high temperatures can be increased with the aid of suitable alloying elements by raising the recrystallization temperature with particle hardening. Molybdenum alloys with small additions of titanium, zirconium, and hafnium have significant hot strengths at extrusion temperatures over 1000 °C, in contrast to the usual hot working steels and cobalt- and nickel-base alloys, as clearly shown by the tool material TZM in Fig. 7.130.

These alloying elements form titanium and zirconium solid solutions with a fine dispersion of TiZr carbides that significantly increase the hot strength. In addition, the carbides raise the recrystallization temperature to above 1300 °C. Even at the high deformation temperatures associated with the extrusion of iron alloys, the temperature is below this recrystallization range. Consequently, changes in the structure and the mechanical properties do not occur, even with prolonged high-temperature loading. The creep properties of these materials are significantly better than other hot working materials, as seen in Fig. 7.131. Molybdenum alloys are used in the work-hardened state. The initial strength depends on the deformation from rolling or forging and from the extent of the carbide dispersion. The most common molybdenum alloy is the hot working material TZM. More recently, the more highly alloyed grades ZHM and MHC have become available. Compared to TZM, these hot working materials have even better hot strength and creep properties. Molybdenum alloys can give much better throughputs than forged cobalt alloys under high thermomechanical loads [Kor 97]. Extrusion dies made of TZM have been used with high throughputs for the extrusion of iron alloys but have not prevailed [Bra 66].

7.15.3 Nickel Alloys

The formation of face-centered cubic solid solutions give high-temperature nickel alloys

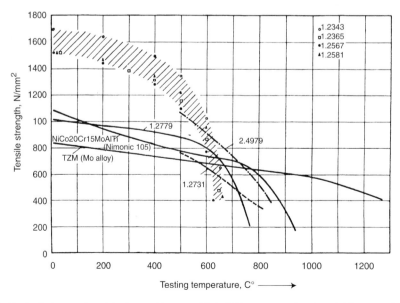

Fig. 7.130 Mechanical properties of the hot working materials in Table 7.13 as a function of different working temperatures from literature data [Schi 82]

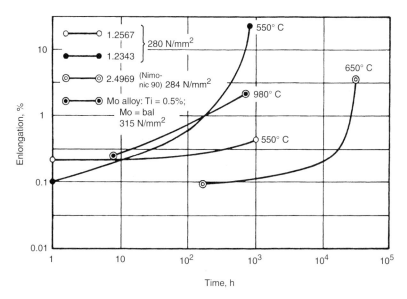

Fig. 7.131 Creep expansion of different hot working materials as a function of the load, temperature, and working time of extrusion tools [Bra 66]

higher recovery and recrystallization temperatures and thus good high-temperature mechanical properties compared to the body-centered cubic hot working steels. Precipitates of intermetallic phases can be produced by the addition of chromium, cobalt, molybdenum, aluminum, titanium, and so on, giving a further increase in the hot strength. The creep strength of nickel alloys is improved by precipitates of the γ-phase Ni_3 (Ti, Al). Increasing amounts of alloying elements, which form the face-centered cubic phases, increase the hot strength of nickel alloys in proportion to their weight content. The nickel alloy 2.4668 is solution heat treated between 960 and 980 °C, cooled in forced air, and age hardened at 700 to 730 °C, with furnace cooling to 610 to 630 °C for 8 h holding time, followed by cooling in air to produce fine precipitates of the γ-phase. The precipitation hardening produces a significant increase in the hot strength as well as the creep strength, so that high-temperature nickel alloys are able to withstand deformation temperatures up to 1200 °C for short periods. These operating conditions occur in dies for the extrusion of copper and titanium alloys [Kor 97, Elm 89].

7.15.4 Metal-Ceramic Composite Materials

In the molybdenum alloys in Table 7.13, the composition of a metal-ceramic material with

the trade name Cermotherm 2015 is listed. This is a composite material produced by powder metallurgy with a molybdenum metal matrix and embedded zirconium oxide particles. The hot working material is very brittle and therefore requires shrink-fitting before use. It has proved very successful for the extrusion of brasses, particularly those containing lead. In the extrusion of these alloys, dies with Cermotherm inserts can give throughputs 1.5 to 3.5 times that of stellite inserts. However, the high notch sensitivity of metal-ceramic materials ensures that Cermotherm inserts are more suited for the extrusion of rod with simple cross sections, including squares and rectangles. Complicated sections are best produced with stellite die inserts. The material is very sensitive to shocks, and this must be taken into account in machining and also during extrusion. Its brittle nature limits the applications. It attains the maximum hot strength at approximately 600 °C, and the hot strength is higher than its strength at room temperature, even at temperatures of approximately 1200 °C. It is therefore suitable for the extrusion of materials in the temperature range between 600 and 1000 °C. Because the metal-ceramic materials have no tendency to weld to the extruded material, excellent surface finishes on the extrusion can be achieved. In addition, the thermal conductivity is relatively high compared to other materials, although its thermal expansion is low. This must be taken into account during shrink-fitting of die inserts.

7.15.5 Hard Metals

Hard metals consist of metallic hard materials, usually carbide based. They are produced by powder metallurgy using sintering processes. High-wear-resistant materials can be produced in this way. The focus for the use of hard metal inserts is their application as a material for the production of tools for volume production. Die inserts are used, for example, for the production of round wire from copper alloys, solder wire in lead and tin alloys, and extruded tubes in aluminum alloys. Cobalt-alloyed hard metals based on titanium carbide are particularly suitable. Hard metals have a low toughness and therefore must be compressed in the die body by shrink-fitting. Because these materials also have a low thermal expansion, they must be particularly highly prestressed in the shrink-fitting [Rei 82, Kol 91, Kor 97].

7.15.6 Pure Ceramic Hot Working Materials

In addition to metal-based special materials, pure ceramic materials of zirconium oxide and aluminum oxide have proved successful for extrusion at high temperatures well above 1000 °C. Ceramic materials are characterized by an extremely low surface-wetting capability. Therefore, materials extruded with them have good surface finishes. Ceramic materials, unlike metals, do not have any slip planes. Stress concentrations in ceramic materials cannot be reduced by localized slip. Instead, spontaneous brittle fracture occurs when the fracture strength is exceeded. Oxide ceramics can only be used successfully as compressively prestressed, that is, shrink-fitted, die inserts. The materials also have a low thermal expansion, which must be taken into account during the shrink-fitting of ceramic die inserts. On the other hand, they are dimensionally very stable at high operating temperatures as a result of the low thermal expansion.

Zirconium oxide ceramic is primarily suitable for the extrusion of copper alloys and, in particular, of brasses, including CuZn37 and CuZn39Pb3, as well as for the extrusion of graphite and austenitic steels. Zirconium-base hot working materials are sintered at approximately 1700 °C. They are stabilized with magnesium oxide to reduce the sensitivity to thermal shock. Their basic chemical composition can be found in Table 7.13. The grain of the material must be fine to achieve a high density of the sintered material, and a fine grain ensures a good surface finish on the extrusion. Coarser grain can be pulled out of the working surfaces of the die by the flow of the extruded material, which damages the surfaces of the extruded product.

The successful application of extrusion dies and die inserts in aluminum oxide (Al_2O_3) ceramics for the manufacture of wire in copper, copper alloys, and aluminum alloys has been described in the literature. A significantly longer die life and better surface finish of the semifinished product can be achieved compared to dies in tungsten-alloyed hot working steels. For example, in the extrusion of aluminum conductor wires with extrusion dies in conventional hot-working steel, the wire surface progressively deteriorates after approximately 1000 m extruded length. However, with Al_2O_3 die inserts, a die life from 30 to 110 km with a constant high-quality wire surface can be achieved, depending on the wire dimensions.

In general, ceramic materials can only be prepared with diamond grinding discs and lapped with diamond paste. Consequently, die inserts must be manufactured as closely as possible to the finished shape by compaction and sintering [Dör 82, Kor 97].

7.16 Further Developments

The wide range of very different hot working materials used for the manufacture of extrusion tooling demonstrates the continuous endeavors of extrusion and tooling experts to find even more efficient tool materials. It is recognized that the hot working materials needed for the manufacture of extrusion tooling must have sufficient creep/fatigue properties to withstand the load cycles in production. If the temperatures fall in the range of crystal recovery of the specific hot working material, then creep will occur under mechanical loading. The creep strength is therefore much more a decisive factor than the 0.2% hot proof stress and the hot tensile stress for hot working materials subjected to high thermomechanical loads [Kor 97]. Figure 7.131 compares the temperature- and time-dependent creep strain of some of the hot working materials used today.

Work is being carried out on the powder metallurgy production of hot working steels to increase tempering resistance, in particular [Sei 88]. In addition, there is research into increasing the hot toughness by alloy optimization of the more highly alloyed hot working steels, for example, those in the fourth group in Table 7.15, so that they can be used for large aluminum hollow dies. Further developments in CVD coatings are expected in the surface treatment of extrusion tooling for the hot working of aluminum alloys, although the coating conditions are difficult. The high coating temperatures of approximately 1000 °C require a mechanically finished die for coating that can be heat treated after the surface treatment.

7.17 Hot Working Materials for Different Extruded Materials for the Manufacture of Extrusion Tooling for Direct and Indirect Forming

In section 7.1.1, the extrusion tooling is classified into those for direct external and internal shape production, for example, extrusion dies and mandrels, and those for indirect shape production as well as auxiliary and support tooling. Extrusion tooling for direct shape production comes into direct contact with the extruded material during the extrusion process, as do some of the tooling for indirect shape production, including the container liner and the dummy block. Depending on the material being extruded, these tools are thermomechanically highly loaded, whereas the tools with no contact with the extruded material are not subjected to the same temperatures but can still be mechanically highly loaded. The cross section of a direct tube press in Fig 7.132 gives an overview of this.

The selection of the suitable hot working material for the manufacture of the extrusion tool depends on these stresses. Every hot working material has its own individual hot strength range in which the important parameters for hot working, including the hot proof stress, hot strength, hot fatigue strength, creep strength, hot toughness, and hot wear resistance, have a balanced relationship to each other. This balance must be taken into account, particularly with hollow dies for aluminum alloys, in order to avoid premature die failures. The alloy steel plants provide relevant data and guidelines in their material brochures. The steel application lists 201 and 202 also help with data on the hot strength, hot toughness, creep strength, and hot elongation for the hot working materials currently used. This does not, however, exclude the specific experience accumulated within an extrusion plant for types of tooling and the material extruded with them, which adds to the data from the supplier. This results in specific demands from the user as, for example, written down in the technical supply guidelines of the DGM for hot working materials for the manu-

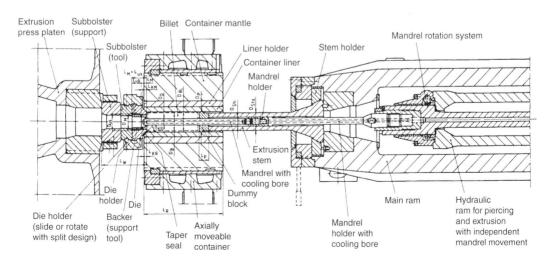

Fig. 7.132 Complete tool set of a direct rod and tube extrusion press with internal piercer as well as liquid-cooled tapered mandrel. The terminology corresponds to DIN 24540. Source: Sauer

Table 7.16 Hot working materials for direct deformation extrusion tooling

Extrusion tools	Lead-zinc and tin alloys Tool material	Magnesium and aluminum alloys Tool material	Initial strength, N/mm²	Copper alloys Tool material	Initial strength, N/mm²	Iron alloys Tool material
Extrusion dies	1.2343 Stellite 3/stellite 6 (for solder wires)	1.2343/1.2367	1500–1800	1.2365/1.2888/1.2889 1.2731 2.4668	1450–1550 ~1050 1300–1400	1.2343/1.2731 (forged or cast)
Feeder chambers	1.2323/1.2343	1.2343	1500–1700	Not suitable	...	Not suitable
Die inserts	Not common	In general, not common	...	Cermotherm (brass wire) MHC/ZrO₂ (German silver) 2.4668/2.4973/2.4979 Stellite 3/stellite 6	1200–1500	TZM
Die body	Not common	In general, not common	...	1.2343/1.2367/1.2889 1.2731	1450–1550 ~1200	1.2343
Mandrel	1.2343	<60 mm diameter, 1.2367 >60 mm diameter, 1.2343	<60 mm diameter, 1600–1800 >60 mm diameter, 1500–1600	<60 mm diameter, 1.2367 >60 mm diameter, 1.2343/1.2367	<60 mm diameter, 1600–1700 >60 mm diameter, 1500–1600	1.2344/1.2367
Mandrel tips	Not common	1.2343/1.2367	1600–1800	1.2889 2.4973/2.4979	1400–1500 1200–1500	Not common
Porthole dies	1.2343	1.2343/1.2367 1.2885	1500–1800	Not suitable	...	Not suitable
Bridge dies	1.2343	1.2343/1.2367 1.2885	1500–1800	2.4668/2.4973	1200–1500	Not suitable

Table 7.17 Hot working materials for indirect deformation extrusion tooling

Also for auxiliary and support tooling

Extrusion tools	Extruded material					
	Lead-zinc and tin alloys	Magnesium and aluminum alloys		Copper alloys		Iron alloys
	Tool material	Initial strength, N/mm²	Tool material	Initial strength, N/mm²	Tool material	Tool material
Backer	1.2343	1400–1500	1.2343	1300–1500	1.2343/1.2714	1.2343
Bolster	1.2343/1.2714	1400–1500	1.2343/1.2714	1300–1500	1.2343/1.2714	1.2343/1.2714
Subbolster	1.2714	1400–1500	1.2714	1300–1500	1.2343/1.2714	1.2343/1.2714
Pressure plate in extrusion press platen	1.2714	1400–1500	1.2714	1200–1300	1.2714	1.2714
Die holder	1.2343	1400–1500	1.2343	1400–1500	1.2343/1.2365, 1.2367/1.2885	1.2343/1.2367
Tool holder	1.2343	1400–1500	1.2343	1400–1500	1.2343/1.2367	1.2343
Container mantle	1.2343	1100–1230	1.2343	1100–1200	1.234/1.2367	1.2343/1.2367
Container liner holder	1.2343	1300–1430	1.2343	1300–1400	1.2343/1.2367	1.2343/1.2367
Container liner	1.2343	1400–1530	1.2343/1.2367	1400–1500, 1000–1100	1.2343/1.2367, 1.2779	1.2343/1.2367
Extrusion stem	1.2343	<700 N/mm², 1500–1600; >700 N/mm², 1600–1700	<700 N/mm², 1.2343; >700 N/mm², 1.2343/1.2367	<700 N/mm², 1500–1600; >700 N/mm², 1600–1700	<700 N/mm², 1.2367; >700 N/mm², 1.2367	1.2343/1.2367
Dummy blocks	1.2343	1500–1600	1.2343/1.2367 (fixed dummy block)	1500–1700, 1300–1500	1.2343/1.2367, 2.4668	1.2344/1.2367
Cleaning blocks	Not necessary	1400–1500	1.2343	1400–1500	1.2343/1.2367	Not necessary
Mandrel holder	1.2343/1.2714	1250–1350	1.2343/1.2714	1250–1350	1.2343/1.2714	1.2343/1.2714
Mandrel bars	1.2343/1.2714	1250–1350	1.2343/1.2714	1250–1350	1.2343/1.2714	1.2343/1.2714

Source: Sayer

Table 7.18   Hot working materials for extrusion containers

For the application: IB = Liner ZB = Liner holder M = Mantle	Extruded metal(a)			
	Characteristic data for current hot working materials(b)			
	Maximum working temperature, °C	Material No.	Strength heat treated to, N/mm²	Permitted load at operating temperature(c), N/mm²
IB Easily extruded aluminum alloys	500	1.2367	1300–1500	850
IB Moderately difficult aluminum alloys	500	1.2367	1300–1500	850
IB Moderately difficult aluminum alloys, indirect	450	1.2344	1300–1500	850
IB Difficult-to-extrude aluminum alloys	500	1.2367	1300–1500	850
IB Difficult-to-extrude aluminum alloys, indirect	450	1.2344	1300–1500	850
IB Easily extruded copper alloys	600	1.2779	1000–1100	550(d)
IB Easily extruded copper alloys, indirect	600	1.2779	1000–1100	550(d)
IB Moderately difficult copper alloys	650	1.2779	1000–1100	500(d)
IB Difficult-to-extrude copper alloys	700	1.2779	1000–1100	425(d)
IB Easily extruded iron alloys	550	1.2343	1300–1500	700
IB Difficult-to-extrude iron alloys	600	1.2367	1300–1500	800
IB Nickel alloys	650	1.2779	1000–1100	500(d)
ZB Moderately difficult aluminum alloys	500	1.2343	1100–1300	800
ZB Difficult-to-extrude aluminum alloys	500	1.2343	1100–1300	800
ZB Difficult-to-extrude aluminum alloys, indirect	450	1.2343	1100–1300	800
ZB Moderately difficult copper alloys	550	1.2367	1100–1300	800
ZB Difficult-to-extrude copper alloys	600	1.2367	1100–1300	750
ZB Easily extruded iron alloys	500	1.2343	1100–1300	800
ZB Difficult-to-extrude iron alloys	500	1.2367	1100–1300	850
ZB Nickel alloys	550	1.2367	1100–1300	800
M Easily extruded aluminum alloys	500	1.2343/1.2323(d)	1000–1200	750/600
M Moderately difficult aluminum alloys	500	1.2343	1000–1200	750
M Moderately difficult aluminum alloys, indirect	450	1.2343/1.2323(e)	1000–1200	750/700
M Difficult-to-extrude aluminum alloys	500	1.2343	1000–1200	750
M Difficult-to-extrude aluminum alloys, indirect	450	1.2343	1000–1200	750
M Easily extruded copper alloys	450	1.2343/1.2323(e)	1000–1200	750/700
M Easily extruded copper alloys, indirect	450	1.2343/1.2323(e)	1000–1200	750/700
M Moderately difficult copper alloys	500	1.2343	1000–1200	750
M Difficult copper alloys	550	1.2367	1000–1200	750
M Easily extruded iron alloys	450	1.2343/1.2323(de)	1000–1200	750/700
M Difficult-to-extrude iron alloys	450	1.2343	1000–1200	750
M Nickel alloys	500	1.2367	1000–1200	800

(a) Table 7.10 gives data on the contributing factors, including billet temperature, specific extrusion pressure, extrusion time, as well as the friction and shear forces. (b) Only a limited range of materials are listed. (c) 85% of the 0.2% hot proof stress, with the exception of the austenitic steel 1.2779. (d) Data taken from the steel application lists 201 and 202 (VDE h). (e) Alternative for less severe thermal stresses. Source: Groos

facture of extrusion tooling for hot working aluminum alloys [DGM 97]. In individual cases, the tool-specific requirements can even exceed these. Tables 7.16 and 7.17 give a general overview of the hot working materials available today for the manufacture of extrusion tooling for the processing of metallic materials.

Table 7.18 illustrates the extent to which an extrusion plant and also the experienced tool manufacturer must proceed in the selection of the correct hot working material for the manufacture of an efficient extrusion tool according to the material-specific processing conditions.

REFERENCES

[Ake 83]: R. Akeret, Einfluß der Querschnittsform und der Werkzeuggestaltung beim Strangpressen von Aluminium (Influence of the Cross-Section and the Tool Design in the Extrusion of Aluminum), Part 1, *Aluminium,* Vol 59 (No. 9), 1983, p 665–669; Part 2, *Aluminium,* Vol 59 (No.10), 1983, p 745–750

[Ake 85]: R. Akeret, Einfluß des Neigungswinkels und der Länge der Lauffläche auf die Reibung im Preßkanal (Influence of the Inclination Angle and the Bearing Length on the Friction in the Aperture), *Aluminium,* Vol 61 (No. 3), 1985, p 169–172

[Ame 71]: A. Ames, I. Bielen, and G. Sauer, Vorschlag zur Normung von Werkzeugen für Leichtmetall-Strangpressen in Abhängigkeit der Preßkräfte (Proposal for Standardization of Tools for Aluminum Extrusion as a Function of the Press Power), Z. *Metallkde.*, Vol 62 (No. 10), 1971, p 716–720.

[Bar 81]: G. Barten, Einflüsse auf Festigkeit und Zähigkeit von härtbaren Warmarbeitsstählen (Influences on the Strength and Toughness on Heat-Treatable Hot-Working

Steels), *ZWF,* Vol 76 (No. 2), 1981, p 89–100

[Ber 76/1]: H. Berns, Ursachen des Zeitstandverhaltens von Warmarbeitsstählen und Vergleich von hochwarmfesten Legierungen (Causes for the Creep Properties of Hot-Working Steels and Comparison of High Temperature Alloys), *ZWF,* Vol 71 (No. 5), 1976, p 212–217

[Ber 76/2]: H. Berns, Auslegung von Blockaufnehmern und Druckgußkammern unter Berücksichtigung des Kriechens (Design of Containers and Pressure Casting Chambers Taking Creep into Account), *ZWF,* Vol 71 (No. 12), 1976

[Ber 76/3]: H. Berns, Werkstofftechnische Betrachtung zur Auslegung von Blockaufnehmern für das indirekte Strangpressen von Messing (Material Scientific Considerations in the Design of Container for the Indirect Extrusion of Brass), *Z. Metallkde.,* Vol 67 (No. 5), 1976

[Ber 76/4]: H. Berns, Zeitstanduntersuchungen an Warmarbeitsstählen (Creep Studies on Hot-Working Steels), *ZWF,* Vol 71 (No. 2), 1976, p 64–69

[Ber 82]: H. Berns, "Warmarbeitsstähle und—legierungen" ("Hot-Working Steels and Alloys"), VDI-Report 432, 1982, p 43–49

[Bra 66]: H. Braun and W. Schulte, Molybdänmatrizen für das Strangpressen von Stahlprofilen (Molybdenum Dies for Steel Section Extrusion), *Stahl Eisen,* Vol 86 (No. 15), 1966, p 967–980

[Bre 79]: H. Brendel and H. Winkler, *Wissenspeicher Tribotechnik,* Springer Verlag, Berlin, 1979

[Bri 75]: H. Briefs and M. Wolf, *Warmarbeitsstähle* (*Hot-Working Steels*), Verlag Stahleisen, Düsseldorf, 1975, p 47

[Brs 81]: H. Brandis, B. Huchtemann, and A. Steinen, Technologie der Wärmebehandlung warm-und hochwarmfester Stähle (Technology of the Heat-Treatment of High Temperature and Very High Temperature Steels), *Thyssen Edelstahl Tech. Ber.,* Vol 7 (No. 1), 1981, p 28–30

[Bun 81]: W. Bunk, I. Hansen, and M. Gregor, *Tribologie,* Band 1 (*Tribology,* Vol 1), Springer Verlag, Berlin, 1981

[Cae 77]: A. Caery, Vorgetragen anläßlich des Internationalen Kolloquiums über Warmarbeitsstähle am 1 und 2 (Presented at the International Colloquium on Hot-Working Steels on 1 and 2), Dec 1977 (St. Etienne)

[Det 89]: D. Deterding, Gebräuchliche Warmarbeitsstähle zum Einsatz für Druckgießformen mit besonderem Hinweis auf den Warmarbeitsstahl 1.2367 (Conventional Hot-Working Steels for Use in Pressure Die Casting Molds with Specific Reference to the Hot-Working Steel 1.2367), *Giesserei,* Vol 76 (No. 24), 1989, p 848–849

[Dez 71]: P. Détrez and M.Th. Leger, *Fonderie,* Vol 26, 1971, p 395–403

[DGM 97]: DGM, Technische Lieferrichtlinien—Warmarbeitswerkstoffe zum Bau von Strangpreßwerkzeugen für die Warmumformung von Aluminium-Werkstoffen (Technical Supply Guidelines—Hot-Working Materials for the Manufacture of Extrusion Tooling for the Hot-Working of Aluminum Materials), *Dtsch. Ges. Materialkd.* March 1997

[Dör 82]: E. Dörre, "Keramische Werkzeugwerkstoffe" ("Ceramic Tool Materials"), VDI-Report 439, 1982, p 61–67

[Dub 86]: *Dubbel,* 15th ed., p 198, 219–220, 228

[Eck 97]: W. Eckenbach, Werkzeuge für das Strangpressen, Neuere Entwicklungen der Widerstandsheizungen von Rezipienten (Tools for Extrusion, New Developments in the Resistance Heating of Containers), *Aluminium,* Vol 73 (No. 7/8), 1997, p 470–472

[Elm 89]: E. El-Magd, K.Th. Kaiser, and H.W. Walkendorf, Einfluß der Vorbehandlung auf die Struktur hochwarmfester Nickellegierungen (Influence of the Pretreatment on the Structure of High Temperature Nickel Alloys), *Metall.,* Vol 43 (No. 12), 1989, p 1149–1152

[Eys 67]: F.W. Eysell, Herstellung und Behandlung von Strangpreßwerkzeugen: III Behandlung von Strangpreßwerkzeugen durch Salzbadnitrieren (Manufacture and Treatment of Extrusion Tools, Part III: Treatment of Extrusion Tools by Salt Bath Nitriding), *Z. Metallkde;* Vol 58 (No. 5), 1967, p 285–288

[Gah 90]: K.-H. Zum Gahr, *Reibung und Verschleiß bei metallischen und nichtmetallischen Werkstoffen* (*Friction and Wear in Metallic and Nonmetallic Materials*), DGM-Informationsgesellschaft Verlag, 1990

[Gie 95]: Gieck, *Technische Formelsammlung* (*Technical Collection of Formulae*), 30th ed., 11–15, 17

[Gri 82]: W. Grimm, A. Mukhoty, and D. Roempler, Einfluß verschiedener Schmelzvarianten auf die mechanischen Eigenschaften von Einsatzstählen (Influence of Different Melt Versions on the Mechanical Properties of Case-Hardening Steels), *ZWF,* vol 77 (No. 4), 1982, p 194–199

[Güm 81]: P. Gümpel and K. Rasche, Entwicklungsstand bei Warmarbeitsstählen (Development of Hot-Working Steels), *Thyssen Edelstahl Tech. Ber.,* Vol 7 (No. 2), 1981, p 151–160

[Hab 77]: E. Haberling, Zeitstand-und Dauerfestigkeit von Warmarbeitsstählen bei erhöhten Temperaturen (Creep and Fatigue Strength of Hot-Working Steels at Elevated Temperatures), *Thyssen Edelstahl Tech. Ber.,* Vol 3 (No. 2), 1977, p 125–129

[Hab 80]: K.-H. Habig, *Verschleiß und Härte von Werkstoffen* (*Wear and Hardness of Materials*), Carl Hanser Verlag, München, Wien, 1980

[Hab 81]: E. Haberling, Zähigkeitsprüfung von Warmarbeitsstählen (Toughness Testing of Hot-Working Tool Steel), *Thyssen Edelstahl Tech. Ber.,* Vol 7 (No. 2), 1981, p 166–167

[Hab 87]: E. Haberling, Zeitstandfestigkeit von Warmarbeitsstählen (Creep Strength of Hot-Working Steels), *Thyssen Edelstahl Tech. Ber.,* Vol 13 (No. 2) 1987, p 118–121

[Har 84]: K.E. Haberfellner and F.M. Schindler, "State and Development of Tooling Materials," International Aluminum Extrusion Technology Seminar (Atlanta, GA), 1984

[Hol 96]: K. Holthe and S. Tjotta, "The Heat Balance during Multiple Press Cycles," International Aluminum Extrusion Technology Seminar, (Chicago, IL), 1996

[Hub 80]: U. Huber-Gommann, H.J. Grosemann, and G. Schulz, Nitrieren im Ammoniakgasstrom (Nitriding in an Ammonia Gasflow), *ZWF,* Vol 75 (No. 9), 1980, p 407–410

[Kle 86]: M. Kleyer, Moderne Strangpreßmatrizen (Modern Extrusion Dies), *VDI-Ber.,* Vol 128 (No. 10), 1986, p 88–93

[Kol 91]: H. Kolaske and K. Dreyer, Neuerungen auf dem Hartmetallgebiet (Developments in Hard Metals), *Ing. Werkst.,* Vol 3 (No. 5), 1991, p 58–61

[Kor 95]: W. Kortmann, Werkzeugwerkstoffe für das Strangpressen, *Grundlagen des Strangpressens,* Kontakt + Studium (Tool Materials for Extrusion, *Fundamentals of Extrusion,* Contact and Study), Expert-Verlag, 1995, p 84–93

[Kor 97]: W. Kortmann, *Vergleich herkömmlicher Warmarbeitsstähle zu Sonderlegierungen im Strangpreßbereich* (*Comparison of Conventional Hot-Working Steels and Special Alloys in Extrusion*), Sonderheft der Schmidt + Clemens GmbH + Co., 1997

[Kra 89]: R. Kranz, F. Wendl, and K.D. Wupper, Einfluß der Erodierbedingungen auf die Zähigkeit von Werkzeugstählen (Influence of the Erosion Conditions on the Toughness of Tool Steels), *Thyssen Edelstahl Tech. Ber.,* Vol 15 (No. 2), 1989, p 126–131

[Kre 78]: W. Krebs, *Giesserei,* Vol 65, 1978, p 645–652, 733–739

[Lan 81]: G. Lang, Abschätzung der Reibung im Preßkanal beim direkten und indirekten Strangpressen von Al99.6 (Estimation of the Friction in the Die Aperture in Direct and Indirect Extrusion), *Aluminium,* Vol 57 (No. 12), 1981, p 791–796

[Lan 84]: G. Lang, Reibung im Preßkanal beim direkten und indirekten Strangpressen (Friction in the Die Aperture in Direct and Indirect Extrusion) of Al99.6, AlMgSi0.5, and AlZn4.5Mg1, *Aluminium,* Vol 60 (No. 4), 1984, p 266–268

[Lau 76]: K. Laue and H. Stenger, Strangpressen, *Verfahren—Maschinen—Werkzeuge* (*Extrusion—Processes—Machining—Tooling*), Aluminium-Verlag GmbH, 1976, p 293–294

[Mit 97]: W. Mitter, K. Haberfellner, R. Danzer, and C. Stickler, Lebensdauerprognose für Warmarbeitsstähle (Service Life Prognosis for Hot-Working Steels), *HTM,* Vol 52 (No. 4), 1997, Carl Hanser Verlag, München

[Mül 95]: K. Müller et al., *Grundlagen des Strangpressens* (*Fundamentals of Extrusion*), Expert-Verlag, 1995, p 140–168

[Ort 77]: R. Ortmann, Untersuchungen zum Aushärtungsverhalten des Preßmatrizenstahles (Investigations into the Age-Hardening Behavior of Extrusion Die Steels) X50NiCrWV1313, *ZWF,* Vol 72 (No. 9), 1977, p 496–498

[Rei 82]: N. Reiter, Hartmetalle als Werkzeugwerkstoff (Hard Metals as Tool Material), *VDI-Ber.,* No.439, 1982, p 145–158

[Sar 67]: G. Sauer, Herstellung und Behandlung von Strangpreßwerkzeugen IV: Erhöhung der Standzeiten von Aluminium-Preßwerkzeugen durch Salzbadnitrieren (Manufacture and Treatment of Extrusion Tools, IV: Increasing the Service Life of Aluminum Dies by Salt Bath Nitriding), *Z. Metallkde.,* Vol 58 (No. 5), 1967, p 289–296

[Schi 82]: A. Schindler, G. Fertl, and H. Kröhnke, Werkzeugwerkstoffe für das Strangpressen (Extrusion Tool Materials), *VDI-Ber.,* No.432, 1982, p 91–101

[Sei 88]: H. Seilstorfer, PM-Warmarbeitswerkstoffe (Hot-Working Tool Materials), *Metall,* Vol 42 (No. 2), 1988, p 146–152

[Ste 96]: B. Steinert, Einflußmöglichkeiten zur optimalen Werkzeugabstützung in Leichtmetall-Strangpressen (Possible Methods for Achieving Optimum Tool Support in Aluminum Extrusion), *Aluminum,* Vol 72 (No. 5), 1996

[Stz 90]: A. Steinmetz and A. Biswas, Rechnerische Simulation des Strangpreßvorgangs (Computer Simulation of the Extrusion Process), *Aluminum,* Vol 66 (No. 3), 1990

[The 93]: W.W. Thedja, K. Müller, and D. Ruppin, Die Vorgänge im Preßkanal beim Warmstrangpressen von Aluminium (The Processes in the Die Aperture in Hot Extrusion of Aluminum), Part 1 and Part 2, *Aluminum,* Vol 69, 1993, p 649–653

[VDE 85]: Verein deutscher Eisenhüttenleute (VDEh): *Leitfaden für eine Betriebsfestigkeitsrechnung,* 2. Auflage (*Guidelines for an Operational Strength Calculation,* 2nd ed.), Verlag Stahleisen mbH, Düsseldorf, 1985

[Wan 72]: D. Wanders, "Berechnung und Optimierung von Hochtemperaturwerkzeugen am Beispiel von Strangpreßmatrizen" ("Calculation and Optimization of High-Temperature Tools Using Extrusion Dies as an Example"), Dissertation, Technische Universität Clausthal, 1972

CHAPTER 8

Quality Management in Extrusion

Detlef Smolarek

8.1 Quality

THE AIM OF EVERY EXTRUSION PLANT is the economic production of competitive products to the required quality.

The expectation of the customer, however, extends beyond the product-specific requirements. In addition to the product and service provided, the customer considers the social and corporation aspects of the company. This includes the social politics, integration into the region, and environmental issues. The quality of a company is the sum of these properties. It can be used as a yardstick for comparing companies.

A company can separate itself from the competition by setting strategic goals for the company quality. To maintain and continually develop the company's quality level, everybody involved in the order processing must be conscious of the entire quality philosophy. Table 8.1 shows an analysis of the approach to quality. The customer requirements for the producer of the semifinished product and the consequences for the supplier are shown in Table 8.2.

It can be seen that the requirements for the manufacturers of the semifinished products have increased and will continue to increase. They will be expected to provide a greater product and production competence and be responsible for the product quality.

8.2 Quality Management

8.2.1 Quality Management System

A quality management system (QMS) can be introduced into a company for various reasons. Usually, these systems are introduced because the customers demand a quality system to ensure that consistent product quality is achieved.

However, a very important point is that only the institutionalizing of the ongoing improvement process will actually contribute to the long-term success.

Table 8.1 Analysis of the approach to quality

Area	Step 1	Step 2	Step 3
Customer	Profit is more important than customer satisfaction No marketing	Customer requirements investigated Customer satisfaction measurements started	The principle of "internal customer" is encompassed by the organization (next operational step is the customer)
Management	Quality—a necessary evil	Quality—a cost problem, defect prevention	Quality—a high-level value prevention
Organization	Functional quality control Final inspection	Functional/teams Quality control has responsibility for quality Self-control	Permanent teams All employees are responsible for quality
System	Quality department, no quality costs monitored	Quality politics, quality-control system established, quality costs monitored	Ongoing continuous improvements Maximum possible output Shortest throughput times

The selection of a QMS can, for example, follow QS 9000. The following conditions must be fulfilled in the selection of the QMS:

- Complete understanding and implementation of the customer's requirements
- Reproducible, documented production parameters
- Controlled internal processing, with delegation of responsibilities
- Promotion of employees' competence toward individual responsibility
- Further development of the QMS
- Organizational responsibility
- Economic and competitive production

Of the QMSs, ISO 9000 is the system that most completely fulfills the company's functions.

Most companies in Europe were previously certified to ISO 9000 through the European Network for Quality System Assessment (EQNet). The important International Organization for Standardization (ISO) standards for quality management and quality control are:

- ISO 9000—guidelines for selection and application
- ISO 9001—model for statement on quality control in production, assembly, and customer service
- ISO 9002—model for statement for quality control in production and assembly
- ISO 9003—model for statement for quality control in final inspection
- ISO 9004—quality management and elements of the quality-control system

8.2.2   Introduction of a QMS

The introduction of a QMS that covers all the operations of a company must be planned in various development phases. The foundation is a planned, long-term concept into which the company-specific requirements can be integrated. The goal must be not only to obtain a certificate of compliance but also to create a management tool that can be constructively used by the employees and that brings the desired results to the organization. In order to develop a practical and acceptable QMS, the opportunities within ISO 9000 should be used.

Modern quality techniques can be readily used as supplementary methods within the 20 elements of ISO 9001. This provides the basic procedures:

- Definition of the vision of the quality culture desired
- Derivation of the individual strategies for quality management
- Co-operation with the individual lines on the development of the individual QMS elements
- Integration of quality management tasks into the lines, for example, testing procedures and responsibility for quality
- Function of quality control from the viewpoint of control and consultation
- Installation of a monitoring system for performance control in all areas

The documentation for the organizational and operational structures required by ISO 9000 should not be a separate handbook for external use but an operational manual and reference book for daily use by all employees.

Figure 8.1 shows a structure for quality-control documentation classified into internal documentation (quality control using internal data) and external documentation (in the form of product catalogs, quality-control documentation, and brochures). Figure 8.2 shows the path to a quality culture in eight phases:

- *Phase 1:* The structured QMS according to ISO 9000 forms a solid foundation that can be built on. The regular certification by accredited bodies must be ensured by ongoing revision.
- *Phase 2:* Personnel are trained by internal education and are then in a position to fulfill the tasks required. The management sets the example.
- *Phase 3:* Training and application of new process-orientated quality techniques are implemented to complement the system-orientated elements of ISO 9000.

Table 8.2   Customer requirements and the consequences for the producer of the semifinished products

Customer requirements	Consequences for semifinished product producer
Price reduction	Production cost reduction
No product defects	Zero-defect production
No incoming goods inspection	Documentation of production data and setting up quality test center
Low capital allocation	Just-in-time production
Reduction of the extent of manufacture	Production of functional complete assemblies
	Increase in the product and production competence

- *Phase 4:* Evidence of progress is provided by the installation of a permanent target-versus-actual comparison as well as the visualization of the results in individual departments. Problems are clearly revealed, and improvement measures are shown.
- *Phase 5:* Trained moderators lead quality circles that optimize individual processes within a process chain, with the personnel involved.
- *Phase 6:* Documentation of the optimized production sequences and testing for robustness and retention of knowledge is performed.
- *Phase 7:* Internal audits according to ISO 9000 lend themselves to monitoring the process. Complementing the normal audits of system audits, product audits, and process audits, self-inspection audits, interface au-

dits, activity audits, or audits to determine training requirements that can be carried out.
- *Phase 8:* The extension of the ongoing improvement to the entire organization is not the final stage of the development but only a stage in the continuous development.

The continually changing boundary conditions necessitate a repeated return to the optimization process, starting at phase 5.

8.2.3 Process Chain

As part of the realization of a QMS, it is recommended to follow the operating sequences within the organization. Figure 8.3 shows the complete process chain for order processing within the quality circle.

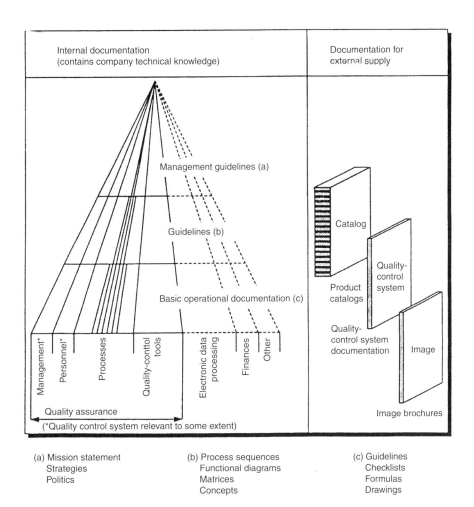

Fig. 8.1 Structure of the control documentation

The complete process can be divided into process steps. Interfaces occur at the transitions between the process steps.

The management of interfaces plays a very important role in achieving short transit times and defect-free production processes. However,

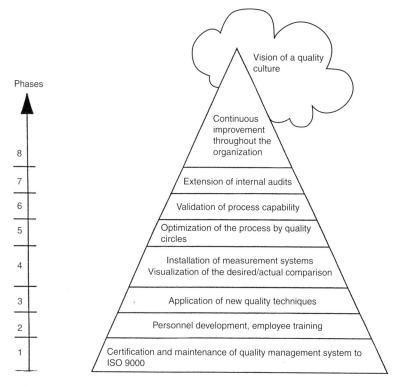

Fig. 8.2 Vision of a quality culture [Smo 94]

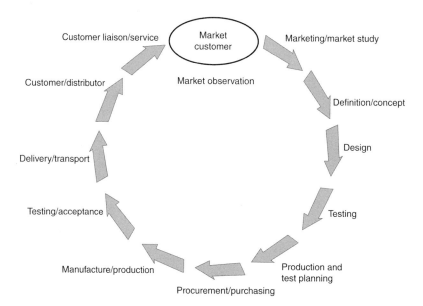

Fig. 8.3 Complete process chain for order processing within the quality circle [Egg 87]

the initial approach should be to reduce the number of interfaces.

Examples for low-interface team organizations in an extrusion plant include the following.

Order Processing. For a specific semifinished product, cooperation between the personnel in purchasing, process planning, production, and transport is realized in a centralized order-processing department with an office close to the production.

Casting House. Casting teams are formed that are responsible for the weekly detailed planning, covering the charging of the melting furnace, casting and charge testing (analysis, ultrasonic testing), and homogenizing of the logs up to cutting of the extrusion billets.

Extrusion. Weekly detailed planning meetings by the press crew establish individual controls testing of the quality characteristics (e.g., shape, roughness, surface quality, weld quality) during contract processing, up to the point of section packing. Regular monitoring of internal customer requirements by communication with internal customers prevents unnecessary additional actions.

8.2.4 Product Liability

With the introduction of the German product liability law on January 1, 1990, the European Union's rules on product liability for the protection of the user were extensively extended. In this law, the change from negligence liability to no-fault causal liability came into effect. The damage associated with product defect establishes the causal liability of the producer. The customer no longer must prove the responsibility of the producer, but the manufacturer has to provide evidence that all measures were taken during processing in order to exclude any defect.

The product liability demands from all plants and manufacturers involved with a product, even if only for a short time, the organizational procedures in the areas of quality control, product documentation, and risk management, from planning to transfer to the customer. The current levels of science and technology are applicable.

The product liability law applies in the case of damage to a third party, not between the two contractual partners. The no-fault liability of the manufacturer expires after 10 years (forfeiture), calculated from the point in time at which the product that caused the failure had been brought into circulation.

Above all, the relationship between the contractor (customer) and the semifinished product producer (extrusion plant) must be considered, because a semifinished product producer is not usually responsible for either the design or the manufacture of a component or even for the assembly and direct distribution of end products, including plant, machinery, and so forth.

It is important that the customer order is clearly defined with supplementary information, including drawings, technical specifications, relevant standards, information on required values in terms of the chemical composition, mechanical properties, shape, and positional tolerances, as well as the required surface condition. Component-critical characteristics should be provided in the specification or on the drawing.

Quality agreements currently represent a standard binding agreement at the interface between supplier and customer. The agreements control product-specific requirements in detail, including, for example:

- Extent of supply
- Testing responsibility
- Documentation
- Liability limitation
- Lot size
- Delivery requirements
- Collaboration on testing and product planning
- Quality-control system requirements
- Procedure for technical process variations
- Auditing
- Additional requirements

The contract review within the extrusion plant must clarify the technical feasibility. In the case of foreseeable deviations as well as technical process limitations, a corresponding written counterproposal or a cancellation must be submitted to the customer (this applies in particular to the aircraft and automobile industries). References to limitations (mechanical properties, analysis variations, charge variations, strength-reducing inclusions, residual internal stresses) should be specified in writing.

The order-conforming processing of the customer order is the controlling requirement. Manufacturers can only be relieved from their product liability in very specifically defined cases, depending on the applicable law (in Germany, according to the product liability law). The burden of proof rests with them. The following application possibilities must be taken into account:

- The supplier has not sold the finished product and is only a subcontractor.

- The supplier has demonstrably not made any errors up to the point of sale. In addition, the defect was not detectable according to the current state of science and technology.
- The product corresponds to a national standard; it must refer to a law or a binding detailed regulation for the manufacture. Standards including ISO, DIN, or European Standards (EN) have only a limited legal quality, because the user has the option of selecting deviations with equal or higher standards. The fulfillment of these standards can only be considered as the minimum requirements.
- There is no liability for the so-called development risks present that existed at the time of bringing to the market but could not be identified by the state of technology and science at the time. The controlling point of the assessment is the time of bringing to the market and not of production.
- If it can be proved that the defect results from the design of the component into which the semifinished product was fitted (damage during installation or during the operational life) as well as by the operational instructions of the end producer, then this relieves the responsibility.

The indemnification liability cannot be excluded by written references in the context of the general commercial and supply terms and conditions or by warnings.

The German product liability law of 1990 § 19 concedes the objection to the development risk (§ 1 Par. 2 No. 5) and stipulates an upper liability limit of 160 million Deutsche marks for personal injury.

8.2.5 Economics

The introduction of a QMS is associated with different costs, depending on the size of the company and the level of development. In addition to the one-off introduction costs, there is ongoing expenditure referred to as quality costs.

Figure 8.4 shows the division of quality costs into quality cost groups and quality cost elements.

8.3 Quality Control

8.3.1 Organization

In a functionally structured large organization, the quality-assurance quality-control (QC) department is an independent department rep-

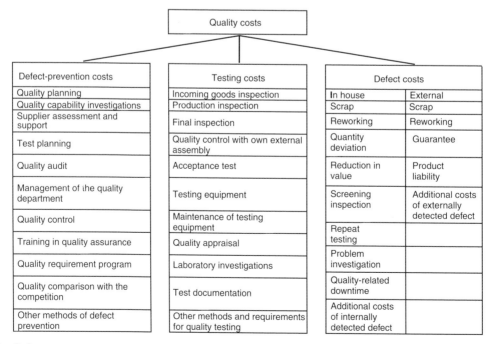

Fig. 8.4 Division of quality costs

resented on the management board (Fig. 8.5). In smaller companies, it forms part of the production department. Integration into departments is also possible.

According to the requirements of the quality system standards, the preference is for the QC to have a largely independent position within the company structure. Apart from the fundamental considerations of the tasks that are centralized and those that are decentralized, decisions must also be made on which tasks are to be delegated, for example, to the production personnel. It should be clarified from the outset whether the personnel involved report directly to the QC department or have only a technical supporting role.

The most effective and economic organization structure depends on the circumstances specific to the organization:

- Company divisions that must be included, for example, development, production, procurement, training, process technology, and so on
- Range of responsibilities of the QC, for example, testing, training, advice
- Present/future organization structure
- Size of the organization
- Product mix referred to the safety risks
- Fulfillment of the system standards

The QC can be further divided according to the following plan:

- With extensive delegation of quality testing to the production areas, the QC can be reduced to technical support.
- The quality technology could then be extended into the area of quality promotion by training the inspectors in the work place (self-inspection).
- The QC can then be considered more as an advisory department with the minimum number of personnel.

8.3.1.1 Process Organization

In the context of a quality system, numerous processes occur with different degrees of importance, including:

- Contract review
- Testing plan
- Development projects
- First-sample test
- Incoming goods inspection
- Traceability
- Documentation
- Modifications
- Monitoring of measurement equipment
- Certification
- Complaints

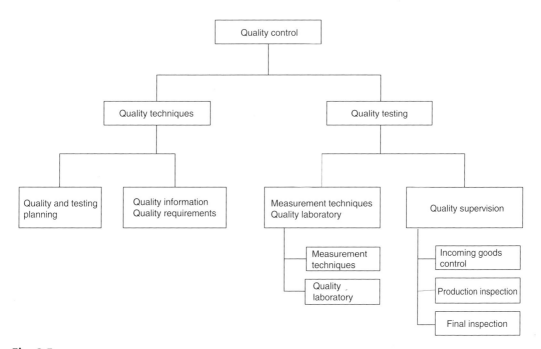

Fig. 8.5 Quality-control division

The operational processes described run throughout the entire company across the functional organization. Many of these processes have the function of a quality-control loop. Figure 8.6 shows an example of a quality-control loop in production.

8.3.2 Responsibilities

8.3.2.1 General Requirements

In recent years, quality control has developed from a piece-related testing station to a company-wide QMS. The personnel of the quality department have been continually confronted with task extensions. Pure, factual knowledge for the solution of the problems of individual components no longer suffices. The management of a quality department in a company producing semifinished products requires knowledge of the fundamentals of materials science and deformation technology as well as destructive and nondestructive materials testing. In addition, it is necessary to have experience in organizational queries, project management, company strategy, personnel development, methods for process improvement, and general financial procedures, particularly when an organization intends to work toward total quality management (TQM) via system certification (Fig. 8.7).

The quality-related strategic knowledge is increasing compared to the production-related knowledge. Questions such as "Can quality control provide an effective risk management covering product liability?" require extensive experience.

Organizations with a higher realization degree of TQM are increasingly involved with system-related responsibilities, including maintenance and further development of a QMS, promotion of the TQM philosophy, and motivation of employees.

In addition to the knowledge of quality control and production and information technology, the social-competence ability in combination with team capability and coaching are moving into the foreground.

New areas, including environmental management, will be integrated into a QMS in the future and will then form part of the responsibilities of a quality manager.

8.3.3 Audits

Auditing need not be used only as a method for analyzing the application of quality systems but can be extended to an organization-wide management instrument. Audits provide a method for the systematic monitoring of the required-versus-actual state at various levels (Fig. 8.8).

The monitoring of the QMS provides information on product quality, employee qualification, as well as logistical quality characteristics including delivery times, on-time deliveries, flexibility to changes and increases in capacity, reaction to customer complaints, and interdisciplinary cooperation.

Auditing then develops into an instrument for strategic control. The QC plans the audit, monitors its periodic execution to plan, and prepares an annual report on the results and actions.

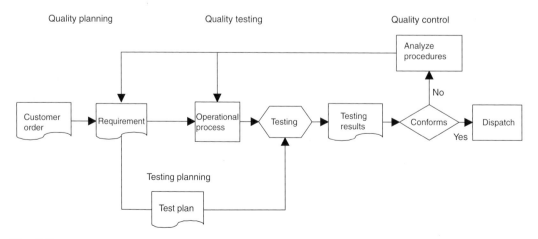

Fig. 8.6 Example of a quality-control automatic loop

On one hand, the integration of the line managers as trained auditors is supported by the increased demand for internal/external customer orientation and, on the other, is upheld by the ongoing improvement process. In addition, the responsibility for quality management has wider support (Table 8.3).

The individual departmental and reciprocal auditing of different organizational units can be carried out by the line managers. A control system then develops from the continuous-improvement process throughout the entire organization. This further develops the competence of the employees involved. The emphasis is on both self-inspection of the quality and also the time-cost parameters. Planning and control responsibilities are the focal point of this audit and not the "supervision."

Considered in its entirety, the following benefits can be achieved. Regular internal and external auditing produces a measurable statement of the ongoing improvement process. The reciprocal comprehension associated with an improved information exchange is a positive side effect of interdisciplinary audits. New ideas and methods flow from innovative departments into other areas. The total knowledge increases. Specific knowledge is available throughout the entire organization by knowledge transfer.

8.3.3.1 QMS Audit

A QMS audit is intended to determine the effectiveness of the QMS throughout the processing of an order/organization. The system audit is an independent test of the quality system of an organization or organizational unit, with specific focus on the interfaces. The weaknesses identified are listed in a report that acts as a basis for those responsible to establish and introduce the necessary corrective actions.

This type of audit is required by ISO 9000, for example. The 20 sections of this standard are accordingly examined. The auditor first acquaints himself with the prescribed quality requirements (handbooks, procedures, customer requirements, specifications, goals, etc.). The actual state of the quality system is examined for:

- Completeness
- Suitability

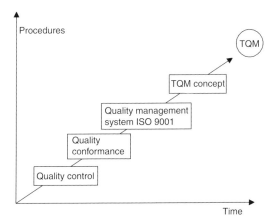

Fig. 8.7 The way to total quality management (TQM)

Table 8.3 Audit classification and auditors

QM, quality management; UM, environmental management

Level	Type of audit	Auditors
Complete organization	QM-system audit	
	Certification	External
	Internal audits	Experienced personnel from all departments
	UM-system audit	
	Certification	External
	Internal audits	Experienced personnel from all departments
Departments	Process audit	
	Technical	Personnel from the relevant departments
	Administrative Cross functional	
	Product audit	Personnel from the quality department
Personnel	Self-inspector audit	Experienced personnel from the relevant departments

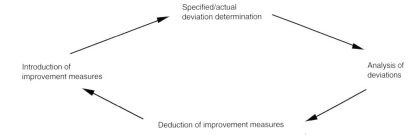

Fig. 8.8 Auditing

- Maintenance of the specified procedures

Finally, if the implementation does not agree with the requirements, corresponding corrective actions are initiated by discussions with those concerned.

8.3.3.2 Environmental System Audit

The auditing of the environmental management system (EMS) to ISO 14001 should monitor the following points on conformance:

- Extent of fulfillment of objectives and part objectives, including maintenance of statutory requirements, obligation to continuous improvement, and so on
- Continuous suitability of the EMS with changes in the boundary conditions and knowledge
- Inclusion of the concerns of relevant circles of interest

The importance of environmental politics, environmental goals, and processes should be taken on board at those levels of management that have specified them. The organization and procedures of the audit are very similar to a QMS.

8.3.3.3 Process Audit

This audit is the testing of a process or a series of such processes in production and administration. It is used in particular where specific key processes take place, for example, quotation and order processing or extrusion and drawing. It should first and foremost establish whether the production is under control and whether the actions/control are appropriately matched to the requirements of the quality criteria and quality evidence.

These process competence investigations are often part of customer requirements. The process audit should be used as early as possible, similar to the sample or first-sample verification.

8.3.3.4 Product Audit

The product audit can be considered as a shortened version of the process audit. In the product audit, the quality of products or components is tested at a specific part of the product production. At the same time, the documentation used up to this point and, if applicable, the fabrication and testing equipment used are also tested.

A product audit is carried out to:

- Establish the quality level of the products to be supplied
- Verify that the products to be supplied meet the specified quality standard
- Establish the quality level of the products delivered to testing stations
- Determine the capability of testing stations to identify quality defects and to make quality decisions
- Assess the quality-control procedures
- Assess whether controlled production is taking place
- Determine the reproducibility of the test results

The concept of the product audit is also to determine whether the necessary means and procedures are available to produce and assess a quality product.

Table 8.4 Failure modes and effect analysis for the extrusion process

Step failure	Type of defect, mode	Effect of defect	Root cause of defect	Procedures to prevent defect
1	Dimensional variation, cross section	Scrap	Tool defect press conditions	Sampling, periodic testing
2	Straightness deviation, bend	Increased straightening cost, scrap	Section guiding	Visual inspection, stretching, straightening
3	Twist	Increased straightening cost	Tool defect	Stretching, straightening
4	Roughness	Scrap	Tool damage, metal buildup on tool	Periodic visual inspection, cleaning
5	Die lines	Scrap	Tool damage, metal buildup on tool	Periodic visual inspection, cleaning
6	Graphite bands, flakes	Scrap	Section guiding (cannot be avoided completely)	Cleaning
7	Mechanical damage	Scrap	Section guiding, handling	. . .
8	Pick-up	Scrap	Billet	. . .
9	Transverse cracking	Scrap	. . .	. . .
10	Incorrect billet, incorrect charge	Scrap	. . .	. . .
11	Lubricant inclusions	. . .	. . .	. . .

Table 8.5 Elements of inspection planning (with reference to DIN 55350)

Elements of inspection planning	Planning aids and methods	
Selection of testing characteristics	Planning-guidelines	Testing characteristics 1, 2, 3
	Product-specific instructions	Failure modes and effect analysis
	Characteristic/defect catalog	Operations plan
Establishing the extent of testing	Sample selection plan	AQL(a)
	Guide to AQL specification	DIN 48080
	Testing instructions	
Determination of the means of testing	Overview of the means of testing	Monitoring of the means of testing
	Guidelines for monitoring the means of testing	
Collation of testing texts	Feature-specific testing guidelines	
	Standard text elements	Quality
Specification of the time of testing	Contract- or noncontract-specific testing	Quality cost table
	Testing costs	Initial calculation
	Integration into operation plan	
	Testing interval	
Specifications for processing results	Contractual agreements, customer specifications	Statistical process control documents
	Release procedures	Measurement protocols
	Compressed evaluation of the results	Monthly per product group/customer
	Storage of the documents	
Selection of the testing location	Capacity	Operational plan
	Testing personnel	Self-inspector or quality personnel
	Incoming goods control	
	Intermediate inspection	
	Final inspection	
	First-sample inspection	

(a) AQL, acceptable quality level

Table 8.6 Classification of the inspection to the production operation

Operation	Inspection	Inspection module
Melting	Analysis	Exact inspection
Casting	Analysis	specifications
	Visual control	per operation
	Ultrasonic testing	
Homogenization		
Extrusion	Dimensional inspection	
	Surface control	
Stretching	Degree of stretching	
	Dimensional control	
Age-hardening	Tensile testing	
	Conductivity	

8.3.3.5 Inspector Audit

This audit is a test that an employee can carry out at their place of work in the factory and in the office.

It monitors whether the inspectors can achieve the quality targets at their place of work and whether they can measure, assess, and compare the results of their work with the quality goals. If noncompliances with the specified-versus-actual quality goals exist, the inspector knows the corrective action capabilities at their place of work. They carry out simple corrections themselves but also understand the limits and when they must bring the problem to the attention of the manager.

8.3.4 Testing

8.3.4.1 Failure Modes and Effect Analysis

The various tasks of a quality department also include the organization of the tests throughout the process chain. Failure modes and effect analysis (FMEA) can be used to determine the need for particular tests and their extent. With the FMEA potential defects, their effects and causes as well as the preventive measures are systematically determined. This can be product-specific (Table 8.4).

The tests determined from the FMEA are complemented by the customer-specific requirements.

8.3.4.2 Inspection Planning

Quality control can be divided into the following tasks: quality planning, quality inspection, and quality management. Quality inspection can be divided into three areas: planning, procedure, and evaluation of the inspection (Table 8.5).

The responsibility of the inspection planning includes:

- Short-term product-related inspection plan preparation, inspection plan adoption, and programming of measurement equipment
- Methodical long-term planning of the inspection method, planning of means of inspection and monitoring, and development planning

The planning function encompasses:

- Selection of the inspection criteria
- Specification of the extent of the inspection

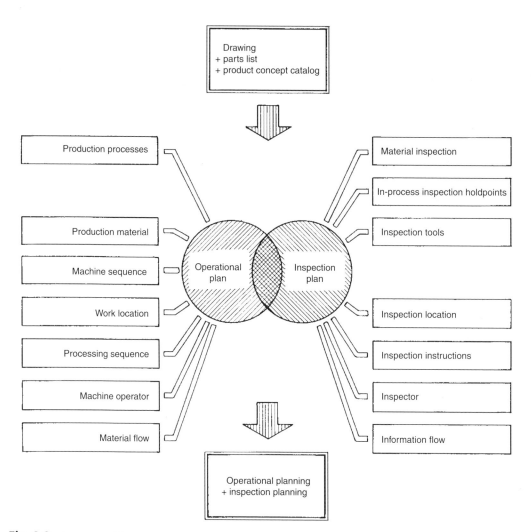

Fig. 8.9 Comparison of the planning content

Table 8.7 Layout of an inspection report

Company name	Inspection report Product:		No.: Customer: Order No.:	
Inspection after operation: Extrusion			Type of inspection: Intermediate inspection	
Sequential No.	Inspection feature	Specified value	Testing equipment	Degree of testing Number of pieces/lot
1	Visual inspection	Free of scratches	. . .	. . .
2	Diameter	600 mm	Vernier caliper	100%
3	Hardness measurement	100 HB	. . .	. . .
4	Internal roughness	RA = 0.4 ∞	Roughness measurement system	5
	Statistical process control card produced by quality control	. . .	. . .	. . .

- Selection of the method of inspection
- Specification of the processing of the results
- Selection of the inspection location
- Selection of the inspection personnel
- Production of the inspection documentation
- Calculation of the inspection time
- Calculation of the inspection costs

Basically, the decision must be made whether the inspection should be carried out by the production personnel in the form of self-inspection or by an independent quality inspector. The goal of every inspection must be to carry out the required tasks within the machine cycle time or order-processing time so that there is no negative influence on the productivity.

The structure of the inspection plans can take the following forms (Table 8.6):

- *Modular format:* The individual inspections can be prepared independently of the operation plan, subsequently extracted from the electronic data processing, and attached to the corresponding customer orders.
- *Finished inspection and working plan:* The inspection plans are linked to the production plans according to a search hierarchy. An inspection document is prepared at the level of

the individual operations per inspection characteristic (Fig. 8.9, Table 8.7).

8.4 Outlook

According to ISO 9000, quality management in the near future will develop further toward process-oriented management. A uniform comprehensive management system oriented toward the individual process steps that are important in an organization (individual commercial processes) should be established, to receive not only the element of the QMS but also additional elements, including environmental management (ISO 14000) and other areas such as safety and maintenance in the form of modules. A total system is then developed into which the individual modules along a process chain can be integrated.

REFERENCES

[Bar 94]: R. Barben, *SAQ-Bull.,* Feb 1994, p 34
[Egg 87]: I. Eggs, and K. Rosemann, *CIM Manage.,* Vol 2, 1987, p 27
[Smo 94]: D. Smolarek, *SAQ Bull.,* April 1994, p 7

APPENDIX A

List of Formula Symbols

A_{Billet}	Billet cross-sectional area
A_{Stem}	Stem cross-sectional area
A_0	Container cross-sectional area
A_S	Section cross-sectional area
b	Heat penetration coefficient
b_B	Heat penetration coefficient for billet material
b_R	Heat penetration coefficient for container material
C	Die profile relative load factor
c	Specific heat capacity
c_B	Specific heat capacity of the billet material
c_R	Specific heat capacity of the container material
D_A	Die exit diameter
D_a	Tube external diameter
D_B	Initial billet diameter
D_D	Mandrel diameter
D_{DS}	Mandrel holder diameter
D_i	Tube internal diameter
D_{Ma}	Die external diameter
D_0	Container diameter
D_o^*	Equivalent container diameter
D_S	Extruded bar diameter
D_S^*	Equivalent extruded bar diameter
F_{HSt}	Axial force on the hollow stem
$\hat{F}_{\text{HSt}}$	Maximum axial force on the hollow stem
$\bar{F}_{\text{HSt}}$	Constant axial force on the hollow stem during the quasi-stationary deformation process
F_M	Axial force on the die
$\hat{F}_M$	Maximum axial force on the die
$\bar{F}_M$	Constant axial force on the die during the quasi-stationary deformation process
f_p	Profile factor
F_R	Axial force required to overcome the friction between the billet and the container
$F_{R\max}$	Maximum value of the axial force required to overcome the friction between the billet and the container
F_{St}	Stem load
$F_{\text{St max}}$	Maximum stem load
$F_{\text{St min}}$	Minimum stem load
F_U	Axial deformation load
$\bar{F}_U$	Constant deformation load during the quasi-stationary deformation process
$F_{V\text{St}}$	Sealing stem load
$\hat{F}_{V\text{St}}$	Maximum axial load on the sealing stem
$\bar{F}_{V\text{St}}$	Constant axial load on the sealing stem during the quasi-stationary deformation process
k_f	Flow stress
k_{f0}	Flow stress of the extruded material outside the deformation zone
$\bar{k}_f$	Mean flow stress of the extruded material in the deformation zone
l_B	Billet length (initial billet length)
l_{MF}	Length of the outermost die guiding surface
l_0	Length of the upset billet in the container
l_R	Discard length
l_S	Extruded length
l_U	Length of the deformation zone
p	Hydrostatic pressure
$\hat{p}$	Maximum value of the hydrostatic pressure
$\bar{p}$	Constant hydrostatic pressure to be referred to during the quasi-stationary deformation process
p_r	Radial compressive stress
p_{St}	Specific stem pressure (specific stem pressures referred to the container cross-sectional area)
$\hat{p}_{\text{St}}$	Maximum specific stem pressure (maximum specific stem pressure referred to the container bore cross-sectional area)

$\dot{p}_{VSt}$	Specific sealing stem pressure (specific stem pressure referred to the container cross-sectional area)	W_S	Upset work
		W_U	Deformation work
		α	Half-die opening angle
$\hat{p}_{VSt}$	Maximum specific sealing stem pressure (maximum specific stem pressure referred to the container bore cross-sectional area)	ϑ	Temperature
		ϑ_B	Initial billet temperature
		$\Delta\vartheta_B$	Temperature increase of the billet material from shearing along the container wall
$\bar{p}_{VSt}$	Specific constant sealing stem pressure to be referred to during the quasi-stationary deformation process	ϑ_E	Temperature of the billet material as it enters the deformation zone
p_x	Axial compressive stress	ϑ_{MK}	Temperature with which the billet material enters the die aperture
p_{XE}	Compressive stress acting in the die exit plane	$\Delta\vartheta_{MK}$	Temperature increase from the friction between the billet material and the die aperture wall
p_{XEid}	Ideal axial compressive stress acting in the die exit plane		
		ϑ_R	Container temperature
Q_B	Heat that flows from the shear zone into the billet	ϑ_S	Extrusion exit temperature
		ϑ_{SA}	Temperature of the outer zone of the extruded section
Q_R	Heat that flows from the shear zone into the container		
		$\Delta\vartheta_U$	Temperature increase of the billet material in the deformation zone
Q_u	Deformation heat		
Q_r	Heat developed during shearing	ρ	Density
Q_λ	Heat that flows from the billet into the container	ρ_B	Density of the billet material
		ρ_R	Density of the container material
R_{eH}	Upper yield stress	φ_g	Logarithmic principal strain
$R_{p0.2}$	0.2% proof stress	$\bar{\varphi}_g$	Mean logarithmic principal strain
S_l	Upset displacement	$\dot{\varphi}_g$	Logarithmic principal strain rate
s_D	Mandrel displacement	$\bar{\dot{\varphi}}_g$	Mean logarithmic principal strain rate of the billet material in the deformation zone
s_{St}	Stem displacement		
t	Time		
u_{St}	Stem speed		
u_{vst}	Sealing stem speed	$\varphi_{g\,ges}$	Logarithmic total principal strain
u_s	Extrusion exit speed	μ_0	Coefficient of friction between the billet material and the container
V	Extrusion ratio		
W_R	Friction work	η_v	Deformation efficiency
		τ_S	Shear stress

Approximate Composition of Materials

Table 1 Approximate composition of aluminum alloys

Material	Similar UNS No.	Si	Fe	Cu	Mn	Mg	Cr	Zn	Other	Al
5182	A95182	0.2 max	0.35 max	0.15 max	0.5 max	4.0–5.0	0.1 max	0.25 max	0.1 Ti max; others 0.05 each, total 0.15 max	...
6009	A96009	0.6–1.0	0.50 max	0.15–0.6	0.20–0.8	0.40–0.8	0.10 max	0.25 max	0.10 Ti max; others 0.05 each, total 0.15 max	...
6016	A96016	1–1.5	0.5 max	0.2 max	0.2 max	0.25–0.6	0.1 max	0.2 max	0.15 Ti max; others 0.05 each, total 0.15 max	...
AA6013	A96013	0.6–1.0	0.5 max	0.6–1.1	0.20–0.8	0.8–1.2	0.1 max	0.25 max	0.10 Ti max; others 0.05 max each, total 0.15 max	bal
AA6056	A96056	0.7–1.3	0.5 max	0.50–1.1	0.40–1.0	0.6–1.2	0.25 max	0.10–0.7	(Ti + Zr) 0.20 max; others 0.05 max each, total 0.15 max	bal
AA6113 reinforced with 25% SiC	A96113	0.6–1.0	0.30 max	0.6–1.1	0.10–0.6	0.8–1.2	0.10 max	0.25 max	0.10 Ti max, 0.05–0.50 O; others 0.05 max each, others total 0.15 max. Note: reinforced with 25% SiC	bal
AA8090	A98090	0.20 max	0.30 max	1.0–1.6	0.10 max	0.6–1.3	0.10 max	0.25 max	2.2–2.7 Li, 0.10 Ti max, 0.04–0.16 Zr; others 0.05 max each, others total 0.15 max	bal
Al99	A91200	...	...	0.05 max	0.05	...	...	0.1 max	Fe + Si 1.00 max, 0.05 Ti max	bal
Al99.5	A91050	0.25 max	0.4 max	0.05 max	0.05 max	0.05 max	...	0.07 max	Cu + Fe + Si + Zn 0.50 max; others 0.03 max each	bal
Al99.6	A91060	0.25 max	0.35 max	0.05 max	0.03 max	0.03 max	...	0.05 max	0.03 Ti max; others 0.03 max each	bal
Al99.8	A91085	0.15 max	0.15 max	0.03 max	0.02 max	0.02 max	...	0.06 max	Cu + Fe + Si + Zn 0.20 max; others 0.03 max each	bal
Al99.85	A91085	0.05 max	0.07	0.01 max	0.02 max	0.01 max	0.02	0.02 max	0.03 Ga max; others total 0.01 max	bal
Al99.98	A91098	0.010 max	0.006 max	0.003 max	...	...	...	0.010 max	0.003 Ti max; others 0.003 max each	bal
Al99.98R	A91098	0.010 max	0.006 max	0.003 max	...	...	...	0.01 max	0.003 Ti max; others 0.003 max each	bal
Al99Cu	A91100	...	...	0.05–0.20	0.05	...	...	0.1	Si + Fe 0.95 max	bal
AlCu2LiMg1.5	A92061	0.20 max	0.30 max	1.8–2.5	0.10 max	1.1–1.9	0.10 max	0.25 max	1.7–2.3 Li, 0.10 Ti max, 0.04–0.16 Zr max; others 0.05 max each, others total 0.15 max	bal
AlCu2Mg1.5Ni	A92618	0.1–0.25	0.9–1.3	1.9–2.7	...	1.3–1.8	...	0.1 max	0.9–1.2 Ni, 0.04–0.1 Ti; others 0.05 max each, others total 0.05 max	bal
AlCu4Mg1	A92024	0.5	0.5	3.8–4.9	0.3–1.2	1–1.8	...	0.2	0.2 Ni	bal
AlCu4PbMgMn	A92007	0.8 max	0.8 max	3.3–4.6	0.50–1.0	0.40–1.8	0.10 max	0.8 max	0.20 Bi max, 0.20 Ni max, 0.8–1.5 Pb max, 0.20 Sn max, 0.20 Ti max; others 0.10 max each, others total 0.30 max	bal
AlCu4SiMg	A92014	0.5–1.2	0.7	3.8–5	0.3–1.2	0.2–0.8	...	0.2	0.2 Ni	bal
AlCuBiPb	A92011	0.40 max	0.7 max	5.0–6.0	...	...	...	0.30 max	0.2–0.6 Bi, 0.20–0.6 Pb; others 0.05 max each, others total 0.15 max	bal
AlCuMg1	A92017	0.20–0.8	0.7 max	3.5–4.5	0.40–1.0	0.40–1.0	0.10 max	0.25 max	Ti + Zr 0.25 max; others 0.05 max each, others total 0.15 max	bal
AlCuMg2	A92024	0.50 max	0.50 max	3.8–4.9	0.30–0.9	1.2–1.8	0.10 max	0.25 max	0.15 Ti max; others 0.05 each, others total 0.15	bal
AlCuMgPb	A92007	0.8 max	0.8 max	3.3–4.6	0.10 max	0.40–1.8	0.10 max	0.8 max	0.20 Bi max, 0.2 Ni max, 0.8–1.5 Pb, 0.20 Sn max, 0.20 Ti max; others 0.10 max each, others total 0.30 max	bal
AlCuSiMn	A92014	0.50–1.2	0.7 max	3.9–5.0	0.40–1.2	0.20–0.8	0.10 max	0.25 max	0.15 Ti max; others 0.05 each, others total 0.15	bal
AlFeSi	A98011	0.4–0.8	0.5–1.0	0.10 max	0.10 max	...	...	0.10 max	0.05 Ti max; others 0.06 max each, others total 0.25 max	bal
AlLi2.5Cu1.5Mg1	A98090	0.20 max	0.30 max	1.0–1.6	0.10 max	0.6–1.3	0.10 max	0.25 max	2.2–2.7 Li, 0.10 Ti max, 0.04–0.16 Zr; others 0.05 max each, others total 0.15 max	bal
AlMg1	A95005	0.4	0.7	0.2	0.2	0.5–1.1	0.1	0.2	...	bal
AlMg1.5	A95050	0.4	0.7	0.2	0.3	1.1–1.8	0.1	0.2	...	bal

AlMg1Mn1	A93004	0.4–0.8	0.7	0.15–0.4	1.2	1.1	…	0.25	…	bal
AlMg1SiCu	A96061	0.5	0.5	0.1	0.15	0.8–1.2	0.04–0.35	0.25	…	bal
AlMg2.5	A95052	…	…	…	0.5	2.2–2.8	0.35	0.2	…	bal
AlMg2.5Cr	A95052	…	…	…	…	2.5	0.25	…	…	bal
AlMg2.7Mn	A95454	0.25 max	0.40 max	0.10 max	0.50–1.0	2.4–3.0	0.05–0.20	0.25 max	0.20 Ti max; others 0.05 max each, others total 0.15 max	bal
AlMg2.7MnCr	A95454	…	0.5	0.1	0.75	2.7	0.12	0.2	…	bal
AlMg3	A95754	0.5	…	…	0.5	2.6–3.4	0.35	0.2	…	bal
AlMg3.5Mn	A95154	…	0.5	…	0.3	3.5	…	0.2	…	bal
AlMg3Mn	A95454	0.5	0.5	0.1	0.3–1	2.4–3.4	0.25	0.2	…	bal
AlMg4.5	A95083	0.5	0.5	0.1	0.3–1	4–4.9	0.25	0.2	…	bal
AlMg4.5Mn	A95083	0.5	0.5	0.1	0.3–1	4–4.9	0.25	0.2	…	bal
AlMg4.5Mn	A95083	0.5	0.5	0.1	0.3–1	4–4.9	0.25	0.2	…	bal
AlMg4.5Mn0.7	A95083	0.40 max	0.40 max	0.10 max	0.10–1.0	4.0–4.9	0.05–0.25	0.25 max	0.15 Ti max; others 0.05 max each, others total 0.15 max	bal
AlMg5	A95056	0.5	0.5	0.1	1	4.5–5.5	0.35	0.2	…	bal
AlMg5Mn	A95182	0.20 max	0.35 max	0.15 max	0.20–0.50	4.0–5.0	0.10 max	0.25 max	0.10 Ti max; others 0.05 max each, others total 0.15 max	bal
AlMgSi	A96063	0.3–0.7	0.5	0.058 max	…	0.4–0.9	0.1	0.2	…	bal
AlMgSi0.5	A96060	0.30–0.6	0.10–0.30	0.10 max	0.10 max	0.35–0.6	0.05 max	0.15 max	0.10 Ti max; others 0.05 max each, others total 0.15 max	bal
AlMgSi0.7	A96005	0.50–0.9	0.35 max	0.30 max	0.05 max	0.40–0.7	0.30 max	0.20 max	0.1 Ni max, 0.10 Ti max, 0.12–0.050 (Cr + Mn); others 0.05 max each, others total 0.15 max	bal
AlMgSi0.8	A96009	0.8–1	0.25	0.05	0.15	0.6–0.7	0.03	0.1	0.05 Ti; others 0.05 max each, others total 0.15 max	bal
AlMgSi1	A96181	0.8–1.2	0.5 max	0.1 max	0.2–1.0	0.6–1.0	0.1 max	0.2 max	0.2 Ti max; others 0.05 max each, others total 0.15 max	bal
AlMgSi1Cu	A96030	0.40–0.8	0.7	0.15–0.40	0.15 max	0.8–1.2	0.04–0.35	0.25 max	0.15 Ti max; others 0.05 max each, others total 0.15 max	bal
AlMgSiCu	A96261	0.4–0.7	0.4 max	0.15–0.40	0.20–0.35	0.7–1.0	0.10 max	0.2 max	0.10 Ti max, Ti includes Zr; others 0.05 max each, others total 0.15 max	bal
AlMgSiCuMn	A96261	0.55	…	0.25	0.25	0.85	…	…	…	bal
AlMgSiPb	A96012	0.6–1.4	0.50 max	0.10 max	0.40–1.0	0.6–1.2	0.30 max	0.30 max	0.7 Bi max, 0.40–2.0 Pb, 0.20 Ti max; others 0.05 max each, others total 0.15 max	bal
AlMn	A93103	0.50 max	0.7 max	0.10 max	0.9–1.5	0.30 max	0.10 max	0.20 max	0.1 Ti max, 0.10 (Ti + Zr) max; others 0.05 max each, others total 0.15 max	bal
AlMn1	A93004	0.6	0.7	0.1	0.8–1.5	0.3	…	0.2	…	bal
AlMn2Mg1	A93004	0.30 max	0.7 max	0.25 max	1.0–1.5	0.8–1.3	…	0.25 max	Others 0.05 max each, others total 0.15 max	bal
AlSi10Mg	A94046	9.0–11.0	0.60 max	0.10 max	0.6 max	0.15–0.40	…	0.1 max	0.05 Ni max, 0.05 Pb max, 0.05 Sn max, 0.20 Ti max	bal
AlSi12	A14130	11.0–13.5	0.70 max	0.10 max	0.5 max	0.10 max	…	0.1 max	0.1 Ni max, 0.1 Pb max, 0.05 Sn max, 0.20 Ti	bal
AlSi5	A94043	3.5–5.5	0.5	0.1	0.3	0.7	…	0.1	…	bal
AlSi5Mg	A94543	3.5–6.0	0.6 max	0.1 max	0.6 max	0.5–0.9	…	0.1 max	0.1 Ni max, 0.1 Pb max, 0.05 Sn max, 0.2 Ti max	bal
AlSi7	A94047	6.5–7.5	0.5 max	0.10 max	0.6 max	0.6 max	…	0.3 max	0.05 Ni max, 0.05 Pb max, 0.05 Sn max, 0.20 Ti	bal
AlSiMgMn	A96082	0.7–1.3	0.50 max	0.10 max	0.40–1.0	0.6–1.2	0.25 max	0.20 max	0.10 Ti max; others 0.05 max each, others total 0.15 max	bal
AlZnMgCu1.5	A97075	0.40 max	0.50 max	1.2–2.0	0.30 max	2.1–2.9	0.18–0.28	5.1–6.1	0.20 Ti max, 0.25 (Ti + Zr) max; others 0.05 max each, others total 0.15 max	bal

(continued)

Table 1 Continued

Material	Similar UNS No.	Si	Fe	Cu	Mn	Mg	Cr	Zn	Other	Al
AlZn4.5Mg1	A97020	0.35 max	0.40 max	0.20 max	0.05–0.50	1.0–1.4	0.10–0.35	4.0–5.0	0.08–0.20 Zr, 0.08–0.25 (Ti + Zr); others 0.05 max each, others total 0.15	bal
AlZn5.5MgCu	A97075	0.40 max	0.50 max	1.2–2.0	0.30 max	2.1–2.9	0.18–0.28	5.1–6.1	0.20 Ti max; for extruded, forged products (Ti + Zr) 0.25 max; others 0.05 max each, others total 0.15	bal
AlZn5Mg3Cu	A947022	0.50 max	0.50 max	0.50–1.0	0.10–0.40	2.6–3.7	0.10–0.30	4.3–5.2	0.20 (Ti + Zr) max; others 0.05 max each, others total 0.15 max	bal
AlZn8MgCu	A97049	0.40 max	0.50 max	1.2–1.9	0.50 max	2.1–3.1	0.05–0.25	7.2–8.4	For extruded, forged products (Ti + Zr) 0.25 max; others 0.05 max each, others total 0.15	bal
AlZnMgCu0.5	A97022	0.50 max	0.50 max	0.20 max	0.10–0.40	2.6–3.7	0.10–0.30	4.3–5.2	0.20 (Zr + Ti) max; others 0.05 max each, others total 0.15 max	bal
AlZnMgCu1.5	A97075	0.40 max	0.50 max	1.2–2.0	0.30 max	2.1–2.9	0.18–0.28	5.1–6.1	0.20 Ti max, 0.25 (Ti + Zr) max; others 0.05 max each, others total 0.15 max	bal
AlZnMgCu2.5	A97050	...	...	2.3	...	2.3	...	6.2	0.12 Zr	bal
E-AlMgSi0.5	A96060	0.30–0.6	0.10–0.30	0.10 max	0.10 max	0.35–0.6	0.05 max	0.15 max	0.10 Ti max; others 0.05 max each, others total 0.15 max	bal
EN AW 1050 A	A91050	0.25 max	0.40 max	0.05 max	0.05 max	0.05 max	...	0.07 max	0.05 Ti max; others 0.03 max each	bal
EN AW 1085	A91085	0.10 max	0.12 max	0.03 max	0.02 max	0.02 max	...	0.03 max	0.02 Ti max, 0.03 Ga max, 0.05 V max; others 0.01 max each	bal
EN AW 1098	A91098	0.010 max	0.006 max	0.003 max	...	...	...	0.015 max	0.003 Ti max; others 0.003 max each	bal
EN AW 1350	A91350	0.10 max	0.40 max	0.05 max	0.01 max	...	0.01 max	0.05 max	0.05 B max, 0.03 Ga max, 0.02 Ti max, 0.02 V max, 0.02 (Ti +V) max; others 0.03 max each, others total 0.10 max	bal
EN AW 2007	A92007	0.8 max	0.8 max	3.3–4.6	0.50–1.0	0.40–1.8	0.10 max	0.8 max	0.20 Bi max, 0.20 Ni max, 0.8–1.5 Pb max, 0.20 Sn max, 0.20 Ti max; others 0.10 max each, others total 0.30 max	bal
EN AW 2014	A92014	0.50–1.2	0.7 max	3.9–5.0	0.40–1.2	0.20–0.8	0.10 max	0.25 max	0.15 Ti max; others 0.05 max each, others total 0.15 max	bal
EN AW 2024	A92024	0.50 max	0.50 max	3.8–4.9	0.30–0.9	1.2–1.8	0.10 max	0.25 max	0.15 Ti max, (Ti + Zr) may be limited; others 0.05 max each, others total 0.15 max	bal
EN AW 2091	A92091	...	0.30 max	1.8–2.5	0.10 max	1.1–1.9	0.10 max	0.25 max	1.7–2.3 Li, 0.20 Si max, 0.10 Ti max, 0.04–0.16 Zr, others 0.05 max each, others total 0.15 max	bal
EN AW 2618	A92618	0.1–0.25	0.9–1.3	1.9–2.7	...	1.3–1.8	...	0.1 max	0.9–1.2 Ni, 0.04–0.1 Ti; others 0.05 max each, others total 0.05 max	bal

EN AW 3004	A93004	0.30 max	0.7 max	0.25 max	1.0–1.5	0.8–1.3	. . .	0.25 max	Others 0.05 max each, others total 0.15 max	bal
EN AW 3103	A93103	0.50 max	0.7 max	0.10 max	0.9–1.5	0.30 max	0.10 max	0.20 max	0.10 Ti max, 0.10 Zr max, 0.10 (Ti + Zr) max; others 0.05 max each, others total 0.15 max	bal
EN AW 5005A	A95005	0.30 max	0.45 max	0.05 max	0.15 max	0.7–1.1	0.10 max	0.20 max	Others 0.05 max each, others total 0.15 max	bal
EN AW 5019	A95019	0.40 max	0.50 max	0.10 max	0.10–0.6	4.5–5.6	0.20 max	0.20 max	0.20 Ti max, 0.10–0.6 (Cr + Mn); others 0.05 max each, others total 0.15 max	. . .
EN AW 5052	A95052	0.25 max	0.40 max	0.10 max	0.10 max	2.2–2.8	0.15–0.35	0.10 max	Others 0.05 max each, others total 0.15 max	bal
EN AW 5056A	A95056	0.5	0.5	0.1	1	4.5–5.5	0.35	0.2	· · ·	bal
EN AW 5083	A95083	0.40 max	0.40 max	0.10 max	0.40–1.0	4.0–4.9	0.05–0.25	0.25 max	0.15 Ti max; others 0.05 max each, others total 0.15 max	bal
EN AW 5454	A95454	0.25 max	0.40 max	0.10 max	0.50–1.0	2.4–3.0	0.05–0.20	0.25 max	0.20 Ti max; others 0.05 max each, others total 0.15 max	bal
EN AW 5754	A95754	0.40 max	0.40 max	0.10 max	0.50 max	2.6–3.6	0.30 max	0.20 max	0.15 Ti max, 0.10–0.6 (Cr + Mn); others 0.15 max each, others total 0.15 max	bal
EN AW 6005A	A96005	0.50–0.9	0.35 max	0.30 max	0.50 max	0.40–0.7	0.30 max	0.20 max	0.10 Ti max, 0.12–0.50 (Cr + Mn); others 0.05 max each, others total 0.15 max	bal
EN AW 6012	A96012	0.6–1.4	0.50 max	0.10 max	0.40–1.0	0.6–1.2	0.30 max	0.30 max	0.7 Bi, 0.40–2.0 Pb, 0.20 Ti max; others 0.05 max each, others total 0.15 max	bal
EN AW 6060	A96060	0.30–0.6	0.10–0.30	0.10 max	0.10 max	0.35–0.6	0.05 max	0.15 max	0.10 Ti max; others 0.05 max each, others total 0.15 max	bal
EN AW 6061	A96061	0.40–0.8	0.7 max	0.15–0.40	0.15 max	0.8–1.2	0.04–0.35	0.25 max	0.15 Ti max; others 0.05 max each, others total 0.15 max	bal
EN AW 6063	A96063	0.20–0.6	0.35 max	0.10 max	0.10 max	0.45–0.9	0.10 max	0.10 max	0.10 Ti max; others 0.05 max each, others total 0.15 max	bal
EN AW 6082	A96082	0.7–1.3	0.50 max	0.10 max	0.40–1.0	0.6–1.2	0.25 max	0.20 max	0.10 Ti max; others 0.05 max each, others total 0.15 max	bal
EN AW 7020	A97020	0.35 max	0.40 max	0.20 max	0.05–0.50	1.0–1.4	0.10–0.35	4.0–5.0	0.17 Ti max, 0.08–0.20 Zr, 0.08–0.25 (Ti + Zr); others 0.05 max each, others total 0.15 max	bal
EN AW 7022	A97022	0.50 max	0.50 max	0.50–1.0	0.10–0.40	2.6–3.7	0.10–0.30	4.3–5.2	0.20 (Ti + Zr) max; others 0.05 max each, others total 0.15 max	bal
EN AW 7049A	A97049	0.40 max	0.50 max	1.2–1.9	0.50 max	2.1–3.1	0.05–0.25	7.2–8.4	0.25 Ti max, 0.25 Zr max, 0.25 (Ti + Zr) max; others 0.05 max each, others total 0.15 max	bal
EN AW 7075	A97075	0.40 max	0.50 max	1.2–2.0	0.30 max	2.1–2.9	0.18–0.28	5.1–6.1	0.20 Ti max, (Ti + Zr) may be limited; others 0.05 max each, others total 0.15 max	bal
EN AW 8090	A98090	0.20 max	0.30 max	1.0–1.6	0.10 max	0.6–1.3	0.10 max	0.25 max	2.2–2.7 Li, 0.10 Ti max, 0.04–0.16 Zr; others 0.05 max each, others total 0.15 max	bal

Table 2 Approximate composition of magnesium and magnesium alloys

Material	Similar UNS No.	Al	Mn	Zn	Zr	Other	Mg
Mg	M19980	. . .	. . .	. . .	. . .	. . .	99.9
MgAl3Zn	M11311	2.5–3.5	0.05–0.4	0.5–1.5	. . .	0.1 Cu max, 0.03 Fe max, 0.005 Ni max, 0.1 Si max, others total 0.1 max	bal
MgAl5Zn	. . .	4.5	0.6	1.2	. . .	. . .	bal
MgAl6Zn	M11610	5.5–7.0	0.15–0.4	0.5–1.5	. . .	0.1 Cu max, 0.03 Fe max, 0.005 Ni max, 0.1 Si max, others total 0.1 max	bal
MgAl8Zn	M11800	7.8–9.2	0.12–0.3	0.2–0.8	. . .	0.05 Cu max, 0.005 Fe max, 0.1 Si max, others total 0.30 max	bal
MgZn2Zr	. . .	. . .	. . .	2	0.06	. . .	bal
MgMn2	M15100	0.05 max	1.2–2.0	0.03 max	. . .	0.05 Cu max, 0.005 Fe max, 0.001 Ni max, 0.10 Si max, others total 0.10 max	bal
MgZn3Zr	. . .	. . .	. . .	3	0.7	. . .	bal
AZ31	M11310	2.5–3.5	0.15	0.6–1.4	. . .	0.005 Fe max, 0.05 Cu max; others 0.02 max each, others total 0.10 max	94.895–96.9
AZ61	M11610	5.8–7.2	0.15 max	0.4–1.5	. . .	0.01 Si max, 0.005 Fe max, 0.002 Ni max, 0.003 Cu max; others 0.02 max each, others total 0.10 max	91.13–93.8

Table 3 Approximate composition of titanium and titanium alloys

Material	Similar UNS No.	Al	Cr	Mn	Mo	Sn	V	Zr	Ti	Other
Ti	R50250	. . .	. . .	. . .	. . .	. . .	. . .	. . .	99.9	. . .
TiAl4Mn4	R56440(a)	4.0	. . .	4.0	. . .	. . .	. . .	. . .	bal	. . .
TiAl4Mo4Sn2	R58650	3.0–5.0	. . .	. . .	3.0–5.0	1.5–2.5	. . .	. . .	. . .	0.08 C max, 0.20 Fe max, 0.05 N max, 0.3–0.7 Si max, 0.015 H max, 0.25 O max; others 0.10 max each, others total 0.40 max
TiAl5Sn2.5	R54520	4.5–5.5	. . .	. . .	. . .	2.0–3.0	. . .	. . .	bal	0.08 C max, 0.50 Fe max, 0.05 N max, 0.020 H max, 0.20 O max; others 0.10 max each, others total 0.40 max
TiAl6V4	R56400	5.50–6.75	. . .	. . .	. . .	. . .	3.5–4.5	. . .	bal	0.08 C max, 0.30 Fe max, 0.05 N max, 0.015 H max, 0.20 O max; others 0.10 max each, others total 0.40 max
TiAl6V6Sn2	R56620	5.0–6.0	. . .	. . .	. . .	1.5–2.5	5.0–6.0	. . .	bal	0.05 C max, 0.35–1.0 Cu, 0.35–1.0 Fe, 0.04 N max, 0.015 H max, 0.20 O max; others 0.10 max each, others total 0.40 max
TiAl6Zr4Sn2Mo2	. . .	6	. . .	. . .	2	2	. . .	4	bal	. . .
TiAl7Mo4	. . .	7	. . .	. . .	4	. . .	. . .	. . .	bal	. . .
TiAl8Mo1V1	. . .	8	. . .	. . .	1	. . .	1	. . .	bal	. . .
TiV13Cr11Al3	. . .	3	11	. . .	. . .	. . .	13	. . .	bal	. . .
6242	R54620	5.5–6.5	. . .	. . .	1.8–2.2	1.8–2.2	. . .	3.6–4.4	. . .	0.05 C max, 0.25 Fe max, 0.0125 H max, 0.12 O
IMI 230	. . .	. . .	. . .	. . .	. . .	. . .	. . .	. . .	bal	2.5 Cu
IMI 318	. . .	6	. . .	. . .	. . .	. . .	. . .	. . .	bal	4V
IMI 679	. . .	2.25	. . .	. . .	1	11	. . .	5	bal	0.2 Si
IMI 829	. . .	5.5	. . .	. . .	0.3	3.5	. . .	3	bal	0.3 Si, 1 Nb

(a) Inactive

Table 4 Approximate composition of copper and copper alloys

Material	Similar UNS No.	Al	Fe	Mn	Ni	Pb	Si	Sn	Zn	Other	Cu
CuAg	...	...	...	...	...	...	...	...	...	0.15 Ag	bal
CuAl10Fe3Mn2	C62300	8.5–11	2.0–4.0	2 max	1 max	0.05 max	...	...	0.5 max	Pb + Zn 0.5 max	bal
CuAl10Fe3Mn2	...	10	3	2.5	...	...	...	...	...	...	bal
CuAl10Ni	...	9.5	3.9	1	5	...	...	...	...	...	bal
CuAl10Ni5Fe4	C63000	8.5–11	2.5–5.3	1.5 max	4.0–6.0	...	0.2 max	...	0.5 max	0.15 Pd max, others total 0.3 max	...
CuAl5	C60800	4.0–6.0	0.4 max	0.3 max	0.8 max	0.02 max	0.2 max	0.3 max	0.5 max	0.4 As max, others total 0.3 max	bal
CuAl5As	C60800	4.0–6.0	0.2 max	0.2 max	0.2 max	0.02 max	...	...	0.3 max	0.2 As max, others total 0.3 max	...
CuAl8	C61000	7.0–9.0	0.5 max	0.8 max	0.8 max	0.02 max	0.2 max	...	0.5 max	Others total 0.3 max	bal
CuAl8Fe	C61400	6.5–9.0	1.5–3.5	1.0 max	1.0 max	0.15 max	0.2 max	0.2 max	0.5 max	Others total 0.3 max	bal
CuAl8Si	...	7.5	1	1	...	...	2.5	...	...	...	...
CuAl9Mn	C63280	8.0–10	1.5 max	1.5–3.0	0.8 max	0.15 max	0.2 max	...	0.5 max	Others total 0.3 max	bal
CuBe2	C17200	...	0.6 max	...	0.6 max	...	...	...	...	1.8–2.1 Be, 0.6 Co max, 0.6 (Ni + Co + Fe) max, 0.2–0.6 (Ni + Co), others total 0.5 max	...
CuCr	C18400	...	...	...	...	...	...	...	0.2 max	0.5 Cd max, 0.4–1.2 Cr	bal
CuCrZr	C18100	...	...	...	...	...	...	...	0.03–0.3	0.3–1.2 Cr, others total 0.2 max	...
CuNi1.5Si	C64700	...	...	...	1.0–1.6	...	0.4–0.7	...	...	Others total 0.5 max	bal
CuNi10Fe	C70600	...	1.0–2.0	0.5–1.0	9.0–11.0	0.03 max	...	...	0.5 max	0.05 C max, 0.05 S max	bal
CuNi10Fe1Mn	C70600	...	1–2	0.3–1	9–11	...	...	...	0.5	0.1 C, 0.05 S, 0.05 (Sn + Pb)	bal
CuNi10Zn42Pb	C79800	...	0.5 max	0.5 max	9–11.0	0.5–2.0	...	0.3 max	37.7–45.5	Others total 0.1 max	bal
CuNi12Zn24	C75700	...	0.3 max	0.5 max	11.0–13.0	0.03 max	...	0.3 max	19.87–26	Others total 0.2 max	bal
CuNi12Zn30Pb	C79200	...	0.3 max	0.7 max	11.0–13.0	0.3–1.5	...	0.3 max	26.2–32.7	Others total 0.4 max	bal
CuNi18Zn19Pb	C753500	...	0.3 max	0.7 max	17.0–19.0	0.3–1.5	...	0.2 max	15.3–23.7	Others total 0.4 max	bal
CuNi18Zn20	C76400	...	0.3 max	0.5 max	17.0–19.0	0.03 max	...	0.2 max	16.97–23	Others total 0.2 max	bal
CuNi20	C71000	...	0.5–1.0	0.5–1.5	19.0–21	0.03 max	...	...	0.2	0.1 C, 0.05 S, 0.05 (Sn + Pb)	bal
CuNi20Fe	C71100	...	0.8	1	20.0–22.0	0.03 max	...	...	0.5 max	0.05 C, 0.05 S	bal
CuNi20Fe	...	...	0.3	0.5	21	...	...	...	...	...	bal
CuNi25	C71300	...	0.3 max	0.7 max	25	0.03 max	...	0.2 max	0.5	0.5 C, 0.02 S, 0.05 (Sn + Pb)	bal
CuNi25Zn15	...	...	...	0.5	24.0–26.0	...	...	...	11.7–18	Others total 0.1 max	bal
CuNi2Si	C64700	...	...	0.5–1.5	1.6–2.5	0.03 max	0.5–0.8	...	0.5 max	Others total 0.5 max	bal
CuNi30Fe	C71500	...	0.4–1.0	...	30.0–32.0	0.03 max	...	...	0.5 max	0.06 C max, 0.05 S max	bal
CuNi30Fe2Mn2	C71640	...	1.5–2.5	1.5–2.5	29–32	0.02 max	...	...	0.1 max	0.05 C max, 0.06 S max	bal
CuNi30Mn	...	0.1 max	0.3 max	1.5–3	29–33	...	...	...	0.5	0.05 Mg max	...
CuNi30Mn1Fe	C71500	...	0.4–1	...	29–32	0.1 max	0.1 max	0.1 max	...	0.1 C, 0.08 S, 0.05 (Sn + Pb)	bal
CuNi3Ni	C64710	...	...	...	2.6–4.5	...	0.8–1.3	...	...	Others total 0.6 max	bal
CuNi3Si	...	...	...	...	3.5	...	0.9	...	...	...	bal
CuNi44	C72150	...	0.2 max	0.5–2.0	43.0–45.0	0.01 max	...	...	...	0.05 C max, 0.02 S max	bal

(continued)

Table 4   Continued

Material	Similar UNS No.	Al	Fe	Mn	Ni	Pb	Si	Sn	Zn	Other	Cu
CuNi5Fe	…	…	1.2	0.6	5	0.05 max	…	…	0.2 max	Others total 0.5 max	bal
CuSi3Mn	C65500	0.01	0.25 max	0.5–1.3	…	…	2.7–3.6	…	0.5	0.2 P, 0.2 Sb, 0.05 S	bal
CuSn10	C90250	…	0.2	0.2	2	1	…	9.0–11.0	0.3 max	0.01–0.35 P, others total 0.1 max	bal
CuSn2	C50780	…	0.1 max	…	…	0.05 max	…	1.0–2.5	0.3 max	0.01 Bi max, 0.1 P	bal
CuSn5	C93500	0.01 max	0.1 max	0.2 max	0.2 max	0.2 max	…	4.0–6.0	0.3 max	0.01–0.35 P, others total 0.2 max	bal
CuSn6	C51980	…	0.1 max	…	0.2 max	0.05 max	…	5.5–7.5	0.3 max	0.01–0.35 P, others total 0.2 max	bal
CuSn8	C52100	…	…	…	0.3 max	0.05 max	…	7.5–9.0	0.3 max	…	bal
CuZn1.5	…	…	…	…	…	…	…	…	1.5	…	bal
CuZn10	C22000	0.02 max	0.05 max	…	0.2 max	0.05 max	…	0.05 max	8.63–11	Others total 0.1 max	bal
CuZn20	C24000	0.02 max	0.05 max	…	0.2 max	0.05 max	…	0.05 max	18.63–21	Others total 0.1 max	bal
CuZn20Al	…	2	…	2	…	…	…	…	19.5	…	bal
CuZn20Al2	C68700	1.8–2.3	0.07 max	0.1 max	0.1 max	…	…	…	27.38–29.68	0.020–0.035 As, 0.005 Mg max, 0.01 P max	bal
CuZn28	C25600	0.02 max	0.05 max	…	0.2 max	0.05 max	…	…	26.63–29	Others total 0.1 max	bal
CuZn28Sn	…	…	…	…	…	…	…	1	27.5	…	bal
CuZn28Sn1	C44300	…	0.07 max	0.1 max	0.1 max	…	…	0.9–1.3	25.885–29.08	0.020–0.035 As, 0.01 P	bal
CuZn30	C26000	0.02 max	0.05 max	…	0.2 max	0.05 max	…	0.05 max	28.63–31	Others total 0.1 max	bal
CuZn31Si	…	…	…	…	0.3	0.4	1	…	27	…	bal
CuZn31Si1	C65100	…	0.4 max	…	0.5 max	…	0.7–1.3	…	27.8–33.3	…	bal
CuZn33	C26200	0.02 max	0.05 max	…	0.2 max	0.05 max	…	0.05 max	31.13–34	Others total 0.1 max	bal
CuZn35	…	…	…	…	…	0.4	…	…	34.5	…	bal
CuZn35Ni	…	0.9	0.3	2	2.5	…	…	0.3	34.1	…	bal
CuZn35Ni2	…	0.3–1.5	0.5 max	1.5–2.5	2.0–3.0	…	0.1 max	…	30.9–38.2	…	bal
CuZn36Pb1.5	C34200	0.05 max	0.2 max	…	0.3 max	0.7–2.5	0.1 max	0.1 max	32.85–37.3	Others total 0.1 max	bal
CuZn37	C27200	0.03 max	0.1 max	…	0.3 max	0.1 max	…	0.1 max	35.37–38	Others total 0.1 max	bal
CuZn38Pb1	C35000	…	0.2 max	…	…	0.5–1.5	0.1 max	…	38	Others total 0.3 max	bal
CuZn38Pb1.5	C48500	0.05 max	0.3 max	…	0.3 max	1.0–2.0	…	0.2 max	35.65–39.5	Others total 0.2 max	bal
CuZn39Pb3	C38500	0.1 max	0.5 max	…	0.5 max	2.5–3.5	…	0.4 max	36–40.5	Others total 0.2 max	bal
CuZn40	C46600	0.05 max	0.2 max	…	0.3 max	0.3 max	…	0.2 max	37.45–40.5	Others total 0.2 max	bal
CuZn40Al2	C67410	1.3–2.3	1.0 max	1.4–2.6	2.0 max	…	0.3–1.0	0.5 max	31.6–40.5	…	bal
CuZn40Mn	…	…	0.3 max	1.0–2.0	…	…	…	…	37.2–42	…	bal
CuZn40Mn2	C67410	0.1 max	1.5 max	1.0–2.5	1.0 max	0.5 max	0.1 max	0.5 max	35.3–42	…	bal
CuZn40Pb2	C37800	0.1 max	0.4 max	…	0.4 max	1.5–2.5	…	0.3 max	37.3–41.5	Others total 0.2 max	bal
CuZn44Pb2	…	0.5 max	0.5 max	…	0.5 max	1.0–2.5	…	0.4 max	39.6–45	Others total 0.4 max	bal
CuZnPb	C37000	…	0.15 max	…	…	0.8–1.5	…	…	36.35–40.2	99.6 min (Cu + named)	bal
CuZr	C15000	…	…	…	…	…	…	…	…	0.1–0.3 Zr, others total 0.2 max	bal
E-Cu	…	…	…	…	…	…	…	0.2–0.3	0.2–0.4	99.5 min (Cu + Sn + Zn)	bal
SE-Cu	C11000	…	…	…	…	…	…	…	…	…	99.9 min
SF-Cu	C11000	…	…	…	…	…	…	…	…	0.003 P max	99.9 min
OF-Cu	C10400	…	…	…	…	…	…	…	…	…	99.95 min

Table 5 Approximate composition of cobalt alloys

Material	Similar UNS No.	C	Cr	Mo	W	Nb	Fe	Ni	Co	Other
ALX	. . .	2	33	. . .	16.5	. . .	. . .	. . .	bal	. . .
Aknit Co50	. . .	2.2	27	. . .	14	. . .	. . .	. . .	bal	. . .
Celsit P	. . .	2.5	31	. . .	13.5	. . .	. . .	. . .	bal	. . .
Revolta	. . .	0.29	28	5.9	. . .	. . .	. . .	. . .	bal	. . .
Platit	. . .	1.4	28	. . .	5	. . .	. . .	. . .	bal	. . .
Stellite 1	R30001	2.2–2.5	30	. . .	12	. . .	. . .	. . .	bal	. . .
Stellite 251	. . .	0.3	28	. . .	. . .	2	18	. . .	bal	. . .
CoCr20Ni20W	R30816	0.35–0.45	19–32	3.5–4.5	3.5–4.5	3.5–4.5	5 max	19–21	45	1.5 Mn max, 1 Si max

Table 6 Approximate composition of nickel and nickel alloys

Material	Similar UNS No.	C	Co	Cr	Al	Mn	Mo	Si	Ti	Other	Ni
Ni99.2	. . .	0.1 max	. . .	. . .	. . .	0.35 max	. . .	0.2 max	. . .	0.25 Cu max, 0.4 Fe max, 0.1 Mg max, 0.005 S max	99.2
NiAl4Ti	. . .	0.15	. . .	. . .	4.5	0.4	. . .	1	. . .	0.2 Cu, 0.5 Fe, 0.15 Mg	bal
NiCo15Cr15 MoAlTi	. . .	0.16	15	15	5	0.5	4	0.5	4	0.012 B, 1.0 Fe max, 0.5 Zr max	bal
NiCr15Fe	N06062	0.08 max	. . .	14–17	. . .	1 max	. . .	0.5 max	0.3 max	0.05 Cu max, 6–11 Fe, 0.03 P max, 0.01 S max	bal
NiCr20Co18Ti	N07090	0.1 max	15–21	18–21	1.0–2.0	1 max	. . .	1 max	2.0–3.0	0.2 Cu max, 2 Fe max, 0.03 max, 0.01 max	bal
NiCr20Ti	. . .	0.08–0.15	. . .	18–21	. . .	1 max	. . .	1 max	0.2–0.6	0.5 Cu max, 0.5 Fe max, 0.03 P max, 0.01 S max	bal
NiCr20TiAl	N07080	0.1 max	2 max	18–21	1–1.8	1 max	. . .	1 max	1.5–2.7	0.01 B max, 0.2 Cu max, 3 Fe max, 0.03 P max, 0.01 S max	bal
NiCr22Mo9Nb	N06625	0.10 max	1.0 max	20.0–23.0	0.40 max	0.50 max	8.0–10.0	0.50 max	0.40 max	0.5 Fe max, 0.015 P max, 0.015 S max, 3.15–4.15 (Nb + Ta)	. . .
NiCu30Al	N05500	. . .	. . .	. . .	2.0–4.0	. . .	. . .	. . .	0.3–1	27–34 Cu, 0.5–2 Fe	bal
NiCu30Fe	N04400	0.15 max	. . .	. . .	0.5 max	1.25 max	. . .	. . .	. . .	28–34 Cu, 1–2.5 Fe, 0.02 S max	bal
NiFe45	. . .	0.05	. . .	. . .	. . .	1	. . .	0.3	. . .	45.0 Fe	bal
NiMn2	. . .	0.1 max	. . .	. . .	. . .	1.5–2.5	. . .	0.2 max	. . .	0.2 Cu max, 0.3 Fe max, 0.15 Mg max, 0.01 S max	bal
NiMo16Cr16Ti	N06455	0.015 max	2.0 max	14.0–18.0	. . .	1.0 max	14.0–17.0	0.08 max	0.7 max	3.0 Fe max, 0.040 P max, 0.030 S max	. . .
RENE 95	. . .	0.015	8	14	3.5	. . .	3.5	. . .	2.5	0.01 B, 3.5 Nb, 3.5 W, 0.05 Zr	bal
MA 754	N07754	0.04	. . .	20	0.3	. . .	. . .	. . .	0.5	. . .	bal
Nimonic Ap1	. . .	0.02	17	15	4	. . .	5	. . .	3.5	0.0025 B	bal

Table 7 Approximate composition of molybdenum, niobium, tantalum, and zirconium alloys

Material	Similar UNS No.	C	Hf	Sn	Ti	W	Mo	Nb	Ta	Zr	Other
Cermotherm	. . .	0.01	. . .	. . .	. . .	. . .	bal	. . .	. . .	Mo-base metal-ceramic ZrO_2	. . .
NbW15Mo5Zr1	. . .	0.05	. . .	. . .	. . .	15	5	bal	. . .	. . .	. . .
TaHf10W5	. . .	. . .	10	. . .	. . .	5	. . .	. . .	bal	. . .	. . .
TaW10	. . .	. . .	. . .	. . .	. . .	10	. . .	. . .	bal	. . .	. . .
ZrSn1.5	. . .	. . .	. . .	1.5	. . .	. . .	. . .	. . .	. . .	bal	0.20 Ni
ZrNb1	. . .	. . .	. . .	. . .	. . .	. . .	. . .	1	. . .	bal	. . .
TZM	. . .	0.015	. . .	. . .	0.5	. . .	bal	. . .	. . .	0.08	. . .

Table 8 Approximate composition of iron alloys and steels

Material	Similar UNS No.	C	Si	Mn	Cr	Mo	W	V	Co	Ni	Other	Fe
FeNi40Cr13MoTi	N08801	0.10 max	1.0 max	1.5 max	19.0–22.0	...	...	...	1.5 max	30.0–34.0	0.5 Cu max, 0.015 S max, 0.7–1.5 Ti max	bal
FeNi38Cr16	N08330	0.05	2.3	1.2	18	...	...	...	...	37	0.5 Cu max	bal
FeNi32Cr20Ti	...	0.04	0.35	0.75	20.5	...	...	...	...	32	0.5 Cu max	bal
FeNi32Cr20	N08020	0.05	0.5	0.75	21	...	...	...	...	32.5	0.38 Ti, 0.38 Al	bal
X20CoCrWMo109	...	0.2	...	...	9	2	6.7	...	9.5	...	...	bal
X30WCrV53	...	0.3	0.2	0.3	2.4	...	4.3	0.6	...	...	...	bal
X30WCrV93	T20821	0.3	0.2	0.3	2.6	...	8.5	0.4	...	...	...	bal
X32CrMoCoV333	...	0.32	...	...	3	2.8	...	0.6	2.8	...	...	bal
X32CrMoV33	...	0.3	0.3	...	3	2.8	...	0.5	...	...	0.3 N	bal
X38CrMoV 51	T20811	0.4	1	...	5.2	1.3	...	0.4	...	...	...	bal
X40CrMoV51	T20813	0.4	1	...	5.2	1.3	...	1	...	...	...	bal
X40CrMoV53	...	0.4	...	...	5.1	3.2	...	0.7	...	...	...	bal
X45CoCrV-5–5-5	T20819	0.40–0.50	0.30–0.50	0.30–0.50	4.00–5.00	0.40–0.60	4.00–5.00	1.80–2.10	4.00–5.00	...	0.025 P max, 0.025 S max	bal
X50NiCrWV1313	...	0.45	...	...	13	...	1.2	1.2	...	13	...	bal
X50WNiCrVCo1212	...	0.5	...	...	4	0.7	12.5	1.1	1.7	11.5	...	bal
X60NiCrTi2615	...	0.05	0.5–1.1	0.75–1.6	15	1.3	...	0.3	...	25.5	Ti(2.10 + B)	bal
St52	...	0.12–0.15	...	1 max	0.6 max	0.25 max	...	...	...	...	0.25–1 Cu	bal
Ni42	...	0.05 max	...	...	...	...	...	...	...	41–43	...	...
Ni48	...	0.05 max	...	0.5 max	...	...	...	...	...	46–50	...	...
NiAl	...	...	...	...	...	...	...	...	...	24	13 Al, 4 Cu	59
40CrMnMo7	T51620	0.35–0.45	0.20–0.40	1.30–1.60	1.80–2.10	0.15–0.25	...	...	...	...	...	bal
48CrMoV67	...	0.4	0.3	1.5	2	0.2	...	...	...	...	...	bal
48CrMoV51	...	0.45	...	...	1.45	0.75	...	...	...	...	0.30 V	bal
55NiCrMoV6	T61206	0.50–0.60	0.10–0.40	0.65–0.95	0.60–0.80	0.25–0.35	...	...	...	1.50–1.80	0.030 P max, 0.030 S max, 0.07–0.12 V	bal
56NiCrMoV7	T61206	0.50–0.60	...	0.65–0.95	1.00–1.20	0.45–0.55	...	...	...	1.50–1.80	0.030 P max, 0.030 S max, 0.07–0.12 V	bal
MA 956	S67956	...	...	...	20	...	...	...	...	...	4.5 Al, 0.35 Ti, 0.5 Y	bal

Table 9 Approximate composition of lead, tin, and zinc alloys

Material	Similar UNS No.	Al	Fe	Other	Pb	Sn
L-PbSn40	L54915	0.005 max	...	0.005 Cd max, 0.12 Sb max, 0.005 Zn max, 0.005 (Al + Cd + Zn) max, others total 0.08 max	bal	39.5–40.5
L-Sn50Pb	L55030	0.002 max	0.02 max	0.01 As max, 0.10 Bi max, 0.002 Cd max, 0.05 Cu max, 0.12 Sb max, 0.002 Zn max, 0.002 (Al + Cd + Zn) max, others total 0.08 max	49.644–50.5	bal
L-Sn60Pb	L13600	0.002 max	0.02 max	0.01 As max, 0.10 Bi max, 0.002 Cd max, 0.05 Cu max, 0.12 Sb max, 0.002 Zn max, 0.002 (Al + Cd + Zn) max, others total 0.08 max	39.194–40.5	bal
L-Sn60PbCu2	...	0.002 max	0.02 max	0.01 As max, 0.10 Bi max, 0.002 Cd max, 1.6–2.0 Cu, 0.12 Sb max, 0.002 Zn max, 0.002 (Al + Cd + Zn) max, others total 0.08 max	37.244–38.9	bal
L-SnAg5	L13961	...	...	3.0–5.0 Ag, others total 0.2 max	...	bal
L-SnCu3	...	...	...	2.5–3.5 Cu, others total 0.2 max	...	bal
Pb 99.94	L50045	...	...	0.001 Ag max, 0.05 Bi max, 0.001 Cu max	bal	...
Pb 99.985	L50020	...	...	0.001 Ag max, 0.01 Bi max, 0.001 Cu max	99.99 min	...
Pb 99.99	L50050	...	0.005 max	0.002 Ag max, 0.005 As max, 0.03 Bi max, 0.002 Cu max, 0.005 Sb max, 0.005 Zn max	bal	0.003 max
Pb 99.9Cu	L51125	...	...	0.0025 Ag max, 0.01 Bi max, 0.04–0.08 Cu, others total 0.001 max	bal	0.001
Pb 99.9	L50050	...	0.005 max	0.002 Ag max, 0.005 As max, 0.03 Bi max, 0.002 Cu max, 0.005 Sb max, 0.005 Zn max	bal	0.003 max
ZnAl4Cu1	...	3.5–4.3	...	0.005 Cd max, 0.75–1.25 Cu, 0.02–0.06 Mg, bal Zn	0.003 max	0.001 max

Index